Great Americana

Account of an Expedition from Pittsburgh to the Rocky Mountains

VOLUME II

Edwin James

Account of an Expedition
from Pittsburgh
to the Rocky Mountains

VOLUME II

by Edwin James

READEX MICROPRINT

Account of an Expedition from Pittsburgh to the Rocky Mountains

VOLUME II

ACCOUNT

OF

AN EXPEDITION

FROM

PITTSBURGH TO THE ROCKY MOUNTAINS,

PERFORMED IN THE YEARS 1819 AND '20,

BY ORDER OF

THE HON. J. C. CALHOUN, SEC'Y OF WAR:

UNDER THE COMMAND OF

MAJOR STEPHEN H. LONG.

FROM THE NOTES OF MAJOR LONG, MR. T. SAY, AND OTHER GEN-
TLEMEN OF THE EXPLORING PARTY.

———

COMPILED
BY EDWIN JAMES,
BOTANIST AND GEOLOGIST FOR THE EXPEDITION.

———

IN TWO VOLS.—WITH AN ATLAS
VOL. II.

———

PHILADELPHIA:

H. C. CAREY AND I. LEA, CHESNUT ST.

1823.

CONTENTS OF VOL. II.

CHAPTER I.

Page.

Sandstone formation at the base of the Rocky Mountains—the Platte within the Mountains—Granite between the Platte and Arkansa—Birds, Plants, &c. - - - - - - 1

CHAPTER II.

Excursion to the summit of the Peak—Mineral Springs—Coquimbo Owl—Encampment on the Arkansa, - - - 23

CHAPTER III.

A detachment from the Exploring party ascend the Arkansa to the Mountains—Bell's Springs—Descent of the Arkansa—Grizzly Bear, 42

CHAPTER IV.

Natural mounds—Kaskaia Indian and Squaw—Preparations for a division of the party—Sandstones of the high plains south of the Arkansa—Floetz trap formation, - - - - 58

CHAPTER V.

Sufferings of the party from stormy weather and want of provisions—Indications of an approach towards settlements—Inscribed rocks—Cervus Macrotis—Volcanic origin of Amygdaloid, - 85

CHAPTER VI.

Band of Kaskaias—Indian encampment—unfriendly behaviour of the Kaskaias—Some account of their persons and manners—Salt Plains—Camancias, - - - - - - 101

CHAPTER VII.

Sand plains—Mississippi Hawk—Small leaved elm—wild horses—Hail storm—Climate—Bisons—Grapes—Red sand formation—Gypsum, - - - - - - - 120

CHAPTER VIII.

Inconveniences resulting from want of water—Wood ticks—Plants—Loss of one of the party—Honey bees—Forests—Gray Sandstone—Indications of coal—Limestone, - - - - 139

CHAPTER IX.

Maclura Aurantiaca—Birds—Falls of the Canadian—Green argillaceous sandstone—Northern and Southern tributaries of the Cana-

CONTENTS.

Page.

dian—Cotton wood—Arrival at the Arkansa—Cane brakes—Cherokees—Belle Point, - - - - - 158

CHAPTER X.

Journey down the Arkansa—Thunder storm—Some account of the Kiawa, Kaskaia, Arrapaho and Shienne Indians—New species of Toad, - - - - - - - 173

CHAPTER XI.

Arrapaho war-party—Cow-bunting—Rattlesnakes—Burrowing owl—Departure of Bijeau and Ledoux for the Pawnee villages—Scarcity of timber—Great herds of Bisons—Wolves, - - 192

CHAPTER XII.

Termination of the great bend of the Arkansa—Ietan war party—Little Arkansa—Red river fork—Little Neosho and Little Verdigris, - - - - - - - 206

CHAPTER XIII.

Indian hunting encampment—Brackish water—The party pressed by hunger—Forked tailed Fly-catcher—An elevated, almost mountainous range of country—Desertion of three men—Red water, 221

CHAPTER XIV.

The party meet with Osage Indians—Some account of this nation—Manner of taking wild horses, - - - - 237

CHAPTER XV.

Verdigris river—Mr. Glenn's trading house—New species of Lizard—Neosho, or Grand river—Salt works—Large spider—Illinois creek—Ticks—Arrival at Belle Point, - - - 250

CHAPTER XVI.

Journey from Belle Point to Cape Girardeau—Cherokee Indians—Osage war—Regulators—Settlements of White river, - 260

CHAPTER XVII.

Hot Springs of the Washita—Red river—Exploring Expedition of 1806—Arrival at Cape Girardeau—Dissolution of the Party, 287

SUPPLEMENTARY CHAPTERS.

Page.

CHAPTER XVIII.

General description of the country traversed by the exploring Expedition, extracted from a report of Major Long to the Hon. J. C. Calhoun, Secretary of War; dated Philadelphia, January 20th, 1821,   -   -   -   -   -   -   -   331

I. Of the country situated between the Ohio river and the Alleghany Mountains,   -   -   -   -   -   -   332

II. Of the country situated between the Ohio, Mississippi, and the Lakes,   -   -   -   -   -   -   -   333

III. Of the country situated between the Mississippi and Missouri rivers,   -   -   -   -   -   -   -   -   340

IV. Of the country situated between the Missouri and Red rivers, west of the Mississippi, and east of the meridian of the Council Bluff, 342

V. Of the country situated between the meridian of the Council Bluff and the Rocky Mountains,   -   -   -   -   350

VI. Of the Rocky Mountains,   -   -   -   361

VII. Of the Indians inhabiting the section of country last described, 363

VIII. Of the Arrapahoes, Kaskaias, Kiaways, Ietans, and Shiennes,   367

IX. Observations embracing several traits of character common to the Indians of the Western country,   -   -   -   368

X. Of the Mississippi, Missouri, and Ohio rivers,   -   -   376

XI. Of the Great Valley, or basin of the Mississippi,   -   -   379

CHAPTER XIX.

Observations on the geology of the country traversed by the Expedition,   -   -   -   -   -   -   -   384

SECTION I. Of the Secondary formations connected with the Rocky Mountains—1, Of the Great American Desert—2, Sandstones of the Rocky Mountains—3, Floetz trap rocks,   -   -   -   386

SECTION II. Of the Primitive parts of the Rocky Mountains,   -   405

SECTION III. Of the Ozark Mountains—1, Carboniferous limestone— 2, Argillaceous sandstone—3, Petrosilex—4, Native argil?—5, Inclined sandstone—6, Argillite—7, Granite,   -   -   408

SECTION IV. Of the Alleghany Mountains—1, Granular limestone— 2, Metalliferous limestone—3, Transition argillite—4, Transition sandstone,   -   -   -   -   -   -   -   -   432

APPENDIX—Containing

Astronomical and Meteorological records—Vocabularies of Indian languages, and a general Index;—conclusion of the volume.

EXPEDITION

FROM

PITTSBURGH TO THE ROCKY MOUNTAINS.

CHAPTER I.

*Sandstone formation at the base of the Rocky Mountains—
The Platte within the mountains—Granite between the
Platte and the Arkansa —Birds—Plants*, &c.

THE inclined sandstone at the base of the Rocky Mountains we found much wider and its summits incomparably
more elevated than our previous opinions, or a distant view
had led us to expect. This extensive range, rising abruptly
from the plain, skirts the base of the mountain like a vast
rampart, and from a person standing near it, intercepts the
view of the still more grand and imposing features of the
granite ridge beyond. It consists of rocks in which the comminuted fragments of primitive aggregates are intermixed
with the reliquiæ of the animals of a former world, known
to us only by the monuments which these remains exhibit.
The stratifications, with which this rugged and precipitous
wall of sandstone is distinctly seamed, penetrate the mass
with various degrees of obliquity; not unfrequently the laminæ are entirely vertical, as if the whole had receded from
its original position, and these immense rocky masses, had, by
the operation of some powerful agent, been broken off from
their former continuity, with the strata now found in a horizontal position in the plains.

It is difficult, when contemplating the present appearance and situation of these rocks, to prevent the imagination from wandering back to that remote unascertained period, when the billows of the primeval ocean lashed the base of the Rocky Mountains, and deposited, during a succession of ages, that vast accumulation of rounded fragments of rocks alternating with beds of animal remains, which now extend without interruption from the base of this range to the summits of the Alleghanies; and endeavouring to form some conception of that subsequent catastrophe which has so changed the relative elevation of the two great formations that the margin of the secondary has been broken off and thrown into an inclined or vertical position.

The valley between this parapet of sand-rock and the first granitic ridge is near a mile wide. It is ornamented with numerous isolated columnar rocks, often of a snowy whiteness, standing like pyramids and obelisks, interspersed among mounds and hillocks, which seem to have resulted from the disintegration of similar masses.

The range of sandstone appears to have been originally of uniform elevation and uninterrupted continuity, stretching along the base of the mountains from north to south, but it has been divided transversely by the bed of the Platte, and all the larger rivers in their descent to the plains.

From our camp, we had expected to be able to ascend the most distant summits then in sight, and return the same evening, but night overtook us and we found ourselves scarcely arrived at the base of the mountain. The lowest part of the sandstone stratum, exposed at the western declivities of the hills, and in the points nearest the granite, contains extensive beds of coarse conglomerate or pudding-stone, often of a reddish colour. The more compact parts of the rock present remains of terebratulæ and other submarine animals. Among these, few are entire or in good preservation. We observed here, several singular, scorpion-like animals, inhabiting under stones and dried bison's dung. They have a formidable appearance, and run actively. They belong to the class Arachnides, genus Galeodes, which has been heretofore observed only in warm climates; not one was known to inhabit this continent.*

About the sandstone ledges we collected a geranium† intermediate between the crane's bill and herb robert, the beautiful calochortus, [C. *elegans*, *Ph.*] and a few other valuable plants.

The Platte at the foot of the mountains is twenty-five yards wide, having an average depth of about three feet; its water clear and cool, and its current rapid. Its descent for twenty miles below cannot be less than eight feet per mile. Its valley is narrow and serpentine, bounded by steep and elevated hills, embosoming innumerable little lawns often of a semicircular form, ornamented by the narrow margin of shrubbery along the Platte.

The narrow valley, which intervenes between the ridges

---

* Genus *Galeodes*, OLIV.

1. G. *pallipes.* SAY. Hairy; mandibles horizontal; fingers regularly arquated; abdomen subdepressed, livid.

DESCRIPTION. *Body*, pale yellowish brown, hairy; *feet*, paler; whitish, first pair smallest, fourth pair largest, and longest; *abdomen*, livid, hairy, subdepressed; *palpi*, more robust than the three anterior pairs of legs, of subequal diameter, but rather thicker towards the tip, more hairy than the feet; *eyes* and *tubercle* blackish; *mandibles*, dilated with numerous rigid setæ; and with parallel setæ projected over the fingers; *fingers*, regularly arquated, reddish brown at tip, and with a reddish brown line above and beneath; within armed with many robust teeth; *thorax*, with a deep sinus at the anterior angles.

2. G. *subulata*, hairy; mandibles, horizontal; thumb nearly rectilinear; destitute of teeth.

This species has the strongest resemblance to the preceding, both in form, magnitude, and colouring; but the superior finger of the mandibles is unarmed and rectilinear, or very slightly flexuous; the inferior finger is arquated, with about two robust teeth.

† G. *cæspitose*, sub-erect, pubescent, sparingly branched above. Radical leaves reniform deeply 5-7 cleft. The flower is a little larger than that of G. *robertianum*, and similarly coloured, having whitish lines towards the base of the corrolla. We also saw here the Campanula *decipiens*. Pers. Lysimachia *ciliata*, *Ph.* Troximon *glaucum*, *N.* with two or three belonging to genera with which we were unacquainted.

of sandstone before mentioned, is a little more fertile than the plains along the river. It is covered with fine and short grasses, and varied with here and there a copse of small oaks or hazles. There are also some columnar masses of white sandstone, twenty or thirty feet high, standing remote from each other, having the debris around their bases covered with shrubby oaks.

We observed here the obscure wren,* a bird more closely related to the great Carolina wren of Wilson than any other we have seen; but the characters drawn from the primaries, and from the marking of the tail sufficiently distinguish it from that species. The bill is somewhat longer, and the general tint of the plumage of a much more sombre hue. It frequents the arid country in the vicinity of the mountains, and is often seen hopping about upon the branches and singularly compressed semi-procumbent trunks, of a species of juniper.

The bill of this species approaches the form which characterizes the genus *Certhia*, in which Wilson has placed its kindred species, the Carolina wren.

On the morning of the 7th of July, the party remaining in the encampment of the preceding day, Dr. James and Mr. Peale, accompanied by two riflemen, were sent out to examine the mountains. These appeared most acces-

---

* Genus Troglodytes. Cuv.

T. *obsoleta*. SAY. Above, dusky-brownish, slightly undulated with pale, tinted with dull ferruginous on the top of the head and superior portion of the back; sides of the head dull whitish, with a broad brown line passing through the eye to the origin of the neck; primaries plain, being entirely destitute of undulations or spots; feathers of the tail-coverts pale, each with four or five fuscous bands; chin, neck beneath, and breast whitish, each feather marked by a longitudinal line of light brown; belly white, flanks a little tinged with ferruginous; inferior tail-coverts white, each feather bifasciate with black brown; tail simple, broadly tipped with ferruginous yellow, and with black before the tip; the remaining portion colour of the wings and obsoletely banded; these bands are more distinct on the two middle feathers which are destitute of the black and yellowish termination; exterior plume marked by four yellowish white spots on the exterior web, and by two larger ones on the inner web; the tip is dusky.

Length six inches; bill from the corner of the mouth rather more than one inch.

sible on the north side of the river, which was opposite our encampment. The river was here about four feet deep, and the strength of the current such as to render it impossible for a man to keep on his feet, in the deepest part of the stream. As some of the party destined for the mountains could not swim, it was thought hazardous for them to attempt to cross by fording. To obviate this difficulty two men were sent with a long rope, which they were directed to stretch across the river, making the ends fast on either shore. This was readily accomplished, one of the men swimming across with an end of the rope in his teeth. By the aid of this the detachment were enabled to keep their feet in crossing, though with extreme difficulty as the bed of the river was uneven and rocky. They all however arrived in safety on the left bank about sunrise.

After passing the region of inclined sandstone, which is about two miles in width, they began to rise upon what may be considered the base of the mountain. As the day advanced the heat became oppressive, and they found themselves somewhat exhausted, before they had crossed the sandstone hills, which appeared so inconsiderable from our encampment, that the labour of crossing them had been almost forgotten in estimating the toils of the day. The first range of primitive rocks they found far more abrupt and rugged than the sandstone hills they had already passed. Its sides are destitute of vegetation, except a few prickly pears and yuccas, with here and there a stinted oak or juniper, and so steep that great exertion as well as the utmost caution are necessary in ascending.

The rock is an aggregate of feldspar and hornblend, approaching in character some of the common varieties of Sienite. On the eastern side, where the feldspar is in the greatest proportion, it is flesh-coloured and its structure crystalline, the fractured surface of the mass being uneven like that of coarse granite; advancing towards the west, horn-

blend was found more and more predominant, and so arranged
as to have, in the mass, a laminated appearance. The natural
fissures or cleavages between the laminæ run nearly in a perpendicular direction, giving the rock the columnar structure
of trap, or greenstone. As they proceeded, a few interesting insects and plants occurred to reward their labors.
But these impenetrable and naked rocks are the abodes of
few living beings either animal or vegetable. In the crevices where a scanty soil has accumulated, is here and there
planted, a hardy evergreen, whose short and gnarled trunk,
and recurved inflexible branches, seem to proclaim the storms
it has withstood, and the centuries during which it has ve-
getated.

The design of the party had been to cross the first range
of the mountains and gain the valley of the Platte beyond,
but this they found themselves unable to accomplish. After
climbing successively to the summit of several ridges, which
they had supposed to be the top of the mountain, they still
found others beyond higher and more rugged. They therefore
relinquished the intention of crossing, and began to look for
the best way to descend to the bed of the river, which lay on
their left hand. Here they halted to rest for a few moments,
and exposed a thermometer in the shade of a large rock.
The mercury fell to 72°; in camp, at the same hour, it stood
at 86°. They were so much elevated above the river, that
although they could see it plainly, it appeared like a small
brook of two or three yards in width, white with foam and
spray caused by the impetuosity of its current and the rough-
ness of its channel. They could distinguish two principal
branches of the Platte, one coming from the northwest, the
other from the south. A little below the confluence of these
branches the river turns abruptly to S. E., bursting through a
chasm in a vast mural precipice of naked columnar rocks.

About noon the detachment commenced their descent,
which cost them no less exertion than their ascent in the

morning. Their fatigue was aggravated by thirst, as they met with no water nor any shade except that of projecting rocks in the higher parts of the mountain. They chose a different route from that which they had taken in ascending, intending to descend to the river, with the hope of being able to travel along its bed. They were obliged to assist each other in lowering themselves down precipices, which they would have found it impossible to pass singly. On the southern declivity of the mountain they met with a few ripe currants, but these were hard and juiceless, of a sweetish taste, and aggravated instead of alleviating their thirst, and were probably the cause of a violent headach with which several of the party were affected soon after eating them. There were also found a few large and delicious raspberries, of a species approaching the flowering raspberry, [Rubus *odoratus*] but with smaller leaves and a more branching stem.

After descending from the more precipitous parts about the summit of the mountain, they crossed a long and rugged tract, buried, and rendered almost impassable by boulders and fragments which had fallen from above, and were at length so fortunate as to find a spring of cool water, and a shade in a narrow ravine, where they sat down to rest, and dine on the provision they had brought.

The men who were with them stopped in the same ravine, a few rods below. One of these, immediately after drinking the water, was violently attacked with headach, vomiting, and purging, which increased to such an alarming degree that he was presently unable to stand upon his feet. As it was feared he would not soon recover strength enough to walk, Mr. Peale undertook to return alone to camp, and give notice of his situation, and return with medicine and assistance.

He descended along a rough and obstructed ravine until he arrived at the Platte, but found the valley so confined as to be impassable, and again directed his course across the

mountains, towards the northeast, and after a most rugged
and fatiguing march of about six miles, arrived at camp late
in the afternoon. Here he found several of the party suffering in a similar manner, but not so severely as the man he
had left in the mountains. Two men were immediately
despatched with some medicines in search of the disabled
party.

The spot where they halted was several miles within the
mountains, and elevated nearly to the limit of phænogamous
vegetation. The common hop, [H. *lupulus*] was growing in
perfection, also the box elder, [Acer *negundo*, *Ph*] the common sarsaparilla of the Eastern states, [Aralia *nudicaulis*]
the spikenard [A. *racemosa*,] and many other plants common to the Alleghanies and Green mountains. After waiting
about two hours, the sick man had so far recovered as to be
able to stand upon his feet, and to walk a little. They therefore relieved him of his gun and other luggage, and moved
by short stages towards camp, where they arrived at a late
hour of the night.*

The men, who had been sent out to their assistance, returned some time afterwards, having sought for them without success. In the morning of the same day, soon after
the departure of Dr. James' detachment, two of the party
passed into the mountains, on the left side of the river; they
experienced much difficulty, and underwent much labour in
scaling the steep ascents, and some hazard in descending the
precipitous declivities, which marked their course. The
timber was small, scrubby, and scattered in the most favour-

---

* Among many plants collected in this excursion, some of them new to
us, we recognized the bear-berry [Arbutus *uva-ursi* L.] an inhabitant of
the mountainous districts of New York and New England, also the Dodeca-
theon *integrifolium. Ph.*, and a beautiful little plant, referrible to the genus Mentzelia of Plumier. On the higher parts of the mountain, an oak is
common, approaching in character the Quercus *banisteri, mx.*, also a
small undescribed acer, the Juniperus *communis*, and J. *virginiana.* In the
ravines, the Rhus *toxico-dendron*, spiræa *opulifolia*, &c.; and at the base
of the mountains, the Prenanthes *runcinatum*, Saxifraga *nivalis, L.* a cer-
astium, &c.

ed situations, and many of the solitary pines, which occupied an elevated position, had evidently been the sport of furious tempests, being rived and seamed by lightning.

To the right, and easy of access, was a projecting rock, supporting a single humble cedar in one of its fissures, from which a stone let fall was received into the torrent of the river which washed its base. The huge rampart of naked rocks, which had been seen from below to stretch across the valley, was now in nearer view, the river whirling abruptly around the acute angle of its extremity, and offering, at its superior edge, an embattled outline. They ascended a primitive mountain which seemed to be of superior elevation, in order to overlook the western ranges, but they here found their horizon bounded by the succeeding mountain, towering majestically above them. To the east, over the tops of a few inferior elevations, lay expanded, like an ocean, the vast interminable prairie, over which we had so long held our monotonous march. The undulations which vary its surface now disappeared, and the whole lay like a map before the observer. They could trace the course of the Platte, and number the streams they had crossed, and others which they had before passed near, by the slight fringing of timber or bushes which margined their banks, and by an occasional glimpse of their streams, shining like quicksilver, and interrupting and varying the continuity of the plain, as they pursued their serpentine course. The atmosphere was remarkably serene, and small clouds were coursing over the surface of the heavens, casting their swiftly-moving shadows upon the earth, and enhancing the beauty of the contrast, which the long lines of timber afforded, to the general glare of light. After contemplating for some time the beauty and extent of the scene, their attention was attracted by a moving point, rendered occasionally visible by reflecting the rays of the retiring sun. This object was our white flag waving in a gentle breeze and revealing the position of our camp, the only spot in the boundless landscape, where the eye could rest on the work of human hands.

Astronomical observations were attempted at camp, but in the middle of the day the moon was too near the sun, and in the evening the sky was cloudy.

The sickness experienced by almost all the party, was, probably, occasioned by eating currants, which were abundant about the camp. It is not to be supposed, this illness was caused by any very active deleterious quality in the fruit, but that the stomach, by long disuse, had, in a great measure, lost the power of digesting fruits. Several continued unwell during the night.

On the morning of the 9th, we resumed our journey, travelling somewhat east of south, along a small tributary of the Platte.*

The bed of this stream lies from south to north, along a narrow valley, bounded on each side by high cliffs of sandstone. The rock is similar to that already mentioned, its

---

* A beautiful species of pigeon was shot near the mountain. The head is of a purplish-cinereous colour; the back of the neck and its sides brilliant golden green, the feathers at base brownish purple; above this patch, and at base of the head, is a white semi-band; the under part of the neck is pale vinaceous-purplish, this colour becomes paler as it approaches the vent, which, with the inferior tail-coverts, is white; anterior portion of the back, the wing-coverts and scapulars, are brownish-ash, the larger wing-feathers dark brown, approaching black, the exterior edges whitish; the lower part of the back, the rump and tail coverts, inferior wing-coverts and sides, bluish-ash, paler beneath the wings; the shafts of the body feathers and tail coverts are remarkably robust, tapering rather suddenly near the tips; the tail is medial, rounded at tip, consisting of twelve feathers, a definite black band at two thirds their length from the base, before which the colour is bluish-ash and behind it dirty whitish; the bill is yellow, tipped with black, somewhat gibbous behind the nostrils; the irides red; the feet yellow; claws black.

This species seems to be most intimately allied to the ring-tailed pigeon (C. *caribæa*.), from which it differs in the colour of the legs and bill, and in not having the gibbosity at the base of the latter, so remarkable; it is possible that it may be an intermediate link between the ring-tailed pigeon and the stock pigeon of Europe, with the latter of which it has in common the exterior white edging to the greater wing feathers. It may be distinguished by the name of band-tailed pigeon (Columba *fasciata*.) and may be seen with other specimens of natural objects, collected in this expedition, in the Philadelphia Museum.

strata having, however, less inclination than is observed nearer the base of the mountain. It is the margin of that great formation of secondary which occupies the plains, and appears as if broken off and thrown into an inclined position, by some convulsion which changed the relative elevation of the stratum. It is of great thickness, its laminæ in an almost vertical position, occupying a surface of two or three and sometimes many miles in width. On the eastern declivities of the first ranges of hills, in places which may be supposed to have been the surface of the stratum in its original position, the rock is usually of a close grain and compact texture, and of a yellowish-white or light gray colour.

We saw many masses of sandstone bearing a striking resemblance to colossal ruins, also some insulated hills with perpendicular sides and level summits. These seem to be the remains of an extensive portion of the sandstone stratum which formerly covered the country to the level of their highest summits. They occur at considerable distance from the base of the primitive mountains, and their summits are occupied by horizontal strata. For a small portion of the upper part of their elevation their sides are nearly perpendicular, but their bases are surrounded by an extensive accumulation of debris, sometimes rising nearly to the summit. After ascending the small stream, before mentioned, to its source, we crossed an inconsiderable ridge, which separates it from the valley of Defile creek: this we ascended to the place where its principal branch descends from the mountain, where we encamped.

Several of the tributaries to Defile creek appear to discharge as much water as is seen in the stream below their junction. This appearance is common to many of the larger creeks, their broad and sandy beds allowing much of the water to sink and pass off through the sand. In the evening a favorable opportunity, the first for several days, presented, and obsesvations for latitude were taken.

In that part of Defile creek, near which we encamped, are numerous dams, thrown across by the beaver, causing it to appear rather like a succession of ponds than a continued stream. As we ascended farther towards the mountains, we found the works of these animals still more frequent. The small willows and cotton-wood trees, which are here in considerable numbers, afford their most favorite food.

In visiting one of those peculiar tabular hills which mark the border of the secondary region, we crossed a ridge of sandstone about three hundred feet in height, with strata inclined to the west. To this succeeds a valley about one mile wide, having a scanty growth of pine and oak. The ascent of the hill is steep and rugged; horizontal strata of sandstone and coarse conglomerate are exposed on its sides, and the summit is capped by a thin stratum of compact sandstone surmounted by a bed of greenstone. The loose and splintery fragments of this rock sometimes cover the surface and make a clinking noise under the feet like fragments of pottery.

The summit of the hill is of an oval form, about eight hundred yards in length and five hundred in breadth. The elevation is about one thousand feet, and the height of the perpendicular precipice, from the summit of the debris to the top of the hill, about fifty.

From this hill the High Peak mentioned by Capt. Pike was discovered, and its bearing found to be S. 50° W.

Several of the party ascended Defile creek until they arrived at the mountains, into which they penetrated as far as was found practicable. As they travelled along the bed of this stream, they found the several rock formations beautifully exposed, and in the following order, commencing from the alluvial of the plain on the east.

First—Horizontal sandstone, embracing extensive beds of coarse conglomerate, and commonly of a light gray or reddish-yellow colour.

Second—Fine compact gray sandstone, containing a few impressions of organic remains, resembling those in the sandstones of coal formations. This rock is inclined at an angle of near twenty degrees towards the west. It forms continuous ranges of hills, not difficult of ascent from the east, but their western declivities are abrupt and precipitous.

Third—Lofty and detached columns of sandstone of a reddish or deep brown colour. These are irregularly scattered throughout a narrow woodless valley. Some of them rise probably three hundred feet above the common level of the plain, and are so steep on all sides as to preclude the possibility of ascent; others are accessible at some points, and one of these we ascended.

Fourth—Coarse white pudding-stone, or conglomerate and sandstone of a deep red colour, alternating with each other, and with beds of fine white sandstone, and resting against the granite in a highly inclined position. This rock contains well preserved remains of terebratula, productus, and other bivalve shells. These are usually found on or near the surface of large nodules of a fine flinty stone, closely resembling petrosilex. The same rock also contains an extensive bed of iron ore, and from its eastern side flows a copious brine spring.

About this spring, which had evidently been much frequented by animals, we saw the skulls of the male and female Big-horn;* the bones of elk, bisons, and other animals.

The granite, which succeeds the sandstone last mentioned, is of a dark reddish-brown colour, containing a large proportion of feldspar of the flesh coloured variety, and black mica. The crystalline grains or fragments of the feldspar

---

* Big-horn. This animal has been rudely figured by Venegas on his second plate, who informs us that it is known to the natives of California by the name of Taye; another figure, but also a bad one, was given by Mr. Geoffroy in the Ann. de Museum, under the name of *Ovis montana.*

Two specimens, a male and female, were taken to Philadelphia by Lewis and Clark, which are set up in the museum of that city.

are large and detached easily; consequently, the rock is in a state of rapid disintegration. This granite rises abruptly in immense mountain masses, and, undoubtedly, extends far to the west.

The little river, on which we encamped, pours down the side of this granitic mountain through a deep, inaccessible chasm, forming a continued cascade of several hundred feet. From an elevation of one or two thousand feet, on the side of the mountain, we were able to overlook a great extent of secondary region at its base. The surface appeared broken for several miles, and in many of the vallies we could discern columnar and pyramidal masses of sandstone, sometimes entirely naked, and sometimes bearing little tufts of bushes about their summits.*

* A female bird was shot on the mountain which closely resembles, both in size and figure, the female of the black game (Tetrao *tetrix*). It is, however, of a darker colour, and the plumage is not so much banded, the tail also seems rather longer, and the feathers of it do not exhibit any tendency to curve outward, which, if we mistake not, is exhibited by the inner feathers of the tail of the corresponding sex of the black game

Its general colour is a black-brown, with narrow bars of pale ocraceous; plumage near the base of the beak above tinged with ferruginous; each feather on the head with a single band and slight tip; those of the neck, back, tail-coverts, and breast, two bands and tip; the tips on the upper part of the back and on the tail-coverts are broad and spotted with black, with the inferior band often obsolete; the throat and inferior portion of the upper sides of the neck are covered with whitish feathers, on each side of which is a black band or spot; a white band on each feather of the breast, becoming broader on those nearer the belly; on the belly the plumage is dull cinereous with concealed white lines on the shafts; the wing coverts and scapulars, about two-banded with a spotted tip and second band, and with the tip of the shaft white; the primaries and secondaries have whitish zig-zag spots on their outer webs, the first feather of the former short, the second longer, the third, fourth, and fifth equal, longest; feathers of the sides with two or three bands and white spot at the tip of the shaft; inferior tail coverts white with a black band and base, and slightly tinged with ocraceous on their centres; legs feathered to the toes, and with the thighs pale, undulated with dusky; tail rounded, with a broad terminal band of cinereous, on which are black zig-zag spots; on the intermediate feathers are several ocraceous spotted bands, but these become obsolete and confined to the exterior webs on the lateral feathers, until they are hardly perceptible on the exterior pair; a naked space above and beneath the eyes. It may be distinguished by the name of the dusky grouse (Tetrao *obscurus*).

When this bird flew it uttered a cackling note a little like that of the domestic fowl: this note was noticed by Lewis and Clark in the bird which

In the evening, a thunder-cloud rose in the east, which appeared for some time to approach, the thunder being loud and frequent, but at length moved off towards the southeast, continuing visible in the horizon during great part of the night.

11th.   From our encampment, we travelled nearly south, and, crossing a small ridge dividing the waters of the Platte from those of the Arkansa, halted to dine on a tributary of the latter.   In an excursion from this place we collected a large species of columbine, somewhat resembling the common one of the gardens.   It is heretofore unknown to the Flora of the United States, to which it forms a splendid acquisition.   If it should appear not to have been described, it may receive the name of Aquilegia *cœrulea.** Our road, during the morning, lay for about twelve miles, along

they speak of under the name of the cock of the plains, and to which Mr. Ord has applied the name of Tetrao fusca, a bird which, agreeably to their description, appears to be different from this, having the legs only half booted: the "fleshy protuberance about the base of the upper chop," and "the long pointed tail" of that bird may possibly be sexual distinctions.

It appears by the observations of Lewis and Clark that several species of this genus inhabit the country which they traversed, particularly in this elevated range of mountains from whence, amongst other interesting animals, they brought to Philadelphia a specimen of the spotted grouse (T. *canadensis.*) which, together with the above described bird, are now preserved in the Philadelphia Museum, thus proving that the spotted grouse is an inhabitant of a portion of the territory of the United States.

* A. *cœrulea.*—Leaves twice ternate; flowers terminal, remote; nectaries strait and very long. It inhabits sandy woods of pine, and spruce within the mountains, rising sometimes to the height of three feet.

In passing from the head waters of the branch of the Platte called Defile creek, to those of one of the northern tributaries of the Arkansa, we noticed some change in the soil, and soon met with many plants we had not before seen.   Several of these, as the common juniper, and the red cedar, (Juniperus *Virginiana*, Ph.) the black and hemlock spruce (Abies *nigra* and A. *canadensis*); the red maple (Acer *rubrum* Mx.) the hop hornbeam (Ostrya *virginica.* L.) the Populus *tremuloides* Mx. Pinus *resinosa* Pyrola *secunda.* Orchis *dilatata*, &c. are common to mountainous districts in all the northern parts of the territory of the United States.   A campanula, probably the C. *uniflora*, bearing a single flower about as large as that of the common hare-bell, occurs very frequently.   Many others are here found which require more careful and extensive comparison with the plants of Mexico, Siberia, and other countries than we have yet had the opportunity to make.

the foot of the primitive mountains, having on our left hand some of the sandstone ridges and hills already described. On our right the brown and naked granite rose in shapeless masses far above our heads, and, occasionally, as we passed the deep fissures worn by the descending torrents, we caught a view of the distant summits, glittering with perpetual frost. In the vallies, towards the east, were many lofty insular hills with perpendicular sides and level table-like summits. They are sometimes disposed in parallel but interrupted ranges, and sometimes irregularly scattered without any appearance of order. In every instance they appeared to be the remains of extensive beds. of sandstone, portions of which had been preserved from disintegration while the contiguous parts had crumbled down and been washed away.

One of these singular hills, of which Mr. Seymour has preserved a sketch, was called the Castle rock, on account of its striking resemblance to a work of art. It has columns, and porticoes, and arches, and, when seen from a distance, has an astonishingly regular and artificial appearance. On approaching it, the base is found enveloped in an extensive accumulation of soil intermixed with fragments of rapidly disintegrating sandstone. The lower portions of the perpendicular sides of the rock are of loosely cemented pudding-stone, but the summit is capped by a compact and somewhat durable sandstone. This is surmouted by a scanty soil in which grow a few stinted oaks and junipers.

We had seen no bisons for several days, but in the afternoon a few were discovered at a distance from our course, and three men despatched in pursuit of them. They were grazing on the side of a hill near a mile distant. As provisions had become scarce, we watched the progress of the hunters with some anxiety. At length the firing commenced, and we enjoyed a distinct, though distant view, of the animating spectacle of a bison hunt. In a short time the hunters joined us, their horses loaded with meat.

In the afternoon we moved on, descending the little stream on which we had halted for dinner. Like the small branches of the Platte it is inhabited by great numbers of beaver, but has more timber and a more fertile soil than any stream of similar magnitude we had lately passed. Some light showers occurred in the middle of the day, and at evening a thunder storm was observed, in the same manner as on the preceding day, to collect in the east, and after we had listened to its thunders for some time it moved off in the direction of the Arkansa, but no rain fell where we were. In the course of the day several elk were seen, and at evening we killed an antelope. Robins are here frequent, and a Jerboa was seen resembling the *Gerbillus canadensis*. Many fine plants were collected, several of which are hitherto undescribed.*

Towards evening our guide discovered we had already passed considerably beyond the base of the Peak, near which it had been our intention to halt. As we were particularly desirous of visiting the mountains at the point designated in many maps as the " *Highest Peak,*" we resolved to return upon our course, but as it was now near sunset we thought it advisable to encamp for the night.

Our journey had been pursued in a bison path, and although not in the direction of our proper course, serving only to pro-long our march without advancing us towards the end of our

* One of these is a large and conspicuous plant of the natural family of the *Cruciferæ*, which may be referred to the new Genus Stanleyea of Nuttall, and distinguished as S. *integrifolia*. *Stem* simple, *leaves* entire, ovate, oblong, tapering to both ends: *stem* angular; *flowers* in a terminal raceme, which is a little branched below; about six inches in length. *Stipe* of the silique, about as long as the pedicel. *Flowers* large, yellow. The whole plant, seen at a little distance, has a remote resemblance to Lysimachia *thyrsifolia* The leaves are five or six inches long, two or three wide, glaucous and veined, in surface and colour, nearly resembling those of the common cabbage, which they are not wholly unlike in taste. The calyx is large, and of a brighter yellow than the other parts of the flower. It inhabits the summits of the sandstone ridges along the base of the mountains. The S. *pinnatifida*, *N.*, the original type of this genus was found by its discoverer, Mr. Nuttall, to act as a violent emetic. It had been eaten by several of the party, who accompanied him, as a substitute for cabbage.

pilgrimage, yet brought us nearer to that romantic scenery which for many days we had chiefly contemplated with a distant eye. We entered the secondary range along the margin of a deep ravine, which wound with a serpentine course towards the base of the mountain Our progress was sometimes impeded by huge rocky masses, which had been precipitated from some neighbouring height, and sometimes a dense forest of very limited extent, or an immense impending wall, or oblique buttress of rock, which, by its proximity to the eye, vied with the grandeur of the ascending piles beyond. We retraced our path of the preceding day until a small stream running towards the northeast offered us a change of scenery, and a course more in the direction we wished to pursue. The great inequalities of the surface, and the precipitous character of several of the passes, thoroughly tested our confidence in our sure-footed Indian horses and mules. The rude pathway skirted along the base of a high cliff, on whose side, far above our heads, projected a narrow ledge of rocks, frowning defiance to all attempts to ascend. This ledge declined gradually as we proceeded, until it terminated abruptly on the edge of a profound gulf. Here appeared to be the only spot at which the ridge could be ascended. On the brow of the cliff a fragment of rock, and a small portion of earth were suspended, by the binding roots of a solitary pine, offering a frail and precarious foothold. This we chose to ascend, startling and hazardous as the attempt appeared, rather than retrace our steps for several miles, and search for a passage in some other direction. The projecting ledge by which we ascended, had barely sufficient width to admit the passage of a single individual at a time. When we had gained the summit, we allowed our horses a moment's rest, in the partial shade of some straggling oaks; and contemplated, not without a feeling of terror, the danger we had passed. We thus pursued the route marked out for us by the bisons, which always trace the most direct and best course, until turning the side of a mountain of moderate elevation, the ocean of prairie again spread before us. This monotonous plain, of which we had been hitherto so weary, now burst upon the sight, and for a moment exhibited a cheerful and pleasant contrast to the rude mountain ruins, we had, with such toil and hazard, been clambering over. This charm was, however, soon to be dispelled. On descending to the plain, it became, as usual, desirable to find a good situation for an encampment, abounding with grass for the horses, and convenient to a water course. For this purpose, one of the party rode to a small line of timber, about a mile on our left, which ran in a parallel direction to our line of march. He overtook us again at the distance of two or three miles, having discovered a copious stream of water. It was about three miles below the point at which the water had been discovered, that we gained the line of timber, only to experience the mortification of disappointment, in finding a naked bed of sand, the stream having no doubt sunk into the earth, some distance above. We had therefore to undergo the pains of abstinence still longer, until we again sought the timber farther below, where the water had reappeared on the surface.

Near this encampment we first observed the great shrubby cactus,* which forms so conspicuous a feature in the vegetable physiognomy of the plains of the Arkansa. Its trunk is six or eight feet in height, and at the root five or six inches in diameter. It is much branched, the ultimate divisions, consisting of long cylindric articulations. The flowers are as large as those of C. *ferox*, of a purple colour, and are on the ends of the articulations. These last are arranged somewhat in whorls, about the ends of the smaller branches. The surface of every part of the plant, aside from its terrific armature of thorns, is marked by little prominences of near

* Cactus *cylindricus* of Humboldt?

an inch in length, and about one fourth of an inch in breadth, rising considerably and bearing a cluster of radiating spines. At their insertion, these thorns are surrounded by pungent setæ, as in C. *ferox*. The whole plant is so thickly beset with strong spines pointing in every direction, that no animal of any considerable size, can approach it unharmed. It does not form thickets, but each plant is a cluster by itself, and when first seen at a distance, they were mistaken for bisons. We were informed by one of our engagees, who had travelled into the Spanish provinces as far as Monterey, that this plant is common there, and its fruit much esteemed.

The Cacti are considered characteristic of warm and dry climates, like those of Egypt and California.* Perhaps there is no part of the world, where plants of this family, constitute so large a proportion of the vegetable products of the soil, as in the arid plains of the Arkansa. These plains are sufficiently dry, but like those of the Platte and Upper Missouri, where *cacti* are almost equally abundant, they are visited by severe cold in winter.

Another highly interesting plant, which occurs in the most barren and desolate parts of the plain, is a cucurbitaceous vine, resembling some of our common squashes, bearing a small fruit, which is round and smooth, and as large as an orange. It is perennial, having a somewhat ligneous root, four or five inches in diameter, and descending often more than four feet into the earth. We were so fortunate as to meet with it in flower, and also with ripened fruit. It has the acutely margined seed of the Genus *Cucumis*, but in other respects, is closely allied to cucurbita.† In addition

---

* Humboldt's Personal Narrative, Vol. i. p. 362. Philadelphia edition.

† Cucumis? *perennis*, American colycinth.
Calyx seated upon the germ, rugose, coloured, campanulate, exterior divisions subulate.
Masc. Three filaments short and closely cohering, covering the central disc.
Fem. Style short; stigmas three—bipartite.

to these we collected the Zygadenus *elegans, Ph.*, Asclepias *tuberosa*, and some others.

From an elevated ridge, which we passed in the morning, some bisons had been seen at the distance of five miles; and as we were in want of game, Mr. Peale with two hunters, rode forward in pursuit of them. They overtook the herd near a small creek, and attacked one of the largest, which was at length killed. On examining the body, twenty balls were found to have entered in different parts, before the animal fell. They arrived at camp, bringing the meat, at a little after noon.

From this camp we had a distinct view of " the Highest

Fruit, large, orbicular, smooth, about four celled; seeds ovate, gibbous, margin acute; dissepiments spongy, seeds in a double order.

Leaves alternate, triangularly cordate; margin undulate; tendrils axillary, trichotomous.

Stems numerous, procumbent, grooved.

Flowers nearly as large as those of Cucurbita *pepo.*

Fruit nearly sessile round, smooth, and green, resembling a small unripe watermelon.

The leaves are rough, of a glaucous green colour, bitter and nauseous to the taste, and the whole plant emits a fetid, disagreeable odour.

Root somewhat ligneous, very large, six feet in length, and often four inches in diameter, descending perpendicularly into the earth. It inhabits the arid and sandy wastes, along the base of the Rocky Mountains, from the confluence of the Arkansa and Boiling spring fork, to the sources of Red river. By means of its long and somewhat succulent root, is is peculiarly adapted to the soil it occupies, and thrives with considerable vigour in wastes, whose thirsty and burning soils, bid defiance to almost every other vegetable. It flowers in July, and continues flowering and perfecting fruit during the summer. Some plants of this interesting species, are growing in the garden of the University at Philadelphia, also in that of Dr. Ewing, from seeds brought by Major Long, but they have not yet flowered. The leaves are thick and robust, from six to eight inches long, and four or five in width, on foot stalks equalling the leaves in length. They are crowded along the stems, and usually stand erect. It does not appear, that any insect, or animal, preys upon the leaves or other parts of this plant. It forms by its deep green, a striking contrast to the general aspect of the regions it inhabits, which are exceedingly naked and barren. This plant has been mentioned by Mr. Brackenridge, under the name of " Arkansa simblin," from the information of hunters, but no detailed account of it has hitherto been given.

The petioles, and the extremities of the stems, are usually affected with morbid enlargements, resembling galls. They may perhaps be caused, by the irritation of the intense reflected light and heat of the sun, in the situations where the plant usually grows. In the gardens it has not hitherto produced these enlargements.

Peak." It appeared about twenty miles distant, towards the northwest; our view was cut off from the base, by an intervening spur of less elevation, but all the upper part of the Peak was visible, with patches of snow, extending down to the commencement of the woody region.

At about one o'clock **P. M.**, a dense black cloud was seen to collect in the southwest, and advancing towards the Peak, it remained nearly stationary over that part of the mountains, pouring down torrents of rain. The thunder was loud and frequent, and though little rain fell near our camp, the creek soon began to swell, and before sunset it had risen about six feet, and again subsided nearly to its former level. When the stream began to rise, it was soon covered with such a quantity of bison's dung, suddenly washed in from the declivities of the mountains and the plains at its base, that the water could scarcely be seen.

As one of the objects of our excursion was to ascertain the elevation of the Peak, it was determined to remain in our present camp for three days, which would afford an opportunity for some of the party to ascend the mountain.

CHAPTER II.

Excursion to the summit of the Peak—Mineral Springs—
Coquimbo Owl—Encampment on the Arkansa.

AT an early hour on the morning of the 13th, Lieutenant
Swift, accompanied by the guide, was despatched from camp,
to measure a base near the Peak, and to make there a part of
the observations requisite for calculating its elevation. Dr.
James being furnished with four men, two to be left at the
foot of the mountain to take care of the horses, and two to
accompany him in the proposed ascent to the summit of the
Peak, set off at the same time.

This detachment left the camp before sunrise, and taking
the most direct route across the plains, arrived at eleven
o'clock, at the base of the mountain. Here Lieutenant Swift
found a place suited to his purpose, where also was a convenient spot for those who were to ascend the mountain, to
leave their horses in a narrow valley, dividing transversely
several sandstone ridges, and extending westward to the base
of the Peak.

After establishing their horse camp, the detachment moved up the valley on foot, arriving about noon at the Boiling
spring, where they dined on a saddle of venison, and some
bison ribs, they had brought ready cooked from camp.

The Boiling spring is a large and beautiful fountain of water, cool and transparent, and highly aerated with carbonic
acid. It rises on the brink of a small stream, which here descends from the mountain, at the point where the bed of this
stream divides the ridge of sandstone, which rests against
the base of the first granitic range.

The water of the spring deposits a copious concretion of

carbonate of lime,* which has accumulated on every side, until it has formed a large basin overhanging the stream. This basin is of a snowy whiteness, and large enough to contain three or four hundred gallons, and is constantly overflowing. The spring rises from the bottom of the basin, with a rumbling noise, discharging about equal volumes of air and of water, probably about fifty gallons per minute, the whole being kept in constant agitation. The water is beautifully transparent, and has the sparkling appearance, the grateful taste, and the exhilarating effect of the most strongly ærated artificial mineral waters.

Distant a few rods from this, is another spring of the same kind, which discharges no water, its basin remaining constantly full, and air only escaping from it. We collected some of the air from both of these springs, in a box we had carried for the reception of plants, but could not perceive it to have the least smell, or the power of extinguishing flame, which was tested by plunging into it lighted splinters of dry cedar.

The temperature of the water of the larger spring at noon was 63°, the thermometer at the same time in the shade, stood at 68°; immersed in the small spring, at 67°. This difference in temperature, is owing to the difference of situation, the higher temperature of the small spring, depending entirely on its constant exposure to the rays of the sun, and to its retaining the same portion of water, while that in the large spring is constantly replaced by a new supply.

After we had dined, and hung up some provisions in a

---

* It is well known, that water in which carbonic acid is dissolved, has the power of holding in solution, a portion of lime, somewhat proportioned in quantity to the acid. In this instance, the water no sooner comes in contact with the atmosphere, than it parts with a portion of its fixed air, consequently losing the power of holding in solution the lime, which is immediately deposited. The lime may perhaps be derived from the cement of the sand rock, or possibly from the granite. Captain Hodgson, found a rivulet among the high and exclusively granitic mountains of the Hymalaya, near the sources of the Ganges, so impregnated with calcareous matter, as to deposit an incrustation on every thing it touched. See *Annals of Philosophy, for July* 1822, p. 36.

large red cedar tree, near the spring, intending it for a supply on our return, we took leave of Lieutenant Swift and began to ascend the mountain. We carried with us, each a small blanket, ten or twelve pounds of bison meat, three gills of parched-corn meal, and a small kettle.

The sandstone extends westward from the springs, about three hundred yards, rising rapidly upon the base of the mountain. It is of a deep red colour, usually compact and fine, but sometimes embracing angular fragments of petrosilx and other silicious stones, with a few organic impressions. The granite which succeeds it, is coarse, and of a deep red colour. Some loose fragments of gneiss, were seen lying about the surface, but none in place. The granite at the base of the mountain, contains a large proportion of feldspar of the rose-coloured variety, in imperfect cubic crystals, and disintegrating rapidly under the operation of frost and other causes, crumbling into small masses of half an ounce weight or less.

In ascending, we found the surface in many places, covered with this loose and crumbled granite, rolling from under our feet, and rendering the ascent extremely difficult. We began to credit the assertions of the guide, who had conducted us to the foot of the Peak; and left us with the assurance, that the whole of the mountain to its summit, was covered with loose sand and gravel, so that though many attempts had been made by the Indians and by hunters to ascend it, none had ever proved successful. We passed several of these tracks, not without some apprehension for our lives, as there was danger when the foot-hold was once lost of sliding down, and being thrown over precipices.

After clambering with extreme fatigue over about two miles, in which several of these dangerous places occurred, we halted at sunset in a small cluster of fir trees. We could not, however, find a piece of even ground large enough to lie down upon, and were under the necessity of securing ourselves from rolling into the brook, near which we encamped, by means of a pole placed against two trees. In this situation we passed an uneasy night, and, though the mercury fell only to 54°, felt some inconvenience from cold.

On the morning of the 14th, as soon as daylight appeared, having suspended in a tree, whatever articles of clothing could be dispensed with, our blankets and provisions, except about three pounds of bison flesh, we continued the ascent, hoping to be able to reach the summit of the Peak, and return to the same camp in the evening. After passing about half a mile of rugged and difficult travelling, like that of the preceding day, we crossed a deep chasm, opening towards the bed of the small stream we had hitherto ascended, and following the summit of the ridge between these, found the way less difficult and dangerous.

Having passed a level tract of several acres, covered with the aspen poplar, a few birches and pines, we arrived at a small stream running towards the south, nearly parallel to the base of the conic part of the mountain, which forms the summit of the Peak. From this spot, we could distinctly see almost the whole of the Peak, its lower half thinly clad with pines, junipers, and other evergreen trees; the upper a naked conic pile of yellowish rocks, surmounted here and there with broad patches of snow; but the summit appeared so distant, and the ascent so steep, that we despaired of accomplishing the ascent, and returning on the same day.

In marshy places about this part of the mountain, we saw an undescribed white flowered species of caltha, some Spediculariæ, the shrubby cinquefoil, (Potentilla *fruticosa, Ph.*) and many alpine plants.

The day was agreeably bright and calm. As we ascended rapidly, a manifest change of temperature was perceptible, and before we reached the outskirts of the timber, a little wind was felt from the northeast. On this part of the mountain, the yellow flowered stone-crop, (Sedum *stenope-*

talum, Ph.) is almost the only herbaceous plant which occurs. The boundary of the region of forests, is a defined
line encircling the peak in a part which, when seen from the
plain, appeared near the summit, but when we arrived at
it, a greater part of the whole elevation of the mountain,
seemed still before us. Above the timber the ascent is steeper,
but less difficult than below, the surface being so highly inclined, that the large masses when loosened roll down, meeting no obstruction, until they arrive at the commencement of
the timber. The red cedar, and the flexile pine,* are the
trees which appear at the greatest elevation. These are small,
having thick and extremely rigid trunks, and near the commencement of the woodless part of the mountain, they have
neither limbs nor bark on the side exposed to the descending
masses of rocks. These trees have not probably grown in a
situation so exposed, as to be unable to produce or retain
bark or limbs on one side; the timber must formerly have
extended to a greater elevation on the sides of this peak,
than at present, so that those trees, which are now on the
outskirts of the forest, were formerly protected by their more
exposed neighbours.

A few trees were seen above the commencement of snow,
but these are very small and entirely procumbent, being sheltered in the crevices and fissures of the rock. There are also
the roots of trees to be seen at some distance, above the part
where any are now standing.

A little above the point where the timber disappears entirely, commences a region of astonishing beauty, and of great
interest on account of its productions; the intervals of soil
are sometimes extensive, and are covered with a carpet of
low but brilliantly flowering alpine plants. Most of these
have either matted procumbent stems, or such as including
the flower, rarely rise more than an inch in height. In many

* Pinus *flexilis*, J.

of them, the flower is the most conspicuous and the largest part of the plant, and in all, the colouring is astonishingly brilliant.

A deep blue is the prevailing colour among these flowers, and the Pentstemon *erianthera*, the mountain Columbine, (Aquilegia *cœrulea*) and other plants common to less elevated districts, were here much more intensely coloured, than in ordinary situations.

It cannot be doubted, that the peculiar brilliancy of colouring, observed in alpine plants, inhabiting near the utmost limits of phænogamous vegetation, depends in a great measure on the intensity of the light transmitted from the bright and unobscured atmosphere of those regions, and increased by reflection from the immense impending masses of snow. May the deep cœrulean tint of the sky, be supposed to have an influence in producing the corresponding colour, so prevalent in the flowers of these plants?

At about two o'clock we found ourselves so much exhausted, as to render a halt necessary. Mr. Wilson who had accompanied us as a volunteer, had been left behind some time since, and could not now be seen in any direction. As we felt some anxiety on his account, we halted and endeavoured to apprize him of our situation; but repeated calls, and the discharging of the rifleman's piece produced no answer. We therefore determined to wait some time to rest, and to eat the provisions we had brought, hoping in the meantime he would overtake us.

Here, as we were sitting at our dinner, we observed several small animals, nearly of the size of the common gray squirrel, but shorter and more clumsily formed. They were of a dark gray colour, inclining to brown, with a short thick head, and erect rounded ears. In habits and appearance, they resemble the prairie dog, and are believed to be a species of the same genus. The mouth of their burrow is usually placed under the projection of a rock, and near these we afterwards saw several of the little animals, watching our approach and uttering a shrill note, somewhat like that of the ground squirrel. Several attempts were made to procure a specimen of this animal, but always without success, as we had no guns but such as carried a heavy ball.

After sitting about half an hour, we found ourselves somewhat refreshed, but much benumbed with cold. We now found it would be impossible to reach the summit of the mountain, and return to our camp of the preceding night, during that part of the day which remained; but as we could not persuade ourselves to turn back, after having so nearly accomplished the ascent, we resolved to take our chance of spending the night, on whatever part of the mountain, it might overtake us. Wilson had not yet been seen, but as no time could be lost, we resolved to go as soon as possible to the top of the Peak, and look for him on our return. We met, as we proceeded, such numbers of unknown and interesting plants, as to occasion much delay in collecting, and were under the disagreeable necessity of passing by numbers which we saw in situations difficult of access. As we approached the summit, these became less frequent, and at length ceased entirely. Few cryptogamous plants are seen about any part of the mountain, and neither these nor any others occur frequently on the top of the Peak. There is an area of ten or fifteen acres, forming the summit, which is nearly level, and on this part scarce a lichen is to be seen. It is covered to a great depth with large splintery fragments of a rock, entirely similar to that found at the base of the Peak, except, perhaps, a little more compact in its structure.

By removing a few of these fragments, they were found to rest upon a bed of ice, which is of great thickness, and may, perhaps, be as permanent and as old as the rocks, with which it occurs.

It was about 4 o'clock P. M., when we arrived on the summit. In our way we had attempted to cross a large field of snow, which occupied a deep ravine, extending down half a mile from the top, on the south-eastern side of the Peak. This was found impassable, being covered with a thin ice, not sufficiently strong to bear the weight of a man. We had not been long on the summit, when we were rejoined by the man, who had separated from us near the outskirts of the timber. He had turned aside and lain down to rest, and afterwards pursued the ascent by a different route.

From the summit of the Peak, the view towards the north, west, and southwest, is diversified with innumerable mountains, all white with snow; and on some of the more distant, it appears to extend down to their bases. Immediately under our feet on the west, lay the narrow valley of the Arkansa, which we could trace running towards the northwest, probably more than sixty miles.

On the north side of the Peak, was an immense mass of snow and ice. The ravine, in which it lay, terminated in a woodless and apparently fertile valley, lying west of the first great ridge, and extending far towards the north. This valley must undoubtedly contain a considerable branch of the Platte. In a part of it, distant probably thirty miles, the smoke of a fire was distinctly seen, and was supposed to indicate the encampment of a party of Indians.*

To the east lay the great plain, rising as it receded, until, in the distant horizon, it appeared to mingle with the sky. A little want of transparency in the atmosphere, added to the great elevation from which we saw the plain, prevented our distinguishing the small inequalities of the surface. The Arkansa with several of its tributaries, and some of the branches of the Platte, could be distinctly traced as on a map, by the line of timber along their courses.

---

* It is related in Du Pradt's History of Louisiana, page 71, that in the year 1724, a large tribe of Indians, called Padoucas, resided in several villages on the heads of the Konzas river, that they removed thence to the sources of the Platte, where they are said still to exist. [See Brackenridge's views, page 147. Lewis and Clark's Map, &c.] But these accounts need confirmation.

On the south the mountain is continued, having another summit (probably that ascended by Captain Pike,) at the distance of eight or ten miles. This, however, falls much below the High Peak in point of elevation, being wooded quite to its top. Between the two lies a small lake, about a mile long and half a mile wide, discharing eastward into the Boiling-spring creek. A few miles farther towards the south, the range containing these two peaks terminates abruptly.

The weather was calm and clear, while we remained on the Peak, but we were surprised to observe the air in every direction filled with such clouds of grasshoppers, as partially to obscure the day. They had been seen in vast numbers about all the higher parts of the mountain, and many had fallen upon the snow and perished. It is perhaps difficult to assign the cause, which induces these insects to ascend to those highly elevated regions of the atmosphere. Possibly they may have undertaken migrations to some remote district, but there appears not the least uniformity in the direction of their movements.* They extended upwards from the summit of the mountain, to the utmost limit of vision, and as the sun shone brightly, they could be seen by the glittering of their wings, at a very considerable distance.

About all the woodless parts of the mountain, and particularly on the summit, numerous tracks were seen resembling those of the common deer, but they most probably have been those of the big-horn. The skulls and horns of these animals we had repeatedly seen near the licks and saline springs at the foot of the mountain, but they are known to resort principally about the most elevated and inaccessible places.

The party remained on the summit only about half an hour.

---

* Notes referring particularly to this grasshopper, and to many other insects, and many other animals, collected on the Platte, and about the mountains, were subsequently lost, in the robbery committed by three of the soldiers, who deserted from the party in the country of the Osages. It is on this account that the name of the insect alluded to, cannot be given, as it is now impossible to identify the specimen.

In this time the mercury fell to 42°, the thermometer hanging against the side of a rock, which in all the early part of the day, had been exposed to the direct rays of the sun. At the encampment of the main body in the plains, a corresponding thermometer stood, in the middle of the day, at 96°, and did not fall below 80°, until a late hour in the evening.

Great uniformity was observed in the character of the rock about all the upper part of the mountain. It is a compact, indestructible aggregate of quartz and feldspar, with a little hornblend in very small particles. Its fracture is fine granular or even, and the mass exhibits a tendency to divide when broken into long, somewhat splintery fragments. It is of a yellowish-brown colour, which does not perceptibly change by long exposure to the air. It is undoubtedly owing to the close texture and the impenetrable firmness of this rock, that so few lichens are found upon it. For the same reason it is little subject to disintegration by the action of frost. It is not improbable that the splintery fragments which occur in such quantities on all the higher parts of the Peak, may owe their present form to the agency of lightning; no other cause seems adequate to the production of so great an effect.

Near the summit, some large detached crystals of feldspar, of a pea-green colour, were collected; also large fragments of transparent, white and smoky quartz, and an aggregate of opake white quartz, with crystals of hornblend.

About five in the afternoon we began to descend, and a little before sunset arrived at the commencement of the timber, but before we reached the small stream at the bottom of the first descent, we perceived we had missed our way. It was now become so dark, as to render an attempt to proceed extremely hazardous, and as the only alternative, we kindled a fire, and laid ourselves down on the first spot of level ground we could find. We had neither provisions nor blankets; and our clothing was by no means suitable for passing the night in so bleak and inhospitable a situation. We could not, however, proceed without imminent danger from precipices, and by the aid of a good fire, and no ordinary degree of fatigue, we found ourselves able to sleep during a greater part of the night.

At day-break on the following morning the thermometer stood at 38°; as we had few comforts to leave, we quitted our camp as soon as the light was sufficient to enable us to proceed, and had travelled about three hours, when we discovered a dense column of smoke rising from a deep ravine on our left. As we concluded this could be no other than the smoke of the encampment where we had left our blankets and provisions, we descended directly towards it. The fire had spread and burnt extensively among the leaves, dry grass, and small timber, and was now raging over an extent of several acres. This created some apprehension lest the smoke might attract the notice of any Indians, who should be at that time in the neighbourhood, and who might be tempted by our weakness to offer some molestation. But we soon discovered a less equivocal cause of regret, in the loss of our *caché* of provisions, blankets, clothing, &c. which had not escaped the conflagration. Most of our baggage was destroyed, but out of the ruins we collected a scanty breakfast, of the half consumed fragments of the bison's meat. We chose a different route for the remaining part of the descent, from the one we had taken in going up, and by that means avoided a part of the difficulty arising from the crumbled granite; but this was nearly counterbalanced by the increased numbers of yuccas and prickly pears.

We arrived, a little after noon, at the Boiling spring, where we indulged freely in the use of its highly ærated and exhilarating waters. In the bottom of both these springs a great number of beads and other small articles of Indian ornament were found, having unquestionably been left there as sacrifices or presents to the springs, which are regarded with a sort

of veneration by the savages. Bijeau assured us he had repeatedly taken beads and other ornaments from these springs
and sold them to the same savages, who had thrown them in.

A large and much frequented road passes the springs and
enters the mountains, running to the north of the high Peak.
It is travelled principally by the bisons, sometimes also by
the Indians who penetrate here to the Columbia.

The men who had been left at the horse camp, about a
mile below the springs, had killed several deer, and had a
plentiful supply of provisions. Here we dined; then mount-
ing our horses proceeded towards the encampment of the
main body, where we arrived a little after dark, having completed our excursion within the time prescribed.

Among the plants collected in this excursion, several appear to be undescribed. Many of them are strictly alpine,
being confined to the higher parts of the mountain, above the
commencement of snow.

Most of the trees which occur on any part of the mountain are evergreen, consisting of several species of abies,
among which may be enumerated the balsam fir, (A. *balsa-
mea, Ph.*) the hemlock, white, red, and black spruce, (A. *canadensis. A. alba. A. rubra* and A. *nigra,)* the red cedar, and
common juniper, and a few pines. One of these, which appears
to have been hitherto unnoticed in North America, has, like
the great white or Weymouth pine, five leaves in a fascicle,
but in other respects there is little resemblance between
them. The leaves are short and rather rigid, the sheathes
which surround their bases, short and lacerated; the stro-
biles erect, composed of large unarmed scales, being somewhat smaller than those of P. *rigida,* but similar in shape,
and exuding a great quantity of resin. The branches which
are covered with leaves chiefly at the ends, are numerous
and recurved, inclining to form a dense and large top: they
are also remarkably flexile, feeling in the hand somewhat
like those of the Dirca *palustris.* From this circumstance,

the specific name *flexilis*, has been proposed for this tree, which is in several respects remarkably contrasted with the **P**. *rigida*. It inhabits the arid plains subjacent to the Rocky Mountains, and extends up their sides to the region of perpetual frost. The fruit of the Pinus flexilis is eaten by the Indians and French hunters about the Rocky Mountains, as is that of another species of the same genus by the inhabitants of some parts of Europe.

The creek, on which the party encamped during the three days, occupied in making the excursion above detailed, is called Boiling-spring creek, having one of its principal sources in the beautiful spring already described. It is skirted with a narrow margin of cotton-wood and willow trees, and its banks produce a small growth of rushes on which our horses subsisted, while we lay encamped here. This plant, the common rush, (Equisetum *hiemale*, *Ph.*) found in every part of the United States, is eaten with avidity by horses, and it is often met with in districts where little grass is to be had. When continued for a considerable time, its use proves deleterious.

The recent tracks of a grizzly bear were observed near the camp, and at no great distance one of those animals was seen and shot at, by one of the hunters, but not killed.

In the timber along the creek, the sparrow hawk, mocking bird, robin, red-head woodpecker, dove, winter wren, towhe-bunting, yellow-breasted chat, and several other birds were seen.

Orbicular lizards were found about this camp, and had been once or twice before noticed near the base of the mountains.

A smoke supposed to be that of an Indian encampment was seen, rising from a part of the mountains at a great distance towards the northwest. It had been our constant practice since we left the Missouri, to have sentinels stationed about all our encampments, and whenever we were not on the march by day, and until nine o'clock in the evening it was the duty of one of the three Frenchmen, to reconnoitre at a distance from camp in every direction, and to report immediately when any thing should be discovered, indicating that Indians were in the vicinity. Precautions of this kind are highly necessary to prevent surprisal, and are invariably practised by the Indians of the west, both at their villages and on their march.

On the 14th, Lieutenant Swift returned to camp, having performed the duties on which he was sent.

A base was measured near the camp, and observations taken for ascertaining the elevation of the Peak. These are detailed in the appendix to this volume, and in Major Long's report, may be seen an account of the method used to estimate the actual elevation of the point at which these observations were made. The entire elevation of the Peak above the level of the ocean, ascertained in the manner there described, is eleven thousand five hundred feet.

Complete sets of observations for latitude and longitude were taken, which gave 38° 18' 9" north, and 105° 39' 49" west from Greenwich, or 28° 39' 45" from Washington, as the position of our camp. The bearing of the Peak from this point is north, 67° west, and the distance about twenty-five miles.

In all the prairie-dog villages we had passed, small owls had been observed moving briskly about, but they had hitherto eluded all our attempts to take them. One was here caught, and on examination found to be the species denominated Coquimbo, or burrowing owl, (Strix *cunicularia*.)

This fellow citizen of the prairie dog, unlike its grave and recluse congeners, is of a social disposition, and does not retire from the light of the sun, but endures the strongest mid-day glare of that luminary, and is in all respects a diurnal bird. It stands high upon its legs, and flies with the rapidity of the hawk. The Coquimbo owl, both in Chili and

St. Domingo, agreeably to the accounts of Molina and Viellot, digs large burrows for its habitation and for the purposes of incubation; the former author gives us to understand that the burrow penetrates the earth to a considerable depth, whilst Viellot informs us, that in St. Domingo the depth is about two feet.

With us the owl never occurred but in the prairie-dog villages, sometimes in a small flock, much scattered and often perched on different hillocks, at a distance, deceiving the eye with the appearance of the prairie dog itself, in an erect posture. They are not shy, but readily admit the hunter within gunshot, but on his too near approach, a part or the whole of them rise upon the wing, uttering a note very like that of the prairie dog, and alight at a short distance, or continue their flight beyond the view.

The burrows, into which we have seen the owl descend, resembled in all respects those of the prairie dog, leading us to suppose either that they were common, though, perhaps, not friendly occupants of the same burrow, or that the owl was the exclusive tenant of a burrow gained by the right of conquest. But it is at the same time probable, that, as in Chili, the owl may excavate his own tenement.

From the remarkable coincidence of note, between these two widely distinct animals, we might take occasion to remark, the probability of the prairie dog being an unintentional tutor to the young owl, did we not know that this bird utters the same sounds in the West Indies, where the prairie dog is not known to exist.

It may be, that more than a single species of diurnal owl has been confounded under the name of cunicularia, as Viellot states his bird to be somewhat different from that of Molina, and we cannot but observe that the eggs of the birds described by the latter are spotted with yellow, whilst those of the former are immaculate.

As our specimens do not in all respects correspond with

the descriptions of the above mentioned authors of the Coquimbo owl, we have thought proper to subjoin such particulars as seem necessary to be noted in addition to the description already given by those authors.*

The general colour is a light burnt-brown, spotted with white; the larger feathers five or six banded, with white, each band more or less widely interrupted by the shaft, and their immediate margins, darker than the other portions of the feather; the tips of these feathers are white or whitish; the exterior primary feather is serrated, shorter than the three succeeding ones, and equal in length to the fifth; the bill is tinged with yellow on the ridges of both mandibles; the tarsi and feet distinctly granulated, the former naked behind, furnished before near the base with dense short feathers, which towards the toes become less crowded, and assume the form of single hairs, these on the toes are absolutely setaceous and scattered; the lobes beneath the toes are large and granulated.

In the plains about our encampment, were several natural mounds, greatly resembling some of the artificial works so common in the central portions of the great valley of the Mississippi. About the summits of these mounds were numerous petrifactions, which were found to be almost exclusively casts of bivalve shells, approaching the genus Cytherea, and usually from one half to one and an half inches in diameter.

On the evening of the fifteenth, finding all our stock of meat injured by too long keeping, four men were sent out on horseback to hunt. At the distance of six miles from camp, they found a solitary bison, which they killed, but concluding from its extreme leanness and the ill savour of the flesh, that the animal was diseased, they took no part of it. On the following morning they returned unsuccessful. We

---

* We have to regret that the plan of this work, will not admit of the introduction of figures, of the many interesting animals that were obtained, described, and delineated during the expedition.

were now reduced to the necessity of feeding on our scanty allowance of a gill of parched maize per day to each man, this being the utmost our limited stores would afford.

On the sixteenth of July, we moved from our encampment on Boiling-spring creek, in a south-western direction to the Arkansa. This ride of twenty-eight miles, which we finished without having once dismounted from our horses, occupied about ten hours of a calm sultry day, in every respect like the preceding, in which the thermometer in the shade had ranged from 90 to 100°. Our route lay across a tract of low, but somewhat broken sandstone of an uncommonly slaty structure. It is fine-grained with an argillaceous cement, and of a light gray or yellowish-white colour. It contains thin beds of bituminous clay slate, and we saw scattered on the surface some small crystals of Selenite. It is traversed by numerous deep ravines in which at this time not a drop of water was to be found.

The soil is scanty and of incurable barrenness. The texture of the rock is so loose and porous, as to unfit it for retaining any portion of the water which falls upon it in rains. A few dwarfish cedars and pines are scattered over a surface of loose dusty soil intermixed with thin lamellar fragments of sandstone, and nearly destitute of grass or herbage of any kind. Our sufferings from thirst, heat, and fatigue were excessive, and were aggravated by the almost unlimited extent of the prospect before us, which promised nothing but a continuation of the same dreary and disgusting scenery. Late in the afternoon we arrived at the brink of the precipice which divides the high plains from the valley of the Arkansa. This is here narrow, and so deeply sunk in the horizontal sandstone, that although there are trees of considerable size growing along the river, they do not rise to the level of the surface of the great plain, and from a little distance on either side the valley is entirely hid. Here our thirst and impatience were for some time tantalized with the view of the cool and verdant valley

and copious stream of the Arkansa, while we were searching up and down for a place where we could descend the precipice.

At length, a rugged ravine was discovered, down which
we with some difficulty wound our way to the base of the
cliff, where lay a beautiful level plain, having some scattered
cotton-wood and willow trees, and affording good pasture
for our horses. Here we encamped, and the remainder of
the afternoon was spent in making preparations to despatch
a small party up the Arkansa to the mountains on the succeeding day.

A small doe was killed near camp, which, though extremely lean, proved an important addition to our supply of provisions.

The place where we encamped was supposed to have been
near where Pike's block house formerly stood, but we sought
in vain for the traces of any thing resembling the work of a
white man.

Some of the birds taken at this encampment are described
in the subjoined note.*

* 1. *Fringilla psaltria*, SAY. A very pretty little bird was frequently
seen hopping about in the low trees or bushes, singing sweetly, somewhat
in the manner of the American goldfinch, or hemp-bird, (Fringilla *trist s.*)
The tints and the distribution of the colours of its plumage resemble in a
considerable degree those of the autumnal and less brilliant vesture of
that well known species. It may however be distinguished in addition to
other differences, by the black tip of its tail feathers, and the white wing
spot.   .
The head is capped with black; the cheeks are dusky; the bill yellow,
with a black tip; the iris, burnt umber; neck above. and half its side, back
and rump olivaceous, more or less intermixed with dusky; smaller wing-
coverts blackish edged with olivaceous; greater wing-coverts brown-black
tipped with white, forming a narrow band; primaries fuscous, and, excepting the exterior one, slightly edged with white; third, fourth, and fifth
feathers, white towards the base, so as to exhibit a white spot beyond the
wing-coverts; secondaries, margined with white exteriorly towards their
tips; tail-coverts black, varied with olivaceous on their shafts; tail, emarginate, feathers blackish, slightly edged with dull whitish; the three exterior ones pure white on their inner webs excepting at base and tip; all beneath yellow; feet pale.
A specimen is deposited in the Philadelphia Museum.
2. *Fringilla frontalis*. SAY. Crimson-necked Finch; head, throat, neck

beneath and upper portion of the breast brilliant crimson, most intense near the bill and over the eyes; rump and tail coverts paler crimson; between the bill and the eyes gray; bill dark brown colour; lower mandible paler; occiput, neck above and each side brown tinged with reddish, the feathers margined with pale; back dusky, brownish; wings and tail fuscous, the latter feathers edged on the inner side with white; the primaries broadly margined within towards the base with white and exteriorly edged with grayish; coverts and tertials edged with dull grayish; inferior portion of the breast, the belly and vent whitish, each feather with a broad fuscous line

Female. Dusky brown, the feathers margined each side with dull whitish; wings fuscous, the margining and edging of the feathers not so distinct as in the male; all beneath, excepting the tail and wing feathers whitish, each feather with a brown streak.

This bird is much more clearly allied both in size and colouring to the Purple Finch (F. *purpurea*) than to the Crimson-headed Finch (F. *rosea*) and may prove to be only a variety of it when a comparison of many individuals can be made. The male, from which the above description is drawn out, may not be in its ultimate state of plumage, as it seems probable that the middle of the head, the upper part of the neck, and the back, in the perfect plumage, is more obviously tinted with crimson, than we have observed those parts to be. It differs, however, from the Purple finch in the tint of the crimson colour, which is far more lively and brilliant, and also in having each feather of the belly, vent, and inferior tail-coverts broadly streaked with brown. We apply to it provisionally the name of F. *frontalis*—A prepared specimen of this bird is in the Philadelphia Museum.

CHAPTER III.

A detachment from the exploring party ascend the Arkansa to the Rocky Mountains—Bell's Springs—Descent of the Arkansa—Grizzly Bear.

On the morning of the 17th, Captain Bell, with Dr. James and two men, left the encampment of the party proposing to ascend the Arkansa to the mountains. They were furnished with provisions for two days, according to the scanty allowance to which now we were reduced.

The river valley was found so narrow and so obstructed by the timber and the windings of the stream as greatly to obstruct the travelling. We therefore resolved to leave it, and pursue our journey in the open plain at a distance from the river. The course of the Arkansa for the first twenty miles from the mountain is but little south of east. It enters the plain at one extremity of an extensive amphitheatre formed by the continued chain of the mountains on the west and northwest and by the projecting spur which contains the High Peak on the east. This semicircular area is about thirty miles in length from north to south and probably twenty wide at its southern extremity. The mountains which bound it on the west are high, and at this time were partially covered with snow.

The surface of the area is an almost unvaried plain, based on a stratum of argillaceous sandstone. Near the foot of the mountain the same sandstone is observed resting in an inclined position against the primitive rocks. It forms a range like that already mentioned when speaking of the mountains at the Platte separated from the primitive, by a narrow valley. On entering this valley, we found the recent trace of a large party of Indians travelling with skin lodges, who appeared to have passed within a very short time. This trace we followed until we found it entered the mountains in the valley of a small stream which descends to the Arkansa from the northeast. This we left on the east, and traversing a rough and broken tract of sandstone hills, arrived after a toilsome journey of about thirty miles at the spot where the Arkansa leaves the mountains.

Here we found several springs whose water is impregnated with muriate of soda and other salts. They rise near each other in a small marshy tract of ground occupying the narrow valley of the river at the point where it traverses the inclined sandstone ridge. Very little water flows from them, and the evaporation of this has left a crystalline incrustation whitening the surface of the surrounding marsh. The springs are small excavations, which may perhaps have been dug by the Indians or by white hunters. They appear to remain constantly full; they all contain muriate of soda, and the smell of sulphuretted hydrogen is perceptible at a considerable distance from them. They differ in taste a little from each other; hence the account given of them by hunters that one is sour, another sweet, a third bitter, and so on. One contains so much fixed air as to give it considerable pungency, but the water of all of them is unpalatable. The sweetish, metallic taste observed in the water of one or two, appears to depend on an impregnation of sulphate of iron.

The sulphates of magnesia and soda will probably be found to exist in these springs, if their water should hereafter be analyzed; they may also be found to possess some active medicinal properties. They are seven in number, and have received the name of Bell's springs, in compliment to their discoverer. Though the country around them abounds with bisons, deer, &c., they do not appear to be frequented as most saline springs are, by these, or other herbivorous animals.

It was near sunset when Capt. Bell and his party arrived at the springs, and being very much exhausted by their laborious march, they immediately laid themselves down to rest, under the open sky, deferring their examinations for the following morning.

The sandstone near the springs is hard, though rather coarse, and of a dark gray, or brownish-yellow colour.

In ascending the Arkansa on the ensuing morning, we found the rock to become more inclined, and of a redder colour; as we approached the primitive, until at about half a mile from the springs, it is succeeded by the almost perpendicular gneiss rock, which appears here at the base of the first range of the mountains. We have noticed, that this particular spot is designated in the language of hunters, " as the place where the Arkansa *comes out* of the mountains," and it must be acknowledged the expression is not entirely inapplicable. The river pours with great impetuosity and violence through a deep and narrow fissure in the gneiss rock, which rises abruptly on both sides to such a height, as to oppose an impassable barrier to all further progress. According to the delineation of Pike's route on the map which accompanies his work, he must have entered the mountains at this place, but no corroboration can be derived from his journal. It appears almost incredible that he should have passed by this route and neglected to mention the extreme difficulty which must have attended the undertaking. Captain Bell and his party returned to the encampment of the main body, on the 18th.

The immediate valley of the Arkansa, near the mountains, is bounded by high cliffs of inclined sandstone; at a short distance below, these disappear, and a sloping margin of alluvial earth extends on each side to the distance of several miles. Somewhat farther down, horizontal sandstone appears, confining the valley to a very narrow space, and bounding it within perpendicular precipices òn each side. Seven miles from the mountains, on the left bank of the Arkansa, is a remarkable mass of sandstone rocks, resembling a huge pile of architectural ruins. From this point, the bearing of James' Peak* was found to be due north.

The Arkansa valley between our encampment of the 18th and the mountains, a distance of about thirty miles, has a meagre and gravelly soil sustaining a growth of small cotton-wood trees, rushes, and coarse grass. Above the rocky bluffs on each side spreads a dreary expanse of almost naked sand, intermixed with clay enough to prevent its drifting with the wind, but not enough to give it fertility. It is arid and sterile, bearing only a few dwarfish cedars, and must forever remain desolate.

Observations were made at camp, for ascertaining the latitude, longitude, &c. and all the party were occupied in their appropriate pursuits. Among the animals taken here, was the four-lined squirrel, (S. 4-vittatus†) a very small and handsome species, very similar in its dorsal markings, to

---

* " From the information of Indians and hunters who have frequently visited this part of the country, as also from the account given by Pike, relative to this Peak, it appears that no person either civilized or savage, had ever ascended it to its summit, and that the ascent was deemed by them, utterly impracticable. Dr. James having accomplished this difficult and hazardous task, I have thought proper to call the Peak after his name, as a compliment, to which his zeal and perseverance, together with the skilful attention with which he has examined its character and productions, give him the fairest claim. Pike has indeed given us notice that there is such a Peak, but he only saw it at a distance. The unfavourable circumstances under which he came into its neighbourhood, preventing his arrival, even at its base. He attempted to ascertain its altitude, but it is believed that his estimate is very erroneous." *Extract from Major Long's MS. Notes, July,* 15*th,* 1820.

† Genus Sciurus, L.

S. *quadrivittatus.* SAY. *Head* brownish intermixed with fulvous, and with four white lines, of which the superior one on each side, passes from the tip of the nose immediately over the eye to the superior base of the ear, and the inferior one passes immediately beneath the eye to the inferior base of the ear; *ears* moderate, semi-oval; *incissores* reddish-yellow; *back* with four white broad lines, and alternate mixed black and ferruginous ones; *sides* fulvous; *beneath* whitish; *tail* moderate, hair black at the base, then fulvous, black in the middle, and paler fulvous at tip, beneath fulvous with a submarginal black line; *thumb* of the anterior feet a prominent tubercle.

Length from the nose to the base of the tail,   4 1-4 inches,   of the tail, ... 3   of the hair at tip of the tail, .   . 1 nearly.

the *getulus, L.;* but as far as we can judge from the description and figures of the latter species by Buffon, our animal
is distinguished by its striped head, less rounded ears, and
much less bushy, and not striated and banded tail, and by
its smaller size. The getulus is also said to have no thumb
warts.

It is an inhabitant of the Rocky Mountains, about the
sources of the Arkansa and Platte. It does not seem to ascend trees by choice, but nestles in holes and on the edge of
the rocks. We did not observe it to have cheek pouches.

Its nest is composed of a most extraordinary quantity of
the burrs of the Xanthium, branches and other portions of
the large upright cactus, small branches of pine trees, and
other vegetable productions, sufficient in some instances to
fill the body of an ordinary cart. What the object of so great
and apparently so superfluous an assembalge of rubbish, may
be, we are at a loss to conjecture, we do not know what peculiarly dangerous enemy it may be intended to exclude by so
much labour.

Their principal food, at least at this season, is the seeds of
the pine which they readily extract from the cones.

There is also another species,* inhabiting about the mountains, where it was first observed by those distinguished travellers Lewis and Clark, on their expedition to the Pacific
ocean. It is allied to the *Sc. striatus,* and belongs to the same
subgenus, (Tamias, Illig.) but it is of a somewhat larger stature,
entirely destitute of the vertebral line, and is further distinguished by the lateral lines, commencing before the humerus

---

* S. *lateralis.* SAY. *Above* brownish-cinereous, intermixed with blackish; each side of the back a dull yellowish-white dilated line, broader before, margined above and beneath with black, originating upon the neck
anterior to the humerus, and not attaining the origin of the tail; no appearance of a vertebral line; *thigh,* neck anterior to the tip of the white
line, and top of the head tinged with ferruginous; *orbit* whitish; *tail* short,
thin, with a submarginal black line beneath; *nails* of the anterior feet
elongated; *thumb* tubercle furnished with a broad nail; *sides* dull yellowish-white; *beneath* pale, intermixed with blackish.

where they are broadest, by the longer nails of the anterior feet, and by the armature of the thumb tubercle. It certainly cannot with propriety be regarded as a variety of the *striatus*, and we are not aware that the latter species is subject to vary to any remarkable degree in this country. But the species, to which, in the distribution of its colours, it is most closely allied, is unquestionably, the *Sc. bilinatus* of Geoffroy. A specimen is preserved in the Philadelphia Museum.

The *cliff swallow*,* is here very frequent, as well as in all the rocky country near the mountains.

A very beautiful species of emberiza† was caught, rather smaller than the indigo bunting, (Emberiza cyanea) with a note entirely dissimilar. It was observed to be much in the grass, rarely alighting on bushes or trees.

* *Hirundo lunifrons.* SAY. *Above* brownish-black, more or less varied with violaceous on the back and wing-coverts; the top of the head exclusively blackish violaceous; a large white frontal lunule; *bill* black; *rump* and *tail-coverts* pale ferruginous: *chin, throat, and neck beneath* dark ferruginous, extending in a narrow band upon the hind head; *breast* pale rufous-ash; *axilla and inferior wing-coverts* dirty brownish; *shoulders* dull whitish, with small black and pale ferruginous spots; *belly, vent, and flanks* white, obsoletely dashed with brown: *inferior tail-coverts* dusky margined with white, *tail entire,* not surpassing the tips of the wings, the exterior margined with white on the inner web; *wing and tail shafts* brown above, white beneath, the tail feathers in some lights have a slightly banded appearance.
Length five and a half inches.
This species attaches its nests, in great numbers, to the rocks in dry situations under projecting ledges. The nest is composed of mud, and is hemispherical, with the entrance near the top, somewhat resembling a chemist's retort, flattened on one side. and with the neck broken off, for the entrance; this entrance which is perfectly rounded, sometimes projects a little and turns downwards. It is an active bird, flying about the vicinity of its nest, in every direction, like the barn swallow. In many of the nests we found young hatched, and in others only eggs.

† *Emberiza amœna.* SAY. *Head* and *neck* bluish-green: *back* brownish black, more or less intermixed with blue and a little brown ferruginous; *rump* pure blue; *smaller wing coverts* dull blue, brown at base, and tipped with white forming a band; *greater wing coverts* blackish, tipped with white, forming a narrow band; *wing and tail feathers* blackish brown, with blue exterior margins; *belly, inferior tail coverts,* and lower part of the breast, white; *superior portion of the breast pale ferruginous; *neck* bright green; *bill* and *feet* pale.

We also captured a rattlesnake,* which like the *tergemi-nus*, we have found to inhabit a barren soil, and to frequent the villages of the Arctomys of the prairie, but its range appeared to us confined chiefly to the vicinity of the Rocky Mountains. Its rattle is proportionally much larger than that of the species just mentioned, and the head is destitute of large plates. It seems by the number of plates and scales, to be allied to the *atracaudatus* of Bosc and Daud, but their description induces the conclusion that their species is entirely white beneath. It is also allied to the Crotalus *durissus*, *L.* (C. rhombifer Beauv.) but is smaller, and the dorsal spots are more rounded. A specimen is placed in the Philadelphia Museum. A new species of Coluber also occurred.†

The only specimens of organic reliquiæ from this vicinity, which we have been so fortunate as to preserve, are very indistinct in their character, and are only impressions on the gray sandstone. One of them appears to have been a phytoid *Millepore*, and the other a subequilateral bivalve, which may possibly have been a *Mactra*. It is suborbicular, and its surface is marked by concentric grooves or undulations. At

* Genus Crotalus. Lin.

1. C. *confluentus*. SAY. Brownish varied with greenish-yellow, a triple series of brown spots, the anterior vertebral ones confluent, and the posterior ones separated into bands.

Body brownish cinereous, varied with greenish-yellow; a triple series of fuscous spots; dorsal series consisting of about forty-four large, transversely oblong-oval spots, each widely emarginate before and behind, and, excepting the posterior ones, edged with greenish-white, the ten or twelve anterior ones crowded, confluent, those of the thicker part of the body separate, those near the cloaca and upon the tail united with the other spots of the lateral series, and forming bands; lateral series, spots rounded and opposite to those of the back; between the dorsal and lateral series, is a series of obsolete, fuliginous spots, alternating with those of the two other series; *head* above scaly, scales of the superior orbits and of the anterior margin larger striated; *beneath* yellowish-white, immaculate.

Plates of the body 197, of the tail 27.

Genus Coluber. Lin.

† 2. C. *testaceus*. Pale sanguineous, or testaceous above, beneath sanguineous, immaculate.

Plates 198, scales 80?

This is a large species, which inhabits near the Rocky Mountains. It moves with great rapidity, and in general form and size resembles *C. constrictor*. The scales are large. A specimen is in the Philadelphia Museum.

a previous encampment, numerous fragments of shells of a dusky colour, occurred in the same variety of sandstone, and amongst these is an entire valve of a small species of Ostrea, of a shape very like that of a *Pinna*, and less than half an inch in length.

We have a specimen, from another locality, of a very dark coloured, compact, and very impure limestone, containing still more blackish fragments of bivalves, one of which presents the form of a much arquated Mytillus, but as the back of the valves only is offered to examination, it may be a *Chama*, but it seems to be perfectly destitute of sculpture.

Another specimen, from the mountains near the Platte is a reddish brick coloured petrosilicious mass, containing casts and impressions of a grooved Terebratula.

Hunters were kept out during the day on the 17th, but killed nothing. At evening they were again sent out on horseback, but did not return until three P. M. on the following day. They had descended the river twelve miles, finding little game. They had killed one deer, one old turkey with her young brood of six. This supply proved highly acceptable, as we had for some time been confined almost entirely to our small daily allowance of corn meal.

At the commencement of our tour, we had taken a small supply of sea biscuit. At first these were distributed, at the rate of three per day to each man; afterwards two, then one, then one for two days, then one for three, till our stock of bread was so nearly exhausted that it was thought proper to reserve the little that remained, for the use of the sick, should any unfortunately require it. We then began upon our parched maize, which proved an excellent substitute for bread. This was issued, at first, at the rate of one pint per day for four men, no distinction being made in this or any other case between the officers and gentlemen of the party, and the citizens and soldiers attached to it. When we arrived at the Arkansa, about one third part of our supply of this article was exhausted, and no augmentation of the daily issues could be allowed, although our supplies of meat had for some time been inadequate to the consumption of the party.

We had a little coffee, tea, and sugar, but these were reserved as hospital stores: our three gallons of salt were expended. We now depended entirely upon hunting for subsistence, as we had done for meat ever since we left the Pawnee villages, our pork having been entirely consumed before we arrived at that place. We, however, apprehended little want of meat, after we should have left the mountains, as we believed there would be plenty of bisons and other game in the plains, over which we were to travel.

At 2 o'clock P. M. on the 18th, rain began to fall, which continued during the remainder of the day, and made it impossible for us to complete the observations we had begun.

The Arkansa, from the mountains to the place of our encampment, has an average breadth of about sixty yards; it is from three to five feet deep, and the current rapid. At the mountains the water was transparent and pure, but soon after entering the plains it becomes turbid and brackish.

19th. This morning we turned our backs upon the mountains, and began to move down the Arkansa. It was not without a feeling of regret, that we found our long contemplated visit to these grand and interesting objects, was now at an end. More than one thousand miles of dreary and monotonous plain lay between us and the enjoyments and indulgences of civilized countries. This we were to traverse in the heat of summer, but the scarcity of game about the mountains rendered an immediate departure necessary.

A large and beautiful animal* of the lizard kind, (be-

---

* Genus Ameiva. A. *Tesselata*. SAY. Tesselated Lizard. The back and sides of the body and neck, are marked by nine or ten longitudinal lines, and eighteen or twenty transverse ones, dividing the whole surface in a tesselated manner, the interstitial quadrate spaces being black; these lines are light brown on the back, and assume a yellow tint on the sides; the scales of these portions of the body are very small, convex and rounded.

The top of the head is olivaceous, covered by plates, arranged thus:

longing to the Genus Ameiva,) was noticed in this day's
ride. It very much resembles the Lacerta Ameiva, as figured and described by Lacepede, but the tail is proportionably
much longer. Its movements were so extremely rapid, that
it was with much difficulty we were able to capture a few
of them.

We had proceeded about eight or ten miles from our
camp, when we observed a very considerable change in the
character, both of the river and its valley; the former becoming wider, less rapid, and filled with numerous islands; the
latter, bounded by sloping sand hills, instead of perpendicular precipices. Here the barren cedar ridges, are succeeded
by still more desolate plains, with scarce a green, or a living
thing upon them, except here and there a tuft of grass, an
orbicular lizard, basking on the scorching sand, a solitary
Pimelia, a Blaps, or a Galeodes; among the few stinted and
withered grasses, we distinguished a small cæspitose species
of Agrostis, and several others, which are thought to be undescribed. Near the river and in spots of uncommon fertility, the unicorn plant, (Martynia *proboscidea, Ph.*) was
growing in considerable perfection. This plant, which is
sometimes cultivated in the gardens, where it is known by
the name of Cuckold's horns, is a native of the Platte and
Arkansa, and is occasionally seen in every part of the open
country from St. Louis, westward to the mountains.

2 with an intermediate small one at their tips; 1, 2, 1 the largest, 2 and
3, superior orbits of the eyes with four plates, of which the two intermediate ones are much the largest; belly bluish-white; throat and neck tinged with yellow, and covered with somewhat larger scales than those of the
back; anterior feet yellowish within, and covered with minute scales, on
the exterior and posterior sides greenish-white, with confluent black
spots and large scales; posterior feet behind greenish-white, with confluent black spots and minute scales, the anterior side yellowish, covered
with large scales; pores of the thigh very distinct and prominent; tail
elongated, rounded, above light brown, with a few lines of black spots
near the base; beneath yellowish-white, immaculate, the scales carinated.
and placed in transverse series.

   Total length 1 foot—Tail 8½ inches.

A little before noon, we crossed a small stream, which was called Castle Rock creek, from a remarkable pile of naked rocks, and halted for dinner on the bank of the river.

In the morning, Mr. Peale and two hunters, had taken a different route from the remainder of the party, hoping to meet with game. They arrived at a small grove of timber, where it was thought deer might be found. They therefore left their horses in care of one of the hunters, and entered the wood on foot. The man had been left alone but a short time, when he discovered a large grizzly bear approaching rapidly towards him, and without staying to make himself acquainted with the intentions of the animal, mounted his horse and fled.

The grizzly bear* is widely distinct from any known spe-

* Ursus *horribilis*, Ord. *Hair* long, short on the front, very short between, and anterior to the eyes, blacker and coarser on the legs and feet, longer on the shoulders, throat, and behind the thighs, and beneath the belly, and paler on the snout; *ears* short, rounded; *front* arquated, the line of the profile continued upon the snout, without any indentation between the eyes; *eyes* very small, destitute of any remarkable supplemental lid; *iris* burnt sciena, or light reddish brown; *muffle of the nostrils* black, the sinus very distinct and profound; *lips*, particularly the superior one, anteriorly extensile, with a few more rigid hairs or bristles; *tail* very short, concealed by the hair. The hair gradually diminishes in length upon the leg, but the upper part of the foot is still amply furnished. *Teeth, incisores* 6, the lateral one with a tubercle on the exterior side; canines large, robust, prominent; a single false molar behind the canine, remaining molares four, of which the anterior one is very small, that of the upper jaw particularly, that of the lower jaw, resembling the second false molar of the common dog.

Anterior feet, claws elongated, slender; fingers with five suboval naked tubercles, separated from the palm, each other, and from the base of the claws by dense hair; palm on the anterior half naked, transversely oval; base of the palm with a rounded naked tubercle, surrounded by the hair.

Posterior feet, with the sole naked, the nails moderate, more arquated, and shorter than the anterior ones.

The nails do not in the least diminish in width at the tip, but they become smaller towards that part, only by diminishing from beneath.

" Testicles suspended in separate pouches, at the distance of from two to four inches from each other."—*Lewis & Clark?*

They vary exceedingly in colour, and pass through the intermediate gradations, from a dark brown to a pale fulvous, and a grayish.

Dimensions from the prepared specimen.

Length from the tip of the nose, to the origin
  of the tail, - - - - - - 5 feet 2 inches.
Trunk of the tail, exclusive of the hair at tip,   1¾

cies of bear, by the essential character of the elongated anterior claws, and rectilinear or slightly arquated figure of its facial profile. In general appearance, it may be compared to the Alpine bear, (U. *arctos*,) and particularly to the Norwegian variety. The claws, however, of these appear to be of the usual form, and not elongated, and the facial space, included between the eyes is deeply indented; they also differ in their manners, and climb trees, which the grizzly bear is never known to do.

Lewis and Clark frequently saw and killed these bears, during their celebrated expedition across the continent. They mention one which was nine feet long, from the nose to the tip of the tail. The fore foot of another, was nine inches across, its hind foot eleven and three quarter inches long, exclusive of the talons, and seven inches wide. The talons of a third, were six and one-fourth inches long.

They will not always attack even when wounded.

" As they fired, he did not attempt to attack, but fled with a most tremendous roar, and such was its extraordinary tenacity of life, that although he had five balls passed through his lungs, and five other wounds, he swam more than half across the river to a sand bar, and survived twenty minutes. He weighed between five and six hundred pounds at least,

From anterior base of the ear to the tip of the nose,	12 inches.
From anterer canthus of the eye, to the tip of the nose, - - - -	6
Orbit of the eye, - - - - -	3-4
Between the eyes, - - - -	4 2-5
Ears from their superior base, - - -	3
Longest claw of anterior feet, - -	4 1-5
Shortest, " " - -	2 3-4
Longest claw of the hind feet, - -	3
Shortest, " " - -	1 3-4
Hair at tip of tail, - - - -	4 1-2
Length of the hair on the	
top of the head, - -	1 3-4 to 2 inch.
beneath the ears, - -	2 1-2 to 3 1-2 in.
neck above, - - -	3 inch.
shoulders above, - - -	4 1-2
throat, - - - - -	4
Belly and behind the anterior legs—longest hairs,	6

and measured 8 feet 7 1-2 inches, from the nose to the extremity of the hind feet."—*Lewis and Clark.*

One lived two hours, after having been shot through the centre of his lungs, and whilst in this state, he prepared for himself a bed in the earth, two feet deep, and five feet long, after running a mile and a half. The fleece and skin were a heavy burden for two men, and the oil amounted to eight gallons.

Another, shot through the heart, ran at his usual pace nearly a quarter of a mile, before he fell.

This species, they further inform us, in all its variations of colouring, is called *Hohhost*, by the Chopunnish Indians.

These travellers mention another species of bear, which seems to be related to the Alpine bear, and which is most probably a new species. It climbs trees, and is known to the Chopunnish Indians, by the name of *Yackah.*

They also inform us, that the copulating season occurs about the 15th June.

The Indians of the Missouri, sometimes go to war in small parties against the grizzly bear, and trophies obtained from his body are highly esteemed, and dignify the fortunate individual who obtains them. We saw on the necks of many of their warriors, necklaces composed of the long fore claws, separated from the foot, tastefully arranged in a radiating manner, and one of the band of Pawnee warriors, that encountered a detachment of our party near the Konza village, was ornamented with the entire skin of the fore foot, with the claws remaining upon it, suspended on his breast.

It is not a little remarkable, that the grizzly bear, which was mentioned at a very early period by Lahontan, and subsequently by several writers, is not even at this day, established in the Zoological works, as a distinct species; that it is perfectly distinct from any described species, our description will prove. From the concurrent testimony of those who have seen the animal in its native haunts, and who have had an opportunity of observing its manners, it is without doubt, the most daring and truly formidable animal, that exists in the United States. He frequently pursues and attacks hunters, and no animal whose swiftness or art is not superior to his own, can evade him. He kills the bison, and drags the ponderous carcase to a distance, to devour it at leisure, as the calls of hunger may influence him.

The grizzly bear is not exclusively carnivorous, as has by some persons been imagined, but also, and perhaps in a still greater degree, derives nourishment from vegetables, both fruits and roots; the latter he digs up by means of his long fore claws.

That they formerly inhabited the Atlantic states, and that they were then equally formidable to the Indians, we have some foundation for belief, in the tradition of the Delaware Indians, respecting the Big Naked bear, the last one of which they believe formerly existed east of the Hudson river, and which Mr. Heckewelder assures us, is often arrayed by the Indians, before the minds of their crying children, to frighten them to quietness.

Governor Clinton in the notes appended to his learned *Introductory Discourse,** says, " Dixon, the Indian trader, told a friend of mine, that this animal had been seen fourteen feet long; that notwithstanding its ferocity, it has been sometimes domesticated, and that an Indian belonging to a tribe on the head waters of the Mississippi, had one in a reclaimed state, which he sportively directed to go into a canoe belonging to another tribe of Indians, then about returning from a visit: the bear obeyed, and was struck by an Indian; being considered one of the family, this was deemed an insult, was resented accordingly, and produced a war between these nations."

A half grown specimen was kept chained in the yard of the Missouri Fur Company, near Engineer Cantonment, last

* V. Trans. of the New York Literary and Philos. Society.

winter; he was fed chiefly on vegetable food, as it was observed, that he became furious when too plentifully supplied with animal fare. He was in continual motion during the greater part of the day, pacing backward and forward to the extent of his chain. His attendants ventured to play with him, though always in a reserved manner, fearful of trusting him too far, or of placing themselves absolutely within his grasp; he several times broke loose from his chain, on which occasions he would manifest the utmost joy, running about the yard in every direction, rearing up on his hind feet, and capering about. I was present at one of these exhibitions; the squaws and children belonging to the establishment ran precipitately to their huts, and closed the doors: he appeared much delighted with his temporary freedom, he ran to the dogs, which were straying about the yard, but they avoided him. In his round he came to me, and rearing up, placed his paws on my breast; wishing to rid myself of so rough a play-fellow, I turned him around, upon which he ran down the bank of the river, plunged into the water, and swam about for some time.

Mr. John Dougherty had several narrow escapes from the grizzly bear. He was once hunting with a companion, on one of the upper tributaries of the Missouri, he heard the report of his companion's rifle, and looking round, he beheld him at a little distance, endeavouring to escape from one of these bears, which he had wounded as it was advancing on him. Mr. Dougherty, attentive only to the preservation of his friend, immediately hastened to divert the attention and pursuit of the bear to himself, and arrived within rifle shot distance, just in time to effect his generous object; he lodged his ball in the animal, and was obliged to fly in his turn, whilst his friend, relieved from imminent danger, prepared for another onset by charging his piece, with which he again wounded the bear, and relieved Mr. Dougherty from pursuit. In this most hazardous encounter, neither of them were injured, but the bear was fortunately destroyed.

Several hunters were pursued by a grizzly bear, that gained rapidly upon them; a boy belonging to the party, who possessed less speed than his companions, seeing the bear at his heels fell with his face to the soil; the bear reared up on his hind feet over the boy, looked down for a moment upon him, then bounded over him in pursuit of the fugitives.

A hunter just returned from a solitary excursion to the Qui Court river, informed me at Engineer Cantonment, that going one morning to examine his traps, he was pursued by a bear, and had merely time to get into a small tree, when the bear passed beneath him, and without halting or even looking up, passed on at the same pace.

Another hunter received a blow from the fore paw of one of these animals, which destroyed his eye and cheek bone.

In proof of the great muscular power with which this animal is endowed, a circumstance related to us by Mr. John Dougherty, may be stated. He shot down a bison, and leaving the carcass, went to obtain assistance to butcher it, but was surprised on his return to find, that it had been dragged entire, to a considerable distance, by one of these bears, and was now lodged in a concavity of the earth, which the animal had scooped out for its reception.

Notwithstanding the formidable character of this bear, we have not made use of any precautions against their attacks, and although they have been several times prowling about us in the night, they have not evinced any disposition to attack us, at that season.

They appear to be more readily intimidated by the voice, than by the appearance of men.

CHAPTER IV.

*Natural mounds—Kaskaia Indian and squaw—Preparations
for a division of the party—Sandstones of the high plains
south of the Arkansa—Floetz Trap Formation.*

In the afternoon of the 19th of July, we passed the mouth
of the river St. Charles, called by Pike the Third fork, which
enters the Arkansa from the southwest. It is about twenty
yards wide, and receives, eight miles above its confluence,
the Green-horn, a small stream from the southeast. The
Green-horn rises in the mountains, and passes between the
Spanish Peaks into the plains. These two peaks had been for
several days visible, standing near to each other, and appearing entirely insulated. If they are not completely so, the
other parts of the same range must fall far below them in
elevation; they are of a sharp, conic form, and their summits white with snow, at midsummer.

We travelled twenty-five miles, the general direction of
our course being a little south of east, and encamped at five
P. M. in a grassy point on the north side of the river. The
soil of the islands and the immediate valley of the river
were found somewhat more fertile than above. Immediately
after encamping the hunters were sent out, who soon returned with two deer and a turkey.

In the evening, the altitude of Antares was taken.
Throughout the night we were much annoyed by mosquitoes, the first we had met for some weeks in sufficient numbers to be troublesome.

We left our encampment on the following morning at five,
the weather warm and fair. Soon afterwards we passed the
mouth of a creek on the south side, which our guide inform-

ed us, is called by the Spaniards Wharf creek, probably from the circumstance of its washing perpendicular precipices of moderate height, which is said to be the case. It is the stream designated in Pike's map as the Second fork. A party of hunters in the employ of Mr. Choteau, who were taken prisoners by the Spaniards in the month of May, 1817, were conducted up this creek to the mountains, thence across the mountains, to Santa Fe.

Near the place where we halted to dine, a large herd of elk were seen, but unfortunately they took the wind of us, and disappeared, giving us no opportunity to fire upon them.

Along the river bluffs, we saw numerous conic mounds, resembling those of artificial formation, so frequently met with near the Ohio and Mississippi, but differing from them by their surface, from the apex to the base, being terminated by a strait or concave, instead of a convex curve, which is usual in those of artificial origin. The natural mounds of which we speak, appear usually to contain a nucleus of sandstone, which is sometimes laid bare on the summit or on the sides, and sometimes entirely concealed by the accumulated debris resting upon it. This stone often contains petrified remains of marine animals.

At the end of this day's ride of twenty-six miles, we found the river valley more than a mile in width, and the distant bluffs which bound it, low, and of gradual ascent. The boulders, pebbles, and gravel, so abundant near the base of the mountain, had been growing gradually less prevalent, and diminishing in size till they had now almost entirely disappeared, their place being supplied by a fine sand intermixed with clay, which here composed the surface. The soil is extremely barren, the islands, and the immediate margin of the river, bearing an inconsiderable growth of cottonwood and willows, the great mass of the country being almost destitute of vegetation of any kind.

Hunters were sent out, immediately on encamping, and

returned at dark, bringing a wild cat, an old turkey, and five of her chickens.

A bird was taken, closely resembling in point of colouring, a species preserved in the Philadelphia museum under the name of *ruby-crowned fly-catcher*, said to be from the East Indies, but the bill differs in being much less dilated. We can hardly think it a new species, yet in the more common books we do not find any distinct description of it. It is certainly allied to the Tyrannus *griseus*, and *sulphuratus* of Vieillot, but in addition to other essential characters, it is distinguished from the former, by its yellow belly, and from the latter, by the simplicity of the wing and tail feathers, and the absence of bands on the side of the head; the bill is also differently formed from either of those species, if we may judge from Vieillot's figures.*

21st. We left our encampment at five A. M. and having descended six or eight miles along the river, we met an Indian and squaw, who were, as they informed us, of the tribe called Kaskaias, by the French, Bad-hearts. They were on horseback, and the squaw led a third horse, of uncommon beauty. They were on their way from the Arkansa below, to the mountains, near the sources of the Platte, where their nation sometimes resides. They informed us that the greater part of six nations of Indians were encamped about thirteen days' journey below us, on the Arkansa. These were the Kaskaias, Shiennes, Arrapahoes, Kiawas,

---

* Genus Tyrannus.

T. *verticalis*, SAY. Head above, pure, pale, plumbeous, the vertex with a bright orange spot; back pale plumbeous, very slightly tinged with olivaceous; wings brown, tertials margined exteriorly with white; inner webs of the primaries towards the base whitish, narrowed at their tips, the first feather remarkably so; tail-coverts and tail deep brown-black, exterior web of the lateral tail feather white, a dusky line before the eye; chin whitish; neck beneath, colour of the head; breast, belly, and inferior tail-coverts, bright yellow; bill furnished with bristles above, and each side at base; superior mandible perfectly rectilinear above from the base to near the tip, where it rather suddenly curves much downward.

Total length 8 inches; bill from the anterior edge of the nostril to the tip, 11-20 of an inch.

the Bald-heads, and a few Shoshones, or Snakes. These nations, the Kaskaia informed us, had been for some time embodied, and had been engaged on a warlike expedition against
the Spaniards on Red river, where a battle was fought, in
which the Spaniards were defeated with considerable loss.

We now understood the reason of a fact which had appeared a little remarkable; namely, that we should have traversed
so great an extent of Indian country, as we have done since
leaving the Pawnees, without meeting a single savage. The
bands above enumerated, are supposed to comprise nearly
the whole erratic population of the country about the sources
of the Platte and Arkansa, and they had all been absent from
their usual haunts, on a predatory excursion against the
Indians of New Mexico.

At our request, the Kaskaia and his squaw returned with
us several miles, to point out a place suitable for fording the
Arkansa, and to give us any other information or assistance
in their power to communicate. Being made to understand
it was the design of some of the party to visit the sources
of Red river, he pretended to give us information and advice
upon that subject; also to direct us to a place where we
might find a mass of rock-salt, which he described as existing on one of the upper branches of Red river.

At ten o'clock we arrived at the ford, where we halted to
make a distribution of the baggage and other preparations
requisite to the proposed division of the party which was
here to take place. Our Kaskaia visitor, with his handsome
and highly ornamented wife encamped near us, having erected a little tent covered with skins. They presented us some
jerked bison meat, and received in return a little tobacco and
other inconsiderable articles. A small looking-glass, which
was among the presents given him, he immediately stripped
of the frame and covering, and inserted it with some ingenuity into a large billet of wood, on which he began to
carve the figure of an alligator. Capt. Bell bought of him

the horse which they had led with them, and which, according to their account, had recently been caught from among the wild horses of the prairie. This made some new arrangement of their baggage necessary, and we were surprised to witness the facility and despatch with which the squaw constructed a new pack-saddle. She felled a small cotton-wood tree, from which she cut two forked sticks. These were soon reduced to the proper dimensions, and adapted to the ends of two flat pieces of wood about two feet in length, and designed to fit accurately to the back of the horse, a longitudinal space of a few inches in width being left between them to receive the ridge of the back. The whole was fastened together without nails, pins, or mortises, but by a strong covering of dressed horse-hide sewed on wet with fibres of deer's sinew.

The Indian informed us he was called " The Calf." He appeared excessively fond of his squaw, and their caresses and endearments they were at no pains to conceal. It was conjectured by our guide, and afterwards-ascertained by the detachment that descended the Arkansa, that this mutually fond couple had married in violation of the laws and usages of their tribe; she being already the wife of another man, had stolen the horse they sold us, and deserted their band to escape punishment.

The low grounds, on the upper part of the Arkansa, have a sandy soil, and are thinly covered with cotton-wood, intermixed with the aspen poplar (P. *tremuloides. Mx.*) and a few willows. The undergrowth is scattering and small, consisting principally of the Amorpha *fruticosa* and a syngeneceous shrub, probably a vernonia. Along the base of the mountains and about this encampment, we had observed a small asclepias, not easily distinguished from A. *verticillata*, but rarely rising more than two or three inches from the ground. Here we saw also the A. *longifolia* and A. *viridiflora* of Pursh. The scanty catalogue of grassy and herbaceous plants comprises two sunflowers (H. *gigantus* and H. *peti-olaris.)* the great Bartonia, the white argemone, the Cactus *ferox*, the Andropogon *furcatum* and A. *ciliatum*, Cyperus *uncinatus*, Elymus *striatus*, and a few others.

Soon after arriving at this encampment, we commenced the separation of our baggage, horses, &c., preparatory to the division of the party. It was now proposed, pursuant to the plan already detailed, that one division, consisting of Mr. Say, Mr. Seymour, Lieutenant Swift, the three Frenchmen, Bijeau, Le Doux, and Julien, with five riflemen, the greater part of the pack-horses, and heavy baggage under the direction of Capt. Bell, should proceed down the Arkansa, by the most direct route, to Fort Smith, there to wait the arrival of the other division, while Major Long, accompanied by Dr. James, Mr. Peale, and seven men, should cross the Arkansa, and travel southward in search of the sources of Red river.

While several of the party were engaged in making these preparations, hunters were sent out, who were so far successful that they soon returned, bringing two deer, one antelope, and seven turkeys. The opportunity of an unoccupied moment was taken to collect from Bijeau an account of some parts of the Rocky mountains which we had not seen.

Joseph Bijeau (or Bessonet, which is his hereditary name, the former having been derived from a second marriage of his mother,) had performed in a very adequate and faithful manner the services of guide and interpreter, from the Pawnee villages to this place. He had formerly been resident in these regions, in capacity of hunter and trapper, during the greater part of six years.

He had traversed the country lying between the north fork of the Platte and the Arkansa, in almost every direction. His pursuits often led him within the Rocky Mountains, where the beaver are particularly abundant. He appears possessed not only of considerable acuteness of observation, but of a degree of candour and veracity which gives credibility to his accounts and descriptions. To him we are indebted for the following account of the country within the mountains.

The region, lying west of the first range of the Rocky Mountains and between the sources of the Yellow-stone, on the north, and Santa Fe, on the south, consists of ridges of mountains, spurs, and vallies. The mountains are usually abrupt, often towering into inaccessible peaks, covered with perpetual snows. The interior ranges and spurs are generally more elevated than the exterior : this conclusion is at least naturally drawn from the fact that they are covered with snow to a greater extent below their summits. Although that point which we have denominated James' Peak has been represented as higher than any other part of the mountains, within one hundred or one hundred and fifty miles, we are inclined to believe it falls much below several other peaks, and particularly that which was for many days observed by the party, when ascending the Platte.

The vallies within the Rocky Mountains are many of them extensive, being from ten to twenty or thirty miles in width, and are traversed by many large and beautiful streams. In these vallies, which are destitute of timber, the soil is frequently fertile and covered with a rich growth of a white flowering clover, upon which horses and other animals feed with avidity. The vallies have an undulated surface and are terminated on all sides by gentle slopes, leading up to the base of the circumjacent mountains. Timber may be had, on the declivities of the hills, in sufficient quantity to subserve the purposes of settlement. The soil is deep, well watered, and adapted to cultivation.

The Indians, who inhabit within the mountains, are roving bands, having no permanent places of residence, and subsisting entirely on the products of the chase. The people called Padoucas have been often represented as residing in the district now under consideration, but are not at this time to be found here, unless this name be synonymous with that of the Bald-heads or some other of the six nations already enumerated.

On the morning of the 22nd, one of two hunters, who had been sent out on the preceding day, but had not returned, came into camp to give notice that a bison had been killed at the distance of eight miles on the other side of the river. Men were accordingly despatched with pack-horses to bring in the meat. Astronomical observations were resumed, and all the party were busily employed in the discharge of their ordinary duties, or in preparations for the approaching separation.* A vocabulary of the Kaskaia lan-

* The New-York bat, (Vespertilio Novaboracensis.) which occurs here, does not vary in any degree from the general characters and appearance, of individuals of the Atlantic states. The specimen we obtained, is most unequivocally furnished with incissores in the superior jaw, which by Pennant were denied to exist in the species of this name. These teeth being small, and hardly rising to a level with the line of the intervening callosity, might be readily overlooked by a casual observer, who does not aid his vision by the use of the lens. In adducing this fact, it must not be understood that we affirm the existence of those teeth in individuals of this species generally, we only refer to the single specimen before us.

A small bat was shot this evening, during the twilight, as it flew rapidly in various directions, over the surface of the creek. It appears to be an immature specimen, as the molares are remarkably long and acute; the canines are very much incurved, and the right inferior one is singularly bifid at tip, the divisions resembling short bristles. This species is beyond a doubt distinct from the Carolina bat (V. Caroliniana, Geoff.) with which the ears are proportionally equally elongated, and, as in that bat, a little ventricose on the anterior edge, so as almost to extend over the eye, but the tragus is much longer, narrower, and more acute, resembling that of the V. *emarginatus*, Geoff., as well in form as in proportion to the length of the ear. We call it V. *subulatus*, and it may be thus described.—Ears longer then broad, nearly as long as the head, hairy on the basal half, a little ventricose on the anterior edge, and extending near to the eye; tragus elongated, subulate; the hair above blackish at base, tip dull cinereous; the interfemoral membrane hairy at base, the hairs unicoloured, and a few also scattered over its surface, and along its edge, as well as that of the brachial membrane; hair beneath black, the tip yellowish-white; hind feet rather long, a few setæ extending over the nails; only a minute portion of the tail protrudes beyond the membrane.

Total length, . . . 2 9-10 inches.
Tail, ... 1 1-5

guage was filled up with words obtained from the Calf, who still remained with us.*

This encampment was about eighteen miles above the confluence of that tributary of the Arkansa, called in Pike's maps "The First fork," and, by our computation, near one hundred miles from the base of the mountain. James' Peak was still visible, bearing north, 68° west, and the Spanish peaks, the westernmost of which bore south, 40° west. The observations made here received the most minute and careful attention. The moon was at this time too near the sun to admit of taking her distance from that luminary, and too near Antares for an observation. The distance of Spica Virginis was too great, and the star was too near the horizon, yet we trust accurate deductions may be made from the distances, which are given at the end of the volume.

On the evening of both days, which our Kaskaia guest spent with us, we observed him to commence soon after sunset, a monotonous and somewhat melancholy chant, which he continued for near an hour. He gave us some account of a battle, which had lately been fought between the Tabbaboos, (Anglo-Americans,) and the Spaniards, in which great guns were used, and when the Spaniards, though superior in number, had been beaten. He appeared well acquainted with the use of fire arms, and challenged one of the party to a trial of skill, in shooting at a mark with the rifle. He had a fusee, kept very carefully in a case of leather, and carried when travelling by his squaw. He was also armed with a bow and some light arrows for hunting, which he carried constantly in his hand. He took leave of us, on the morning of the 23d, having received several presents, with which he appeared highly pleased.

The Arkansa, between this point and the mountains, has

---

* The results of several sets of observations gave as the position of this encampment 38° 12' 22" north latitude, and 103° 46' 15". west longitude from Greenwich, or 26° 46! 15!! from Washington.

a rapid current, whose velocity, probably, varies from four to six miles per hour. It may be forded at many places, in a moderate stage of water. The average breadth of the river is from sixty to seventy-five yards. At many places, however, it is much enlarged, including numerous islands. It pursues a remarkably serpentine course within its valley, forming a succession of points on both sides of the river, which, together with the islands, are usually covered with cottonwood. The bed of the river is gravelly, or composed of water-worn stones, which diminish in size, as you recede from the mountains. The water is turbid, but in a less remarkable degree, than that of the Platte. The bed of the river, has, in many instances, changed its place, and the old channel is sometimes occupied by stagnant water, and sometimes by a small stream, which is rendered transparent by passing through the sand and gravel, forming the recently raised bank of the river.

On the 24th, the movements of the party were resumed; Major Long with the division destined for Red river, crossed the Arkansa, at five A. M. On arriving at the opposite bank, three cheers were given, which our late companions returned, from the other side. We lost sight of them as they were leaving the camp, to descend the Arkansa.

Major Long's division of the party consisting of ten men, took with them six horses and eight mules, most of them in good condition for travelling. A few had sore backs, but one horse only was unfit for service.

Our course, which was a little to the east of south, was nearly at right angles to the direction of the Arkansa. It was our intention to cross to, and ascend the First Fork, a considerable stream entering the Arkansa, eighteen miles below our last encampment. After leaving the river, we found the surface to rise gradually, till at the distance of six or eight miles, it is broken by a few small gravelly ridges; these are of little elevation, and their summits overlook an extensive waste of sand, terminated towards the south and east, only by the verge of the sky, towards the west and northwest, by the snowy summits of the Spanish mountains. As our way led across the general course of the streams, we met with no water, except such as was still standing in puddles, which had been filled by the late rains. Near one of these we halted to dine. The thermometer hanging in the shade of our tent, which was the most perfect, and indeed the only shade we could find, stood at 100°. The little water we could procure was thick with mud, and swarming with the larvæ of mosquitoes, but this we regretted the less, as we had no cooking to perform. We dined upon jerked meat from our packs. Some animals seen at a distance, were at first mistaken for bisons, but were found by the hunters sent in pursuit of them, to be horses, and too wild and vigilant to be taken.

A species of cone flower (Rudbeckia *tagetes*,) with an elongated receptacle, and large red-brown radial florets, was observed, about the margin of the stagnant pool, near which we halted.*

We also collected the Linum *rigidum?* and a semiprocumbent species of Sida, which appears to be undescribed. It is a little larger than the S. *spinosa*, to which it has some general resemblance.

The whole tract, passed in this day's journey of twenty-seven miles, is sterile and sandy. At sunset we were so fortunate as to meet with another small pool of water, at which we pitched our tent, and kindled a fire with the dung of the

---

* R. *tagetes*, Hirsute, *stem* much branched, somewhat grooved; *radical leaves* subentire spatulate, linear or pinnatifid; *cauline leaves* interruptedly pinnatifid, the divisions irregular in form and position, but usually linear; *branches* alternate or scattered; *peduncles* grooved, short, few flowered, terminal: *ray flowrets* [5-8] recurved, red-brown: *disk* dark-brown: *receptacle* columnar but proportionally much shorter than that of R. *columnaris*, to which species the one under consideration is allied. *Plant* about twelve inches high, growing in clusters, and having by its numerous branches and finely divided leaves, a remote resemblance to Anthemis *cotula*.

bison. Since leaving the Arkansa, we had scarcely seen as much wood, as might have supplied us with fuel for a single night. We passed in the course of the day, not less than four or five paths, leading southwest towards the Spanish settlements. Some of them appeared to have been recently travelled by men with horses, such paths being easily distinguished from those of bisons or wild horses.

Our camp was near the head of a dry ravine, communicating towards the southeast, with a considerable stream, which we could distinguish at the distance of eight or ten miles, by a few trees along its course. Continuing our journey on the ensuing day, we soon found ourselves in a tract of country, resembling that on the Arkansa near the mountains. A similar horizontal slaty sandstone occurs, forming the basis of the country. There is also a variety of this stone, somewhat crystalline, resembling that of St. Michael's, in the lead mine district, but exhibiting no trace of metallic ores. These rocks are deeply channelled by the water courses, but at this time the streams contain little water. These ravines are, the greater number of them, destitute of timber, except a few cedars, attached here and there in the crevices of the rock. The larger vallies which contain streams of water, have a few cotton-wood and willow trees. The box elder, the common elder, (Sambucus *canadensis*,) and one or two species of Viburnum, are seen here.

It was perhaps owing to our having followed more carefully than they deserved, the directions of the Calf, that we did not arrive as early as we had expected, upon the stream we designed to ascend. In the middle of the day on the 25th, we fell in with a smaller river, at the distance of thirty-six miles from the point where we had left the Arkansa, this we concluded, could be no other than that tributary, whose mouth is said to be distant eighteen miles from the same spot. This stream, where we halted upon it to dine, is about ten yards wide, and three feet deep, but appeared at this time considerably swollen. Its immediate valley is about three hundred yards in width, bounded on both sides by perpendicular cliffs of sandstone, of near two hundred feet elevation. A very large part of the area included between these showed evidence in the slime and rubbish, with which its surface was covered, of having been recently inundated. This stream, like all others of similar magnitude, having their sources in high mountains, is subject to great and sudden floods.

A short time before we halted, our two hunters, Verplank and Dougherty, were sent forward to hunt, and joined us with a deer, soon after we had encamped.

After dinner we moved on, ascending the creek, whose valley was sufficiently wide for a little distance, to afford us an easy and unobstructed passage. The stream runs nearly from south to north, in a deep but narrow and tortuous valley, terminated on both sides, by lofty and perpendicular precipices, of red sand rock. This sandstone, appears entirely to resemble that before described, as occuring in an inclined position, along the base of the mountains, on the Arkansa and the Boiling-spring creek. Here it is disposed in horizontal strata of immense thickness. It varies in colour from a bright brick red, to a dark brown, and is sometimes gray, yellow, or white. It consists essentially of rounded particles of quartz and other silicious stones, varying in size from the finest sand to gravel stones, and large pebbles. Extensive beds of pudding stone occur in every part of it, but are abundant somewhat in proportion, to the proximity of the high primitive mountains. In the lower parts of the stratum, these beds of coarse conglomerate, appear to have the constituent gravel and pebble stones more loosely cemented, than in portions nearer the upper surface. Wherever we have met with them in immediate contact with the granite of the Rocky Mountains, they are nearly destitute of cement, and of a colour approaching to white. This remark, it is highly probable, may not be applicable to many extensive beds of pudding stone, which lie near the base of the mountains. In the instances which came under our notice, the absence of colour and the want of cement, may very probably have been accidental. The finer varieties of the sandstone are often met with in the immediate neighbourhood of the granite, and are of a compact structure, and an intense colour. Red is the prevailing colour in every part of the stratum, but stripes of yellow, gray, and white, are frequently interspersed. In hardness and other sensible properties, it varies widely at different points. In many instances it is entirely similar to the sandstone about New Brunswick, in New Jersey, at Nyac, and along the Tappan bay in New York, and particularly that variety of it which is quarried at Nyac, and extensively used in the cities of New York and Albany, for building. It contains a little mica in small scales. Oxide of iron predominates in the cement, and the ore denominated the brown oxide, occurs in it, in reniform, botryoidal and irregular masses.

A few miles above our mid-day encampment, we entered the valley of a small creek, tributary from the southeast to the stream we had been ascending, but this we found so narrow and so obstructed by fallen masses of rocks, and almost impenetrable thickets of alders and willows, as to render our progress extremely tedious and painful. We were several times induced to attempt passing along the bed of the stream, but as the mud was in many places very deep, this was done at the cost of the most violent and fatiguing exertions, on the part of our horses, and the risk to ourselves of being thrown with our baggage into the stream. With the hope of finding an easier route across the hills, we ascended with much difficulty a craggy and abrupt ravine, until we had attained nearly the elevation of the precipitous ramparts, which hemmed in the narrow valley of the creek; but all we gained by this ascent, was the opportunity of looking down upon a few of our companions, still lingering below, diminished to the stature of dwarfs by the distance, and by contrast with the rude and colossal features of the scene. The surface of the country, extending on both sides from the summit of the precipices, consisted of abrupt conic piles, narrow ridges, and shapeless fragments of naked rocks, more impassable than the valley below. Counselled therefore by necessity, we resumed our former course, ascending along the bed of the creek.

Among other birds, which occurred in this day's march, we noticed the *yellow-bellied fly-catcher*, and the *obscure wren*.

One of the small striped ground squirrels already noticed, was killed, and an individual belonging to another species* distinguished by the extraordinary coarseness and flattened form of the fur, and by three black lines on each side of the tail. These lines at their tips, are of course, united over the surface of the tail, as in the Barbary squirrel. It nestles in holes and crevices of the rocks, and does not appear to ascend trees voluntarily.

It inhabits frequently about the naked parts of the sandstone cliffs, or where are only a few cedar bushes. In the pouch of the specimens killed, we found the buds and leaves of a few small plants common among the rocks.

Following up the bed of the creek, we ascended by a gradual acclivity, to the surface of the stratum of red sandstone. It is separated by a somewhat distinct boundary from the finer and more compact gray variety which rests upon it.

---

* Genus Sciurus.

S. *grammurus*. SAY. Line-tailed squirrel. Body cinereous, more or less tinged with ferruginous; fur very coarse, much flattened, canaliculate above, plumbeous or blackish at base; then whitish, or ferruginous; tip brownish; above the neck and shoulders the whitish is prevalent; from the middle of the back, the sides, and the exterior surface of the legs, the ferruginous colour prevails, the terminal brown of the feet being obsolete; superior and inferior orbits of the eye white; tail moderate whitish; fur triannulate with black, the base and tip of each hair being whitish; beneath, whitish tinged with ferruginous; thumb tubercle armed; iris burnt umber: pupil black.

Length to the origin of the tail, 11 1-2 inches.
　　　　Of the tail, 　.　　. 　9 inches.

This gray sandstone appears from the organic relicts it contains, as well as from its relative position, to have been of more recent deposition than the red. Its prevailing colours are gray or yellowish white, its stratifications distinct, and its cement often argillaceous.

After entering upon this variety, we found the valley of the creek less serpentine in direction, but narrower and more obstructed by detached fragments than below. The impaling cliffs on each side were also more. uniformly perpendicular, putting it out of our power to choose any other path than the rugged one which lay before us. As with every step of our advance upon this route we were gaining a little in point of elevation, we hoped by following it, to reach at length, its termination in the high and open plain which we had no doubt existed, extending over the greater part of the surface of the country wherever the strata of sandstone were still unbroken. At five P. M., supposing we had arrived very near this wished-for spot, and finding an indifferent supply of grass for our horses, we halted for the night, having travelled fifteen miles.

26th. The water of the large stream we had crossed and ascended for some distance on the preceding day, was turbid, and so brackish, as to be nauseous to the taste. The same was observed, though in a less remarkable degree, of the little tributary we had followed up to our encampment. After leaving the region of red sandstone, we found the water perceptibly purer. In the districts occupied by that rock, we have observed several copious springs, but not one whose waters were without a very manifest impregnation of muriate of soda, or other saline substances. In the gray, or argillaceous sandstone, springs are less frequent, but the water is not so universally impure.

A beautiful Dalea, two or three Euphorbias, with several species of Eriogonum, are among the plants collected about this encampment. Notwithstanding the barrenness of the soil, and the aspect of desolation which so widely prevails, we are often surprised by the occurrence of splendid and interesting productions springing up under our feet, in situations that seemed to promise nothing but the most cheerless and unvaried sterility. Operating with unbounded energy, in every situation, adapting itself with wonderful versatility, to all combinations of circumstances; the principle of life extends its dominion over inhospitable tracts, which seem as if designed for the perpetual abode of inorganic desolation; distributing some of its choicest gifts to the most ungenial regions, fitting them, by peculiarity of structure, for the maintenance of life and vigor, in situations apparently the most unfavored.

At nine o'clock in the evening of the 25th, a fall of rain commenced. We were now ten in company, with a single tent, large enough to cover half the number. In order, however, to make the most equal distribution of our joint possessions, it was so arranged that about the half of each man was sheltered under the tent, while the remainder was exposed to the weather. This was effected, by placing all our heads near together in the centre of the tent, and allowing our feet to project in all directions, like the radii of a circle.

On the ensuing morning, we commenced our ride at an early hour, being encouraged still to pursue the course up the ravine, by a bison path, which we believed, would at length conduct us to the open plain. Our progress was slow, and laborious, and our narrow path so hemmed in with perpendicular cliffs of sandstone, that our views were nearly as confined, and the surrounding objects as unvaried, as if we had been making our way in a subterranean passage. Two black-tailed deer, with a few squirrels, and some small birds, were all the animals seen in the course of the day. Some enormous tracks of the grizzly bear, with the recent signs of bisons, afforded sufficient proof, that these animals, though unseen, were near at hand.

Our courses were nearly south, during the day, and the distance we travelled, estimated on them, fifteen miles. The actual distance passed, must have been much greater, as our real course was extremely circuitous, winding from right to left, in conformity to the sinuosities of the valley.

At four o'clock, we arrived at the head of the stream, which we had hitherto ascended. As we were conscious, that after leaving this, and emerging into the open country, we could not expect to meet with water again, in a distance of several miles, it was resolved to halt for the night, and the hunters were sent out. Soon afterwards, it began to rain. At sunset, the hunters returned, having killed a female of the black-tailed, or mule deer. The flesh of this, we found in tolerable condition, and extremely grateful to our hungry party.

On the morning of the 27th, we rose at three o'clock, and hastened our preparations for an early start. The morning was clear and calm, and the copious dew, which was beginning to exhale from the scanty herbage of the valley, gave the air a delightful freshness. The mercury, as on several of the preceding mornings, stood at about 55°.

At sunrise, we resumed our toilsome march, and, before ten o'clock, had arrived at a part of the valley beyond which it was found impossible to penetrate. The distance we had travelled would have been, in a direct line, about three miles. In passing it, we had followed no less than ten different courses, running in all possible directions. This fatiguing march had brought us to a point where the valley was so narrow and so obstructed with large detached fragments of rocks, as to be entirely impassable on horseback: we were therefore under the necessity of halting, and, as the place afforded some grass, our horses were turned loose to feed, while several persons were sent to discover, if possible, some passage by which we might extricate ourselves from the ravine. At length one returned, having found, at the distance of a mile and a half below, a pass where, it was thought, our horses could be led up the cliff.

On the preceding day, we had commenced our accustomed march in a valley bounded by perpendicular cliffs of red sandstone, having an elevation of at least two hundred feet from the surface of the valley. As we ascended gradually along the bed of the stream, we could perceive we were arriving near the surface of this vast horizontal stratum and, at night, we pitched our tent at the very point where the red sandstone began to be overlaid, in the bed of the creek, by a different variety. This second variety, the gray sandstone, was in a horizontal stratum, evidently more than two hundred feet in thickness. It is usually a more compact and imperishable stone than the red, its fragments remaining longer entire and retaining the angles and asperities of the surface, which in the other variety are soon softened down by the rapid progress of disintegration. It is easy to perceive that the sandstone formation, including the two varieties above mentioned, must be, at this point, of immense thickness; fifteen hundred feet is probably a very moderate estimate for the aggregate elevation of some extensive portions of the gray sandstone, above that part of the valley at which the red first appears. From this point downwards the extent of the latter variety may be very great; but no estimate can be formed which would be in any measure entitled to confidence.

After we had dined, we retraced our two last courses, and succeeded in ascending the cliff, at the place which one of the hunters had pointed out, taking, without the least regret, our final leave of the " Valley of the souls in Purgatory."*

* This tributary of the Arkansa, designated on the old maps as the First Fork, as we learned from Bijeau, is called, among the Spaniards of New Mexico, " The river of the souls in purgatory." We emerged from the gloomy solitude of its valley, with a feeling somewhat akin to that which attends the escape from a place of punishment.

From the brow of the perpendicular precipice, an ascending slope of a few rods conducted us, through scattering groves of junipers, to the border of the open plain. Here, the interminable expanse of the grassy desert burst suddenly upon our view. Instead of a narrow crooked avenue, hedged in by impending cliffs and frightful precipices, a boundless and varied landscape lay spread before us. The broad valley of the Arkansa, studded with little groves of timber, and terminated, in the back ground, by the snowy summit of James' Peak, lay in our rear. The Spanish Peaks and numerous spurs of the Rocky Mountains, with the shining pinnacles of the more distant ranges, limited our view on the right. On our left and before us, lay the extended plain diversified with vast conic mounds, and insular table-like hills, while herds of bisons, antelopes, and wild horses, gave life and cheerfulness to the scene.*

After travelling one and a half miles, into the plain, on a due south course, we halted to take the bearing of several remarkable points. Due east, was a solitary and almost naked pile of rocks, towering to a very considerable elevation above the surface of the plain. James' Peak bore north 71° west; the west Spanish Peak south, 87? west; magnetic variation, 13½° east. As we proceeded, we were surprised to witness an aspect of unwonted verdure and freshness, in the grasses and other plants of the plain, and in searching for the cause of this change, discovered we had arrived at a region differing, both in point of soil and geological features, from any portion of the country we had before seen. Several circumstances had induced us to conjecture that

---

* A large undescribed species of Gaura is common about the banks of all the creeks we had seen since leaving the Arkansa. It attains, ordinarily, the size of G. *biennis,* but is clearly distinct both from that and all other North American species. It has a broader leaf than any other species of the genus met with in this country. The flowers are small, of a purple colour, and incline to form a terminal spike. The whole plant is covered with a dense silky pubescence, and is remarkably soft to the touch. We propose to call it Gaura *mollis.*

rocks of the newest floetz trap formation existed in some portion of the secondary region, along the eastern declivity of the Rocky Mountains, but, until this time, we had met with no positive confirmation of the opinion. We were glad to be at length relieved from the tiresome sameness of the sand formation, and promised ourselves, in the treasures of a new and more fertile variety of soil, the acquisition of many important plants.

At five **P. M.** we met with a little stagnant water, near which we encamped, having travelled about ten miles nearly due south from the point where we had left the valley of the creek. The hunters went out on foot, in pursuit of bisons, several herds being in sight, but returned at dark, having effected no more than to break the shoulder of a young bull, who ran off pursued by a gang of wolves. Several of the party, being informed of the route the animal had taken, and instigated, in common with the wolves, by the powerful incitement of hunger, resolved to join the chase, and to dispute with their canine competitors the possession of the prey. When they had nearly overtaken the bison, they saw him several times thrown to the ground by the wolves, and afterwards regaining his feet. They soon came near enough to do execution with their pistols, and frightened away the wolves, only to make a speedier end of the harassed animal. It was now past nine o'clock, but the starlight was sufficient to enable them to dress the meat, with which they returned loaded to camp, and spent the greater part of the night in regaling on the choice pieces.

28th. From an elevated point, about eight miles south of our encampment, the high peak at the head of the Arkansa was still visible. From a computation of our courses and distances, we found we could not be less than one hundred and thirty miles distant from its base, but the air, at that time, was remarkably clear, and our elevation above the common level of the plain very considerable. By referring to Pike's " Journal of a voyage to the sources of the Arkansa," it will be seen that this peak is the most prominent and conspicuous feature in a great extent of the surrounding country. " It is indeed so remarkable as to be known to all the savage nations for hundreds of miles around, and to be spoken of, with admiration, by the Spaniards of New Mexico, and was the bounds of their travels northwest. Indeed, in our wanderings in the mountains, it was never out of sight, except when in a valley, from the 14th November to the 27th January." See page 171.

Notwithstanding this representation, and that the peak in question was seen by ourselves, at the distance of one hundred and thirty miles, we are inclined to think, that, in point of elevation, it falls far below many portions of the interior ridges of the mountains, which are visible from its summit, and from the plains of the Platte, and that it is, by standing a little detached from the principal group of the mountains, it acquires a great portion of the imposing grandeur of its appearance.

We passed, in the morning, some tracts of gray sandstone, having, however, met with several inconsiderable conic hills, belonging to that interesting formation, called by Werner the Floetz Trap rocks. We perceived before us a striking change in the aspect and conformation of the surface; instead of the wearisome uniformity, the low and pointless ridges, which mark the long tract of horizontal sandstone we had passed, we had now the prospect of a country varied by numerous continued ranges of lofty hills, interspersed with insulated cone-like piles, and irregular masses of every variety of magnitude and position. .This scenery is not to be compared, in point of grandeur, with the naked and towering majesty of the great chain of the Andes, which we had lately left, but, in its kind, it is of uncommon beauty. The hills, though often abrupt and high, are sometimes smooth and grassy to their summits, having a surface unbroken by a

single rock or tree, large enough to be seen at the distance
of a mile.

At noon, we halted near the base of a hill of this description. It is of greenstone, and the sand-rock on which it rests
is disclosed at the bottom of a ravine, which commences
near the foot of the hill. This latter rock is of a slaty structure, and embraces narrow beds of bituminous clay slate,
which contains pieces of charcoal or the carbonized remains
of vegetables, in every possible respect resembling the charcoal produced by the process of combustion in the open air.
In the ravines, and over the surface of the soil, we observed
masses of a light, porous, reddish-brown substance, greatly
resembling that so often seen floating down the Missouri, by
some considered a product of pseudo-volcanic fires, said to
exist on the upper branches of that river.* We also saw
some porphyritic masses with a basis of greenstone, containing crystals of feldspar.

In the afternoon, several magpies, shore-larks, and cow-
buntings were seen. One of the cow-buntings followed us
five or six miles, alighting on the ground near the foremost
of our line, and within a few paces of the horses' feet, where
he stood gazing at the horses until all had passed him, when
he again flew forward to the front, repeating the same movements many times in succession.

We had now arrived near that part of the country where,
according to the information of the Kaskaia, we expected to
find the remarkable saline spring, from which, we were told,
the Indians often procured large masses of salt. The Kaskaia had, by the aid of a map traced in the sand, given us a
minute account of the situation of the spring, and of the surrounding country, stating that the salt existed in masses at the
bottom of a basin-like cavity, which contained about four
and a half feet of reddish water. Thus far we had not found
a single feature of the country to correspond, in the slightest

* See Bradbury's travels, p. 161. second edition.

degree, to his descriptions, and as we had been careful to follow the general direction of the course pointed out to us, it was probably his intention to deceive.

Our course, which was a little east of south, led us across several extensive vallies, having a thin dark-coloured soil, closely covered with grasses and strewed with fragments of greenstone. Descending, towards evening, into a broad and deep valley, we found ourselves again immured between walls of gray sandstone, similar in elevation and all other particulars to those which limit the valley of Purgatory creek. It was not until considerable search had been made, that we discovered a place where it was possible to effect the descent, which was at length accomplished, not without danger to the life and limbs of ourselves and horses. The area of the valley was covered with a sandy soil, in which we again saw the great cylindric Cactus, the Cucumis, and other plants common to the sandy districts, but rarely found in the scanty soils of the Trap formation. Pursuing our way, along this valley, we arrived, towards evening, at an inconsiderable stream of transparent and nearly pure water descending along a narrow channel, paved with black and shapeless masses of amygdaloidal and imperfectly porphyritic greenstone.* This was the first stream we had, for a long time, seen traversing rocks of secondary formation, whose waters were free from an impregnation of muriate of soda and other salts. From the very considerable magnitude of the valley, and the quantity of water in the creek, it is reasonable to infer that its sources were distant at least twenty miles to the west, and the purity and transparency of its waters afford sufficient evidence that it flows principally from a surface of Trap rocks.

* From a subsequent comparison of the direction of several water courses which descend from this elevated district, we have been induced to consider the creek mentioned in the text as one of the most remote sources of the great northern tributary of the Canadian river.

Having crossed the creek, with some difficulty, we halted on the bank to set up our tent and prepare ourselves for a thunder-shower, which was already commencing. After the rain, the sky became clear, and the sun, which was near setting, gilded with its radiance the dripping foliage of a cluster of oaks and poplars which stood near our tent. The grassy plain, acquiring unwonted verdure from the shower, and sparkling with the reflection from innumerable suspended rain drops, disclosed here and there a conic pile or a solitary fragment of black and porous Amygdaloid. The thinly wooded banks of the creek resounded to the loud notes of the robin, and the more varied and melodious song of the mocking bird; the stern features of Nature seemed to relax into a momentary smile to cheer us on our toilsome journey.

On the morning of the 29th, our course (S. 35° E.) brought us at the distance of three miles from our camp to the foot of the cliff, which separates the valley from the high plain. This mural barrier, has an elevation of about two hundred feet, and is impassable except at particular points, where it is broken by ravines. One of these we were fortunate in finding without being compelled to deviate greatly from our course, and climbing its rugged declivity, we emerged upon the broad expanse of the high plain. Turning with a sort of involuntary motion towards the west, we again caught a view of the distant summits of the Andes, appearing on the verge of our horizon. The scene before us was beautifully varied with smooth valleys, high conic hills, and irregular knobs scattered in every direction as far as the eye could comprehend. Among these singular eminences nothing could be perceived like a continuous unbroken range; most of them stand entirely isolated, others in groups and ranges, but all are distinct hills, with unconnected bases. The surface of the country generally, and more especially in the immediate vicinity of these hills, is strewed with fragments of compact or porphyritic greenstone. These are in some places accumulated in such quantities as greatly to retard the traveller.

At half past eleven A. M., a violent storm with high and cold wind, came on from the northeast, and continued for two hours. Soon after its commencement we halted to dine, but were unable to find a spot affording wood, until so much rain had fallen as to wet our clothing and baggage. Fire was almost the only comfort we could now command, our provision being so nearly exhausted, that about an ounce of jerked bison meat was all that could be allowed each man for his dinner.

The rain ceasing, we again resumed our march, but had not proceeded far, when we were overtaken by a second storm from the N. E., still more violent than the first, and attended with such pelting hail, that our horses refused to proceed in any direction, except that of the wind, so that rather than suffer ourselves to be carried off our course, we were compelled to halt and sit patiently upon our horses; opposing our backs to the storm, we waited for its violence to abate. As soon as the hail ceased, we moved on; the water pouring in streams from our mockasins and every part of our dress. The rain continued until dark, when being unable to find wood, and having no occasion for water, we halted, and without the delay of cooking supper or eating it, we set up our tent, and piled ourselves together under it in the most social manner imaginable. During the day, the mercury had fallen from 70° to 47°, indicating a change of temperature, which was the more severely felt as we were hungry, wet, and much fatigued. As we had neither dry clothing nor blankets, we could find no other method of restoring the warmth to our benumbed bodies than by placing them together in the least possible compass. We spent a cheerless night, in the course of which Mr. Peale experienced an alarming attack of a spasmodic affection of the stomach induced probably by cold and inanition. He was somewhat relieved by the free use of opium and whiskey.

We left our comfortless camp at an early hour on the ensuing morning, and traversing a wide plain strewed with fragments of greenstone, amygdaloid, and the vessicular substance already mentioned as the pumice stone of Bradbury, we arrived in the middle of the day, in sight of a creek, which like all water courses of this region, occupies the bottom of a deep and almost inaccessible valley; with the customary difficulty and danger, we at length found our way down to the stream, and encamped.

We were much concerned, but by no means surprised, to discover that our horses were rapidly failing under the severe services they were now made to perform; we had been often compelled to encamp without a sufficiency of grass, and the rocky ways, to which we had for some time accustomed them, were destroying their hoofs. Several were becoming lame, and all much exhausted and weakened.

Verplank, our faithful and indefatigable hunter, was so fortunate, as to kill a black-tailed deer, at a distance from our course. A horse was, however, sent for the remainder of the meat, (Verplank having brought the greater part of it on his shoulders) and we once more enjoyed the luxury of a full meal.

CHAPTER V.

Sufferings of the party from stormy weather and want of provisions—Indications of an approach towards settlements—Inscribed rocks—Cervus Macrotis—Volcanic origin of Amygdaloid.

THE valley in which we halted is narrow, and bounded on both sides by cliffs of greenstone, having manifestly a tendency to columnar or polyedral structure. It falls readily into large prismatic masses, but obstinately resists that further disintegration, which must take place before it can be removed by the water. For this reason the valley is much obstructed by the fallen masses retaining their angular form, and little intermixed with soil.

The stream which exists in this valley, for a part of the year at least, but which was now dry, runs towards the southeast. Having arrived at that part of the country which has by common consent, been represented to contain the sources of the Red river of Louisiana, we were induced by the general inclination of the surface, and the direction of this creek to consider it as one of those sources, and accordingly resolved to descend along its course, hoping it would soon conduct us to a country abounding in game, and presenting fewer obstacles to our progress, than that in which we now were. Our sufferings from the want of provisions, and from the late storm, together with the enfeebled condition of our horses, had discouraged us from prolonging, farther than was necessary, our journey towards the southwest.

The country between the sources of Purgatory creek, and the stream on which we were encamped, is a wide and elevated formation of trap rocks, resting upon horizontal sandstone. It has a loose and scanty soil, in which sand, gravel, and rolled pebbles are rarely seen, except in the vicinity of some points, where the sandstone appears to have been uncovered by the action of currents of water. In traversing it we had collected many new and interesting plants, among these were a large decumbent mentzelia, an unarmed rubus, with species of astragalus, pentstemon, myosotis, helianthus, &c. Beside the common purslane, which is one of the most frequent plants about the mountains, we had observed on the Arkansa a smaller species, remarkably pilose about the axils of the leaves, which are also narrower than in P. *oleracea.* A very small cuscuta also occurs almost exclusively parasitic on the common purslane.

31st. In attempting to descend the creek from our last encampment, we found the valley so obstructed with fragments of greenstone, as to be wholly impassable. We accordingly ascended into the plain, and continuing along the brink of the precipice, arrived in a few hours at a point where the substratum of sandstone emerges to light, at the base of an inconsiderable hill. It is a fine gray sandstone, having an argillaceous cement, and its laminæ are so nearly horizontal, that their inclination is not manifest to the eye. It is smooth and fissile, and in every respect remarkably contrasted to the massive and imperfectly columnar greenstone, which it supports.

The greenstone of this district is not universally marked by any tinge of green in the colouring, but often, as in the instance of which we are now speaking, its colour is some shade of gray, varying from light gray to grayish black. The hornblend and feldspar which enter into its composition, are minutely and intimately blended. Its minute structure is rarely, if ever, distinctly crystalline; most frequently it is compact, and the fracture nearly even,

The hunters were kept constantly in advance of the party,

and, in the course of the morning, they killed a small fawn and a heron. At one o'clock, we arrived at the confluence of a creek, tributary from the east to the stream we were following, and descending into its valley, by a precipitous declivity of about four hundred feet, encamped for the remainder of the day. This valley is bounded by perpendicular cliffs of sandstone, surmounted by extensive beds of greenstone. The fragments of the latter have fallen down into the valley, and, being less perishable than the sandstone, they constitute the greater part of the debris accumulated along the base of the cliffs.

The sand-rock, which in some places is exposed in perpendicular precipices, is soft and friable, being very readily scratched with the point of a knife, and has been rudely inscribed, propably by the Indians, with emblematical figures commemorative of some past event. Several of the figures, intended to represent men, are distinguished by the sign of the cross inscribed near the head; some are represented smoking, and some leading horses, from which we infer, that the inscriptions are intended to commemorate some peaceful meeting of the Indians with the Spaniards of New Mexico, for the purposes of trade, where horses were either given as presents or bartered for other articles. Some meeting of this kind has, probably, happened here at no very distant period, as corn-cobs were found near our encampment : from this circumstance, it would appear that the distance to the Spanish settlements cannot be very great.

Mr. Peale, who had been unwell since the cold storm of the 28th, now found some little relief in the opening of an abscess which had formed on his jaw.

As several of our horses had been lamed in descending into the valley, and by the rough journey of the preceding day, it was thought necessary to allow ourselves a day of rest. Since arriving in the country inhabited by the hitherto undescribed animal, called the black-tailed or mule deer, we had been constantly attentive to the important object of procuring a complete specimen for preservation and description. Hitherto, though several had been killed, none had been brought to camp, possessing all the characters of the perfect animal. Supposing we should soon pass beyond their range, a reward had been offered to the hunter who should kill and bring to the camp an entire and full grown buck.

Verplank killed one of this description, on the afternoon of the first of August, near enough our camp to call for assistance and bring it in entire. They did not arrive until dark, and we had such pressing necessity for the flesh of the animal, that we could not defer dressing it until the next morning. The dimensions were accordingly taken, and a drawing made by Mr. Peale, by the light of a large fire. Verplank informed us that in company with the buck which he killed, were five does, two of the common red deer, (C. Virginianus,) and three of the other kind.*

* Since our return to Philadelphia, the following description of the animal has been drawn out from the dried skin, which, however, is so much injured by depredating insects, that it has not been judged proper to mount it entire. The head has therefore been separated from the remaining portion of the skin, and may be seen in the Philadelphia Museum, placed under the foot of a Prairie wolf, (Canis *latrans*. Say.) which has been well prepared by Mr. T. Peale.

Cervus *macrotis*. Say. Antlers slightly groved, tuberculated at base, a small branch near the base, corresponding to the situation and direction of that of C. *Virginianus*; the curvature of the anterior line of the antlers is similar in direction, but less in degree, to that of the same deer; near the middle of the entire length of the antlers, they bifurcate equally, and each of these processes again divides near the extremity, the anterior of these smaller processes being somewhat longer than the posterior one. The ears are very long, extending to the principal bifurcation, about half the length of the whole antler; the lateral teeth are larger, in proportion to the intermediate teeth, than those of the C. *Virginianus* are; eyelashes black, the aperture beneath the eye is larger than that of the species just mentioned and previous; the hair also is coarser and is undulated and compressed, like that of the elk (C. *major*.); the colour is light reddish-brown above; sides of the head, and hair on the fore portion of the nose above, dull cinereous: the back is intermixed with blackish-tipped hairs, which form a distinct line on the neck, near the head: the tail is of a pale reddish-cinereous colour, and the hair at the tip of the tail is black: the tip of the trunk of the tail is somewhat compressed, and is beneath

We observed about this camp a yellow flowering sensitive plant, apparently a congener to the saw brier (Schranika *uncinata.*) of the Platte and Arkansa. Its leaves are twice pinnated, and manifestly irritable. We also added to our collection two new species of Gaura, much smaller than G *mollis,* which is also found here.

Several rattlesnakes were seen and many orbicular lizards. These are evidently of two distinct species, differing from each other in the length of the spines, and the position of

almost destitute of hair: the hoofs are shorter and wider than those of the Virginianus, and more like those of the *Elk.*

Length from the base of the antlers to the origin of the	
basal process	2 inches.
of the basal process	2 1-2
from the basal process to the principal bifurcation	4 1-2 to 5.
from the principal bifurcation to the two other bifurcations, respectively	4 1-2 to 5 1-2
terminal prongs of the anterior branch	4 to 4 1-2
of the posterior branch	2 1-2 to 3
from the anterior base of the antlers to the tip of the superior jaw	9 1-4
from the anterior canthus of the eye to the tip of the jaw	6 1-4
from the base of the antler to the anterior canthus	3
of the ears, more than	7 1-2
of the trunk of the tail	4
of the hair at the tip of the tail, from	3 to 4

This is probably the species mentioned by Lewis and Clark, vol. i. p. 77, under the name of Black-tailed deer, and, more frequently, in other parts of the work, by that of Mule deer. It is, without doubt, a new species, not having been, hitherto, introduced into the systems.

Having mentioned the *Elk,* it may be proper, in this place, to express our opinion, that bad as the figure of that animal, given by Catesby, under the name of Cervus major, certainly is, it was really intended to represent the same species with that which Gmelin calls C. *canadensis.* We have never heard of any animal being observed in the southern or western states, that could be mistaken for it, neither did we meet with, or hear of the existence of any animal, which could be, by any person whatever, confounded with this species, if we except the Black-tailed deer, which by an extremely inattentive observer, viewed transiently, and at a great distance, might possibly be mistaken for it. But the Black-tailed deer, we cannot admit ever to have been known to Catesby, when we take into consideration the boundaries of the remote territory to which its range is limited. Catesby's figure also is far more like the *Elk* than the Black-tailed deer.

the nostrils. Scarce any two of either species are precisely similar in colour, but the markings are permanent. Both species possess, in a slight degree, the power of varying the shades of colour. We could find no conspicuous difference marking the different sexes in the species with long spines; the other we have not had sufficient opportunity to examine.

Aug. 2d. The rain which had fallen during great part of the preceding day and night, had considerably raised the water in the small creek, on which we were encamped. At sunrise we collected our horses, and proceeded down the valley, the direction of our course, being south, 80° east. At the distance of two or three miles we found the valley much expanded in width, and observed a conspicuous change in the sandstone precipices, which bound it. This change is the occurrence of a second variety of sand-rock, appearing along the base of the cliff, and supporting the slaty argillaceous stratum above described. These rocks have the same relative position, and nearly the same aggregate elevation, as the two very similar varieties in the valley of Purgatory creek: indeed the conclusion, that they are the continuation of the same strata, can scarcely be avoided. The lowermost or red sand-rock, is here very friable and coarse. Its prevailing colour is a yellowish gray or light brown. It often consists almost exclusively of large rounded particles of white or transparent quartz, united by a scanty cement, which usually contains lime, and sometimes, but not always, oxide of iron. In some instances the cement seems to be wanting. Its stratifications are very indistinct, compared to those of the gray sandstone, and like them disposed horizontally.

On entering the wider part of the valley, we perceived before us, standing alone in the middle of the plain, an immense circular elevation, rising nearly to the level of the surface of the sandstone table, and apparently inaccessible on all sides. On its summit is a level area of several acres bearing a few cedar bushes, probably the habitation of birds only.

Leaving this we passed three others in succession, similar in character, but more elevated and remarkable.

After passing the last of these, the hills ceased abruptly, and we found ourselves once more entering on a vast unvaried plain of sand. The bed of the creek had become much wider, but its water had disappeared. Meeting at length with a stagnant pool, we halted to dine, but found the water more bitter and nauseous to the taste, than that of the ocean, as it could neither be used for cooking or to drink; we made but a short halt, dining on a scanty allowance of roasted venison, which we ate without bread, salt, water, or any thing else. Some fragments of amygdaloid, were strewed along the bed of the stream, but we saw no more of that rock, or of the other members of the Floetz Trap formation in place. They may extend far towards the southwest, but of this we have no conclusive evidence. The aspect of these rocks particularly of the amygdaloid or toad-stone, is so peculiar, and its disposition so remarkably dissimilar to that of the sandstones, with which it is associated, as strongly to suggest the idea of a different origin.

In the midst of one of the violent storms, we encountered in passing this trap formation, we crossed the point of a long but low ridge of amygdaloid, so singularly disposed as to suggest to every one of the party, the idea, that the mass had once been in a fluid state, and that when in that state it had formed a current, descending along the bed of a narrow ravine, which it now occupied, conforming to all the sinuosities and inequalities of the valley, as a column of semifluid matter would do. Its substance was penetrated with numerous vessicular cavities, which appeared in some instances elongated in the direction of the ridge. Its colour is nearly black; and when two masses are rubbed together, they emit a smell somewhat like the soot of a chimney. These

appearances are so remarkable, that it is not surprising
these rocks should have been considered of volcanic origin,
and it is this supposition, unquestionably, from which has
originated the statement contained in the late map of the
United States, by Melish, that the district about the sources
of Red river, is occupied by volcanic rocks; this information
having probably been derived from the accounts of hunters.

The vallies which penetrate into the sandstone, supporting
the trap rocks, have usually a sandy soil, while that of the
more elevated portions, though inconsiderable in quantity, is
not sandy nor intermixed with pebbles or gravel. Among the
few scattered and scrubby trees, met with in this district, are
oaks, willows, and the cotton-wood; also a most interesting
shrub or small tree, rising sometimes to the height of twelve
or fourteen feet. It has dioiceous flowers, and produces a leguminous fruit, making in several particulars a near approach
to Gleditschia, from which, however, it is sufficiently distinguished by the form of the legume, which is long and
nearly cylindiric, and by the seeds, which are enclosed in
separate cells, immersed in a saccharine pulp, but easily detached from the valves of the legume. In these particulars
it discovers an affinity to the tamarind of the West Indies.
The legume or pod, which is from six to ten inches long,
and near half an inch in diameter, contains a considerable
quantity of a sugar-like pulp, very grateful to the taste when
ripe. The leaves are pinnated, and the trunk beset with
spines, somewhat like the honey locust, but the spines are
simple. Our Spanish interpreter, informed us that it is found
about Monterey, and in other parts of the internal provinces,
where it must have been noticed by Humboldt; but we have
not been able to have access to his account of it.

In the afternoon, we travelled thirteen miles, descending
along the valley in a southeast direction. We extended our
ride farther than we had wished; finding no suitable place

to encamp. After sunset we found a small puddle of stagnant water in the bed of the creek, which though extremely impure, was not as bitter as that near which we halted in the middle of the day. Neither wood nor bison dung could be found, so that being unable to kindle a fire, we were compelled to rest satisfied with the eighth part of a sea biscuit each for supper, that being the utmost our supplies would allow. In the afternoon one of our hunters had killed a badger, which was all the game we had, and this we were compelled to reserve until we could make a fire to cook it.

3d. Little delay was occasioned by our preparations for breakfast. The fourth part of a biscuit, which had been issued to each man on the preceding evening, and which was to furnish both supper and breakfast, would have required little time had all of it remained to be eaten, which was not the case. We were becoming somewhat impatient on account of thirst, having met with no water which we could drink, for near twenty-four hours. Accordingly getting upon our horses at an early hour, we moved down the valley, passing an extensive tract, whose soil is a loose red sand, intermixed with gravel and small pebbles, and producing nothing but a few sunflowers and sand-cherries still unripe. While we should remain upon a soil of this description, we could scarcely expect to meet with water or wood, for both of which we began to feel the most urgent necessity, and as the prospect of the country before us promised no change, it is not surprising we should have felt a degree of anxiety and alarm, which, added to our sufferings from hunger and thirst, made our situation extremely unpleasant. We had travelled greater part of the day enveloped in a burning atmosphere, sometimes letting fall upon us the scorching particles of sand which had been raised by the wind, sometimes almost suffocating by its entire stagnation, when we had the good fortune to meet with a pool of stagnant water, which though muddy and brackish, was not entirely impotable, and afford-

ed us a more welcome refreshment, than is often in the power
of abundance to supply. Here was also a little wood, and
our badger, with the addition of a young owl, which we had
the good fortune to take, was very hastily cooked and eaten.

4th. We were still passing through a barren and desolate
region, affording no game, and nearly destitute of wood and
water. Its soil is evidently the detritus of a stratum of red
sandstone, and coarse conglomerate, which is still the basis
and prevailing rock. It appears to contain a considerable
proportion of lime, and fragments of plaister-stone and Selenite are often seen intermixed with it.

Our morning's ride of sixteen miles, brought us to a place
where the water of the river emerges to view, rising to the surface of that bed of sand, beneath which it had been concealed
for a distance of more than one hundred miles. The stream
was still very inconsiderable in magnitude, the water brackish and mixed with so large a quantity of red earth, as to
give it the colour of florid blood. The general direction of
its course inclining still towards the southeast, we were now
induced to believe it must be one of the most considerable
of the upper tributaries of Red river. A circumstance tending to confirm this opinion, was our falling in with a large
and much frequented Indian trace crossing the creek, from
the west, and following down along the east bank. This
trace consisted of more than twenty parallel paths, and bore
sufficient marks of having been recently travelled, affording
an explanation of the cause of the alarming scarcity of game
we had for some time experienced. We supposed it to be
the road leading from the Pawnee Piqua village, on Red
river to Santa Fe.

Two shrubby species of Cactus, smaller than the great cylindric prickly pear, noticed near the Rocky Mountains, occur in the sandy plains, we were now traversing. One of these
which is about four feet high, and very much branched, has
long and solitary spines, a small yellow flower, and its fruit,

which is about as large as the garden cherry, is very pleasant to the taste. The fruit of the C. *ferox*, which is also
found here, was now ripe, being nearly as large as an egg,
and of a deep purple colour. The jatropha stimulosa, a congener to the manihot or Cassada of the West Indies, a cassia,
an amorpha, and many new plants were here added to our
collections.

A few wild horses had been observed in the course of the
day, and towards evening one was seen following the party,
but keeping at a distance. At night, after our horses had been
staked in the usual manner near the camp, we perceived him
still lingering about, and at length approaching the tent, so
closely, that we began to entertain hopes of capturing him
alive. In attempting this, we stationed a man with a noosed
rope, in the top of a cotton-wood tree, under which we tied
a few of our horses, but this plan did not succeed.

On the following morning, one of our hunters fortunately
discovered the same horse standing asleep under the shade
of a tree, and having shot him, returned immediately to
camp with the intelligence. We had all suffered so severely
from hunger, and our present want of provisions was so
great, that we ate indiscriminately and greedily of this unaccustomed food, and congratulated each other on the acquisition of so seasonable a supply. We felt a little regret at
killing so beautiful an animal, who had followed us several
miles on the day before, and had lingered with a sort of confidence about our camp; but all our scruples yielded to the
admonitions of hunger.

The day being Sunday, and the plain about our camp affording a supply of grass for our jaded horses, we resolved
to remain encamped, seizing the opportunity of making observations for latitude, &c. The morning was calm and clear,
the mercury at 69° Fah. For five mornings preceding, it had
been at 58° and in the middle of each day rose above 90°.
The moon was now too near the sun to admit of observations

by lunar distances, but the meridional altitude of the sun's lower limb, taken with great care, and under circumstances favorable to accuracy, gave 35° 16′ 19″ for the latitude of our encampment.

The river bed, at this place, was found by admeasurement, sixty yards in width, twenty of which were naked sand-bar, the remaining forty covered with water, having an average depth of about ten inches. The current is moderate, the water intensely red, having nearly the temperature and the saltness of new milk. It suspends a very considerable quantity of clay, derived from the cement of the sand-rock, but notwithstanding its impurities, it is more grateful to the taste than any we had met with since leaving the mountains, and though drank in large quantities, produced no unpleasant effect.

Some spots in the low plains had here considerable fertility, depending probably in some degree on the intermixture of a large proportion of calcareous matter, with the soil resulting from the disintegrated sand-rock. Though no extensive formation of limestone appears, yet the sandstone has not only in many instances a calcareous cement, but is traversed by numerous veins, both of Gypsum and carbonate of lime.

The occurrence of the elm and the diospyros indicated a soil at least approaching towards one adapted to the purposes of agriculture. Among great numbers of interesting plants, we found here a gentiana, with a flower much larger than g. *crinita*, an orobanche, probably the o. *ludoviciana*, *N.*, a new croton, an ipomopsis and many others. Notwithstanding the scarcity of game, which we had so long felt, we daily saw numbers of antelopes, with some signs of bear, deer, and turkies; but these animals had acquired all the vigilance which results from the habit of being often hunted, and the entire want of thick forests, and even of solitary trees or inequalities of the surface to cover the approach of the hunter, rendered abortive most of our attempts to take them.

The common partridge, (Perdix *virginianus*) was seen near this encampment; also the dove, which had never disappeared entirely in all the country we had passed.

Rising at the customary hour on the morning of the 7th, we perceived that a part of our horses were missing. As we were apprehensive they had been stolen by Indians, a small party was immediately sent to discover the route they had taken. Pursuing along their path, the men overtook them at the distance of two or three miles, as they were straying on in search of pasture.

On leaving our camp we endeavoured to regain the trace, on which we had for several days travelled; but though we spent much time in the search, and travelled several miles off our course we were not able to find it. This we had occasion to regret, as the surface of the country is mostly of a loose sand, bearing tufts of wormwood, and other plants, rendering the travelling difficult where there is no road. In order to shun the numerous ravines which now began to occur, we chose our route at some distance from the bank of the river, where we found the vallies deeper and more abrupt, though less frequent.

In the course of our morning's ride of twenty miles, we saw several gangs of wild horses, and with these we distinguished numbers of colts and some mules. In passing through a village of prairie dogs, of which we saw great numbers, Mr. Peale killed a burrowing owl. The bird, though killed instantly, had fallen into one of the marmot's burrows, but had luckily lodged within the reach of the arm. On opening it, the intestines were found filled with the fragments of grasshoppers' wings, and the hard parts of other insects. We have never been able from examination to discover any evidence, that these owls prey upon the marmots, whose villages they infest.

After proceeding near twenty miles, we directed our course towards the river, which we had kept at some distance on our left. Arriving at it at two o'clock, we encamped, and sent out the hunters, as we had some hope of procuring a supply of provisions, less repugnant to our prejudices than horse-flesh; the hunters, however, as well as others of the party, spent the remaining part of the afternoon in an unavailing search for game.

The hills, which bound the immediate valley of the river at this place, have an elevation of from one to two hundred feet above the surface of the water. They are usually co-vered with a deep sandy soil, but disclose in their sides, points and precipices of red sandstone, containing large quantities of very beautiful Selenite. The other more com-mon varieties of sulphate of lime, are also of frequent oc-currence. Crystals of carbonate of lime, are met with in veins traversing the sandstone.

In this region, the cenchrus tribuloides, a most annoying grass, supplies the place of the Cactus *ferox*, and the troublesome stipas of the Platte. The cenchrus bears its seed in small spikelets, which consist of a number of rigid radi-ating spines. These clusters of barbed thorns are detached at the slightest touch, falling into our mockasins, adhering to our blankets and clothing, and annoying us at every point. The clott-bur, (Xanthium *strumiarum*) which had occur-red in every part of our route, began now to ripen and cast off its muricated fruit, adding one more to the sources of con-stant molestation.

A formidable centipede, (Scolopendra) was caught near the camp, and brought in alive by one of the engagees. It was about eight inches in length, and nearly three-fourths of an inch in breadth, being of a flattened form, and of a dark brown colour. While kept alive, it showed great viciousness of disposition, biting at every thing which came within its reach. Its bite is said to be venomous.

On the morning of the 8th, we continued our journey, crossing and recrossing the river several times. This we found necessary, as the occurrence of steep and rocky ravines made it impossible to pass along the bank parallel to the course of the river, which here became more meandering, winding about the points of rocky and impassable promontories.

Few trees occur along this part of the valley, but grapevines were becoming numerous, and some of them loaded with fruit. Among these we saw signs of the black bear, and one of these animals was shot at but not killed. We also saw some recent tracks of bisons, reviving us with the hope of a return of the days of plenty. We constantly met with the remains of Indian encampments; trees which had been felled with the tomahawk, and other evidences that the country had been recently occupied by savages.

We passed in the afternoon, to a more plain and fertile country than that we had for some days been traversing. The river valley became wide, and bounded on both sides by low and rounded hills, instead of abrupt and perpendicular precipices. The general surface of the country is but little elevated above the river, and is nearly unbroken.

We crossed the beds of several creeks, apparently large streams in the wet season, but now entirely destitute of water. As yet we had not crossed a single tributary discharging any water into the river, nor had we been able to discover any augmentation of the volume of water, which appeared to have been derived from tributaries entering on the other side. The channels of all the creeks, hitherto observed, were beds of sand without water. Several of these " dry rivers," which we passed in the course of the day, have broad vallies, which, if we may judge from a comparison with that we were descending, must have an extent of more than one hundred miles, draining a wide expanse of country of the surplus water in the rainy season, but remaining dry during great part of the year. At five o'clock we encamped, having travelled twenty-six miles due east. The hunters were immediately sent out, but returned without game, having seen nothing.

A beautiful white flowered Gaura,* had been for several days observed along the bank of the river. It is undescribed, and has, before flowering, a very distinct resemblance to common flax.

---

* G. *linifolia*, Nuttall's manuscript.

Stem erect, sparingly branched, smooth. Leaves smooth sessile, alternate linear lanceolate entire, with the midrib translucent. Flowers in a terminal crowded spike; after flowering, the spike extends itself, and in the ripened fruit is scattered, Nut triquetrous, much shorter than the linear bractea.

The flowers are white, having in the calyx a tinge of brownish purple. They are about as large as those of G. *coccinnea*. The plant is three or four feet high, the leaves small and short, and the stem slender.

This is the fifth species of Gaura, we have met with west of the Mississippi. The G. *biennis* of the Eastern States, has not hitherto been found here.

CHAPTER VI.

Band of Kaskaias—Indian encampment—Unfriendly beha-
viour of the Kaskaias—Some account of their persons and
manners—Salt plains—Camancias.

ON the 9th we breakfasted on the last of the horse-beef,
which, having been killed on the 5th, and the weather being
unusually warm, had suffered from long keeping. We ate it
cheerfully, only regretting we had not the prospect of any
thing as good for dinner. All the marksmen of the party
were kept constantly out in search of game, but for several
days had met with no success in hunting.

Our sufferings from want of provisions, and from the apprehension of still more distressing extremities, were now so
considerable, that we gave little attention to any object except hunting. Unfortunately for us, the wind had been high
during the morning, and had blown from west to east, nearly in the direction of our route, so that whatever animals
might have been in the way, had received early intimation
of our approach, and made their escape. We were glad to
observe considerable numbers of prairie wolves, and carrion
birds, as they afforded an almost certain indication of the
proximity of bisons. The recent tracks of a herd of these
animals had been discovered, from which we learned that
they had crossed the river within a day or two, in a crowded
and hurried manner, as if pursued by hunters. We pursued
nearly the same course during the day, and halted for the
night at a late hour, having travelled twenty-eight miles,
and being much exhausted with fatigue, hunger, and the
heat of the day, the mercury at noon having stood at 96°.

At about ten o'clock on the morning following, the hunters, who had preceded the party, discovered on the opposite side of the river, a solitary bison, of which they went immediately in pursuit. The party had made their breakfast of about two ounces of sugar and some grapes, which had been found near camp, and having been for several days reduced to a scanty allowance of provision, they encamped immediately, and awaited with great anxiety the return of the hunters, who soon joined us bringing in the greater part of the carcass of the bison, so extremely lean and ill-flavored that nothing but the most urgent necessity could have induced us to taste it. It was evident that the animal was diseased, and had lingered behind the herd for want of strength to travel. Our situation, however, afforded us not the power of choosing, and from the occurrence of this one we were induced to hope we should soon meet with others in better condition.

We had passed on the preceding day for the first time a small creek discharging some water into the river, and shortly afterwards the sandy bed of another, sixty yards in width, with an extensive valley, but having no water visible above the sand. This morning we also crossed a tributary affording a little water, and a dry channel communicating opposite to our encampment with the bed of the river, which is here paved with small stones, occasioning an inconsiderable fall. Throughout the day the weather was extremely warm, and at sunrise on the following morning the mercury was standing at 71°.

We had not proceeded far on our way, when we discovered on the opposite side of the river, a large party of Indians, approaching in an irregular and interrupted line, which extended more than a mile, from the opposite bank. They had, as was evident, already discovered us, and their outriders were seen plunging into the river at various points, and several soon came up to shake hands with us. The foremost scarcely allowed themselves time to finish this hasty ceremony of salutation, when they rode to reconnoitre some points of bushes and patches of low grape vines on our left, manifestly to ascertain if the whole strength of our party was collected. The main body of the Indians crossed the river more slowly, and as we halted on an elevation near the point where they ascended the bank, the whole passed in review before us. They were all on horseback, and the squaws and children, composing by far the greatest part of the cavalcade, passed us without halting. Every squaw appeared to have under her care a greater or less number of horses, which were driven before her, some dragging lodge-poles, some loaded with packs of meat, and some carrying children. We were amused at observing many small children, too young to be able by their own strength to sit on a horse, lashed by their legs to the saddle, and riding on in entire unconcern. As they passed the deepest part of the river, many of the squaws stooped to fill their vessels with water. These were of the most primitive kind, being formed almost without exception of the stomach or bladder of a bison or other animal.

At length the chief, who was one of the last to cross the river, came up, and shaking us each by the hand, with some appearance of cordiality, invited us to accompany him a short distance on his route, to a place where his party would encamp for the remainder of the day and the ensuing night. The chief was accompanied by an old man, who could speak a little Spanish, by which language we communicated with him. He informed us, his band were a part of the tribe of Kaskaias or Bad-hearts, as they are called by the French, that they had been on an hunting excursion to the sources of the Rio Brassis and the Rio Colorado of Texas, and were now on their way to meet the Spanish traders, at a point near the sources of the river we were descending. They in their turn demanded who we were, whence and whither we were travelling, and were apparently satisfied with our answers, though as afterwards appeared, they did not entirely credit what we had told them of the purposes of our journey.

To our inquiries concerning the river, they answered without hesitation, that it was Red river; that at the distance of ten days travelling, in the manner of Indians with their lodges, (about one hundred miles) we should meet with the permanent village of the Pawnee Piquas; that a large band of Camancias were hunting on the river below, whom we should fall in with in two or three days. Having described to them the route we had pursued, and the great and frequented road on which we had travelled, they said that when we were at the point where that road first crosses the river, we were three days ride from Santa Fe, which was situated behind a low and distant range of hills, that we remembered to have seen from that place.

We hesitated a little to comply with the request of the chief, enforced as it was with some insolence, that we would return and encamp with his party: but as we wished to purchase horses and provisions, and to make the best use of an opportunity to become acquainted with the savages, we at length consented. The ground they chose for their encampment, was a beautiful open plain, having the river in front and a small creek on the left. We were somewhat surprised to witness the sudden manner in which this plain became covered with their tall conic lodges, raised by the squaws, in perfect silence and good order.

For our accommodation a lodge was spread, enclosing as much space as possible in a semi-circular area, in such a manner, that the skin covering afforded a shade, which was all the shelter needed. In order to enlarge this tent as much as possible, the covering was raised so high upon the poles that its lower margin did not extend to the ground by a space of several feet. To remedy this the squaws brought bushes from a neighbouring thicket, which they placed around the

base of the lodge, in such a manner as effectually to exclude
the sunshine. We were sorry to find afterwards that this
had been done not more from motives of hospitality, than to
aid them in their design of pilfering from our baggage.

These skin lodges, are the only habitations of the wandering savages, during all seasons of the year. Those
of the Kaskaias differ in no respect from those we have
already described, as used by the Otoes and others of
the Missouri Indians. The poles, which are six or eight to
each lodge, are from twenty to thirty feet in length, and are
dragged constantly about in all their movements, so that the
trace of a party with lodges is easily distinguished from that
of a war party. When they halt to encamp, the women immediately set up these poles, four of them being tied together by the smaller ends, the larger resting on the ground,
are placed so far apart as to include as much space as the
covering will surround. The remaining poles are added to
strengthen the work and give it a circular form.

The covering is then made fast by one corner to the end
of the last pole, which is to be raised, by which means it is
spread upon the frame with little difficulty. The structure
when completed is in the form of a sharp cone. At the summit is a small opening for window, chimney, &c., out of
which the lodge poles project some distance, crossing each
other at the point where the four shortest are tied together.
The skin lodge, of which a drawing by Mr. Peale is annexed, is greatly inferior in point of comfort, particularly in winter season, to the spacious mud cabins of the settled Indians.

The poles, necessary for the construction of these moveable dwellings, are not to be found in any part of the country of the Kaskaias, but are purchased from the Indians of
the Missouri, or others inhabiting countries more plentifully
supplied with timber. We were informed by Bijeau, that

five of these poles are, among the Bad-hearts, equal in value to a horse.

The chief of this band is called the Red Mouse. He is of large stature, is somewhat past the middle age of life, and no way deficient in his person, and countenance of those indications of strength, cunning, and ferocity, which form so important a part of greatness in the estimation of the Indians.

Immediately after he had dismounted, on the halting of his party, a small wooden dish was brought him, containing some water. He had received a wound some time before apparently from an arrow, which had passed through the arm. Placing the dish on the ground before him, he dipped his hand repeatedly in the water, then seizing a small image of an alligator, profusely ornamented with white and blue beads, he pressed it in his hand with all the strength of the wounded arm. This we saw him repeat a great number of times. The alligator appeared to be the *great medicine*, on which he relied for the cure of his wound; no dressing or application of any kind was made immediately to the affected part.

As soon as we had placed our baggage in the tent provided for us, we commenced negotiations with Red Mouse, for the purchase of horses. When the articles we proposed to barter were exhibited, he appeared dissatisfied, supposing probably, we had still others in reserve, which he would be able by a little obstinacy to extort from us. He accordingly insisted that more of the packs should be opened, and, at last, undertook to extend his inquiries to our private baggage. This we found it necessary to resist, and a little scuffle ensued, at which many of the Indians, with a throng of women and children, who surrounded us, took fright and ran off with the utmost despatch. They all appeared somewhat surprised and intimidated, and the few who remained in our lodge, entreated us not to be angry at the insolence they had shown, saying we should frighten their women, and that they had mistaken us for traders. We had good reasons for wishing not to carry our resentment farther than was necessary, and accordingly relinquished the attempt to trade with them, informing them, at the same time, that we were hungry. Having received us in a friendly manner, we expected they would, according to the custom of most Indians, have shown their good will by inviting us to a feast. We had, therefore, waited with some impatience for their good cheer, so long that hope began to fail us. It will be recollected we had for some days been almost in a starving condition, and we perceived that the Indians had very plentiful supplies of jerked meat. In compliance with our repeated requests the wife of Red Mouse at length brought us a little half boiled bison meat, from which we had observed her to select the best pieces, and give them to the children. After we had eaten this we returned the wooden dish on which it had been brought, at the same time asking her for more. This second demand procured us a little more jerked meat, which came so reluctantly, that as our hunger was now somewhat appeased, we resolved to ask them for no more.

One of the party having asked for water, the paunch of a bison was brought, containing three or four quarts, from which we all managed to drink, though with some difficulty. Little care or labour had been bestowed on the preparation of this vessel. The papillous coat, which formed the internal surface of the stomach of the animal, had not been removed; nor had it lost from long use its peculiar smell. The organ is suffered to retain its original form, as far as is consistent with the uses to which it is applied; one of the orifices is brought nearly in contact with the other, where it is retained by a stick passed through the margin, the depending part is a sack, sometimes large enough to contain six or eight gallons. It may well be supposed, practice is required to enable a person to drink with ease and adroitness from one of these vessels, and the Indians appeared somewhat amused, at the awkwardness of our attempts, in which we spilt more water in our bosoms, than was conveyed into our mouths.

When filled, these sacks cannot be set upon the ground without suffering the loss of their contents. To remedy this the Kaskaias carry with them, as an indispensable article of furniture, a sort of tripod consisting of three light poles tied together at one end and sharpened at the other, by which they are driven into the ground, and the water-sack is suspended between them. One of these was placed near the entrance of almost every lodge in this encampment.

We had scarcely finished our scanty repast, when the wife of the Red Mouse, showing her trencher to signify that we were her debtors, began to beset us for presents; as we were, however, little pleased with her hospitality, we treated her demands, as she had done ours. A number of small articles were pilfered from us, and the Indians seemed determined to show us little respect, until they perceived we were putting our guns in order for immediate use; at this they expressed some apprehension, and behaved afterwards with less rudeness.

They had thirty-two lodges, and were probably about two hundred and fifty in number, including men, women, and children. Among these we could number only twenty-two armed men, and these kept constantly about us. They were armed, exclusively, with bows and arrows, and, as we believed, had some fear of us, though we were less than half their number. It was, probably, owing to our perceiving, or at least appearing to perceive this, that we escaped from them uninjured. They had many horses, probably more than five hundred and some of them very good.

Towards evening, the chief withdrew from our lodge, when we observed his squaw prepare some food for him, pounding the jerked meat to a powder, with a stone pestle, using a piece of skin instead of a mortar. When reduced to very fine fragments, it was mixed with bison tallow, a little water added, and the whole boiled together.

After the chief had finished his meal, a council was held between all the men of the band. They met behind the chief's lodge, and we were not greatly pleased to perceive that they seemed anxious to conceal their meeting from us. At night we determined to collect all our horses, and placing them as near as we could around our lodge, to watch them until morning, but, upon examination, a few of them only could be found, the remainder, as we believed, having been secreted by the Indians. The crowd, which had been assembled about us during the day, dispersed, as the evening advanced, and, at dark, all became still in and about the encampment. At this time, the chief, whose lodge was near ours, standing at the entrance of his dwelling, harangued with great vehemence, in a voice sufficiently loud and clear to be heard by all his people, who had now retired to their several lodges. As we had no interpreter of their language, we could understand nothing of the import of his speech. Every thing remained quiet during the night, and as soon as day dawned on the following morning, a loud harangue, similar to that in the evening, was pronounced by the chief, and immediately afterwards the whole camp was in motion. The lodges were taken down, the packs placed upon the horses, and the whole body were in a short time ready to move off. As several of our horses, our kettles, and other articles of the greatest importance were missing, we were unwilling to part from our hosts in the hasty manner they seemed to intend. We accordingly summoned the old Indian interpreter, and made our complaint and remonstrance to the chief. He told us our horses had strayed from the camp, and that several of his people were then out, searching for them, and made other excuses, evidently designed to gain time until his band could move off. Perceiving we had no time to lose, Major Long ordered horses and other articles to be seized, correspond-

ing to those we had lost. This timely measure produced the desired effect. Their whole camp had been some
time in motion : the women and children, with all their
baggage, except what we had detained, had moved to a considerable distance, and we found ourselves, at this unpleasant state of the dispute, surrounded by their whole armed
force. We observed greater numbers of arrows in their
hands than on the preceding day, and were not without our
fears that they intended to carry the dispute, respecting our
horses and kettles, to greater lengths than we could wish.
We were, however, agreeably disappointed to learn that all
our lost property had been found. It was accordingly restor-
ed to us and we parted from the Kaskaias as friends.

The time we spent with this band of savages was so short,
as to afford little opportunity of becoming acquainted with
their manners. Their dress is nearly similar to that of the
Pawnees, but consists more exclusively of leather. The
women, instead of the robe, wear a loose frock without
sleeves. It has an opening for the neck, large enough to admit the head, and descends from the shoulders, hanging like
a bag about the body, and reaching below the knees. When
eagerly engaged in their employments this inconvenient article of dress is thrown aside, and the squabbish person
of the female savage is exposed to view, disfigured only by
a small apron of leather worn round the waist. The young
females appear in some measure, exempted from the laborious services performed by the married women, and
consequently, possess a degree of lightness and elasticity in
their persons, which they soon lose after they begin to bear
children, and subject themselves to the severe drudgeries of a
married life. Their breasts become so flaccid and pendulous
that we have seen them give suck to their children, the mother and the child at the same time standing erect upon the
ground. This fact is sufficient to prove that they do not, at
least in some instances, wean their children at a very early
age.

Like all savages, they suffer themselves to be covered with filth and vermin, and as among many northern tribes,* lice are sought for and eaten with avidity, at least by the women; notwithstanding which, some of the young females are far from disgusting in their appearance. They have well turned features, aquiline noses, large and regular teeth, and eyes which, though usually rather small, are clear and brilliant. In the general structure of their features, and in the complexion of their skins, they resemble the Missouri tribes, being of a clearer and brighter red, than many of the eastern Indians. In stature and in symmetry of body they are inferior to the Otoes, Pawnees, and most of the Missouri Indians who reside in permanent villages.

They seemed to have had little intercouse with the whites, as some among them appeared to take great pleasure in exhibiting to their friends the skin of our arms, which they requested us to show them for that purpose. It was probably by means of a mistake, on the part of one of the interpreters, that we received the intimation that they had never before heard of such a people as that to which we belonged. We saw among them few articles of foreign production; these they had, probably, received from Spanish traders. In the whole encampment we saw but one kettle, which belonged to the chief, and their great eagerness to steal our tin cups and other similar articles, sufficiently evinced that such things are scarce, and of great value among them. They have some beads, most of which are bestowed in ornamenting the dress of the children; also some pewter and brass rings, worn principally by the women. They are acquainted with the use of tobacco, and smoked with us according to the universal custom of the Indians, but expressed, by signs, that they found the smoke of unmixed tobacco too strong for them. One of their young men, who was in his ordinary dress when we met the party, visited us soon after

* Des. of Kamschatka. p. 507. Pennant's Arct. Zool. vol. i. p. 204.

we had encamped, dressed in leggings and breech-cloth, with a striped worsted vest and a silver-headed bamboo.

A child was shown us, who spoke Spanish, and who was said to be a prisoner from the Spanish settlements; he was not, however, distinguished from the Kaskaias by any difference of colour or of features. He spoke frequently of the Christians, which convinced us that he had, at least been among the half civilized Indians of New Mexico, who have some acquaintance with the Spanish language, and have been taught enough of the Christian religion to make use of the sign of the cross.

This band of Kaskaias frequent the country about the sources of the Platte, Arkansa, and Rio Del Norte, and extend their hunting excursions to Red river and the sources of the Brassis. The great numbers of images of the Alligator, which they wear, either as ornaments, or as amulets for the cure or prevention of disease and misfortune, afford sufficient proof of their extending their rambles to districts inhabited by that reptile. These images are of carved wood, covered with leather, and profusely ornamented with beads. They are suspended about the neck, and we saw several worn in this manner by the children as well as by adults. It was observed, likewise, that the rude frames of the looking-glasses carried by several of the men, were carved so as to approximate towards the same form.

It is, perhaps, owing to their frequent exposures to the stormy and variable atmosphere of the country about the Rocky Mountains, that these Indians are subjected to numerous attacks of rheumatic and scrofulous diseases. We saw one old woman with a distorted spine, who had, probably, suffered when young from rickets.* A young man of

---

* Baron Humboldt saw no instance of personal deformity among the Chaymas, the Caribs, the Muyscas, or the Mexican, or Peruvian Indians,* and he thence concludes, perhaps hastily, " that bodily deformities are infinitely rare among those races that have the dermoid system highly coloured." This remark is not strictly applicable to the North American Indians, nor to the highly coloured descendants of African races, now so

* Pers. Nar. vol. iii p. 233.

a fine athletic frame, had his neck covered with scrofulous ulcers. While he was with us, he was constantly endeavouring to conceal with his robe this afflicting spectacle. He remained but a short time amongst us, and did not make his second appearance.

An old man came frequently to us with a diseased leg, informing us by signs that it had repeatedly formed large abscesses, which had discharged much matter, and afterwards healed. His frequent applications to us were made with the hope that we would do something for his relief.

The men of this band wear the hair long, and suffer it to hang negligently about the shoulders. Some of them have a braid behind which is garnished with bits of red cloth, small pieces of tin, &c., and descends nearly to the ground, being sometimes eked out with the hair of a horse's tail. Among the old men, were several who had suffered a number of scattering hairs on the face to become of considerable length, a violation of good manners, and a neglect of personal neatness, not often met with among the Indians, and excusable only in the old. In their conduct towards us they were guilty of more rudeness and incivility than we had been accustomed to meet with among the savages of the Missouri.

Though we saw much to admire among this people, we cannot but think them among the most degraded and miserable of the uncivilized Indians on this side of the Rocky Mountains. Their wandering and precarious manner of life, as well as the inhospitable character of the country they inhabit, precludes the possibility of advancement from the profoundest barbarism. As is common among other of the western tribes, they were persevering in offering us their women, but this appeared to be done from mere beastliness and the hope of reward, rather than any motive of hospitality or a

numerous among us. We saw, among the Indians of the Mississippi, several instances of deformity. *Shawiskanan,* a Sioux, who was exhibited at New-York and Philadelphia in 1822, is more deformed than any white man we remember to have seen.

desire to show us respect. We saw among them no article of food, except the flesh of the bison; their horses, their arms, lodges, and dogs, are their only wealth.

In their marches they are all on horseback, the men are expert horsemen, and evince great dexterity in throwing the rope, taking in this way many of the wild horses which inhabit some parts of their country. They hunt the bison on horseback with the bow and arrow, being little acquainted with the use of fire arms. One of them, who had received a valuable pistol, from a member of our party, soon afterwards returned and wished to barter it for a knife. They begged for tobacco, but did not inquire for whiskey. It is probable they have not yet acquired a fondness for intoxicating liquors.

At eight o'clock on the morning of the 12th, we took our leave of the Kaskaias, having recovered from them all the articles they had stolen, except a few ropes, halters, and other small affairs, which, not being indispensably necessary to us, we chose to relinquish, rather than submit to a longer delay, among a people we had so much reason to dislike.

They had shown a disposition, so far from friendly toward us, that we were surprised to have escaped without having found it necessary to use our arms in self-defence, and as we thought it by no means improbable some of their young men might follow us to steal our horses, we moved on rather briskly, intending to travel as far in the course of the day as we conveniently could.

The river valley spread considerably a little below the point where we had encamped. In many places we found the surface a smooth and naked bed of sand, in others covered by an incrustation of salt, like a thin ice, and manifestly derived from the evaporation of water, which had flowed down from the red sandstone hills bounding the valley. These hills were here of moderate elevation, the side towards the river being usually abrupt and naked. The sandstone is fine, of a deep red colour, indistinctly stratified, and traversed in various directions by veins, filled principally with sulphate of lime.

We had seen among the Indians, on the preceding day, quantities of salt, in large but detached crystalline fragments, resembling the common coarse salt of commerce. It had evidently been collected from some place like the one above mentioned, where it had been deposited from solution in water. When we inquired the particular locality, the Indians pointed to the south, and said, it was found near the sources of a river, rising in that direction.

At the place of our evening encampment, we saw the red-necked avoset, (Recurvirostra *americana*) the minute tern, (Sterna *minuta*) and several other strand birds, which we could not approach near enough to distinguish the species. There is also a very evident similarity between the plants found here, and many of those growing in saline soils along the sea coast. We see here several species of atriplex, chenopodium, salsola, kochia, and anabasis, all delighting in a saline soil, and affording on analysis a greater proportion of soda, than most inland plants.

The day had been unusually warm. During all our mid-day halt, protracted on account of the sultriness of the weather, to an unaccustomed length, the mercury had remained at 100°, the thermometer being suspended in the closest shade we could find. It is to be remarked, however, that in almost every one of the numerous instances, when the mercurial column had indicated so high a temperature, a fair exposure could not be had. We often found it necessary to halt upon the open plain, where the intensity of light and heat were much increased by the reflection of the sun's rays from the sand. The temperature indicated by the thermometer suspended in the imperfect shade of our tent, or of a small tree, was, however, somewhat lower than that to which our bodies were exposed, and it will be believed, our sufferings from this source were great, both on our marches and while en-

camped in the middle of the day.　Our tent being too small
to afford its imperfect shade to the whole party, we sometimes suspended blankets, using instead of poles our rifles
and gunsticks, but the protection these could afford against
the scorching glare of a vertical sun, was found extremely inadequate.

At sunset we crossed, what appears to be, at some seasons
of the year, the bed of a large river, at least two hundred
yards wide, but at this time not a drop of water was found
in it.　It has a wide valley, and in every respect, but the
occasional want of water, is a large stream.　A little beyond
this we encamped for the night, having travelled twenty-eight
miles.

13th.　The course of the river had here become considerably serpentine, so that our route along its valley, was of necessity somewhat circuitous.　Wishing to avoid the unnecessary travelling thus occasioned, we turned off from the river,
and ascended the hills, hoping to meet with an Indian trace,
leading across the country by the most direct route.　Our
search was, however unavailing, only affording us an opportunity of examining a portion of the country remote from
the river.　This we found much broken with irregular hills,
abrupt ravines, and deep vallies.　At 10 o'clock we met with
a small stream of water, running towards the river we had
left, and crossing it, perceived the trace of a large party of
mounted Indians, which had ascended the creek within a few
hours previous.　We supposed them to have been the band
of Camancias spoken of by the Bad-hearts, and notwithstanding we had reason to entertain some fear, that they would
have treated us no better than the Kaskaias had done, we
considered ourselves unfortunate, in not having met them.
Much confusion and uncertainty attends the limited information, hitherto before the public, concerning the wandering
bands of savages, who occupy the country between the frontiers of New Mexico and the United States.　Some who have

spoken of these Indians, seem to have included several of the erratic hordes already enumerated, under the name of Hietans or Camancias. From their wandering mode of life, it unavoidably happens, that the same band is met by hunters and travellers, in different parts of the country, at different times, consequently they receive different appellations, and the estimate of their numbers becomes much exaggerated. Of this band, we have no other information to communicate, than that they appeared, from the tracks of their horses and lodge poles, to have been rather more numerous than the party of Bad-hearts we had lately met. A recent grave was discovered by one of our hunters, at no great distance from the river, in which it was supposed one of this band had been buried. At one end of the grave was erected a pole about ten feet in length, crossed near the top by another two feet long. To the foot of this rude cross was tied a pair of mockasins, newly soaled and carefully prepared for the use of the departed, in that long journey, on the *road of the dead*, to which the good wishes of some friend had accompanied him.

Where we halted at noon, were some trees, and several of these were covered with grape vines, loaded with ripe and delicious fruit. The Osage plum was also common, and now beginning to ripen. The temperature of the air within our tent, partially shaded by some small trees, was sufficiently high to keep the mercury at 105° Fah. From twelve o'clock to three P. M. a suffocating stillness prevailed in the air, and we could find no relief from the painful glare of light, and the intense heat, which seemed about to reduce the scanty vegetation to ashes.

In the afternoon, a thick grove of timber was descried at a distance below, and on the opposite side of the river. This cheering sight was like the discovery of land to the mariner, reminding us of the comparative comfort and plenty, which we had learned to consider inseparable from a forest country, and exciting in us the hope that we should

soon exchange our desolate and scorching sands for a more
hospitable and more favoured region. As this little grove
of trees, appearing to us like the commencement of an immense forest, gave reason to expect we should soon find
some small game, Mr. Peale, with one man, went forward
to hunt. Soon after arriving at the wood, they discovered
a flock of turkies, and the rifleman, dismounting to shoot,
left his mule for a moment at liberty. The animal taking a
sudden advantage of the opportunity, turned about and
made the best of his way out of the wood, pursued by
Mr. Peale. This chase continued about five miles, and
ended in putting the mule on the recent trace of the party,
which there was no reason to fear he could be induced
to leave until he had rejoined his companions. Mr. Peale
who was exhausted with the pursuit, followed slowly,
and neglecting to pursue carefully the path of the party,
passed us, after we had turned aside to encamp, still travelling on in the direction of our course. At dark, believing
we were still before him, and knowing we must encamp near
the river, he betook himself to the sandbars, which were now
naked, occupying the greater part of what was sometimes
the bed of the stream. Along these he travelled, occasionally discharging a pistol, and looking about, in constant expectation of seeing the blaze of our evening fire, until the
moon began to sink behind the hills, when finding the light
insufficient to enable him to continue his search, he tied his
horse to a tree and laid down to wait the return of daylight.

At camp guns were discharged, as large a fire kindled as
we could find the means of making, and other measures taken
to give him notice of our position, and late in the evening,
the man, whose mule had been the occasion of the accident,
joined us, but was unable to give any account of Mr. Peale,
or the mule, which had, however, arrived before him. At
seven o'clock, on the morning following, Mr. Peale returned
to us, having convinced himself, by a careful examination of

the river valley, that we were still above. He accordingly retraced his course, until he discovered the smoke of our encampment. He had been much harassed, in the night, by mosquitoes; and bisons having recently occupied the shade of the tree under which he slept, the place afforded as little refreshment for the horse as for himself. Delaying a little to allow him time to make amends for his long abstinence, we left our camp at a later hour than usual, and moving along a wide and somewhat grassy plain, halted to dine near an old Indian breast-work, by the side of a grove of cotton-wood trees, intermixed with a few small-leaved elms. This breast-work is built like that discovered on the Platte, a few days march above the Pawnees. We have met with the remains of similar works in almost every grove of trees about the base of the mountains. Near some of them, we noticed holes dug a few feet into the ground, probably as *caches* or depositaries of provision, the earth which was raised having been removed to a distance, or thrown into the river that that it might not lead to the discovery of the concealed articles. We sometimes saw large excavations of this kind, having an entrance comparatively small, and so placed as to be easily concealed, made by white hunters, to hold their furs, and whatever else they might wish to deposit in safe keeping.

The occurrence of the elm, the phytolacca, the cephalanthus, and other plants, not met with in a desert of sand, gave us the pleasing assurance of a change we had long been expecting in the aspect of the country. The blue jay, the purple martin, a deer, and some turkies were also seen near this encampment. The bed of the river is here, eight hundred yards wide, but the quantity of water visible is much less than in some places above. The magnetic variation, ascertained at this camp, was 12° 30′ east.

CHAPTER VII.

Sand plains — Mississippi hawk — Small-leaved elm — Wild horses — Hail storm — Climate — Bisons — Grapes — Red-sand formation — Gypsum.

EXTENSIVE tracts of loose sand, so destitute of plants and so fine as to be driven by the winds, occur in every part of the saline sandstone formation southwest of the Arkansa. They are, perhaps, invariably the detritus of the sand-rock, deposited in vallies and depressions where the rapidity of the currents of water has been checked by permanent obstacles. This loose sand differs in colour from the sandstone, which is almost invariably red. The difference may have been produced simply by the operation of water suspending and removing the light colouring matter, no longer retained by the aggregation of the sandstone. These fields of sand have most frequently an undulated surface, occasioned, probably, not less by the operation of winds than by the currents of water. A few plum bushes, almost the only woody plants found on them, wherever they take root form points, about which the sand accumulates, and, in this manner, permanent elevations are produced. The yucca *angustifolia* and the shrubby cactus, the white argemone, and the night-flowering Bartonia, are the most conspicuous plants in these sandy wastes.

Our course, on the 15th, led us twice across the bed of the river, which we found one thousand and four hundred paces in width, and without water, except in a few small pools where it was stagnant. This wide and shallow bed is included between low banks, sometimes sloped gradually and sometimes, though rarely perpendicular, and rising scarcely more than four feet from the common level of the bottom of the channel. Driftwood is occasionally seen without these banks, at an elevation of a few feet above them, affording evidence that they are, at times, not only full but overflowed. Whenever they are but partially filled it is easy to see that, what for a great part of the year is a naked sand-beach, then becomes a broad and majestic river. It must flow with a rapid current, and, in floods, its waters cannot be otherwise than of an intense red colour. The immediate valley of the river had now become little less than two miles in width, and had, in some places, a fertile soil. This happens wherever places occur having little elevation above the bed of the river, and which have not recently been covered with drifted sand.

Several species of locust were extremely frequent here, filling the air by day with their shrill and deafening cries, and feeding with their bodies great numbers of that beautiful species of hawk, the Falco *Mississippiensis* of Wilson. It afforded us a constant amusement to watch the motions of this greedy devourer, in the pursuit of the locust his favorite prey. The insect being large and not very active is easily taken; the hawk then poises on the wing, suspending himself in the air, while with his talons and beak he tears in pieces and devours his prey.

Prairie wolves, and vultures, occurred in unusual numbers, and the carcasses of several bisons, recently killed, had been seen. We could also distinguish the recent marks of a hunting party of Indians, the tracks of horses and men being still fresh in the sand. At four P. M. several bisons were discovered at a distance, and, as we were in the greatest want of provisions, we halted and sent the hunters in pursuit, and, being soon apprised of their success, the requisite preparations were made for jerking the meat. Near our camp was a scattering grove of small-leaved elms. This tree (the Ulmus *alata, N.*) is not known in the Eastern States, but is common in many parts of Tennessee, Missouri, and Arkansa. When found in forests intermixed with other trees, it is usually of a smaller size than the Ulmus *Americana*, and is distinguished from it by the smallness of the leaves and the whiteness of the trunk. On the borders of the open country, where large trees often occur entirely isolated, the Ulmus *alata* has decidedly a more dense and flattened top than any other tree we have seen. When standing entirely alone, it rarely attains an elevation of more than thirty or thirty-five feet, but its top, lying close to the ground, is spread over an area of sixty or seventy feet in diameter, and is externally so close and smooth as to resemble, when seen from a distance, a small grassy hillock.

Near our camp was a circular breast-work, constructed like those already mentioned, and large enough to contain eighty or an hundred men. We were not particularly pleased at meeting these works so frequently, as they indicate a country subject to the incursions and ravages of Indian war parties.

16th. The greater part of the flesh of the bison, killed on the preceding evening, had been dried and smoked in the course of the night, so that we had now no fear of immediate suffering from hunger, having as much jerked meat as was sufficient to last several days.

The sky continued clear, but the wind was high, and the drifting of the sand occasioned much annoyance. The heat of the atmosphere became more intolerable, on account of the showers of burning sand driven against us, with such force as to penetrate every part of our dress, and proving so afflictive to our eyes, that it was with the greatest difficulty we could see to guide our horses. The sand is carried from the bed of the river, which is here a naked beach, of more than half a mile wide, and piled in immense drifts along the bank. Some of these heaps we have seen covering the trunk and a portion of the upper branches, of what appeared to be large trees. Notwithstanding we were now three hundred miles distant from the sources of the river, we found very little water, and that being stagnant and frequented by bisons and other animals, was so loathsome, both to sight and smell, that nothing but the most incontrollable thirst, could have induced us to taste it.

At a short distance below the place of our encampment, we passed the confluence of a large creek, entering from the southwest. Though like all the streams of this thirsty region its waters were entirely hid in the sand, yet it is evidently the bed of a large tributary; from its direction, we conclude it can be no other than the one on which the Kaskaias informed us they had encamped the night before we met them. Its name, if it have any among the Indians or Spaniards, we have not learned.

We had for some days observed a few wild horses, and they, as well as the bisons, were now becoming numerous. In the habits of the wild horse, we find little unlike what is seen in the domestic animal. He becomes the most timorous and watchful of the inhabitants of the wilderness. They show a similar attachment to each others' society, though the males are occasionally found at a distance from the herds. It would appear from the paths we have seen, that they sometimes perform long journies, and it may be worthy of remark, that along these paths are frequently found very large piles of horse-dung of different ages, affording sufficient evidence that this animal in a wild state, has, in common with some others, an inclination to drop his excrement where another has done so before him. This habit is sometimes faintly discovered in the domestic horse.

As we were about to halt for dinner, a male bison which had lingered near our path was killed, but the flesh was found in too ill a condition to be eaten, as is the case with all the bulls at this season.

Soon after we had mounted our horses in the afternoon, a violent thunder storm came on from the northwest. Hail fell in such abundance as to cover the surface of the ground, and some of the hailstones, which we examined, were near an inch in diameter. Falling with a strong wind, these heavy masses struck upon our bodies with considerable violence. Our horses, as they had done on a similar occasion before, refused to move, except before the wind. Some of the mules turned off from our course, and had run more than half a mile before they could be overtaken. For ourselves, we found some protection, by wrapping our blankets as loose-ly as possible around our bodies, and waited for the cessa-tion of the storm, not without calling to mind some instances on record, of hailstones, which have destroyed the lives of men and animals. It is not improbable, that the climate of a portion of country, within the range of the immediate influ-ence of the Rocky Mountains, may be more subject to hail-storms in summer, than other parts of the continent, lying in the same latitude. The radiation of heat from so extensive a surface of naked sand, lying along the base of this vast range of snowy mountains, must produce great local inequalities of temperature: the diminished pressure of the atmosphere, and the consequent rapidity of evaporation, may in these elevated regions also be supposed to have an important influence on the weather. We have not spent sufficient time in the coun-try near the eastern border of the Rocky Mountains, to enable us to speak with confidence of the character of its climate. It is, however, sufficiently manifest that in summer it must be extremely variable, as we have found it; the thermometer often indicating an increase of near fifty degrees of tempera-ture, between sunrise and the middle of the day. These ra-pid alternations of heat and cold must be supposed to mark a climate little favourble to health, though we may safely as-sert that this portion of the country is exempt from the ope-ration of those causes, which produce so deleterious an atmosphere in the lower and more fertile portions of the Mississippi basin. If the wide plains of the Platte, the upper Arkansa, and the Red river of Louisiana, should ever become the seat of a permanent civilized population, the diseases most incident to such a population, will probably be fevers attended with pulmonary and pleuritic inflammations, rheumatism, scrofula, and consumption. It is true that few if any instances of pulmonary consumption, occur among the Indians of this region; the same remark is probably as true of the original native population of New York and New England.

Though much rain fell during this storm, it was so rapidly absorbed by the soil, that little running water was to be seen. The bed of the river was found smooth and unobstructed, and afforded us for several days the most convenient path for travelling. As we descended, we found it to expand in some places to a width of near two miles. Bisons became astonishingly numerous, and in the middle of the day countless thousands of them were seen, coming in from every quarter to the stagnant pools, which filled the most depressed places in the channel of the river. The water of these was of course too filthy to be used in cooking our meat, and though sometimes compelled to drink it, we found little alleviation to our thirst. At our encampments we were able to furnish ourselves with water of a better quality by digging in the sand, where we seldom failed to meet with a supply at a few feet from the surface.

On the 17th we halted in the middle of the day to hunt, as, although we had killed several bisons on our marches of the preceding days, none of them had been found in good condition. The flesh of the bulls in the months of August and September, is poor and ill-flavoured; but these are much more easily killed than the cows, being less vigilant, and sometimes suffering themselves to be overtaken by the hunter without attempting to escape. As the herds of cows were now seen in great numbers, we halted and the hunters went out and killed several. Our camp was on the southwest side of the river, under a low bluff, which separates the half wooded valley from the open and elevated plains. The small elms along this valley were bending under the weight of innumerable grape vines, now loaded with ripe fruit, the purple clusters crouded in such profusion as almost to give colouring to the landscape. On the opposite side of the river was a range of low sand hills, fringed with vines, rising not more than a foot or eighteen inches from the surface. On examination we found these hillocks had been produced, exclusively by the agency of the grape vines arresting the sand, as it was borne along by the wind, until such quantities had been accumulated as to bury every part of the plant except the ends of the branches. Many of these were so loaded with fruit, as to present nothing to the eye but a series of clusters so closely arranged as to conceal every part of the stem. The fruit of these vines is incomparably finer than that of any other, either native or exotic, which we have met with in the United States. The burying of the greater part of the trunk, with its larger branches, produces the effect of pruning, in as much as it prevents the unfolding of leaves and flowers on the parts below the surface, while the protruding ends of the branches enjoy an increased degree of light and heat from the reflection of the sand. It is owing undoubtedly to these causes that the grapes in question are so far superior to the fruit of the same vines in ordinary circumstances.

The treatment here employed by nature to bring to perfection the fruit of the vine may be imitated, but without the same peculiarities of soil and exposure, can with difficulty be carried to the same magnificent extent. Here are hundreds of acres covered with a surface of moveable sand, and abounding in vines, placed in more favorable circumstances, by the agency of the sun and the winds, than it is in the power of man, to afford to so great an extent. We indulged ourselves to excess, if excess could be committed in the use of such delicious and salutary fruit, and invited by the cleanness of the sand, and a refreshing shade, we threw ourselves down, and slept away with unusual zest, a few of the hours of a summer afternoon.

Our hunters had been as successful as could be wished, and at evening we assembled around a full feast of " marrow bones," a treat whose value must forever remain unknown to those who have not tried the adventurous life of the hunter. We were often surprised to witness in ourselves a proof of the facility, with which a part at least of the habits of the savage could be adopted. Having been in several instances compelled to practice a tedious abstinence, the return of plenty found us well disposed to make amends for these temporary privations, and we lingered almost involuntarily at every meal, as if determined not only to make amends for the deficiency of the past, but to secure so ample a supply as would enable us to defy the future.

The grapes and plums, so abundant in this portion of the country, are eaten by turkies and black bears, and the plums by wolves, as we conclude from observing plumstones in the excrement of these animals. It is difficult to conceive whence such numbers of predatory animals and birds, as exist in every part of the country where the bisons are present, can derive sufficient supplies for the sustenance of life; it is indeed sufficiently evident, their existence is but a protraction of the sufferings of famine.

The great flowering hibiscus is here a conspicuous and highly ornamental plant, among the scattering trees in the low ground. The occurrence of the black walnut for the first time, since we left the Missouri, indicated a soil somewhat adapted to the purposes of agriculture. Portions of the river valley, which are not covered with loose sand, have a red soil, resulting from the disintegration of the prevailing rocks, red sandstone and gypsum, intermixed with clay, and are covered with a dense growth of fine and nutritious grasses.

Extensive tracts of the great woodless plain, at a distance
from the river, appear to be based on a more compact variety of sandstone, usually of a dark gray colour, and less per-
vious to water than the red. For this reason some copious
springs are found upon it, and a soil by no means destitute
of fertility, yielding sustenance to inconceivable numbers of
herbivorous animals, and through them to innumerable birds
and beasts of prey. It must be supposed, however, that the
herds of bisons, daily seen about the river, range over a much
greater extent of country than was comprised within our limited views; the want of water in many places, may compel
them to resort frequently to the river in dry weather, though
at other times they may be dispersed in the high plains.

18th. In speaking of a country, whose geography is so little known, as that of the region southwest of the Arkansa,
we feel the want of ascertained and fixed points of reference.
Were we to designate the locality of a mineral or any other
interesting object, as twenty or thirty days' journey from
the Rocky Mountains, we should do nearly all in our power; yet this sort of information would probably be thought
vague and useless. The smaller rivers of this region have as
yet received no names from white hunters; if they have names
among the Indians, these are unknown to us. There are no
mountains, hills, or other remarkable objects, to serve as
points of *reckoning*, nearer than the Rocky Mountains and the
Arkansa. The river itself, which we supposed to be the Red
river of Natchitoches, is a permanent land mark, but it is a
line, and aids us only in one direction in our attempts to designate locality. The map accompanying this work was projected in conformity to the results of numerous astronomical
observations for latitude and longitude, but many of these
observations were made at places, not at present to be known
by any names we might attempt to fix upon them. More extensive and minute examination, than we have been able to bestow, might establish something like a sectional division,

founded on the distribution of certain remarkable plants. The great cylindric cactus, the American colycinth, (Cucumis *perennis*,) and the small-leaved elm, might be used in such an attempt, but it is easy to see that the advantages resulting from it, would be for the most part imaginary.

Discussions of this sort have been much insisted on, and may be important as aiding in the geography of climates and soils, but can afford little assistance to topography.

The geological features of the region under consideration, afford some foundation for a natural division, but this division must be so extremely general, as to afford little satisfaction. We could only distinguish the red sandstone, the argillaceous sandstone, and the trap districts, and though each of these have distinctive characters, not easy to be mistaken, they are so irregular in form and position, as to be in no degree adapted to aid in the description, and identifying of particular places. On the contrary it is to be regretted, there are no established points, to which we might refer, in communicating what we have observed of the position of these formations, and indicating the particular localities of some of the valuable minerals they contain.

The red sandstone, apparently the most extensive of the rocky formations of this region, shows, wherever it occurs, indications of the presence of muriate of soda, and almost as commonly discloses veins and beds of sulphate of lime. This substance had been growing more and more abundant, since we left the region of the trap rocks at the sources of the river. It was now so frequent as to be conspicuous in all the exposed portions of the sand-rock, and was often seen from a distance of several miles. It occurs under various forms; sometimes we met with the most beautiful selenite, disposed in broad reticulating veins, traversing the sandstone. The granular and fibrous varieties, whose snowy whiteness contrasts strongly with the deep red and brown of the sandstone, are sometimes seen in thin horizontal laminæ, or scattered about the surface, sometimes included in larger masses of the common amorphous plaister stone. This last is usually of a colour approaching to white, but the exposed surfaces are more or less tinged with the colouring matter of the sand-rock, and all the varieties are so soft as to disintegrate rapidly, when exposed to the air. Recent surfaces show no ferruginous tinge, in other words, this colour does not appear to have been contemporaneous to the formation of the sulphate of lime, but derived from the cement of the sandstone, and to have penetrated no farther than it has been carried by the infiltration of water.

We left our encampment at five o'clock; the morning fair; thermometer at 62⁰. Our courses, regulated entirely by the direction of the river, were north, fifty-five east, eleven miles, then north, ten east, seven miles, in all eighteen miles before dinner.* The average direction of our course, for some days, had been rather to the north than south of east. This fact did not coincide with our previous ideas of the direction of Red River, and much less of the Faux Ouachitta or False Washita, which, being the largest of the upper branches of Red River from the north, we believed might be the stream we were descending. From observations taken at several points along the river we had ascertained that we must travel three or four days' journey to the south, in order to arrive at the parallel of the confluence of the Kiamesha with the Red river,† and we were constantly expecting a change in the direction of our courses. The confident assurance of the Kaskaias, that we were on Red River, and but a few days' march above the village of the Pawnee Piquas, tended to quiet the suspicions we began to feel on this subject. We had now travelled, since meeting the Indians, a greater distance than we could suppose they had intended

* The magnetic variation was here from 12° to 13° east.

† The latitude of this point was ascertained by Major Long, in December, 1819, to be a few minutes below 34° north.

to indicate by the admeasurement of ten " lodge days," but we were conscious our communications with them had been made through inadequate interpreters, and it was not without reason we began to fear we might have received erroneous impressions. In the afternoon, however, the river inclined more to the direction we wished to travel; and we had several courses to the south of east. At sunset we pitched our tent on the north side of the river, and dug a well in the sand, which afforded a sufficient supply of wholesome, though brackish water. Throughout the night the roaring of immense herds of bisons, and the solemn notes of the hooting owl, were heard, intermixed with the desolate cries of the prairie wolf, and the screech owl. The mulberry and the guilandina growing near our camp, with many of the plants and birds we had been accustomed to see in the frontier settlements of the United States, reminded us of the comforts of home, and the cheering scenes of social life, giving us, at the same time, the assurance that we were about to arrive at the point where we should take leave of the desert.

19th. The mercury at sunrise stood at 71°. The morning was calm, and the sky tinged with that intense and beautiful blue which marks many of our summer skies, and is seen with greater pleasure, by those who know that home, or a good tavern, is near, than by such as have no prospect of shelter, save what a tent or a blanket can afford. We were now looking, with much impatience, for something to indicate an approach towards the village of the Pawnee Piquas; but instead of this the traces of Indians seemed to become less and less frequent. Notwithstanding the astonishing numbers of bison, deer, antelopes, and other animals, the country is less strewed with bones than almost any we have seen, affording an evidence that it is not a favourite hunting ground of any tribe of Indians. The animals also appeared wholly unaccustomed to the sight of men. The bisons and wolves

moved slowly off to right and left, leaving a lane for the party to pass; but those on the windward side often lingered
for a long time almost within the reach of our rifles, regarding us with little appearance of alarm. We had now nothing to suffer, either from the apprehension or the reality of
hunger, and could have been content that the distance between ourselves and the settlements should have been much
greater than we supposed it to be.

In the afternoon, finding the course of the river again
bending towards the north, and becoming more and more
serpentine, we turned off on the right side, and choosing
an east course, travelled across the hills, not doubting but we
would soon arrive again at the river. We found the country,
at a distance from the bed of the river, somewhat elevated
and broken; but, upon climbing some of the highest hills,
we again saw the landscape of the unbounded and unvaried
grassy plain spread out before us. All the inequalities of the
surface have evidently been produced by the excavating
operation of currents of water, and they are consequently
most considerable near the channels of the large streams.
This remark is applicable to the vallies of all the large rivers
in the central portions of the great horizontal formation
west of the Alleganies. We find, accordingly, that on the
Ohio, the Missouri, the Platte, the Konzas, and many of
the rivers tributary to the Mississippi, the surface becomes
broken in proportion as we proceed from the interior towards
the bed of the river; and all the hills bear convincing evidence
that they have received their existence and their form from the
action of the currents of water, which have removed the soil
and other matters formerly occupying the vallies, and elevating
the whole surface of the country nearly to a common level.
Regarding in this view the extensive vallies of the Mississippi, and its tributaries, we naturally inquire how great a
length of time must have been spent in the production of
such an effect, the cause operating as it now does? It is

scarce necessary to remark that where the vallies of the rivers in question are bounded on both sides, as they often are, by perpendicular cliffs of sandstone or limestone in horizontal strata, the seams and markings on one side correspond with those on the other, indicating the stratifications to have been originally continuous.

A ride of a few miles, in a direction passing obliquely from the river, brought us to a point which overlooked a large extent of the surrounding country. From this we could distinguish the winding course of a small stream uniting numerous tributaries from the ridge we occupied, and pursuing its way towards the southeast along a narrow and well wooded valley. The dense and verdant foliage of the poplars and elms contrasted faintly with the bright red of the sandstone cliffs, which rose on both sides, far surpassing the elevation of the tallest trees, and disclosing here and there masses of sulphate of lime of a snowy whiteness. Looking back upon the broad valley of the river we had left, the eye rested upon insulated portions of the sandy bed, disclosed by the inflections of its course, or the opening of ravines, and resembling pools of blood rather than wastes of sand. We had been so long accustomed to the red sands that the intensity of the colouring ceased to excite attention, until a distant view afforded us the opportunity of contrasting it with the general aspect of the country.

The elevated plains we found covered with a plenteous, but close fed crop of grasses, and occupied by extensive marmot villages. The red soil is usually fine, and little intermixed with gravel and pebbles, but too sandy to retain moisture enough for the purposes of agriculture. The luxuriance and fineness of the grasses, as well as the astonishing number and good condition of the herbivorous animals of this region clearly indicate its value for purposes of pasturage. There can be no doubt that more valuable and productive grasses than the native species can, with little trou-

ble, be introduced. This may easily be effected by burning
the prairies, at a proper season of the year, and sowing the
seeds of any of the more hardy cultivated graminæ. Some of
the perennial plants common in the prairies, will, undoubtedly, be found difficult to exterminate; their strong roots penetrating to a great depth, and enveloping the rudiments of
new shoots placed beyond the reach of a fire on the surface.
The soil of the more fertile plains is penetrated with such
numbers of these as to present more resistance to the plough
than the oldest cultivated pastures.

We had continued our march until near sunset, expecting
constantly to come in view of the river, which we were persuaded must soon make a great bend to the south; but perceiving the night would overtake us in the plains, we began
to search for a place to encamp. The bison paths in this
country are as frequent, and almost as conspicuous, as the
roads in the most populous parts of the United States. They
converge from all directions to the places where water is to
be found, and by following their guidance we were soon led
to a spot where was a small spring, dripping from the side
of a cliff of sandstone. The water collected in a little basin
at the foot of the cliff, and flowing a few rods down a narrow ravine disappeared in the sand. Having established our
camp, we travelled down this ravine, searching for plants,
while any daylight remained. The rocks were beautifully
exposed, but exhibited no appearance unlike what we had
been accustomed to see along the river; the red indistinctly
stratified sand-rock, spotted and veined with plaister stone
and selenite. About the shelvings and crevices of the rocks
the slender corrolla of the Œnothera *macrocarpa* and the
purple blossoms of the Pentstemon *bradburii* lay withering
together, while the fading leaves and the ripening fruit reminded us that the summer was drawing to a close.

On the morning following we resumed our march, alter-
ing our course from S. E. to N. E. The want of water in

the hills compelled us again to seek the river. Falling in
with a large bison path which we knew would conduct us by
the easiest and most direct route, we travelled about fifteen
miles, and encamped at noon on the bank of the river. In
returning to the low grounds we passed some grassy pastures carpeted with the densest and finest verdure, and
sprinkled with herds of deer, antelopes, and bisons. In some
places the ground was covered with a purple mat of the
prickly leaves and branches of a procumbent Eryngo intermixed with the tall and graceful Centaurea *speciosa,** with
here and there a humble Dalea, or an ascending Petalostemon.
As we approached the river we discovered a fine herd of bisons in the grove where we intended to place our camp, some
lying down in the shade, others standing in the pool of
water which extended along under the bank. Dismounting
from our horses and approaching under cover of the bushes
we shot two of the fattest, but before we had time to reload
our pieces, after the second fire, we perceived a bull running
towards us, evidently with the design to make battle; we,
however, gave him the slip, by escaping into the thick bushes,
and he turned off to follow the retiring herd.

It is only in the rutting season that any danger is to be apprehended from the strength and ferocity of the male bison.
At all other times, whether wounded or not, their efforts are,
to the last, directed solely towards an escape from their
pursuers, and at this time it does not appear that their rage
is provoked, particularly by an attack upon themselves, but
their unusual intrepidity is directed indiscriminately against
all suspicious intruders.

We had now, for some days, been excessively annoyed
with large swarms of blowing flies, which had prevented our

* This elegant Centaurea has a head of flowers nearly as large as that
of the Cnicus *lanceolatus,* so commonly naturalized in the east. Some
specimens, from seeds brought by Major Long, have flowered in Mr.
Peale's garden, near Germantown. The plant will be easily naturalized,
and found highly ornamental.

carrying fresh game along with us for more than a single day. It had been our custom at meals to place our boiled or roasted bison meat on the grass, or the broken boughs of a tree, in the middle of our circle; but this practice we now found it inexpedient to continue, as before we could finish our repast our table often became white with the eggs deposited by the flies. We were commonly induced to dispense with our roast meats, unless we chose to superintend the cooking ourselves; and afterwards it required the exertions of one hand to keep away the flies while with the other we helped ourselves to what we wished to eat. Our more common practice was to confine ourselves to the single dish of hunters' soup, suffering the meat to remain immersed in the kettle until we were ready to transfer it to our mouths.

Gnats had been rather frequent, and we began to feel once more the persecutions of the ticks, the most tormenting of the insects of this country.

The little pool near our tent afforded all the water that could be found within a very considerable distance. The bisons came in from every direction to drink, and we almost regretted that our presence frighted away the suffering animals with their thirst unslaked.

21st. The day was warm and somewhat rainy. Soon after leaving our camp we saw three black bears and killed one of them. This is the first animal of the kind we had eaten since we left the Missouri, and the flesh, though now not in the best condition, we found deserving the high encomiums commonly lavished upon it. Experienced hunters prefer it to that of the bison, and indeed to almost every thing, except the tail of the beaver.

Black bears had been frequent in the country passed since the 15th. At this season they feed principally upon grapes, plums, the berries of the cornus *alba* and c. *cirunata* and the acorns of a small scrubby oak common about the sand hills.

They also eat the flesh of animals, and it is not uncommon

to see them disputing with the wolves and buzzards for their share of the carcasses of bisons, and other animals, which have been left by the hunters, or have died of disease. Grapes had evidently been very abundant here, but had been devoured, and the vines torn in pieces by the bears and turkies.

In the middle of the day we found the heat more oppressive, with the mercury at 96°, than we had known it in many instances when the thermometer had indicated a higher temperature by six or eight degress. This sultry calm was, however, soon succeeded by thunder showers, attended with their ordinary effects upon the atmosphere. In the afternoon, the country we passed was swarming with innumerable herds of bison, wild horses, deer, elk, &c., while great numbers of minute sandpipers, yellow-shanked snipes, killdeer plovers (charadrius *vociferus*) and tell-tale godwits, about the river, seemed to indicate the vicinity of larger bodies of water than we had been accustomed of late to see. During the afternoon and the night, there was a continual and rapid alternation of bright, calm, and cloudless skies, with sudden and violent thunder storms. Our horizon was a little obscured on both sides by the hills and the scattered trees which skirted along the sides of the valley. As we looked out of our tent, to observe the progress of the night, we found sometimes a pitchy darkness veiling every object; at others, by the clear light of the stars, and the constant flashing from some unseen cloud, we could distinguish all the features of the surrounding scene; our horses grazing quietly about our tent, and the famished prairie wolf prowling near, to seize the fragments of our plentiful supper. The thunder was almost incessant, but its low and distant mutterings were, at times, so blended with the roaring of the bisons, that more experienced ears than ours might have found a difficulty in distinguishing between them. At a late hour in the night some disturbance was perceived among the horses, occasioned by a herd of wild horses, which had come in and struck up a hasty acquaintaince with their enslaved fellow-brutes.   As it was near daylight we forbore to do any thing to frighten away the intruders, hoping, to have an opportunity to prove our skill in the operation of *creasing*, as soon as the light should be sufficient.   A method sometimes adopted by hunters for taking the wild horse is to shoot the animal through the neck using the requisite care not to injure the spine.   A horse may receive a rifle ball through a particular part of the neck without sustaining any permanent injury; the blow is, however, sufficient to occasion a temporary suspension of the powers of life, during which the animal is easily taken.   This is called creasing; and requires for its successful performance a very considerable degree of skill and precision in the use of the rifle.   A valuable but rather refractory mule, belonging to our party escaped from the cantonment near Council Bluff, a few days before we left that place.   He was pursued by two men through the prairies of the Papillon, across the Elkhorn, and finally to the Platte, where, as they saw no prospect of taking him by other means, they resolved upon creasing.   The ball however swerved an inch or two from its aim and broke the neck of the animal.

CHAPTER VIII.

Inconveniences resulting from want of water—Wood-ticks—
Plants—Loss of one of the Party—Honey bees—Forests—
Gray sandstone—Indications of coal—Limestone.

AUGUST 22. So much rain had fallen during the night
that soon after commencing our morning march we enjoyed
the novel and pleasing sight of a running stream of water.
It had been only two weeks since the disappearance of running water in the river above, but during this time we had
suffered much from thirst, and had been constantly tantalized
with the expectation of arriving at the spot where the river
should emerge from the sand.   By our computation of distances we had travelled more than one hundred and fifty
miles along the bed of this river, without once having found
it to contain running water. We had passed the mouths of
many large tributaries, but they, like the river itself, were
beds of naked sand.   These *dry rivers*, at least the more
considerable of them, are constantly conveying away, silent
and unseen, in the bottom of their deep beds, streams of water of no trifling magnitude.   This is probably the case with
all such as have their sources in the primitive country of
the Rocky Mountains, likewise with those which traverse any
great extent of the floetz trap district, as both of these formations afford a more abundant supply of water than the
sandstone tracts.

In the afternoon we saw a dense column of smoke, rising
suddenly from the summit of a hill, at some distance on the
right side of the river.   As at the moment, the air happened to be calm, the smoke rose perpendicularly in a de-

fined mass, and after continuing, for a few minutes, ceased suddenly. Having recently observed signs of Indians, we took this as a confirmation of our suspicions, that an encampment or a village was not far distant. We had observed that parties of Indians, whether stationary or on their marches, are never without *videttes*, kept constantly at a distance from the main body, for the purpose of giving timely notice of the approach of enemies. Several methods of telegraphic communication are in use among them, one of which is this, of raising a sudden smoke, and for this purpose, they are said to keep in constant readiness, a supply of combustibles. During the remainder of this, and the day following, we were in constant expectation of falling in with Indians. Towards evening on the 23d, we saw an unusual number of horses, probably four or five hundred, standing among the scattered trees along the river bottom. We discovered them while more than a mile distant, and from their dispersed manner of feeding, and the intermixture of various colours among them, we concluded they must be the horses belonging to a band of Indians. We accordingly halted, and put our guns in order for immediate use, and then approaching cautiously, arrived within a few rods of the nearest, before we discovered them to be wild horses. They took flight, and dispersing in several directions, disappeared almost instantly.

At eleven P. M., the double meridian altitude of the moon's lower limb, observed for latitude, was 72° 18' 15''; index error, minus 4'. For the two last days, our average course had inclined considerably to the south. The water visible in the river had increased rapidly in quantity, and the apparent magnitude of the stream was nearly equal to what it had been four hundred miles above.

24th. Our supply of parched corn-meal was now entirely exhausted. Since separating from our companions on the Arkansa, we had confined ourselves to the fifth part of a pint per day, to each man, and the discontinuance of this small allowance, was at first sensibly felt. We, however, became gradually accustomed to the hunter's life in its utmost simplicity, eating our bison or bear meat, without salt or condiments of any kind, and substituting turkey or venison, both of which we had in the greatest plenty, for bread. The few hungry weeks we had spent about the sources of the river, had taught us how to dispense with superfluous luxuries, provided the demands of nature could be satisfied.

The inconveniences resulting from another cause, were more serious. All our clothing had become so dirty, as to be offensive both to sight and smell. Uniting in our own persons, the professions of traveller, hostler, butcher, and cook, sleeping on the ground by night, and being almost incessantly on the march by day, it is not to be supposed, we could give as much attention to personal neatness, as might be wished. Notwithstanding this, we had kept ourselves in comfortable condition, as long as we had met with water, fit for washing our clothes. This had not now been the case for some weeks. The sand of the river bed approaches in character so near to a fluid, that it is in vain to search for, or to attempt to produce any considerable inequalities on its surface. The utmost we had been able to accomplish, when we had found it necessary to dig for water, was to scoop a a wide and shallow excavation, in the bottom of which a very small quantity would collect, but not more than a pint could be dipped up at a time, and since the water had appeared above the sand, it was rare to find it more than an inch or two in depth, and so turbid as to be unfit for use. The excessive heat of the weather, aggravated the inconvenience resulting from the want of clean clothing, and we were not without fears that our health might suffer.

The common post oak, the white oak, and several other species, with the gymnocladus, or coffee bean tree, the cercis, and the black walnut, which indicate a soil of very con-

siderable fertility, now began to occur, and game grew so
abundant, that we had it at any time in our power, to kill as
many bisons, bear, deer, and turkies, as we might wish.

25th. Our daily journies over desolate and uninhabited
plains, could afford little to record, unless we were to set
down the names of the trees we passed, and of the plants
and animals which occured to our notice. Our horses had
become so exhausted by the great fatigues of the tour, that
we found it necessary to content ourselves with a slower
progress than formerly. According to our expectations,
when we first commenced the descent of the river, we should
some time since have arrived near the settlements; these,
however, we could plainly perceive, were still far distant.
The country we were traversing, has a soil of sufficient fertility to support a dense population, but the want of springs
and streams of water, must long oppose a serious obstacle to
its occupation by permanent residents. A little water was to
be seen in the river, but that was stagnant, the rise occasioned by the late rains having subsided.

Leaving our camp at an early hour, we moved down the
valley towards the southeast, passing some large and beautiful groves of timber. The fox squirrel which we had not
seen since we left the Missouri, the cardinal and summer
red-bird, the forked-tail tyrant, and the pileated woodpecker,
with other birds and animals, belonging to a woody country,
now became frequent. The ravens, common in all the open
plains, began to give place to crows, now first noticed.
Thickets of oak, elm, and nyssa, began to occur on the hills,
and the fertile soil of the low plains to be covered with a
dense growth of ambrosia, helianthus, and other heavy weeds.
As we were riding forward at a small distance from the river, two bucks and a fawn happened to cross our path, a few
rods in front of the party. As the wind blew from them to
us, they could not take our scent, but turned to gaze at us,
without the least appearance of alarm. The leader was shot

down by one of the party, when his companion and the fawn, instead of taking fright, came nearer to us, and stood within pistol shot, closely watching our movements, while the hunters were butchering the one we had killed. This unusual degree of tameness we could discover more or less, in all the animals of this region, and it seems to indicate that man, the enemy and destroyer of all things, is less known here, than in other portions of the country we had passed. In some parts of our route, we had seen the antelopes take fright, when we were more than a mile to the windward of them, when they could have received no intimation from us, except by sight, yet it does not appear, that their powers of vision are, in any degree, superior to those of most other ruminant animals.

27th. We were able to select for this day's rest, a delightful situation at the estuary of a small creek from the south. The wide valley of the river here presented a pleasing alternation of heavy forests, with small but luxuriant meadows, affording a profuse supply of grass for our horses. The broad hills swelling gently one above another, as they recede from the river, are diversified with nearly the same intermixture of field and forest, as in the most highly cultivated portions of the Eastern States. Herds of bisons, wild horses, elk, and deer, are seen quietly grazing in these extensive and fertile pastures, and the habitations and the works of men, alone seem wanting, to complete the picture of rural abundance.

We found, however, the annoyance of innumerable multitudes of minute, almost invisible seed ticks, a sufficient counterpart to the advantages of our situation. These insects unlike the mosquitoes, gnats, and sandflies, are not to be turned aside by a gust of wind, or an atmosphere surcharged with smoke, nor does the closest dress of leather afford any protection from their persecutions. A person no sooner sets foot among them than they commence in countless thousands, their silent and unseen march; ascending along the feet and legs, they insinuate themselves into every article of dress, and fasten, unperceived, their fangs upon every part of the body. The bite is not felt until the insect has had time to bury the whole of his beak, and in the case of the most minute and most troublesome species, nearly his whole body seems hid under the skin. Where he fastens himself with such tenacity that he will sooner suffer his head and body to be dragged apart than relinquish his hold. It would, perhaps, be well when they are once thoroughly planted to suffer them to remain unmolested, as the beaks left under the skin produce more irritation than the living animal; but they excite such intolerable itching, that the sufferer cannot avoid aggravating the evil by his efforts to relieve himself from the offending cause. The wound which was at first almost imperceptible, swells and inflames gradually, and being enlarged by rubbing and scratching, at length discharges a serous fluid, and finally suppurates. If the insect is suffered to remain unmolested, he protracts his feast for some weeks, when he is found to have grown of enormous size, and to have assumed nearly the colour of the skin on which he has been feeding. His limbs do not enlarge, but are almost buried in the mass accumulated on his neck, which extending forward, bears against the skin, and at last pushes him from his hold.

Nothing is to be hoped from becoming accustomed to the bite of these wood-ticks. On the contrary, by long exposure to their venomous attacks the skin acquires a morbid irritability, which increases in proportion to the frequency and continuance of the evil, until at length the bite of a single tick is sufficient to produce a large and painful phlegmon. This may not be the case with every one, but it was so with us. The burning and smarting of the skin prompted us to bathe and wash whenever we met with water: but we had not long continued this practice when we perceived it only to augment our sufferings, by increasing the irritation it was meant to allay.*

It is not on men alone that these blood-thirsty insects fasten themselves. Horses, dogs, and many wild animals are subject to the attacks of a tick that sometimes attains a very large size. It is nevertheless sufficiently evident, that like mosquitoes and other blood-sucking insects, by far the greater number of wood-ticks must spend their lives without ever establishing themselves as parasites on any animal, and even without a single opportunity of gratifying that thirst for blood, which, as they can exist and perform all the common functions of their life without its agency, would seem to have been given them merely for the annoyance of every animal that may fall in their way.

Among many other plants common to the low and fertile parts of the United States, we observed the acalypha and the splendid lobelia *cardinalis*, also the cardiospermum *helicacabum*, sometimes cultivated in the gardens, and said to be a native of the East Indies. It is a delicate climbing vine, conspicuous by its large inflated capsules. The acacia, [robinea *pseudacacia*] the honey locust, and the Ohio æsculus are among the forest trees, but are confined to the low grounds. The common black haw [viburnum *lentago*] the persimmon or date plum, and a vitis unknown to us, occurred frequently and were all loaded with unripe fruit. The misseltoe, whose range of elevation and latitude seems to correspond very nearly with that of the miegia and the cypress, occurs here, parasitic on the branches of elms. In the sandy soils of the hills, the formidable jatropha *stimulosa* is some-

---

* In those parts of South America where the absence of crocodiles permits people to enter the river, Humboldt and Bonpland observed, that the immoderate use of baths, while it moderated the pain of the old stings of Zancudoes, rendered them more sensible to new. By bathing more than twice a day the skin is brought into a state of nervous irritability of which no idea can be formed in Europe. It would seem as if all feeling were carried towards the integuments.

See Humboldt's Personal Narrative, p. 105. vol. 5.

times so frequent, as to render the walking difficult. It is covered with long and slender prickles, capable of inflicting a
painful and lasting wound, which is said to prove ruinous to
the feet of the blacks in the West Indies. The cacti and
the bartonias had now disappeared, as also the yucca, the
argemone, and most of the plants which had been conspicuous
in the country about the mountains. The phytolacca *decandra*,
an almost certain indication of a fertile soil, the diodia *te-*
tragona, a monarda, and several new plants were collected in
an excursion from our encampment. The red sand-rock is
disclosed in the sides of the hills, but appears less frequently, and contains less gypsum than above, though it
still retains the same peculiar marks distinguishing it as
the depository of fossil salt. Extensive beds of red argillaceous soil occur, and are almost invariably accompanied by
saline efflorescences, or incrustations. We search in vain, both
in the rocks and the soils for the remains of animals, and it is
rare in this salt formation to meet with the traces of organic
substances of any kind; the rock, itself, though fine and compact, disintegrates rapidly, producing a soil which contains so
much alumine as to remain long suspended in water,
tinging with its peculiar colour all the rivers of this region.
It has been remarked that the southern tributaries of the
Arkansa, particularly the Canadian, the Negracka, and the
Ne-sew-ke-tonga, discharge red waters, at the time of high
freshets in such quantity as to give a colouring to the Arkansa quite to its confluence with the Mississippi. From this
it is inferred that those rivers have their sources in a region
of red sandstone, whose north-eastern limit is not very far removed from the bed of the Arkansa. We attempted to take
sets of equal altitudes, but failed on account of a trifling in-
accuracy in our watch. The variation of the magnetic needle was found to be the same as on the 25th; namely, 11°
30′ east.

Our hunters had been sent out in quest of game, as not-

withstanding the plenty we had enjoyed and the great number of animals we had killed we found it impossible, on account of the heat of the weather and the multiplicity of the
blowing flies, to keep a supply of meat for more than one
day. At evening they returned, having killed a large black
bear. The animal finding himself wounded had turned with
great fury upon the hunter, who, being alone, was compelled
to seek his safety by climbing into a tree. It is well known
that the black bear will sometimes turn upon his pursuers,
and this, it is probable, is more frequently the case at this
season than at any other, as they are now unincumbered
with that profusion of fat which, for a part of the year, renders them clumsy and inactive, and the males are, morover,
excited by that uncommon ferocity which belongs to this
season of their loves.

We had observed that the sand-drifts, extending along all
that part of the river we had passed in the three last weeks,
were, almost exclusively on the northern bank. The country
we were now passing is too fertile and too closely covered
with vegetation, to admit the drifting of the sand, except from
the uncovered bed of the river; yet along the northern side
of the valley we frequently saw naked piles of sand, which
had been wafted to considerable distance by the winds.
From the position of these sand banks. as well as from our
experience, we were induced to believe that the high winds
of this region, are mostly from the south, at least during the
dry season.

We left our encampment at half past five on the morning
of the 28th, and following the river, the aggregate of our
courses for the day was about east, and the distance twenty-
one miles. Our last course led us out of the valley of the
river, and for a few miles across the open plain. Here
we passed a large and uncommonly beautiful village of the
prairie marmots, covering an area of about a mile square,
having a smooth surface and sloping almost imperceptibly

towards the east.   The grass on this plain was fine, thick and close fed.   As we approached, it happened to be covered with a herd of some thousands of bisons; on the left were a number of wild horses, and immediately before us twenty or thirty antelopes and about half as many deer. As it was near sunset the light fell obliquely upon the grass, giving an additional brilliancy to its dark verdure. The little inhabitants of the village were seen running playfully about in all directions, and as we approached, they perched themselves on their burrows and proclaimed their terror in the customary note of alarm.   A scene of this kind comprises most of what is beautiful and interesting to the passing traveller in the wide unvaried plains of the Missouri and Arkansa.

In the course of the day we passed two large creeks, one entering from the south, the other from the north; also several springs on the south side, along the base of a rocky hill, rising abruptly from the bed of the river; but notwithstanding all these tributary supplies, no running water appeared above the sands.

We passed great numbers of carcases of bisons recently slaughtered, and the air was darkened by flights of carrion birds, among which we distinguished the vultur *aura* and the V. *atrata*, the black vulture of the Southern States.   From the great number of carcases and skeletons, we were induced to believe ourselves near the hunting ground of some nation of Indians, and our expectations of seeing the Pawnees of Red River began to revive.

29th. Finding the valley of the river somewhat contracted in width and extremely serpentine, we ascended into the open country on the north side and made our way across the hills, taking a course a little south of east.   At the distance of a mile or two from the river we enjoyed a delightful view of the elevated country beautifully varied with gentle hills, broad vallies, fertile pastures, and extensive woodlands. The soil we found of a superior quality, the timber more abundant than in any region we had passed since we left the Missouri. Extensive forests appeared in the distant horizon, and the prairies in every direction were intersected by creeks and ravines, fringed by lines of timber. The aspect of the country is very similar to that of Grand river and the lower part of the Missouri, but the soil is more fertile. The first elevations rise from forty to fifty feet above the bed of the river, and these are succeeded by others ascending by an almost imperceptible slope towards the interior. Among the trees on the uplands are the black cherry, the linden, and the honey locust all indicating a fertile soil.

A little before we halted to dine, Adams, our interpreter of Spanish, having dropped some article of baggage returned on the track for the purpose of recovering it, and as he did not join us again we concluded he must have missed his way.

At evening we returned to the valley of the river and placed our camp under a small cottonwood tree, upon one of whose branches was a swarm of bees. These useful insects reminded us of the comforts and luxuries of life among men, and at the same time gave us the assurance that we were drawing near the abodes of civilization. Bees, it is said by the hunter and the Indians, are rarely if ever seen more than two hundred and fifty or three hundred miles in advance of the white settlements.

On receiving the first intimation of the absence of Adams, who had been following in the rear of the party, a man was sent back to search for, and bring him to our encampment; but as he could not be found we concluded that he had missed our path, and probably gone forward. We were confirmed in this belief, when on the following morning we discovered the track of a solitary mule, which had passed down along the bed of the river. This we accordingly followed, not doubting but Adams must soon perceive he had passed us, and would wait until we should overtake him.

The loose soft sands of the river bed, yielding to our horses' feet, made the travelling extremely laborious; and the intense reflection of the rays of the sun almost deprived us of the use of our eyes. Mr. Peale's horse soon became unable to proceed at an equal pace with the remainder of the party; but, as no suitable spot for encampment appeared, he dismounted and, by great exertions, was able to urge his animal along in the rear. The travelling in the bed of the river became so extremely inconvenient, that we resolved upon attempting to penetrate the thick woods of the bottom, and ascend to the open plains. We found, however, the woods so close and so interlaced with scandent species of Smilax, Cissus, and other climbing vines as greatly to retard our progress, and we were soon induced to wish ourselves again upon the naked sands. Notwithstanding the annoyance they gave us, we took a pleasure in observing the three American species of Cissus growing almost side by side. The C. *quinquefolia*,* the common woodbine, cultivated as an ornament about yards and summer-houses, grows here to an enormous size, and as well as the C. *hederacea*, seems to prefer climbing on elms. The remaining species, the C. *bipinnata*,† is a smaller plant, and though much branched, is rarely scandent. They all abound in ripe fruit, which, notwithstanding its external resemblance, and its close affinity to the grape, is nauseous to the taste, and does not appear to be sought with avidity even by the bears.

In ascending the hills, we found them based upon a variety of sandstone, unlike the red rock of the salt formation, to which we had been so long accustomed. We observed that a corresponding change also takes place in the conformation of the surface and the general aspect of the country. The hills are higher and more abrupt; the forests more extensive; the streams of water more copious, and more serpentine in direction; in other words, we here begin to recognize the fea-

---

* Ampelopsis *quinquefolia* of Michaux.   † C. *stans* of Persoon.

tures of a mountainous region. The sandstone, which appears in the beds of the streams and the sides of the hills, is coarse and hard, of a dark gray colour, and a horizontally laminated structure. It is deeply covered with a soil of considerable fertility, sustaining heavy forests of oak. Among these trees, the upland white oak is common, but is of rather diminutive size, and often hollow. In a tree of this description we observed as we passed the habitation of a swarm of bees, and, as it was not convenient at that time to stop, we fixed a mark upon it and proceeded to make the best of our way towards the river. On descending the hills, we found the valley of the river much contracted in width, and the bed itself occupying less space by half than where we had left it above.

On the following day, the party remained encamped, to take observations, and afford an opportunity for rest to the horses. Some of the men went back about six miles to the bee-tree we had passed on the preceding day, and brought in a small quantity of honey, inclosed in the skin of a deer recently killed. About our camp we examined several ledges of sandstone of the coarse dark gray variety above mentioned. In some instances, we found it nearly approaching in character the glittering crystalline variety of the lead mine district, but we sought in vain for an opportunity to observe the manner of its connexion with red sandstone.

As we were now at the western base of that interesting group of hills, to which we have attempted to give the name of the almost extinct tribe of the Oarks, and, as we believed ourselves near the extreme southern bend of the river we were descending, we thought it important to ascertain our latitude and longitude by as complete sets of observations as circumstances allowed us to make, and this, the favourable position of the moon enabled us to do in the most satisfactory manner. The results will be seen on the map, and the observations themselves are given in the Apendix.

During the extreme heat of the day the mercury stood at 99° in a fair exposure. This extraordinary degree of heat may have been, in some degree, occasioned by the stagnation of the air between the hills, and, possibly, by the reverberation of the sun's rays from the naked sands; but the instrument was one of an approved character, and was exposed in the deep shade of an extensive grove of trees.

As yet no running water appeared in the river, but, as the pools were large, and some of them little frequented by the bisons, we were no longer under the necessity of digging.

Sept. 1st. The sycamore, the æsculus, the misseltoe, and the parroquet, are conspicuous objects in the deep and heavy forests of the Ohio and Mississippi: with these we now found ourselves surrounded. Bisons were comparatively scarce along this part of the river; but whether this was owing to the near approach of inhabited countries, or to the great extent and almost impenetrable density of the forests on each side of the river, we were unable to determine. At night we still heard the growling of the herds in the distant prairies, and occasionally saw bisons in small bodies crossing the river.

The Kaskaia Indians had told us that before we arrived at the village of the Pawnee Piquas, we should pass a range of blue hills. These we concluded could be no other than hills whose sides were covered with forests, like those we were now passing, and, accordingly, we watched with some anxiety for the appearance of something to indicate the vicinity of an Indian village.

As we pursued our way along the serpentine bed of the river, the valley became narrower, the hills more elevated, and, as we crossed the rocky points of their bases, we observed that the sandstone was of a different character from any we had before seen. It contains more mica than that of the Alleghanies, or that of the secondary hills along the base of the Rocky Mountains. It glitters conspicuously like mica slate when seen in the sunshine, and this, as we found by examination, does not depend entirely on the great proportion of mica it contains, but also, in some degree, on the crystalline structure of the minute particles. Its cement is often argillaceous, and this, as well as the impressions of Strobilaria* and other organic relics we observed in it, induced us to expect the occurrence of coal beds.

On ascending the hills, from the place of our mid-day encampment, we found this sandstone at an elevation of about two hundred feet, according to our estimate, from the bed of the river, succeeded by a stratum of limestone of the common compact blue variety, abounding in casts of anomias, encrinites, &c. This rests horizontally on the summits of the hills, and as it disintegrates less rapidly than the sandstone which forms their bases, it is sometimes left projecting in such a manner as to render access impossible. Climbing to the summit of some of the hills near the river, we had the view, towards the south and east, of a wild and mountainous region, covered with forests, where, among the bright verdure of the oak, the nyssa, and the castanea *pumila*, we distinguished the darker shade of the juniper, and others of the coniferæ.

A little before arriving at the place of our evening encampment, we observed the track of a man who had passed on foot, and with bare feet, down the river. This we were confident could be no other than the track of our lost interpreter, Adams. What accident could have deprived him of his mule we were at a loss to conjecture. We found it equally difficult to account for his pushing forward with such perseverance, when he must have had every reason to believe we were behind him.

2d. The morning was fair, and we commenced our journey by sunrise. At a little distance below our encampment, we passed the mouth of a large tributary from the south.

* Nuttall.

It was about sixty yards wide, and appeared to contain considerable water which was absorbed in the sands immediately at its junction with the larger stream. About the mouth of this creek we saw the remains of several gar fish [Esox *osseus*]. This fish is protected by a skin so flinty and incorruptible, as to be invulnerable to the attack of birds and beasts of prey, and even when the internal soft parts have been dissolved and removed by putrefaction, the bony cuticle retains its original shape like that of the trunk and limbs of the canoe birch, after the wood has rotted away. The gar is usually found in deep water, lying concealed in the places where the small fish resort, and seizing them between his elongated jaws, which are armed with numerous small and sharp teeth. This fish, though not held in high estimation as an article of food, is little inferior, as we have often found by experiment, to the sturgeon of the Hudson. Its unsightly aspect produces a prejudice against it, and in countries of such abundance as those watered by the Mississippi and its tributaries, a creature so disgusting in appearance, and of so unpromising a name, is rarely eaten.

We had passed the mouth of the creek about a mile, when we discovered a little column of smoke ascending among some scattered oaks on the right bank of the river. Approaching the spot, we perceived our lost interpreter, who had parted from us five days before, sitting a few feet in advance of his fire. When we discovered him, his appearance indicated the deepest despondency. He had kindled a fire upon a little rocky eminence, projecting to the verge of the river, and seated himself near it upon the ground with his face turned towards the river, as if in expectation of relief from that quarter. His elbows rested upon his knees, and his hands supported his head. Having sat in long expectation of seeing us, he had fallen asleep, and on being waked, some minutes elapsed before he recovered entire self-possession and consciousness. His long, sun-burnt hair hung loosely about a face, it could scarcely be said to shade, and on which famine and terror had imprinted a frightful expression of ghastliness. Perhaps some consciousness of having acted an imprudent and reprehensible part, prevented any demonstrations of joy he might otherwise have shown at sight of us. Under the apprehension that accidents of this kind might occur it had repeatedly been enjoined upon all the party, never to lose sight of the main body when on the march. But on this occasion, no regard was paid to this necessary regulation.

From his statement, we learned, that after separating from us on the morning of the 29th August, he had returned a mile or two, to search for his canteen, but not finding it, in his hurry to rejoin the party, he had missed the trace, and presently found himself bewildered. Taking the bed of the river as his guide, he urged on his mule without allowing it time to rest, or to feed, till on the third day it refused to proceed, and he left it. He then took his baggage, musket, &c., and pushed forward on foot, evidently with the hope of arriving at the Pawnee village; but by the end of the day, found his strength so exhausted that he could go no farther, and was compelled to encamp. Having expended his ammunition in unsuccessful attempts to shoot turkies, he had been trying to make a substitute for fish hooks by bending up some needles; but this project he had not brought to perfection, and assured us he had not tasted food since the breakfast of the 29th, a period of more than five days.

The Small leaved and the White elm,* the Nettle tree or Hackberry, the Cotton-wood, Mulberry, Black walnut, Pecan, Ash, Sycamore, and most of the trees common to the low grounds of the Mississipi, are intermixed here to form the dense forests of the river valley; while in the more scattered woods of the highlands, the prevailing growth is Oak, with some species of Nyssa, the Dyospiros and a few other small trees.

* Ulmus *americana*, and U. *alata*.

At evening a large flock of white pelicans passed us on their way up the river.

On the morning of the 3d, not having been able to select a suitable place for a Sunday encampment, we moved on, searching for a supply of grass, that we might halt for the day. The hunters preceded the party, and meeting with a herd of bisons, and good pasturage in the same place, killed a bull of a most gigantic stature, and waited until the remainder of the party came up, and encamped near the carcass.

Having arranged our camp, and performed in the way of washing, dressing, &c., the little in our power to do, we made an excursion into the adjoining forest, to collect plants, and to search for honey, which, from the great numbers of bees we had seen, we were conscious must be abundant. Since leaving the open country, we had remarked a very great change in the vegetation. The dense shade, and perhaps, the somewhat confined air of the forest, are unfavorable to the growth of many of those grasses, and those robust perennials, which seem to delight in the arid soils, and the scorching winds of the sandy desert. The sensitive cassia (C. *nictitans*.) the favorite food of the bees, some species of Hedysarum and a few other leguminæ, are however, common to both regions.

A considerable part of the day we spent in unavailing contest with the ticks. The torment of their stings increased upon us if we were a moment idle, or attempted to rest ourselves under the shadow of a tree. We considered ourselves peculiarly fortunate, when we could find the shade of a tree extending some distance on the naked sands of the river bed, for there the ticks were less numerous. In the middle of the day, the mercury again rose to 97°, and the blowing flies swarmed in such numbers about our blankets and clothing, as to allow us no rest.

About the pools near our camp, we saw the little white Egret; the snowy Heron had been common for some days.

Great numbers of cranes, ducks, pelicans, and other aquatic birds, induced us to believe, that larger bodies of water than we had recently seen, must be near.

Bears and wolves were still frequent. Among the latter, we observed a black one of a small size, which we believed to be specifically different from any of those we had seen above. All our attempts to capture this watchful animal, were without success. Since entering the region of forests, we had found the number of small animals, birds, and insects, considerably increased. An enormous, black, hairy spider, resembling the mygale *avicularia* of South America, was often seen, and it was not without shuddering, that we sometimes perceived this formidable insect, looking out from his hole, within a few feet of the spot, on which we had thrown ourselves down to rest.

On the 4th, we met with nothing interesting, except the appearance of running water in the bed of the river. Since the 13th of the preceding month, we had travelled constantly along the river, and in all the distance passed in that time, which could not have been less than five hundred miles, we had seen running water in the river, in one or two instances only; of those, one in it had evidently been occasioned by recent rains, and had extended but a mile or two, when it disappeared.

CHAPTER IX.

Maclura auran tiaca—Birds—Falls of the Canadian—Green argillaceous sandstone—Northern and Southern tributaries of the Canadian—Cotton-wood—Arrival at the Arkansa—Cane-brakes—Cherokees—Belle Point.

The region we were now traversing, is one of great fertility, and we had daily occasion to regret that our visit to it had not been made earlier in the season. Many unknown plants were observed, but their flowering season being past, the fruit of many of them having ripened and fallen, we were deprived of the means of ascertaining the name and place of such as had been heretofore described, and of describing such as were new. We had, however, the satisfaction to recognize some interesting productions, among which we may enumerate a very beautiful species of Bignonia, and the bow-wood or Osage orange.* The rocky hills abound in

---

* Maclura *aurantiaca of Nuttall.* A description of this interesting tree, may be seen in Mr. Nuttall's valuable work, on the Genera of North American plants, page 233, vol. 2d. That description was drawn from specimens, cultivated in the garden of Mr. Choteau, at St. Louis, where, as might be expected, the tree did not attain its full size and perfect character. In its native wilds, the maclura is conspicuous by its showy fruit, in size and external appearance, resembling the largest oranges. The leaves are of an oval form, with an undivided margin, and the upper surface of a smooth shining green; they are five or six inches long, and from two to three wide. The wood is of a yellowish colour, uncommonly fine and elastic, affording the material most used for bows, by all the savages from the Mississippi to the Rocky Mountains. How far towards the North, its use extends, we have not been informed. but we have often seen it among the lower tribes of the Missouri, who procure it in trade from the Osages, and the Pawnees of Red river. The bark, fruit, &c., when wounded, discharges a copious milky sap, which soon dries on exposure and is insoluble in water containing probably, like the milky juices of many of the URTICAÆ a large intermixture of Coatchouc or Gum Elastic. Observing this property in the milky juice of the fruit, we were

trees of a small size, and the cedars are sometimes so numerous, as to give their peculiar and gloomy colouring to the landscape.

We listened, as we rode forward, to the note of a bird, new to some of us, and bearing a singular resemblance to the noise of a child's toy trumpet. This we soon found to be the cry of the great ivory billed woodpecker, (Picus *principalis*) the largest of the North American species, and confined to the warmer parts. The P. *pileatus* we had seen on the 28th August, more than one hundred miles above, and this, with the P. *erythrocephalus*, were now common. Turkies were very numerous. The paroquet, chuck-wills-widow, wood robin, mocking bird, and many other small birds, filled the woods with life and music. The bald eagle, the turkey-buzzard and black vulture, raven, and crow, were seen swarming like the blowing flies, about any spot where a bison, an elk, or a deer had fallen a prey to the hunter. About the river were large flocks of pelicans, with numbers of snowy herons, and the beautiful ardea egretta.

Soon after we had commenced our morning ride, we heard the report of a gun, at a distance of a mile, as we thought, on our left. This was distinctly heard by several of the party, and induced us to believe that white hunters were in the

tempted to apply it to our skin, where it formed a thin and flexible varnish, affording us, as we thought some protection from the ticks.

The fruit consists of radiating, somewhat woody fibres, terminating in a tuberculated and sightly papillose surface. In this fibrous mass, the seeds, which are nearly as large as those of a quince, are disseminated, We cannot pretend to say what part of the fruit has been described, as the "pulp which is nearly as succulent as that of an orange, sweetish, and perhaps agreeable when fully ripe." In our opinion the whole of it is as disagreeable to the taste and as unfit to be eaten, as the fruit of the Sycamore, to which it has almost as much resemblance as to the orange.

The tree rises to the height of twenty-five or thirty feet, dividing near the ground into a number of long slender, and flexuous branches. It inhabits deep and fertile soils along the river valley. The Arkansa appears to be the northern limit of the range of the Maclura, and neither on that river nor on the Canadian, does the tree, or the fruit, attain so considerable a size, as in warmer latitudes. Of many specimens of the fruit examined by Major Long, at the time of his visit to Red river, in 1817, several were found measuring five and a half inches in diameter.

neighbourhood. We had recently seen great numbers of elk, and killed one or two, which we had found in bad condition.

6th. Numerous ridges of rocky hills traverse the country from northeast to southwest, crossing the direction of the river obliquely. They are of a sandstone which bears sufficient evidence of belonging to a coal formation. At the spot where we halted to dine, one of these ranges, crossing the river, produces an inconsiderable fall. As the whole width of the channel is paved with a compact horizontal sandstone, we believed all the water of the river must be forced up to view, and were surprised to find the quantity something less than it had been almost six hundred miles above in the same stream. It would appear, that all the water, which falls in rains, or flows from springs in an extent of country far greater than Pennsylvania, is not sufficient to supply the evaporation of so extensive a surface of naked and heated sands.

If the river, of which we speak, should, at any season of the year, contain water enough for the purposes of navigation, it is probable the fall, occasioned by the rocky traverse above mentioned, will be sufficient to prevent the passage upwards. The point is a remarkable one as being the locality of a rare and beautiful variety of sandstone. The rock which appears in the bed of the river is a compact slaty sandstone of a deep green colour resembling some varieties of chloritic slate. Whether the colour depends upon *epidote chlorite*, or some other substance, we were not able to determine. The sandstone is micaceous, but the particles of mica, as well as those of the other integrant minerals, are very minutely divided. The same rock, as we found by tracing it to some distance, becomes of a light gray colour, and contains extensive beds of bituminous clay slate. Its stratifications are so little inclined that their dip cannot be estimated by the eye. This point, though scarce deserving the name of a cataract, is so marked by the occurrence of a peculiar bed of rocks crossing the river, and by the rapid descent of the current, that it may readily be recognized by any who shall pass that way hereafter. In this view we attach some importance to it, as the only spot, in a distance of six hundred miles, we can hope to identify by description. In ascending, when the traveller arrives at this point, he has little to expect beyond but sandy wastes, and thirsty inhospitable steppes. The skirts of the hilly and wooded region extend to a distance of fifty or sixty miles above; but even this district is indifferently supplied with water. Beyond, commences the wide sandy desert stretching westward to the base of the Rocky Mountains. We have little apprehension of giving too unfavorable an account of this portion of the country. Though the soil is, in some places, fertile, the want of timber, of navigable streams, and of water for the necessities of life, render it an unfit residence for any but a nomade population. The traveller who shall, at any time, have traversed its desolate sands will, we think, join us in the wish that this region may forever remain the unmolested haunt of the native hunter, the bison, the prairie wolf, and the marmot.

One mile below this point, (which we call the falls of the Canadian, rather for the sake of a name than as considering it worthy to be thus designated,) is the entrance from the south of a river fifty yards wide. Its banks are lined with tall forests of cotton-wood and sycamore, and its bottoms are wide and fertile. Its bed is less choked with sand than that of the river to which it is tributary. Six or eight miles farther down, and on the other side, is the confluence of the Great North Fork, discharging at least three times as much water as we found above it. It is about eighty yards wide. The beds of both these tributaries are covered with water from shore to shore; but they have gentle currents, and are not deep, and neither of them have, in any considerable degree, that red tinge which characterises the Canadian. We have already mentioned, that what we consider the sources of the North Fork are in the floetz trap country, nearly opposite those of Purgatory creek of the Arkansa. Of one of its northern tributaries we have received some infor mation from the recent work of Mr. Nuttall, who crossed it in his journey to the Great Salt river of Arkansa, in 1819. " Still proceeding," says he, " a little to the north of west, about ten miles further, we came to a considerable rivulet of clear and still water, deep enough to swim our horses. This stream was called the Little North Fork (or branch) of the Canadian, and emptied into the main North Fork of the same river nearly two hundred miles distant, including its meanders, which had been ascended by the trappers of bea- ver."* From his account it appears that the banks of this stream are wooded, and that the " superincumbent rock" is a sandstone, not of the red formation, but probably belong- ing to a coal district.

Its water, like that of the Arkansa and its northern tribu- taries, when not swelled by rains, is of a greenish colour. This colouring is, sometimes, so intense in the rivers of this region as to suggest the idea that the water is filled with minute confervas, or other floating plants; but when we see it by transmitted light, as when a portion of it is held in a glass vessel, the colour disappears.

Three and an half miles below the confluence of the North Fork is a remarkable rock, standing isolated in the middle of the river, like the Grand Tower in the Mississippi. It is about seventy-five feet high, and fifty or sixty in diameter, and its sides so perpendicular as to render the summit in- accessible. It appears to have been broken from a high promontory of gray sandstone overhanging the river on the north side.

Not being able to find grass for pasture, we rode later than usual, and were finally compelled to encamp on a sandy beach, which afforded nothing but rushes for our horses.

* Journal of Travels into the Arkansa Territory, by Thomas Nuttall. &c. page 200.

8th. The quantity of water in the river, had now become so considerable, as to impede our descent along the bed, but the valley was narrow and so filled with close and entangled forests, and the uplands so broken and rugged, that no other path appeared to remain for us. We therefore continued to make our way, though with great difficulty, and found our horses much incommoded, by being kept almost constantly in the water, as we were compelled to do, to cross from the point of a sand bar on one side the river, to the next on the other. Quicksands also occurred, and in places where we least expected it, our horses and ourselves were made to *bite the dust*, without a moment's notice. These sudden falls, occasioned by sinking in the sand, and the subsequent exertions necessary to extricate themselves, proved extremely harrassing to our jaded horses, and we had reason to fear, that they would fail us, in our utmost need.

Above the falls the width of the river, that is, of the space included between its two banks, varies from three hundred yards, to two miles; below, it is uniformly narrower, scarce exceeding four hundred yards. The beaches are sloping, and often covered with young cotton-wood or willow trees. In the Missouri, Mississippi, and to some extent in the Arkansa, and its tributaries, the islands, sand-bars, and even the banks are constantly shifting place. In the progress of these changes, the young willows and cotton-wood trees, which spring up wherever a naked beach is exposed, may be supposed to have some agency, by confining the soil with their roots, and arresting the dirt and rubbish in times of high water. In the Missouri, the first growth which springs up in these places, is so commonly the willow, that the expressions " willow bar," and " willow island," have passed into the language of the boatmen, and communicate the definite idea of a bar or an island, recently risen from the water. These willows become intermixed with the cotton-wood, and these trees are often almost the exclusive occupants of extensive portions of the low grounds. The foliage of the most common species of willow, (S. *angustata*,) is of a light green colour, and when seen under certain angles, of a silvery gray, contrasting beautifully with the intense and vivid green of the cotton-wood.* Within a few rods of the spot where we halted to dine, we were so fortunate as to find a small log canoe, made fast on shore. From its appearance, we were assured it had been some months deserted by its rightful owner,

* This tree, the Populus *angulata* of Pursh, has received its common name from the downy cotton like appendage to the seed, which being ripened and shed in May or the beginning of June, is then seen floating in the air in great quantities, and often proves somewhat troublesome to the eyes and noses of persons, who are much in the open air. Baron Humboldt, in speaking of the Unona *aromatica* of South America, says, "its branches are straight, and rise in a pyramid, nearly like those of the poplar of the Mississippi, falsely called lombardy poplar." Pers. Nar. p. 163, Vol. 5. As far as our observation has extended, the poplar most common in the country of the Mississippi, and indeed almost the only one which occurs, is the *angulata*, very distinct from the P. *dilatata*, the lombardy poplar of our streets and yards, which is not a native of this country. The branches of the cotton-wood tree are not very numerous, particularly where it occurs in forests, as is the case on the Mississippi, below the confluence of the Missouri, and in the alluvial lands of most of the rivers in the United States, and show less tendency to arrange themselves in a pyramidal form, than those of almost any other tree. In the open country west of the Mississippi, where in the distance of one hundred miles, some dozens of scattered cotton-wood trees may be found; their tops are peculiarly low and straggling, as is the case with individuals of the same species, which have grown in open fields, and by the road sides in various places.

This tree is perhaps as widely distributed, as any indigenous to North America, extending at least from Canada to Louisiana, and from the Atlantic to the lower part of Columbia river. It is, however, so peculiarly frequent in every part of the country, watered by the Mississippi and its tributaries, that it may with as little absurdity, as usually attends names referring to locality, be called the Mississippi poplar. It is probable, that nearly one half of the whole number of trees, in the recent alluvial grounds or bottom lands of the Mississippi and its tributaries, are of this species. Whether it was considered by Humboldt, as identical with the lombardy poplar of our streets, we cannot decide.

The cotton-wood varies in magnitude, in proportion to the fertility of the soil, and on the Ohio, the Mississippi, and the Arkansa, it attains the size of our largest forest trees. It is sometimes exceeded in girth, and in the number and extent of its branches, by the majestic sycamore, but in forests where the two are intermixed, as is commonly the case, it is seen to overtop all other trees.

A cotton-wood tree mentioned in the Journal of the Exploring Party, who ascended Red river in 1806, and spoken of as one of many similar trees, standing in a cornfield, three or four days journey above Natchito-

and from the necessity of our situation, thought ourselves justified in seizing, and converting it to our own use. Our pack-horses had become much weakened, and reduced by long fatigue, and in crossing the river, as we had often to do, we felt that our collections, the only valuable part of our baggage, were constantly exposed to the risk of being wetted. We accordingly made prize of the canoe, and putting on board our packs and heavy baggage, manned it with two men, designing that they should navigate it down to the settlements. Not far from this canoe, we discovered in the adjoining woods, the remains of an old camp, which we perceived had been occupied by white men, and saw other convincing proofs, that we were coming near some inhabited country.

We halted at evening in a small prairie, on the north side of the river, the first we had seen for some time. The difficulties of navigation, arising from the shallowness of the water, prevented the arrival of the canoe and baggage, until a

ches, measured one hundred and forty-one feet and six inches in height, and five feet in diameter,* which is exceeded by few trees, except the sycamore, in the temperate parts of North America. [Freeman's MS. Journal.] Though we have not actual admeasurements to compare with this, we are of opinion, that many trees on the Arkansa, would rather exceed, than fall short of these dimensions. The cotton-wood affords a light and soft timber, not very durable, except when protected from the weather. Before expansion, the buds of this tree are partially covered with a viscid resinous exudation, resembling that so conspicuous on the buds of the P. *balsamifera*, and diffusing in spring and the early part of summer, an extremely grateful balsamic odour.

* According to Pennant, the *gran* or *Norway fir*, (Pinus *abies*, P.) the loftiest of European trees attains only the height of one hundred and sixty feet. [See Introd. to his Arctic Zoology, p. 103.] The pines of Nootka Sound are one hundred and twenty feet high. [Barrington's Misc. 290.] Gov. Phillip relates, that the pines of Norfolk island, are sometimes one hundred and eighty feet high, and nine or ten in diameter at the bottom of the trunk, but these are considered trees of astonishing magnitude. Can it be credited, that a species of pine on the Columbia, is commonly twenty-seven feet in circumference, six feet above the earth's surface, and *two hundred and thirty feet high*, rising one hundred and twenty feet without a limb? We have it on the unquestioned authority of Lewis and Clark, p. 156, V. 2, that they found one tree, whose trunk rose two hundred feet without limbs, and whose entire height was three hundred feet. This tree appears, from their description, to have been an Abies.

late hour. The men had been compelled to wade a great
part of the way, and drag the canoe over the sand.

9th. We had proceeded a mile or two from our encampment, when we discovered a herd of twenty or thirty elk,
some standing in the water, and some lying upon the sand
beach, at no great distance before us. The hunters went forward, and singling out one of the finest bucks, fired upon
him; at which the whole herd plunged into the thicket, and
disappeared. We had, however, too much confidence in the
skill of the hunter, to doubt but his shot had been fatal, and
several of the party dismounting, pursued the herd into the
woods, where they soon overtook the wounded buck. The
noble animal, finding his pursuers at his heels, turned upon
the foremost, who saved himself by springing into a thicket,
which the elk could not penetrate, but in which he soon became entangled by his enormous antlers, and fell an easy
victim. His head was enveloped in such a quantity of cissus,
smilax, and other twining vines, that scarce the tips of his
horns could be seen: thus blindfolded, he stood until most
of those, who had followed into the woods, had discharged
their pieces, and did not finally yield to his foes, until he was
stabbed to the heart with a knife. He was found in excellent
condition, having more than two inches of fat on the brisket.
The meat was carried to the river, and deposited on a projecting point of rocks, with a note addressed to the men who
were behind with the canoe, directing them to add this supply of provisions to their cargo.

At this point, and again at an inconsiderable distance below, a soft green slaty sandstone forms the bed of the river,
and occasions a succession of rapids.

At noon an observation by the meridian altitude of the
sun's lower limb gave us 35° 80′ as an approximation to our
latitude. This was much greater than we had anticipated,
from the position assigned to Red river on the maps, and
tended to confirm the unpleasant fears we had entertained of

having mistaken some tributary of the Arkansa for the Red river.

Thick and extensive cane brakes occurred on all sides, and though the bottoms were wide and covered with heavy forests, we could see, at intervals, the distant sandstone hills with their scattered forests of cedar and oak.

10th. We left our camp at the usual hour, and, after riding eight or ten miles, arrived at the confluence of our supposed Red river with another of a much greater size, which we at once perceived to be the Arkansa. Our disappointment and chagrin, at discovering the mistake we had so long laboured und r, was little alleviated by the consciousness that the season was so far advanced, our horses and our means so far exhausted, as to place it beyond our power to return and attempt the discovery of the sources of Red river. We had been misled by some little reliance on the maps, and the current statements concerning the position of the upper branches of Red river, and more particularly by the confident assurance we had received from the Kaskaia Indians, whom we did not suspect of a wish to deceive us in an affair of such indifference to them. Knowing there was a degree of ambiguity and confusion in the nomenclature of the rivers, we had insisted particularly on being informed whether the river we were descending, was the one on which the Pawnee Piquas had their permanent residence, and this we were repeatedly assured was the case. Several other circumstances, which have been already mentioned, led us to the commission of this unfortunate mistake.

According to our estimate of distances on our courses, it is seven hundred ninety-six and a half miles from the point where we first struck the Canadian to its confluence with the Arkansa. If we make a reasonable allowance for the meanders of the river, and for the extension of its upper branches some distance to the west of the place where we commenced our descent, the entire length of the Canadian will appear to

be about one thousand miles. Our journey upon it had occupied a space of seven weeks, travelling with the utmost
diligence the strength of our horses would permit.

On arriving at the Arkansa, we waited a short time for
our canoe, in which we carried across our heavy baggage,
and then swimming our horses, ascended the bank in search
of a place to encamp, but soon found ourselves surrounded
by a dense and almost impenetrable cane-brake, where no
vestige of a path could be found. In this dilemma, no alternative remained but to force our way forward, by the
most laborious exertions. The canes were of a large size,
and stood so close together, that a horse could not move
forward the length of his body without breaking, by main
force, a great number of them. Making our way, with excessive toil, among these gigantic gramina, our party might
be said to resemble a company of rats traversing a sturdy
field of grass. The cane stalks, after being trod to the earth,
often inflicted, in virtue of their elasticity, blows as severe as
they were unexpected. It is not to be supposed, that our
horses alone felt the inconvenience of this sort of travelling.
We received frequent blows and bruises on all parts of our
bodies, had our sweaty faces and hands scratched by the
rough leaves of the cane, and, oftentimes, as our attention
was otherwheres directed, we caught with our feet, and
had dragged across our shins the flexible and spiny stalks of
the green briar.

This most harrassing ride was commenced at eleven in the
morning, and continued, without a moment's intermission,
till sunset, when finding we were not about to extricate ourselves, we returned near a mile and a half on our track, to
a spot where we had passed a piece of open woods, large
enough to spread our blankets on. Here we laid ourselves
down at dark, much exhausted by our day's journey.

Our fatigue was sufficient to overcome the irritation of the
ticks, and we slept soundly until about midnight, when we

were awakened by the commencement of a heavy fall of rain, from which, as we had not been able to set up our tent, we had no shelter.

On the following morning, after several hours spent in most laborious travelling, like that of the preceding day, we found ourselves emerging from the river bottom, and, to our great satisfaction, exchanging the cane-brakes for open woods. At the foot of the hill, lay a deep morass, covered with the Nelumbo and other aquatic plants. It had, probably, been the former bed of the Arkansa. Observing water in some parts of it, several of the party attempted to penetrate to it, to drink, but the quaking bog was found so deep and soft as to be wholly impassable.

After ascending the hills, we pursued our course nearly due north, through open woods of oak and nyssa, until we reached the prairie, and soon after discovered a large and frequented path, which we knew could be no other than that leading to Fort Smith. On emerging from the low grounds, we had no longer the prospect of boundless and monotonous plains. We were in a region of mountains and forests interspersed with open plains, but these were of limited extent.

12th. We resumed our journey at sunrise. The weather was cool and the morning fair. The wide and densely wooded valley of the Arkansa lay on our right. The course of the river was marked by a long and undulating line of mist, brightening in the beams of the rising sun. Beyond, rose the blue summits of the Point Sucre and Cavaniol mountains, " in the clear light, above the dews of morn." Though the region about us had all the characters of a mountain district, we could discover little uniformity in the direction of the ranges. The Cavaniol and Point Sucre mountains stand on opposite sides of the Poteau, near the mouth of the Meline fork, and are parts of low ridges running from southwest to northeast. On the north side of the Arkansa is a ridge of considerable elevation, nearly parallel in direction to the general course of the river.

In the path we were travelling, we observed tracks indicating that men on horseback had recently passed, and in the course of the morning we met a party of six or eight Indians who informed us they were of the Cherokee nation, and that we should be able to arrive at the military post at Belle Point on the following morning. They were on horseback, carrying guns, kettles, and other articles suited to a hunting excursion, which it was their purpose to make in the territory of the Osages. Two or three of them had round hats; all had calico shirts, or some other article of foreign fabric, as part of their dress, and, in all, a mean and squalid appearance, indicated that they had been in habits of frequent intercourse with the whites. They were unable to speak or understand our language, but communicated with considerable ease by means of signs.

At eleven o'clock we halted, and as our provisions were nearly exhausted, most of the party went out to hunt, but were not fortunate in meeting game. We found, however, some papaw trees, with ripe fruit of an uncommon size and delicious flavor, with which we were able to allay our hunger. The papaw tree attains a much larger size, and the fruit arrives at greater perfection in the low grounds of the Arkansa than on the Missouri, Ohio, and upper Mississippi, where it is also common. The papaws fall to the ground as soon as fully ripe, and are eagerly sought after by the bears, racoons, opossums, &c.

In the afternoon one of our mules failed so far, that the undivided attention, and the most active exertions of two men were required to keep him moving at the rate of a slow walk. This made it necessary we should encamp, and we accordingly selected a spot in a fine open grove, where we pitched our tent. Among other interesting plants, we col-

lected here the beautiful vexillaria* *virginica* of Eaton,
which has the largest flower of any of the legumina of the
United States, as is remarked by Mr. Nuttall. We saw also the menispermum lyoni Hieracium *marianum*, Rhexia
virginica, &c.

As we encamped at an early hour, the party dispered in
various directions in search of game. Nothing was found except a swarm of bees affording as much honey as we chose
to eat for supper. While engaged in felling the tree, we heard
several guns, at a distance, and by sending persons to examine, we learned that they were those of a party of men accompanying Mr. Hugh Glen on his way from Fort Smith,
to the trading house at the mouth of the Verdigris. In the
evening we received a visit from Mr. Glen, whose camp was
distant only about a mile from ours. He was the first white
man, not of our own party, whom we had seen since the 6th
of the preceding June. From him we received a highly acceptable present of coffee, biscuits, a bottle of spirits, &c.;
also the welcome intelligence that Captain Bell, with his division of the exploring party, had arrived at Fort Smith some
days previous.

Early on the 13th, we took up our march in a heavy fall
of rain, which continued until we arrived at the little plantation opposite Belle Point. Here we emerged from the deep
silence and twilight gloom of the forest, and found ourselves once more surrounded by the works of men. The
plantation consisted of a single enclosure covered with a
thick crop of maize intermixed with gigantic stalks of the
phytolacca *decandra*, and Ricinus *palma-christi*, forming a
forest of annual plants, which seemed almost to vie with
miegias and annonas, occupying the adjacent portions of the
river bottom.

Urged by our impatience to see human faces, we called

---

* We have adopted this name from the author of the " Manual of Bota-
ny," as a substitute for that of the 1712 Genus of Persoon which has been
so severely censured by President Smith in Rees' Cyclopedia. It is equally appropriate with the old name.

out to the people in the cottage to direct us to Belle Point, although we knew the path could not be mistaken, and that we were not ten rods from the ferry. Notwithstanding our inquiries might have been thought impertinent, we were very civilly answered by a young woman, who came to the door, and attempted to silence the clamours of the dogs. We were not surprised to find our uncouth appearance a matter of astonishment both to dogs and men.

On arriving at the beach opposite Fort Smith, and making known our arrival by the discharge of a pistol, we perceived the inhabitants of the garrison and our former companions, coming down to the ferry to give us welcome: and being soon carried over, we met from Major Bradford and Captain Ballard, a most cordial reception. Captain Bell, with Mr. Say, Mr. Seymour, and Lieutenant Swift, having experienced numerous casualties, and achieved various adventures, having suffered much from hunger, and more from the perfidy of some of their soldiers, had arrived on the 9th, and were all in good health. The loss most sensibly felt, was that of the manuscript notes of Mr. Say and Lieutenant Swift. Measures for the apprehension of the deserters, and the recovery of these important papers were taken immediately, and a reward of two hundred dollars offered. Mr. Glen had kindly volunteered his assistance, and his influence, to engage the Osages in the pursuit. But these efforts were unavailing.

We arrived at Fort Smith at about nine o'clock, and were soon afterwards invited to a bountifully furnished breakfast-table at Major Bradford's. Our attentive host, knowing the caution necessary to be used by men in our situation, restrained us from a too unbounded indulgence in the use of bread, sweet potatoes, and other articles of diet, to which we had been long unaccustomed. The experience of a few days taught us that we should have been fortunate had we given more implicit heed to his cautions.

It is now necessary to return, and attend Captain Bell's detachment of the party, in their progress down the Arkansa.

CHAPTER X.*

The party proceed upon their route—Thunder storm—Some account of the Kiawa, Kaskaia, Arrapaho, and Shienne Indians—New species of toad.

24th. AFTER the departure of so great a portion of our number, combined with whom, we could hardly be regarded as sufficiently powerful to contend successfully with a force which we were daily liable to encounter, we were well aware of the necessity of exerting an increased vigilance, and of relying still more implicitly upon our individual means of defence than we had hitherto done. Our small band now consisted of Captain Bell, Lieutenant Swift, Mr. Seymour, Mr. Say, and the interpreters Bijeau, Ledoux, and Julien, with five soldiers.

We were cheered by the reflection that we had successfully performed a very considerable and most important part of our expedition, harmonizing well with each other, and unassailed by any urgent visible dangers, such as had been anticipated by ourselves, and predicted by others. We could not, however, look forward to the trackless desert which still separated us from the uttermost boundary of civilization, and which we had no reason to believe was less than one thousand miles in breadth, traversed, in many portions of its extent, by lawless war parties of various nations of Indians, without an emotion of anxiety and of doubt, as to the successful termination of our enterprize.

We were this afternoon assailed by a very severe thunder

* This account of the Expedition down the Arkansa river is from the MS. of Mr. Say.

storm; and Julien, who had skirted the timber for the purpose of hunting, was electrified by a flash of lightning which entered the earth within a few yards of him.

The wind was violent, and blew the drops of rain with so much force into our faces, that our horses refused to proceed, constantly endeavouring to turn themselves about from the storm; we at length yielded to their obstinacy, and halted upon the plain. The storm did not abate until we were thoroughly drenched to the skin, when, after being delayed some additional space of time until a straggler had joined us, we continued our journey.

The striped and spotted ground squirrel, a beautiful little animal, occurred to our notice several times in the course of the day.

Mr. T. Nuttall long since obtained specimens of this species, near the Mandan village, on the Missouri, and in the year 1814 he presented skins of it to several of his scientific friends in London.

He informs me that he has seen tippets worn by the Indians of the Upper Missouri, which were made of the skins of this elegant species, sewn together.

They burrow in the earth, and do not voluntarily climb trees. They inhabit an extensive portion of North America, extending at least from the more northern lakes to the Arkansa river, and most probably in that direction into Mexico, and westward to the Rocky Mountains. They were not uncommon in the vicinity of Engineer Cantonment.

26th. Late in the afternoon we saw, at a great distance before us, evident indications of the proximity of Indians, consisting of conic elevations, or skin lodges, on the edge of the skirting timber, partially concealed by the foliage of the trees. On our nearer approach we observed their horses peacefully grazing; but becoming suddenly frightened, probably by our scent, they all bounded off towards the camp, which was now full in view. Our attention was called off from the horses by the appearance of their masters, who were now seen running towards us with all their swiftness. A minute afterwards we were surrounded by them, and were happy to observe, in their features and gestures, a manifestation of the most pacific disposition; they shook us by the hand, assured us by signs that they rejoiced to see us, and invited us to partake of their hospitality. We, however, replied that we had brought our own lodges with us, and would encamp near them. We selected for this purpose a clear spot of ground on the bank of the river, intending to remain a day or two with this little known people, to observe their manners and way of life. We had scarcely pitched our tents, watered and staked our horses, before presents of jerked bison meat were brought to us by the squaws, consisting of selected pieces, the fattest and the best, and in sufficient quantity for the consumption of two or three days. After the usual ceremony of smoking, they were informed to what nation we belonged; and that further communication would be made to their principal men to-morrow, whom we wished summoned for that purpose. About sundown they all retired, and left us to our repose. The Indians were encamped on both sides of the river, but the great body of them was on the opposite bank, their skin lodges extending in a long single line, the extremities of which were concealed from our view by the timber of the islands in the river, whilst about ten lodges only were erected on the side we occupied, and within a quarter of a mile of our camp.

Soon after our arrival, an Indian, well stricken in years, inquired if we had seen a man and squaw within a day or two on our route; we described to him the appearance of the Calf and his squaw; that is my wife, said he, who has eloped from me, and I will instantly go in pursuit of them. He accordingly procured a companion, and both were soon on their way, well armed and mounted.

27th. Notice having been sent to the opposite party of our

arrival, and of our wish to see the principal men, four chiefs presented themselves at our camp this morning at an early hour, as representatives of the several bands, of the same number of different nations here associated together, and consisting of Kiawas, Kaskaias, or Bad-hearts, Shiennes (sometimes written Chayenne,) and Arrapahoes; several distinguished men accompanied them. We had made some little preparation for their reception by spreading skins for them to sit on, hoisting our flag, and selecting a few presents from our scanty stores. They arranged themselves with due solemnity, and the pipe being passed around, many of them seemed to enjoy it as the greatest rarity, eyeing it as it passed from mouth to mouth, and inhaling its fragrant smoke into their lungs with a pleasure which they could not conceal. One individual, of a tall, emaciated frame, whose visage was furrowed with deep wrinkles, evidently rather the effect of disease than of age, after filling his lungs and mouth top full of smoke, placed his hands firmly upon his face and inflated cheeks as in an ecstasy, and unwilling to part with what yielded the utmost pleasure, he retained his breath until suffocation compelled him to drive out the smoke and inhale fresh air, which he effected so suddenly, and with so much earnestness and singular contortion of countenance, that we restrained ourselves with some effort from committing the indecorum of a broad laugh. We had the good fortune to find one of them who could speak the Pawnee language tolerably well; he had acquired it in his early youth, whilst residing in a state of captivity in that nation, so that by means of our interpreters we experienced no difficulty in acquainting them, that we belonged to the numerous and powerful nation of Americans,* that we had been sent by our great chief, who presides over all that country, to examine that part of his territories, that he might

* In contradistinction from Spaniards, near whose frontier these Indians rove.

become acquainted with its features, its produce, and population; that we had been many moons on our journey, and had passed through many red nations, of whose hospitality we largely partook, &c. This was translated into French, then into Pawnee, and afterwards into Kiawa and the other languages, by their respective interpreters. In reply a chief expressed his surprise that we had travelled so far, and assured us that they were happy to see us, and hoped that as a road was now open to our nation, traders would be sent amongst them.

We assured them that traders would be soon amongst them, provided we could report, on our return, that we had been hospitably treated while travelling through their country.

A few presents, such as knives, combs, vermillion, &c. were then laid before the chiefs, who in return presented us with three or four horses, which terminated the proceedings of the council. We afterwards understood that our guests thought we gave but little, and it is perhaps true that the value of their presents was far greater than ours, yet our liberality was fully equal to our means.

The whole population had now deserted their edifices, and crowded about us, and agreeably to our wishes, which were announced in the council, the women brought jerked meat, and the men skin and hair ropes for halters, to trade with us for trinkets, and we were enabled to obtain a sufficient quantity of each, at a very moderate price. The trading being completed, we expected the crowd to diminish, but it seemed rather to augment, both in magnitude and density, until becoming a very serious inconvenience, we requested the chiefs to direct their people to retire, which they immediately complied with; but, with the exception of the Shienne chief, were not obeyed. All the Shiennes forthwith left us in compliance with the peremptory orders of their chief, who seemed to be a man born to command, endowed with

a spirit of unconquerable ferocity, and capable of inflicting exemplary punishment upon any one who should dare
disobey his orders.   He was tall and graceful, with a
highly ridged aquiline nose, corrugated forehead, mouth
with the corners drawn downward, and rather small, but
remarkably piercing eye, which when fixed upon your countenance, appeared strained in the intenseness of its gaze, and
to seek rather for the movements of the soul within, than to
ascertain the mere lineaments it contemplated.   The other
chiefs seemed to possess only the dignity of office, without
the power of command; the result, probably, of a deficiency
of that native energy with which their companion was so
preeminently endowed; they scarcely dared to reiterate their
admonitions to their followers not to press so closely upon
the white people, but to limit their approaches to the line of
our baggage; still our tents were filled, and our persons
hemmed in by the ardent and insatiable curiosity of the
multitude of both sexes, and of all ages, mounted and on foot.
To an observer of mankind the present scene was abundantly
fruitful and interesting.   We could not but remark the ease
and air of security, with which the equestrians preserved
their equipoise on the naked backs of their horses in their
evolutions beyond the crowd, nor could we restrain a smile,
in the midst of vexatious circumstances, at the appearance
of the naked children mounted on horses, sometimes to the
number of three or four on each, fearlessly standing erect,
or kneeling upon their backs to catch a glance over the heads
of the intervening multitude, at the singular deportment,
costume, and appearance of the white strangers.

In the rear of our tent a squaw, who had become possessed of a wooden small-toothed comb, was occupied in removing from her head a population as numerous as the individuals composing it were robust and well fed; she had
placed a skin upon her lap to receive the victims as they
fell; and a female companion, who sat at her feet, alternately

craunched the oily vermin between her teeth, and conversed with the most rapid and pleasant loquacity as she picked them up from the skin before her.

Our attention was now arrested by a phenomenon, which soon relieved us from the crowd that pressed upon us. A heavy and extensive cloud of dust was observed in the north obscuring the horizon, and bounding the range of vision in that direction; it moved rapidly towards us. An animated scene ensued. The Indians forded the river with as much rapidity of movement as they could exert towards their encampment, horse and foot, the water foaming before them. It soon became obvious that the dust ascended into the atmosphere under the influence of a violent current of air; we, therefore employed a few moments of interval, in strengthening our feeble tenements, to resist the influence of the approaching tempest. They were so nearly filled with our red brethren, that it was with no little difficulty we wedged ourselves into shelter. It soon became necessary to exert our strength in holding down our tents, and supporting the poles, which bowed and shook violently under the pressure of the blast; thunder, lightning, rain, and hail succeeded. During this play of the elements our guests sat in stillness, scarcely articulating a word during the prevalence of the electrical explosions.

Our tents were much admired, and previously to the fall of rain, which exposed their imperfection, in admitting the water modified into the form of a mist, one of the natives offered to exchange an excellent mule for that in which he was sitting. And, as the commonalty could not distinguish us in their minds from traders, another offered two mules, valued equal to four horses, for a double barrelled gun; and a third would willingly have bartered a very good horse for an old and almost worn out camp kettle, which we could by no means part with, though much in want of horses.

These Indians differ, in many particulars, from those of

the Missouri, with whose appearance we had been, for some time, familiar. Their average stature appeared to us less considerable, and although the general appearance of the countenance was such as we had been accustomed to see, yet their faces have, perhaps, somewhat more latitude, and the Roman nose is obviously far less predominant; but still, the direction of the eye, the prominence of the cheek bones, the form of the lips, teeth, chin, and retreating forehead, are precisely similar. They have also the same habit of plucking the hair from various parts of the body; but that of the head, in the female, is only suffered to attain to the shoulders, whilst the men permit theirs to grow to its full extent. They even regard long hair as an ornament; and many wear false hair fastened to their own by means of an earthy matter, resembling red clay, and depending, in many instances, particularly in the young beaux, to their knees, in the form of queues, one on each side of the head, variously decorated with ribbon-like slips of red and blue cloth, or coloured skin. Others, and by no means an inconsiderable few, had collected their long hair into several flat masses of the breadth of two or three fingers, and less than the fifth of an inch in thickness, each one separately annulated with red clay, at regular intervals. The elders wore their hair without decoration, flowing loosely about their shoulders, or simply intermixed with slender plaited queues. In structure and colour it is not distinguished from that of the Missouri Indians, though in early youth it is often of a much lighter colour; and a young man, of perhaps fifteen years of age, who visited us to-day, had hair decidedly of a flaxen hue, with a tint of dusky yellow.

Their costume is very simple, that of the female consisting of a leathern petticoat, reaching the calf of the leg, destitute of a seam, and often exposing a well formed thigh, as the casualties of wind, or position, influence the artless foldings of the skirt; the leg and foot are often naked, but

usually invested by gaiters and mockasins; a kind of sleeve-
less short gown, composed of a single piece of the same
material, loosely clothes the body, hanging upon the shoulders, readily thrown off, without any sense of indelicacy,
when suckling their children, or under the influence of a
heated atmosphere, displaying loose and pendent mammæ. A
few are covered by the more costly attire of coarse red or
blue cloth, ornamented with a profusion of blue and white
beads; the shortgown of this dress has the addition of wide
sleeves descending below the elbow; its body is of a square
form with a transverse slit in the upper edge for the head
to pass through; around this aperture, and on the upper side
of the sleeves, is a continuous stripe, the breadth of the hand,
of blue and white beads, tastefully arranged in contact with
each other, and adding considerable weight, as well as ornament, to this part of the dress; around the petticoat, and in
a line with the knees, is an even row of oblong conic bells,
made of sheet copper, each about an inch and a half in
length, suspended vertically by short leathern thongs as near
to each other as possible, so that when the person is in motion they strike upon each other and produce a tinkling sound.
The young unmarried females are more neatly dressed, and
seem to participate but little in the laborious occupations,
which fall chiefly to the lot of their wedded companions.

The dress of the men is composed of a breech-cloth, skin
leggings, mockasins, and a bison robe. In warm weather, the
three latter articles of dress are sometimes thrown aside as
superfluous, exposing the limbs and body to view and to
the direct influence of the most ardent rays of the sun.
Such are the habiliments that necessity compels the multitude to adopt; but the opulence of a few has gained for themselves the comfortable, as well as ornamental, and highly
esteemed Spanish blanket, from the Mexican traders, and of
which we had previously seen two or three in the possession of Pawnee warriors, worn as trophies. Another spe-

cies of garment, in their estimation equally sumptuous with the blanket, is the cloth robe, which is of ample dimensions, simple in form, one half red and the other blue, thrown loosely about the person, and at a little distance, excepting the singular arrangement of colours, resembling a Spanish cloak.

Some have, suspended from the slits of their ears, the highly prized nacre, or perlaceous fragments of a marine shell, brought probably from the northwest coast.

The Shienne chief revisited us in the afternoon. He informed us that one of his young men, who had been sent to ascertain the route which the bison herds had taken, and their present locality, had observed the trail of a large party of men, whom, by pursuing the direction, he had discovered to be Spaniards on their way towards the position we then occupied, where they must very soon arrive. As we were now in a region, claimed by the Mexican Spaniards as exclusively their own, and as we had for some days anticipated such an event as highly probable, we involuntarily reposed implicit confidence, in the truth of the intelligence communicated by the chief, who regarded that people as our natural enemies. Nevertheless, his story was heard by our little band, as it was proper that it should have been in our situation, and in the presence of Indians, with the appearance of absolute apathy. The chief seemed not to have accomplished some object he had in view, and departed evidently displeased. When he was out of hearing, the Indian interpreter who had become our friend, told us that the story was entirely false, and was without a doubt the invention of the chief, and designed to expedite the trade for a few additional horses, that we were then negociating.

Mr. Say, accompanied by an interpreter, who made a short visit to the small group of lodges near us, was kindly received, though hooted at by the children, and of course snarled and snapped at by the dogs. The skin lodges of these wandering people, are very similar to those of the Missouri tribes, but in those to which he was introduced, he experienced the oppression of an almost suffocating heat, certainly many degress above the temperature of the very sultry exterior atmosphere. A very portly old man, whose features were distinguished by a remarkably wide mouth and lengthened chin, invited him to a small ragged lodge, to see the riches it contained. These consisted of habiliments of red and blue cloth, profusely garnished with blue and white beads, the product of the industry and ingenuity of his squaw, from materials obtained last winter from some white traders, who made their appearance on Red river. The present members of this family, were the old man, one wife and four children, the latter as usual in a state of nudity. The baggage was piled around the lodge, serving for seats and beds, and a pile of jerked meat near the door, served also for a seat, and was occasionally visited by the dirty feet of the children. A boy was amusing himself with that primitive weapon, the sling, of an ordinary form, which he used with considerable dexterity, the effect of which he appeared disposed to try upon the stranger, and was not readily turned from his purpose, by a harsh rebuke and menacing gesture.

He was informed that the party of traders, who had last winter ascended Red river to their country, were *Tabbyboos*, a name which they also applied to us, and which appears to be the same word which, according to Lewis and Clark, in the language of the Snake Indians, means white men, but it was here applied particularly to the Americans. These traders offered various articles, such as coarse cloths, beads, vermillion, kettles, knives, guns, powder, lead, &c.; in exchange for horses and mules, bison robes, and parchment or *parfleche*. Such was the anxiety to obtain the merchandise thus displayed before them, that those enterprising warriors, whose stock of horses was but small, crossed the mountains into Mexico, and returned with a plentiful supply of those animals for exchange, captured from the Spanish inhabitants of that country. This illicit trade in horses was conducted so extensively by that party of traders, that he was told of a single Indian, who sold them fifty mules, besides a considerable number of horses from his own stock.

At his return to camp, he was informed that an old Indian had been there, who asserted that he never before had seen a white man, and on being permitted to view a part of the body, usually covered by the dress, he seemed much surprised at its whiteness.

These Indians seem to hold in exalted estimation, the martial prowess of the Americans. They said that a battle had lately been fought in the country, which lay very far down Red river, between a handful of Americans, and a great war party of Spaniards; that the latter were soon routed, retreating in a dastardly manner, "like partridges running through the grass." They were at present at war with the Spaniards themselves, and had lately killed many individuals of a party of that nation, near the mountains.

In the evening, squaws were brought to our camp, and after we had retired to our tent at night, a brother of the grand chief, Bear's-tooth, continued to interrupt our repose, with solicitations in favour of a squaw he had brought with him, until he was peremptorily directed to begone, and the centinel was ordered to prevent his further intrusion.

The Bear-tooth is the grand chief of the Arrapahoes, and his influence extends over all the tribes of the country in which he roves: he was said to be encamped at no great distance, with the principal body of these nations. He is said to be very favorably disposed towards the white people, and to have afforded protection, and a home in his own lodge, to a poor and miserable American, who had had the good fortune to escape from the barbarity and mistaken policy of the Mexican Spaniards, and from the horrors of a Spanish prison, to find an asylum amongst those whom they regard as barbarians, but to whose commiseration his wretchedness seemed to have been a passport.

28th. This morning at sunrise, we were called from our tents by the cry of *Tabbyboo*, proceeding from two handsome mounted Arrapahoes, who appeared delighted to see us; they had passed our camp in the night, on their way from the camp of the Bear-tooth, with a message from that chief to our neighbours. In consequence of this information or order, the lodges on both sides of the river were struck at six o'clock, and the whole body of Indians, commenced their march up the river, notwithstanding the threatening aspect of the heavens, which portended a storm. We could not but admire the regularity, with which the preparations for their journey seemed to be conducted, and the remarkable facility with which the lodges disappeared, and with all their cumbrous and various contents, were secured to the backs of the numerous horses and mules. As the long drawn caravan proceeded onward, a military air was imparted to the whole, at the distance at which we contemplated it, by the activity of the young warriors, with their lances and shields, galloping or racing along the line for caprice or amusement.

The Kiawa chief and a few attendants, called to make his parting visit. He is an old man, rather short, inelegantly formed, destitute of any remarkable physiognomical peculiarity, and like other chiefs, without any distinction of personal ornament. In common with many of his tribe, his system was subject to cutaneous eruptions, of which several indications, besides a large ulcer, near the angle of the mouth, exhibited the proof. We were soon all driven into our flimsy and almost worn out tents, which afforded us but a very partial shelter from the fall of a heavy shower of rain from the N. W. There we obtained some additional information from the chief, who was disposed to be communicative, to augment the considerable mass, which we had already collected from other Indians, and particularly from Bijeau, respectin these wandering hordes. The chief seemed to take a pleasure in pronouncing to us words of the Kiawa language, and smiled at our awkward attempts to imitate them, whilst we were engaged in committing them to paper. This vocabulary, as well as that of the Kaskaia language, which we had previously obtained from the Calf, had been for some time the objects of our wishes, as Bijeau persuaded us, that they were more difficult to acquire than any other language, and that, although formerly he resided three years with those nations, he never could understand the meaning of a single word, not even |their expressions for *Frenchman* or *tobacco*. Nor does this observation, though, perhaps unintentionally exaggerating the ideas of the abstruse nature of the language, appear absolutely destitute of foundation, since these nations, although constantly associating together, and united under the influence of the Bear-tooth, are yet totally ignorant of each others language, insomuch that it was no uncommon occurrence, to see two individuals of different nations, sitting upon the ground, and conversing freely with each other, by means of the language of signs. In the art of thus conveying their ideas, they were thorough adepts, and their manual display was only interrupted at remote intervals by a smile, or by the auxiliary of an articulated word of the language of the Crow Indians, which to a very limited extent, passes current amongst them.

These languages abound with sounds strange to our ears, and in the noisy loquacity of some squaws, who held an animated debate near our tent yesterday, we distinguished pre-eminently, sounds which may be expressed by the letters koo, koo, koo.

The Shiennes or Shawhays, who have united their destiny with these wanderers, are a band of seceders from their own nation, and some time since on the occurrence of a serious dispute with their kindred on Shienne river of the Missouri, flew their country, and placed themselves under the protection of the Bear-tooth.

These nations have been for the three past years, wandering on the head waters and tributaries of Red river, having returned to the Arkansa, only the day which preceded our first interview with them, on their way to the mountains, at the sources of the Platte river. They have no permanent town, but constantly rove, as necessity urges them, in pursuit of the herds of bisons, in the vicinity of the sources of the Platte, Arkansa, and Red rivers.

They are habitually at war with all the nations of the Missouri; indeed martial occurrences in which they were interested with those enemies, formed the chief topic of their conversation with our interpreters. They were desirous to know of them the names of particular individuals whom they had met in battle, and whom they described; how many had been present at a particular engagement, and who were killed or wounded. The late battle which we have before spoken of, with the Loup Pawnees, also occupied their inquiries; they denied that they were on that occasion aided by the Spaniards, as we understood they had been, but admitted their great numerical superiority, and the loss of many in killed and wounded. Their martial weapons are bows and arrows, lances, war clubs, tomahawks, scalping knives, and shields.*

---

* Chabonneau informs us, that he observed the clitoris and labia of a squaw of the Arrapaho nation, whom he had examined, to be very much elongated and dilated, so as to resemble large valves; this effect he attributed chiefly to the art of the mother, employed during the infancy and youth of the daughter, and to her own subsequent manipulations, and those of her husband.

We do not know that any writer has visited these Indians, since the expedition of Mr. Bourgmont, commander of Fort Orleans of the Missouri, which took place in the year 1724. They were then, and have since continued to be distinguished collectively by the name of Padoucas. Du Pratz informs us, that they were then very numerous, "extending almost two hundred leagues, and they have villages quite close to the Spaniards of New Mexico." And that "from the Padoucas to the Canzes, proceeding always east, we may now safely reckon sixty-five and a half leagues. The river of the Canzes is parallel to this route." From this statement of the course, and estimate of the distance to the country of the Padoucas, it is evident, that at this day the Indians do not habitually wander in that direction, so near to the Missouri as they then did, owing probably to the hostilities of the more martial nations residing on that river.

Tobacco being very scarce, they do not carry with them a pouch, for the convenience of having it always at hand, an article of dress invariably attendant on the Missouri Indian. Bijeau informed us that the smoking of tobacco was regarded as a pleasure so sacred and important, that the females were accustomed to depart from the interior of a lodge when the men indulged themselves with the pipe. The Shienne chief, in consequence of a vow he had made against using the pipe, abstained from smoking while at our council, until he had the good fortune to find a small piece of paper which some one of our party had rejected; with this he rolled up a small quantity of tobacco fragments into the form of a segar, after the manner of the Spaniards, and thus contented himself with infringing the spirit of his vow, whilst he obeyed it to the letter.

The rain having ceased, our guest and his attendants took their leave.

These Indians might readily be induced to hunt the beaver, which are so extremely abundant in their country, but as yet, these peltries seem not to have entered amongst the items of their trade.

In the afternoon we struck our tents, and continued our journey; we were soon overtaken by a thunder storm, which poured down upon us a deluge of rain, and continued, with partial intermissions, during the night.

For the elucidation of what we have said respecting the form and arrangement of the skin, or travelling lodges of the Indians, we subjoin an engraving, representing an encampment of Oto Indians, which Mr. Seymour sketched near the Platte river. In this plate, the group of Indians on the left is intended to represent a party of Konza Indians approaching to perform the calumet dance in the Oto village. It may be proper to remark, that this party when still distant from the Otoes, had sent forward a messenger, with the offer of a prize to the first Oto that should meet them. This circumstance was productive of much bustle and activity among the warriors and young men, who eagerly mounted their horses, and exerted their utmost speed.

Since we have mentioned the Otoes, we will notice the ceremony of marking a distinguished squaw, which was in part witnessed by some of our party at the Oto village. This marking, which we have elsewhere alluded to, consists in picking into the forehead, with a small fascicle of needles, or other small pointed instruments, a portion of minute particles of carbon, from a solution of gun powder, or comminuted and moistened wood coal, so as to form upon the part a small blue spot. On the approach of our party, however, to the group of Indians in which this ceremony was performing, each individual sat perfectly still, with his head inclined, as if indisposed to proceed whilst observed by strangers. In the centre of the group was a piece of wood supported at each end by an upright crotchet, and holding suspended various articles of merchandize, intended to compensate the operator; consisting of red and blue strouding, and many other articles of much value. The squaw, with her family and friends, accompanied by the individual who was to perform the operation, sat in the form of a semicircle, in front of these valuables, and a large decorated pipe was laid on the soil before them. Our party supposed that the value of the merchandize thus offered in exchange for the distinction of a small spot on the forehead, was, in that country, and particularly after having passed through the hands of the traders, estimable at one hundred dollars.

We will further interrupt our narrative in this place, to mention a circumstance, that has been omitted in our account of the manners and habits of the Indians of the Missouri. It serves to show that their attention is not limited to the larger and more imposing objects of the creation, but that it is directed to the " watches, as well as the clocks of nature."

The Oto warrior, *Little black bear*, when looking at our

collection of insects at Engineer cantonment, recognised a
considerable number of them, told which inhabited the water,
and which the land, and noticed many little anecdotes of
their manners with much accuracy; with respect to some,
however, which he pointed out, he entertained strange no-
tions, doubtless in common with his countrymen. Our largest species of dytiscus, he said, sometimes entered the womb
of a pregnant squaw, and destroyed the fœtus. The large
green grasshopper with a pointed head, (Truxalis) he said,
would seize the nipple of a squaw with its mouth, and would
not quit its hold until the body was torn from the head.

29th. The sun arose with renewed splendour, and ushered in another sultry day. Two of the horses, which had been
presented by the chiefs, ran off, and were observed to rise
the bluffs and disappear; men were despatched in pursuit of
them, who after a long and fatiguing chase, returned about
noon, unsuccessful. We reconciled ourselves as we might
to this privation, and after dining, proceeded onward. The alluvial margins of the river are gradually dilating as we descend, and the mosquitoes, which have of late visited our
camp but sparingly, are now increasing in number.

A fine species of toad (Bufo*) inhabits this region. It resembles the common toad (B. *musicus*. Daud.) but differs in
the arrangement of the colours, and in the proportional
length of the groove of the head, which in that species ex-

---

* Bufo *cognatus*. Fuscous, with cinereous lines; head canaliculate,
groove abbreviated before.
    Body above dark brownish, papillous; the papillæ and their discs
black, they are more numerous, prominent, and acute on the sides and
legs, not prominent on the back: a vertebral cinereous vitta, from which
an oblique, cinereous, irregular line is drawn from the vertex to the side
behind the anterior feet; another double one from the middle of the back
to behind the middle of the side, and another from behind the middle of the
back to the posterior thighs; *sides* and legs with irregular cinereous lines;
head with a groove, which hardly extends anteriorly to the line of the
anterior canthus of the eyes; *verrucæ* behind the eyes moderate; *superior
maxilla* emarginate; *beneath* granulated.
    Length from the nose to the cloaca, 3 3-4 inches.
    A specimen is placed in the Philadelphia Museum.

tends to the nose; it is destitute of large verrucose prominences intervening between the verrucæ behind the eyes,
and of the large, irregular, black dorsal spots edged with
white, observable upon the *musicus*. In the arrangement of
the cinereous lines it presents a general resemblance to B.
fuscus. Laur. as represented on pl. 96. of the Encyc.
Method.

It resides in a country almost destitute of timber, where,
with a variety of the *musicus*, it is very much exposed to
the direct rays of the sun.

CHAPTER XI.

Arrapaho war-party—Cowhunting—Rattlesnakes—Burrowing-owl—Departure of Bijeau and Ledoux for the Pawnee villages—Scarcity of timber—Great herds of bisons—wolves.

On the 30th, about sunrise, a dense fog intercepted the view of the surrounding scenery, which was soon dissipated as we moved on, exhibiting all the variety of partially revealed, and unnaturally enlarged objects, so familiar to observers of rural sights. At noon, a beautiful natural grove of cottonwood, lining a ravine in which was some cool but stagnant water, near the bank of the river, invited us to repose during the oppressive mid-day heat. We had hardly stripped our horses of their baggage, and betaken ourselves to our respective occupations, when a voice from the opposite bank of the river warned us of the proximity of Indians, who had been until now unseen. Nine Indians soon appeared, and crossed the river to our camp. They proved to be an Arrapaho war party of eight men and a squaw, of whom one was a Kiawa.* This party informed us that they had left the Bear-tooth's party on a tributary of this river, at the distance of half a day's journey from us, moving upwards. As no apprehension of mischief was entertained from so small a party, they were invited to encamp near us for the remainder of the day, to which, urged by curiosity, and perhaps by the hope of receiving some presents, they readily assented. The squaw busied herself in erecting a little bowery of a sufficient size to contain herself and her husband, who we afterwards dis-

* The Arrapaho or Rappaho nation is known to the Minnetarees of the Missouri, by the name of E-ta-leh, or Bison-path Indians.

covered to be a personage of some eminence in their mystic
arts.

Having supplied our guests with a pipe and some tobacco,
we resumed our occupations. Our attention was however
diverted to the young Kiawa warrior, who had the presump-
tion to seize the Kaskaia horse, which was purchased of the
Calf Indian, loose him from the stake around which he was
grazing, and having the further audacity to lead him near to
our tent, proceeded to make a noose in the halter, which he
placed over the mouth of the animal, that patiently submitted
to his operations. This sudden subjection of the horse
was a subject of more surprise to us, than the outrageous attempt of the Indian, as he had hitherto resisted all our en-
deavors to accomplish the same object, whether conciliatory
or forcible. It seemed to corroborate the truth of the observation, that the horse readily distinguishes the native from the
white man, by his acute sense of smelling. The intention of
the Indian to take possession of the horse was now manifest,
and one of our party stepped forward and seized the halter
near the head of the animal; but the Indian who held
the other extremity of the halter, betrayed no symptoms
of fear, or of an intention to relinquish a possession
which he had thus partially gained. He looked sternly at
his antagonist, and asserted his right to the horse, inasmuch
as he had, he said, formerly owned him, and meant now to
repossess him. Supposing that this altercation might even-
tuate unpleasantly, the remainder of our party stood prepared
to repulse any attempt which the other Indians might make to
support the claim of their companion, whilst Bijeau advanced
with a manly decision and jerked the halter out of the hands of
the Indian. His companions sat enjoying themselves with their
pipe, and did not appear disposed to take any part in the
transaction. He fortunately made no further exertions to obtain possession of the horse, but immediately mounted his
own horse, and rode off in high dudgeon, saying he would

remain no longer with us, for fear we would kill him. Contrary
to our expectations, the other Indians loudly condemned his
conduct; they said that the horse had never been his property,
that they all knew the animal well, that he was a very bad Kiawa, and would either assemble a party to return against us,
or he would return himself that night, to accomplish his purpose. "If he does come," said they, "you need not give
yourselves any trouble, for we will watch for him, and kill
him ourselves.

When the excitement of this incident had subsided, we
felt desirous to examine the contents of the medicine bag of
the man of mysteries, who was at once a magician and the
leader of the party. At our solicitation he readily opened
his sacred depository, and displayed its contents on a skin
before us, whilst he politely proceeded to expatiate on their
powers and virtues in the occult art, as well as their physical efficacy. They consisted of various roots, seeds, pappus,
and powders, both active and inert, as respects their action
on the human system, carefully enveloped in skins, leaves,
&c.; some of which, to his credulous faith, were invested
with supernatural powers. Similar qualities were also attributed to some animal products, with which these were accompanied, such as claws of birds, beaks, feathers, and hair.
But the object that more particularly attracted our attention,
was the intoxicating bean, as it has been called, of which he
possessed upwards of a pint. Julien recognised it immediately. He informed us that it is in such high request
amongst the Oto Indians, that a horse has been exchanged
for eight or ten of them. In that nation they are only used
by a particular society, who, at their nocturnal orgies, make
a decoction of the bean, and, with much pomp and ceremony, administer the delightful beverage to each member. The
initiation fees of this society are rather extravagant, and the
proceeds are devoted principally to the purchase of the bean.
That old sensualist, Shongotonga (Big-horse), is the princi-

pal or presiding member of the society, and the bean is obtained, in some circuitous manner, from the Pawnee Piquas of Red river, who, probably, receive it from the Mexican Indians. With some few trinkets, of little value, we purchased the principal portion of our medicine man's store of beans; they are of an oval form, and of a light red, sometimes yellowish colour, with a rather deeply impressed oval cicatrix, and larger than a common bean. A small number of a differently coloured, and rather larger bean was intermixed with them.

The squaw had in her possession, a quantity of small, flat, blackish cakes, which, on tasting, we found very palatable. Having purchased some of them, we ascertained that they were composed of the wild cherry, both pulp and stone pounded together, until the latter is broken into fragments, then mixed with grease, and dried in the sun.

Not choosing to rely implicitly on the good faith of the strangers, however emphatically expressed, the sentinel was directed to look well to them, and also to keep the horse in question constantly in view during the night, and to alarm us upon the occurrence of any suspicious movements. All, however, remained quiet during the night, and in the morning, the 31st., we resumed our journey. The river now considerably dilates, and is studded with a number of small islands, but the timber and shrubs that skirt it are still less abundant and more scattered. The alluvial formation affords a moderate growth of grass, but the general surface of the country is flat, sterile, and uninteresting. The day was cloudy, with an E. S. E. wind, which at night brought some rain.

Aug. 1st. Set out late, and after having travelled about two miles, a horseman armed with a spear was seen on the Bluffs, at the distance of about a quarter of a mile, who, after gazing at our line for a short time, disappeared. Our Pawnee interpreters being at a considerable distance in the rear, Julien was sent forward to reconnoitre. He mounted the Bluff to the general level of the country, and abruptly halted his horse within our view, as if appearances before him rendered precaution necessary. The Indian again came in sight, and, in full career, rushed towards him, passed him, and wheeling halted his horse. Many other Indians then appeared, who surrounded Julien, and, after a short and hurried conference, they dashed at full speed down the steep bank of the Bluff to meet us, the whole in concert singing the scalp-song. So adventurous and heedless was this movement, that one of the horses stumbled, and fell with great violence, and rolled to the bottom. His rider, no doubt, prepared for such an accident, threw himself in the instant from his seat, so as to fall in the most favorable manner, and avoid the danger of being crushed by the horse. Not the slightest attention was bestowed upon him by his companions, and, indeed, the disaster, however serious it at first appeared, hardly interrupted his song. His horse being but little injured, he almost immediately regained his saddle, and came on but little in the rear of the others, who now had mingled with our party, shaking us by the hand with a kind of earnest familiarity, not the most agreeable. We needed no additional information to convince us that this was a war party; their appearance was a sufficient evidence of the nature of their occupation. One of us asked an individual, if they were Kiawas, and was answered in the affirmative; he asked a second if they were Kaskaias, and a third if they were Arrapahoes, who both also answered affirmatively. This conduct, added to their general deportment, served to excite our suspicions and redouble our vigilance. Two or three other little detached squads were now seen to approach, also singing the scalp-song.

Our interpreters having joined us, it was proposed that we should avail ourselves of the shade of a large tree, which stood near the river, to sit down and smoke with them,

They reared their spears against the tree, with apparent carelessness and indifference, and took their seats in the form of a semicircle on the ground. Having staked our horses in the rear, and stationed the men to protect them and the baggage, we seated ourselves, and circulated the pipe as usual. But as the party opposed to us was nearly quadruple our number, we did not choose to follow their example, in relinquishing our arms, but grasped them securely in our hands, and retained a cautious attitude.

Bijeau ascertained that they were a Shienne war party on their return from an expedition against the Pawnee Loups. They had killed one squaw, whose scalp was suspended to the spear of the partizan or leader of the party, the handle of which was decorated with strips of red and white cloth, beads, and tail-plumes of the war-eagle. He also informed us that he recognized several of them, particularly a chief who sat next to him, whose person, himself and party had formerly seized upon, and detained as a hostage for the recovery of some horses that had been stolen. The chief, however, did not now betray any symptoms of a disposition to retaliate for that act, though, without doubt, he regarded us as in his power.

Our interpreter readily conversed with them, through the medium of a Crow prisoner, whose language he partially understood.

The partizan, who killed the victim of this excursion, and two others, one of whom first struck the dead body, and the other who took off the scalp, were painted deep black with charcoal, and almost the entire body being exposed, rendered the effect more impressive. One of the latter, a tall athletic figure, remained standing behind us, and refused to smoke when the pipe was offered to him, alledging as an excuse, the obligation of a vow he had made against the use of tobacco on the decease of his late father.

We now drew upon our little stores of merchandize for two

or three twists of tobacco and a few knives, which, being laid before the partizan, excited from his politeness, the return of thanks. He was of an ordinary stature, and had exceeded the middle age; his face much pitted with the small-pox, his nostrils distended by a habitual muscular action, which, at the same time, elevated the skin of the forehead and forcibly drew downward that part which corresponds with the inner extremity of the eyebrows, into a kind of gloomy frown. This singular expression of countenance, added to the contrast of the whites of his large eyes, with the black colour, with which his features and body were overspread, seemed to indicate the operations of a mind hardened to the commission of the most outrageous actions. He, however, behaved with much propriety. During these scenes, Mr. Say succeeded in ascertaining and recording many of the words of their language, from an Indian who had seated himself behind him.

The party was armed with spears, bows and arrows, war-clubs, tomahawks, scalping knives, &c.

As many of them now began to ask for tobacco, and for paper to include fragments of it, in the form of segars, for smoking, and not finding it convenient to gratify them in this respect, we thought it prudent to withdraw, lest a quarrel might ensue. We, therefore, mounted our horses, without molestation, having been detained an hour and a half, and proceeded on our journey, with the agreeable reflection, that our deportment had not warranted a supposition that we were conscious of any inferiority in force, but rather that it was dictated by a high courtesy.

A few bisons varied the landscape, which is fatiguing to the eye by its sameness, and, after travelling twenty-three miles, we encamped for the night.

A large green-headed fly (Tabanus.) has made its appearance in great numbers, which exeedingly annoys our already sufficiently miserable horses. Their range seems to be in a great measure restricted to the luxuriant bottoms, and, like the Zimb of Egypt, they appear to roam but little beyond their proper boundaries. If we traversed these fertile portions of the low grounds, which yield a profuse growth of grasses, we were sure of being attacked by them, seizing upon the necks of the horses and dying them with blood; but the refuge of the more elevated surface, and arid barren soil, afforded speedy relief, by banishing our assailants.

Scarcely were our tents pitched, when a thunder-storm, which had been approaching with a strong west wind, burst over us, but was of short continuance.

2nd. After moving a few miles, we halted, and sent out hunters to kill a bison.* The *confluent rattlesnakes* are very abundant, particularly in and about the prairie-dog villages; but neither their appearance, nor the sound of their rattle excites the attention of our horses. The sagacity of Mr. Seymour's mule, however, seems superior to that of his quadruped companions. He appears to be perfectly aware of the dangerous qualities of these reptiles, and when he perceives one of them near him, he springs so abruptly to one side as to endanger his rider. Fortunately none of us have been bitten by them, during our pedestrian rambles.

A recent trail of some war party was this morning observed leading across the river.

The hunters returned unsuccessful, and we proceeded on until sunset, to a distance of twenty miles. Great numbers of bisons were seen this afternoon, and some antelopes.

---

* Amongst the herds of these animals, we very frequently saw flocks of the Cow Bunting (*Emberiza pecora*). The manners of this bird, in some respects, are similar to those of the *Tanagra erythroryncha* of Lord Stanley, in Salt's travels, flying and alighting in considerable numbers on the backs of the bisons, which from their submission to the pressure of numbers of them, seem to appreciate the services they render by scratching and devesting them of their vermin. This bird is here, as well as in the settlements, remarkably fearless. They will suffer us to pass very near to them, and one of them to-day alighted repeatedly on the ground near our horses' feet; he would fly along our line, balance himself on his wings, to gratify his curiosity, within striking distance of a whip.

3rd. The morning was clear and fine, with a temperature of 57 degrees. The antelopes became more numerous as we proceeded; one of them trotted up so near to our line, as to fall a victim to his curiosity. A considerable number of the coquimbo or burrowing-owl occurred in a prairie-dog village of moderate extent. They readily permitted the hunter to approach within gunshot, and we were successful in obtaining a specimen of the bird in good order. On examining the several burrows, at which the owls had been observed to be perched, we remarked in them a different aspect from those at which the prairie dog had appeared; they were often in a ruined condition, the sides, in some instances, fallen in, sometimes seamed and grooved by the action of the water, in its course from the surface to the interior, and, in other respects, presenting a deserted aspect, and, like dilapidated monuments of human art, were the fit abode of serpents, lizards, and owls.

The burrows, at which we saw the prairie dog, were, on the contrary, neat, always in repair, and evinced the operations of industrious tenants. This contrast, added to the form and magnitude of the dwelling, leads us to the belief that the coquimbo owl does not, in this region, excavate its own burrow, as it is said to do in South America and in the West India islands. But, rather, that it avails itself of the abandoned burrows of this species of marmot, for the purposes of nidification and shelter.

On our arrival at our mid-day resting place on the bank of the Arkansa, the water of the river was potable, but in a few minutes it became surcharged with earthy and stercoraceous matter, from the sweepings of the prairie by the late rain, to such a degree, that our horses would hardly drink it. There remained, however, a short distance below, a small stream of beautifully pellucid water, which rapidly filtrated through a fortuitous embankment of sand and pebbles, and strongly contrasted with the flood, with which it was soon again to intermingle. Our travelled distance to-day was twenty-three miles.

4th. Proceeded about six miles, when we forded a small portion of the river to an island, which supported a growth of low and distant trees. Here the tents were pitched, with the intention of halting a day or two, to recruit our miserable horses, and to supply ourselves with a store of jerked meat. The hunters were accordingly sent to the opposite side of the river, and in a short time they succeeded in killing four fat cows, which gave employment to all the men, in preparing the meat for transportation.

A brisk southerly wind prevailed, that rendered the atmosphere less oppressive than usual.

The wind ceased during the night, and the lowing of the thousands of bisons that surrounded us in every direction, reached us in one continual roar. This harsh and guttural noise, intermediate between the bellowing of the domestic bull, and the grunting of the hog, was varied by the shrill bark and scream of the prairie wolves, and the howling of the white wolves, (Canis Mexicanus Var?) which were also abundant. These wild and dissonant sounds, were associated with the idea of the barren and inhospitable wastes, in the midst of which we were then reposing, and vividly reminded us of our remoteness from the comforts of civilized society. Completed the operation of jerking the meat, of which we had prepared two packs, sufficient in weight to constitute a load for one of our horses, and disposed every thing for an early departure to-morrow.

6th. An unusual number of noisy wolves hovered around our encampment of last night, attracted probably by the smell of the meat. Resumed our journey on a fine cloudless morning, with a strong and highly agreeable breeze from the south. We were now traversing the great bend of the river. Travelled twenty-three miles this day, and shot two bulls which were now lean, and their flesh of a disa-

greeable rank taste, and scarcely eatable; we therefore contented ourselves with the tongues and marrow-bones.

7th. The mercurial column of the thermometer at sunrise,
for a few days past, has ranged between 42 and 67 degrees,
and the atmosphere is serene and dry. The services of the
two French Pawnee interpreters, Bijeau and Ledoux, had
terminated agreeably to their contract at Purgatory creek.
But having been highly serviceable to us on our route, it became desirable, particularly on the departure of our companions for Red river, that they should accompany us still
farther, until we should have passed beyond the great Indian
war path, here so widely outspread. This they readily consented to, as they regarded a journey from that point to their
home at the Pawnee villages, as somewhat too hazardous
to be prudently attempted by only two individuals, however
considerable their qualifications, and intimate their familiarity
with the manners of those whom they would probably meet.

But as we now supposed ourselves to have almost reached
the boundary of this region, and they again expressed their
anxiety to return to their village, in order to prepare for their
autumnal hunt, we no longer attempted to induce their further delay. They departed after breakfast, on a pathless journey of about three hundred miles, the supposed distance from
this point to the Pawnee villages of the Platte; apparently
well pleased with the treatment they had received, and expressing a desire again to accompany us, should we re-
ascend the Missouri.

We cannot take leave of them, without expressing our entire approbation of their conduct and deportment, during our
arduous journey; Bijeau particularly, was faithful, active, industrious, and communicative. Besides the duties of guide
and interpreter, he occasionally and frequently volunteered
his services as hunter, butcher, cook, veterinarian, &c., and
pointed out various little services, tending to our comfort
and security, which he performed with pleasure and alacri-

ty, and which no other than one habituated to this mode of life would have devised. During leisure intervals, he had communicated an historical narrative of his life and adventures, more particularly in as far as they were relative to the country which we have been exploring. He particularized the adventures of Choteau and Demun's hunting and trading party, their success in beaver hunting, the considerable quantity of merchandise they took with them, their adventures with the natives, and the singular circumstances attendant on their capture by the Mexican Spaniards, and the transfer of the merchandise to Santa Fe, without, however, venturing to express any conjectures relative to the latter transaction. Much still more important information was derived from him, concerning the manners and habits of these mountain Indians, their history, affinities, and migrations.

A copious addition to our vocabulary of words of the Pawnee language, was obtained from Ledoux, together with an account of the manners and habits of that nation.

All these, however, composed a part of the manuscripts of Mr. Say, that were subsequently carried off by deserters from our camp.

Travelled this day twenty-seven miles. The soil is becoming in many districts more exclusively sandy, the finer particles of which, driven by the wind, have formed numerous large hillocks on the opposite side of the river, precisely resembling those which are accumulated on our sea coast. On the northern side, or that which we are traversing, the prairie still offers its unvaried flatness, and cheerless sterility, so that during a portion of the day's journey, not a solitary bush seen on the river bank, relieved the monotonous scene before us.

Proceeded early on the following morning, and at the distance of twelve miles crossed a creek of clear running water, called by Bijeau, Demun's creek, from the circumstance of that hunter losing here a fine horse. At a considerable dis-

tance above, its stream was slightly fringed with timber, but
at our crossing place, it was like the neighbouring part of the
river, to which it contributed, entirely destitute of trees.
Our journey this day was a distance of twenty-four and a
half miles; towards evening, we crossed another creek, over
which, being much backed up by the river, we experienced
some difficulty in effecting a passage, and were obliged with
this view to ascend its stream some distance. It was moderately wooded, and amongst other trees we observed the elm,
(Ulmus *alata*,) and some plum trees, bearing fruit nearly ripe.

9th. During these few days past, the bisons have occurred
in vast and almost continuous herds, and in such infinite
numbers, as seemed to indicate the great bend of the Arkansa, as their chief and general rendezvous. As we passed
along, they ran in an almost uninterrupted line before us. The
course of our line being parallel to that of the Arkansa, when
we travelled at the distance of a mile or two from the river,
great herds of these animals were included between us and
it; as the prevailing wind blew very obliquely from our left
towards the river, it informed them of our presence, by the
scent which it conveyed. As soon as the odour reached even
the farthest animal, though at the distance of two miles on
our right, and perhaps a half a mile in our rear, he betrayed
the utmost alarm, would start into a full bounding run, to
pass before us to the bluffs, and as he turned round the head
of our line, he would strain every muscle to accelerate his
motion. This constant procession of bulls, cows, and calves
of various sizes, grew so familiar to us at length, as no longer to divert our view from the contemplation of other objects, and from the examination of the comparatively more
minute, but certainly not less wonderful works of nature.

The white and prairie wolves more intelligent than their
associates, judging by the eye of the proximity of danger, as
well as by their exquisite sense of smelling, either dashed

over the river, or unhesitatingly crossed our scent in the rear, and at an easy pace, or dog-trot, chose the shortest route to the bluffs.

The soil during the afternoon's ride was a deep, fine, white sand, which rendered the travelling very laborious, under the debilitating influence of an extreme temperature of 94 degrees of Fahrenheit's scale, and affected the sight by the glare of light, which it so freely reflected. The chief produce of these tracts of unmixed sand, is the sunflower, often the dense and almost exclusive occupant.

The evening encampment was formed at the junction of a small tributary with the river, at the distance of about twenty-four miles from the last mentioned creek. The very trifling quantity of timber, supported by the immediate bank of the river in this region, is almost exclusively the cottonwood; we are therefore gratified to observe on this creek, besides the elm, the walnut, mulberry and ash, which we hail with a hearty welcome, as the harbingers of a more productive territory.

CHAPTER XII.

Termination of the great bend of the Arkansa—Ietan war party—Little Arkansa—Red rivers fork—Little Neosho and Little Verdigris.

AUGUST 10th. THE great bend of the Arkansa terminates here, and as our horses have fed insufficiently for several days past, we lay by for the day, to give them an opportunity of recruiting. S. S. E. winds prevailed, and at noon exerted a considerable force; the extreme heat was 96 degrees. The hunters brought in a deer and bison.

11th. Having jerked our meat, and our horses being refreshed, we set forward at an early hour. The sandy soil and growth of sunflowers, still continues on the river bottoms, and the surface of the opposite bank, still swells into occasional hillocks of naked sand. The rice bird, (*Emberiza oryzivora*, L.) was feeding on the seeds of the sunflower, and the bald eagle was seen sailing high in the air.

We have, hitherto, generally been able to procure a sufficient supply of small drift wood for our culinary purposes, but at this noon-day halting place, we were obliged to dispatch a man across the river, to collect enough to kindle a fire. From our evening encampment, not a tree was within the range of sight.

This day was extremely warm, the mercury at three o'clock indicating 96 degrees, a temperature not decreased by a nimbus in the west, pouring rain with some thunder. In the evening, lightning played beautifully amongst the mingled cirrostratus and cumulus clouds, with which the heavens became overcast.

In the afternoon, we passed the termination of the sand

hills of the opposite shore. A fine male antelope was shot by Lieutenant Swift, and a skunk was also added to our stock of provisions. Distance twenty-five miles.

12th. Passed over a very wide bottom, of which the soil where not too sandy, produces a most luxuriant growth of grasses and other plants, but the river is still in a great measure destitute of trees, of which we passed but three, during the morning's ride, and not a bush over the height of about two and a half feet, being a few willows and barren plum bushes. We were again gratified with the appearance of the *prairie fowl*, running nimbly before us through the grass, the first we have seen since leaving the Platte. The bisons have now very much diminished in number; we passed unheeded, within a few yards of a young bull, whose glazed eye, and panting respiration, showed the operation of some malady, and it was curious to observe, that though he stood erect and firmly on his legs, the wolves which fled on our approach, were acquainted with his defenceless condition, and surrounded him in considerable numbers, awaiting his dissolution, and probably watching their opportunity to accelerate it.

The afternoon was calm, and the mercury at its greatest elevation, stood at 99 degrees. Soon after our departure from our resting place of noon, we observed a large herd of bisons on our left, running with their utmost rapidity towards us, from the distant bluffs. This was a sufficient warning to put us on our guard against another unwelcome war party. Looking attentively over the surface of the country in that direction, a mounted Indian was at length observed to occupy an elevated swell of the surface, at the distance of a mile or two from us. Our peace flag was as usual, immediately displayed, to let him know that we were white people, and to induce him to come to us, whilst we halted to wait for him. Assured by this pacific display, he approached a short distance but again halted, as if doubting our intentions,

Julien was then sent forward towards him, bearing the flag, to assure him of our friendship. The Indian now advanced but with much caution, and obliquely from one side to the other, as if beating against the wind. Another Indian was now observed advancing rapidly, who joined his companion. After some communication, by means of signs with Julien, to ascertain who we were, they approached within gunshot of us, and halting, desired to shake hands with our chief. After this ceremony they rode to an elevated ground, in order to give information to their party, which during this short interview, we had discovered at a long distance towards the bluffs, drawn up in line, in a conspicuous situation. One of the horsemen halted, whilst his companion rode transversely twice between him and the party. This telegraphic signal was immediately understood by the party, that consequently came on towards us. But their movement was so tardy, that it required the exertion of the greater portion of our stock of patience to wait their coming, under the ardour of the heated rays of the sun to which we were exposed. They seemed peaceably disposed, and desired to accompany us to the river bank, in order to smoke with us, but such was the scarcity of timber, that we were unable to avail ourselves of the shade of a single tree.

We now ascertained that they were an Ietan or Camanch (a band of Snake Indians,) war party, thirty-five in number, of whom five were squaws. They had marched to attack the Osages, but were surprised in their camp of night before last, by a party of unknown Indians. In the skirmish that ensued, they lost three men, and had six wounded. They, however, escaped under cover of the darkness, with the further loss of fifty-six horses and all their clothing, which were captured by the enemy.* They were indeed in a naked

* We have since learned from Major O'Fallon, that Ietan, the distinguished Oto partizan had informed him, within a few days of this date, that he had just then returned from a war excursion, in company with a

condition, being destitute of robes, leggings, and mockasins, with nothing to cover their bodies at night, or to protect them from the influence of the sun during the day. The
squaws, however, had managed to retain their clothing, and
one of the warriors had preserved an article of dress, resembling a coat, half red and half blue, ornamented with beads
on the sleeves and shoulders. The usual decoration of beads
about the neck, and in the hair, and ears, were preserved,
and one warrior only was painted with vermillion. The hair
of several was matted into flat braids with red clay, and one
individual had seven or eight pieces of the pearl shell, so
highly valued by these Indians, suspended from his ears. In
every particular of form and feature, they were undistin-
guishable from the Kiawas, Kaskaias, and Arrapahoes. Much
attention was devoted to the wounded, who were each accommodated with a horse, of which animals eight had been
fortunately retained. These objects of sympathy, were assisted in alighting from their horses with great tenderness, particularly one of them, who was shot through the body. Another of them, who was one of the two mounted spies that
first approached us, had lost his brother in the late battle,
and to prove the sincerity of his grief for his loss, he had
cut more than one hundred parallel transverse lines on his
arms and thighs, of the length of from three to four inches,
deep enough to draw blood, and so close to each other, that
the width of the finger could not be interposed between any
two of them.

They were armed with the bow and arrow, lance and
shield, and thirteen guns, but by far the greatest number
carried lances.

They begged stoutly for various articles, particularly clothing, and it was found necessary to separate from them a few

small party of Otoes that he led. And the narration of his adventures satisfactorily proved, that it was he and his party, that reduced the Ietan war
party to the condition, in which they presented themselves to us.

feet, into a distinct body, in order to be prepared to act together in case of necessity. One of us, however, occupied with the appearance of these Indians, still remained amongst them, until one of the Indians attempted to seize his gun, when a slight scuffle ensued, which terminated by violently wresting the piece from the grasp of the Indian, and warily retreating from the midst of them.

All being seated, the pipe was passed round to a few principal persons, who sat directly in front of us. Some presents were likewise laid before the partizan, consisting of a blanket, a skin to make mockasins of, a dozen knives, and five twists of tobacco; and though some of them complained aloud, and with a violent shivering gesticulation, of the cold they suffered during the night, such was the state of our stores, both public and private, that it was not thought prudent further to enlarge our bounty.

One of our number, who was earnestly occupied in endeavouring to obtain a few words of their language, but who succeeded in recording but four, heard one of them whilst in conversation with the partizan, terminate a remark with a word or phrase, so exactly similar in sound to the words *how is it*, that he almost involuntarily repeated them aloud. The speaker seemed pleased with this, and believing from the exact similarity of the sounds, that he understood the language, immediately directed his discourse to him, but was answered only by signs, denoting ignorance of the language.

Their words seem less harsh, more harmonious, and easier of acquisition, than those of their neighbours.

Whilst thus occupied, one of the soldiers who were behind us, called our attention to an Indian who had the effrontery to seize the Kaskaia horse by the halter, and as in a former instance, was making a noose to pass over his head. This procedure was pointed out to the partizan, who taking no notice of it, the fellow was ordered in a peremptory tone of voice and unequivocal manner, to desist, which he reluctantly complied with. Thus, this horse is immediately distinguished, and recognised by all the parties we have met with, since he has been with us.

We had remained about an hour with this party, when in consequence of this conduct, of their importunateness, and some incipient symptoms of disorder amongst them, we judged it prudent to leave them, without further delay, in order to avoid a quarrel.

We therefore mounted our horses, notwithstanding the earnest solicitations of these Indians, that we would pass the night with them, probably anticipating another night attack from some unseen enemy. But hardly had we proceeded an hundred yards, when Julien's voice called our attention to the precarious situation in which he was placed. He had been by an accident detained in the rear, and being separated a short distance from the party, he was now entirely surrounded by Indians, who appeared determined to strip him of every thing, and by pulling at his blanket, bridle, &c. they had nearly unhorsed him. Several of us, of course, at this critical juncture, turned our horses to assist him, and a soldier who was nearest, prepared his rifle to begin the onset. Observing our attitude, many of the Indians were in a moment prepared for battle, by placing their arrows across their bows, and a skirmish would, no doubt, have ensued, had not the partizan, observing our determination, and influenced perhaps by gratitude for the presents he had received, called off his men from Julien, and permitted us, without any further molestation, to proceed on our way.

In consequence of the desperate situation of this party, we could not entertain a doubt, that they would attempt to capture our horses during the night, and to appropriate to themselves our personal equipments. We therefore continued our movement until a later hour than usual, and after a day's journey of twenty-two miles, during which we saw but three trees, we encamped in a selected position, and made the best arrangements in our power, to repulse a night attack. The horses were staked as near to each other, and to ourselves as possible, the packs were arranged in a semi-circular line of defence, and each man reposed on his private baggage; the guard was doubled, and we remained wakeful during the night. No alarm however occurred, and on the following morning we set out early. Our way led over an extensive bottom, from three to twelve miles in breadth, producing a luxuriant growth of grasses now glittering with drops of collected dew. Crossed a creek which is destitute of timber as far as the eye can trace its course. The depth of the water being to all appearance considerable, it became necessary to seek a fording place, which was found about a mile above its confluence. It was here knee-deep, flowing with a moderate current over a bed of sand and gravel, the surface of the water being depressed only about four feet below the general level. About an hundred yards beyond its confluence, we observed a canal of water backed up from the river, which from a little distance, gave a double appearance to the creek. We remained here until a large elk, which had been shot, was cut up and the meat packed upon the horses.

At our mid-day resting place were a few trees and some elevated sand hills, but as the situation was not an eligible one for the protection of the horses from Indian depredation, we moved a few miles further, and encamped as usual on the bank of the river. The day had been very sultry, with an extreme temperature of 95 degrees, and the evening was accompanied by a display of lightning in the north-western horizon.

The bisons are yet numerous, and the white wolves also abundant; packs of the latter are still heard to howl about our camp in the night, responding to the harsh bellowing or grunting of the bulls. Our dogs, that formerly took part in this wild and savage concert, by barking fiercely in return, no longer rouse us from our sleep by noticing it.

14th. A slight dew had fallen. The wind was S. S. E. nearly calm, and our morning's journey was arduous, in consequence of the great heat of the atmosphere. Our dogs, these two or three days past, had evidently followed us with difficulty. Cæsar, a fine mastiff and the larger of the two, this morning trotted heavily forward and threw himself down directly before the first horse in the line: the rider turned his horse aside, to avoid doing injury to the dog, but had he noticed the urgency of this eloquent appeal of the animal for a halt, it would not have passed unregarded. The dog, finding this attempt to draw attention to his sufferings unavailing, threw himself successively before two or three other horses, but still failed to excite the attention he solicited, until a soldier in the rear observed that his respiration was excessively laborious, and his tongue to a great length depended from his widely extended mouth. He therefore took the dog upon his horse before him, intending to bathe him, in the river, which, however, being at the distance of a half mile, the poor exhausted animal expired in his arms, before he reached it. To travellers, in such a country, any domesticated animal, however abject, becomes an acceptable companion, and our dogs, besides their real usefulness as guards at night, drew our attention in various ways during the day, and became gradually so endeared to us, that the loss of Cæsar was felt as a real evil.

The afternoon continued sultry, the extreme heat being 97 degrees. Towards evening, a brisk northeast wind appeared to proceed from a nimbus which was pouring rain in that direction, and produced so instantaneous and great a change in the atmospheric temperature, that we were obliged to button up to the chin; but it revived and refreshed us all. As we were now approaching a well wooded creek, we hoped soon to assuage our impatient thirst; but great was the mortification, upon arriving at the naked bank, to see a dry bed of gravel of at least fifty yards in breadth. Crossing this inhospitable tract, which appears to be occasionally deluged with water, with the intention of passing down the opposite bank of the river, we were agreeably surprised to discover a fine limpid stream of cool water, meandering through a dense growth of trees and bushes, which had before concealed it from view. Here we remarked the Honey locust [Gleditsia *triacanthus*] and Button wood,] Platanus *occidentalis*,] though the principal growth is Cotton-wood, Elm, and Ash.

This stream of water, we believe, is known to a few hunters, who have had an opportunity to visit it, by the name of Little Arkansa.

The distance of the day's journey was twenty-three miles, during which but a single prairie-dog village was seen, and proved to be the last one that occurred on the expedition. Partridges and prairie fowls were numerous.

15th. Much lightning occurred during the night, pervading the eastern heavens, nearly from north to south. At the distance of a mile from last night's encampment we crossed a wooded ravine, and, further on, a small creek, when upon looking back on our right, we saw the appearance of an Indian village, situate near the confluence of the Little Arkansa with the river. Inspired with hope we turned towards the spot, but on arriving there, it proved to be a large hunting camp, which had probably been occupied during the preceding season. It exhibited a more permanent aspect than three others that occurred on our route of the three past days; much bark covered the boweries, and a few pumpkins, watermelons, and some maize, the seeds of which had fallen from unknown hands, were fortuitously growing as well within as without the rude but frail tenements. Of the maize we collected enough to furnish out a very slight but extremely grateful repast, and the watermelons were eaten in their unripe state.

Resuming our ride we crossed three branches of a creek, in one of which two of the horses entered in a part not fordable, and as the banks were steep and miry, it was with much exertion and delay that they were recovered. Oak and Walnut trees abound upon this creek, besides, Elm, Ash, and Locust. A kingfisher [Alcedo *alcyon*] was also seen.

The extreme heat was rather more intense than that of the preceding day, the mercurial column standing for a time at 97½ degrees.

The bluffs hitherto more or less remote from the bed of the river, now approached it so closely, as to render it necessary to pursue our course over them. On ascending upon the elevated prairie, we observed that it had assumed a different appearance, in point of fertility, from that which we had been familiar with, nearer to the mountains. And although the soil is not yet entirely concealed from the view by its produce, yet the grass is from six inches to one foot in height.

But five bisons were seen to-day, a privation which communicates a solitary air to this region, when compared with the teeming plains over which we have passed, and of which these animals formed the chief feature.

Our distance this day on a straight line, may be estimated at fourteen and a quarter miles, though the actual travelled distance was much more considerable.

During the space of about one month, our only regular food, besides meat, has been coarsely ground parched maize meal, of which a ration of one gill per day, was shared to each individual. This quantity was thrown into common stock and boiled with the meat, into a kind of soup. This meal is nutricious, portable, not subject to spoil by keeping a reasonable length of time, and is probably to be preferred as a substitute for bread, to other succedanea by travellers in an uncivilized country. Our store of meal, however, was now exhausted, and we were obliged to resort to a small

quantity of mouldy crumbs of biscuit, which had been treasured up for time of need.

At night almost incessant lightning coruscated in the
north-western horizon.

16th. Several showers of rain with much thunder and vivid
lightning fell during the night; and the early morning continued showery, but the clouds were evidently undergoing the
change from nimbus to cirrostratus, in this instance, the harbingers of a fine day. Several ravines occurred on the morning's journey, containing, in the deeper parts of their bed,
pools of standing water. The first was of considerable size,
with steep banks, and thickly wooded as far up its course as
the view extended. The trees were principally oak, some
walnut, elm, ash, mulberry, button-wood, cotton-wood and
willow.

A horse, presented by the Kiawa chief, could not be prevailed upon to traverse this occasional water course; he evaded the attempts of several men to urge him forward, and
after being thus fruitlessly detained a considerable time, the
animal was shot.

If he had been abandoned, he must have perished for want
of water, having been accidentally deprived of sight, and more
certainly, as that fluid, so indispensable for the support of
animal life, was here of difficult access.

At the ravine, which served as a halting place during the
mid-day heats, we first observed the plant familiarly known
in the settlements, by the name of Poke, (Phytolacca *decandra*.) reclining over the bank with its fecundity in the midst
of a crowded assemblage of bushes, and partially shading a
limpid pool, that mantled a rocky bed below. A large species of mushroom, (Lycoperdon,) was not uncommon, nearly
equal in size to a man's head.

We have now passed the boundary of the summer bison
range, and the wolves, those invariable attendants on that
animal, are now but rarely seen. The antelopes also have

disappeared. The river banks, as well as those of creeks, and some ravines, from near the little Arkansa, are pretty well wooded, with but few interruptions. In many parts the growth is dense, but always, as yet, strictly limited to skirting the water courses.

During the afternoon, we crossed numerous ravines, some of which, judging by the infallible indications of dried grass, and floated wood lodged on high in the croches of the trees, pour down, at certain seasons, large volumes of water, from the prairies into the river.

Near our evening encampment, but on the opposite side of the river, appeared the entrance of a large creek, of the width of ninety or a hundred yards, and of considerable depth; it seems to be well wooded, and its course is nearly parallel to the river for a great distance, before it discharges into it. This stream is called Red Fork; its waters are turbid, opake, and red; great numbers of fresh water tortoises, closely allied to the Testudo *geographica* of Le Sueur, inhabited the basin formed by the entrance of this stream. Immediately below its junction, the bluffs on that side are washed by the stream of the river.

The bottom land on the left bank is still confined to a narrow strip.

The sun having been, during the chief part of the day, obscured by an interrupted sheet of cirrostratus, and a brisk northeast wind prevailing, rendered the day temperate and agreeable. Travelled distance nineteen and a half miles.

Having been entirely unsuccessful in hunting since the 13th instant, we remained in our position during the morning of the succeeding day, and sent out four hunters to procure fresh meat; but, towards noon, they all returned with but three turkeys, of which two were young; they saw no deer, but much elk sign.

At two o'clock, proceeded onward, upon a slightly undulated prairie, over which the eye roves to a great distance without impediment. Indeed, the surface of the country which extends along the upper portions of the Platte and Arkansa rivers, is generally less undulated than that on either side of the Missouri.

The ravines, which intersected our path were not so extensive or profound as those of yesterday, and, in one of them, we observed the common elder (Sambucus).

Should military possession ever be taken of this elevated country, eligible positions might readily be selected for military posts, at several different points below the Little Arkansa, where the bluffs almost impend over the river. Such a position was occupied by our evening encampment. This bluff is naked, of a gently rounded surface, presenting a high, rugged, and inaccessible front upon the river, which it commands to a considerable distance, in both directions. An adequate supply of wood, for fuel and architectural purposes, is afforded by a ravine which flanks its lower side, and by other points.

Two fawns were killed during this afternoon's journey of twelve miles, and a black bear was seen. The bitter-apple vine (Cucumis,) occurred now but rarely.

18th. The inequality of the surface increases as we proceed, the undulations being now much more abrupt and considerable, belted near their summits with a rocky stratum, and assuming much the same character with those spoken of in the account of our expedition to the Konza village. This stratum, which is a gray and ferruginous sandstone, contains petrifactions of marine shells, so completely assimilated with the matrix, in which they repose, and decomposing so entirely simultaneously with it, when exposed to atmospheric action, that even their generic characters cannot be recognized. Amongst other appearances, however, we observed a bivalve, which seemed to differ from Terebratula and its congeners.

At the distance of eleven miles, we crossed a small river,

flowing with a very gentle current over a gravelly bed, with a breadth of fifty or sixty yards, and an extreme depth of three feet. It has been named Stinking Fork. Its western bottom is of very considerable width, well-wooded with the beforementioned description of trees, in addition to which the hackberry (Celtis) here first appears, together with a crowded undergrowth of pea vines, nettles, and rank weeds, which obstruct the passage of the traveller. The eastern bank, upon which our noonday encampment was established, was high, rocky and precipitous, requiring considerable exertion to surmount it.

Here the organic reliquiæ are somewhat more distinct, than those which we examined on the opposite side of this subsidiary river. They are referrible to those generally extinct genera, that inhabited the great depths of the primeval ocean. Amongst them we recognized a smooth species of *Anomia*, of the length of half an inch, a species of *Terebratula*, an *Encrinus*, and numerous insulated spines of a Linnæan *Echinus?*

At two o'clock, pursued our journey under an extreme heat of 92 degrees, which was hardly mitigated by the gentle fanning of a slight S. E. breeze. The appearance of the country had now undergone a somewhat abrupt change. Low scrubby oaks, the prevailing trees no longer exclusively restricted, as we have hitherto observed them, to the mere margin of a water course, now were seen extending, in little clusters or oases, in the low grounds. In the ravines, which are numerous, profound, abrupt, and rocky, we observed the hickory (Caria of Nuttall.), which had not before occured since our departure from the forests of the Missouri.

The bluffs are steep and stony, rendering the journey much more laborious to our horses, that were almost exhausted by traversing a plain country, and their hoofs already very much worn by constant friction with the grass, will, we fear, be splintered and broken, by the numerous loose and angular stones which they cannot avoid. Near the summits of some of these bluffs, the stratum of rock assumes an appearance of such remarkable regularity as to resemble an artificial wall, constructed for the support of the superincumbent soil, and remind us of the extraordinary similar products of Chinese industry, mentioned by Barrow, intended for the acquisition of horizontal garden spaces on the sides of hills and mountains.

At the distance of eight miles from the small river before mentioned, we encamped for the night, on the east side of a creek which we call Little Verdigris.

It is about 40 yards in breadth, and not so deep as the Little Neosho; its bed is gravelly, but the foot of each bank is so miry, that we experienced some difficulty in crossing. There is but a slight skirting of forest, which denotes to the distant spectator the locality of this creek.

One of the hunters returned with the information, of his having discovered a small field of maize, occupying a fertile spot at no great distance from the camp; it exhibited proofs of having been lately visited by the cultivators; a circumstance which leads us to believe that an ascending column of smoke seen at a distance this afternoon, proceeded from an encampment of Indians, whom, if not a war party, we should now rejoice to meet. We took the liberty, agreeably to the custom of the Indians, of procuring a mess of the corn, and some small but nearly ripe watermelons, that were also found growing there, intending to recompense the Osages for them, to whom we supposed them to belong.

During the night we were visited by a slight shower of rain from the southwest, accompanied by distant thunder.

CHAPTER XIII.

Indian hunting encampment—Brackish water—The party pressed by hunger—Forked tailed flycatcher—An elevated, almost mountainous range of country—Desertion of three men —Red water.

August 19th. Several small cornfields were seen this morning along the creek. At a short distance from our place of encampment, we passed an Indian camp, that had a more permanent aspect than any we had before seen near this river. The boweries were more completely covered, and a greater proportion of bark was used in the construction of them. They are between sixty and seventy in number.

Well worn traces or paths lead in various directions from this spot, and the vicinity of the cornfields induces the belief that it is occasionally occupied by a tribe of Indians, for the purposes of cultivation as well as of hunting.

The increasing quantity of forest, partially obscuring the course of the river, renders it now no easy task to trace its inflexions.

After proceeding twelve miles, over a rugged country, at present destitute of water, we were rejoiced to find at our dining place, a puddle of stagnant rain water, which had been protected from the action of the sun, by the elevated and almost impending bank of the ravine, in which it was situate, and which, though " mantled o'er with green," was yet cool and grateful to our pressing thirst.

We left our cool and shady retreat, and again betook ourselves to the prairies, under a temperature of 96°. Our remaining dog, *Buck*, had been, since the regretted death of his companion, treated with all the kindness and attention due to an humble friend. He was very frequently accommodated with a ride on horseback before one of the men when he betrayed unusual exhaustion. But, notwithstanding all such attention, for which he seemed touched with feelings of gratitude, he experienced Cæsar's fate and was necessarily abandoned.

The evening camp was pitched upon a luxuriant grassy plain of the margin of the river. On tasting the water it was perceived to be slightly saline, though the proportion of that condiment was not so considerable as to render it unpleasant to the palate. This saline intermixture is, no doubt, due to the Red Fork, inasmuch as the river, above the entrance of that stream, appeared entirely destitute of saline contamination, and no stream enters on this side in which the slightest apparent degree of brackishness is to be detected by the taste.

The cotton tree is less numerous in this vicinity, than we have seen it higher up the river, and being intermixed with other trees, forms but an insignificant feature of the forest.

20th. Heavy rain, accompanied with much thunder and lightning, commenced early in the night, and continued until daylight this morning. Hunters, who had been sent out, detained us until nine o'clock, when they returned unsuccessful; in consequence of which, and of our having made a sparing meal last evening, on a turkey that had been shot, we were obliged to depart fasting on our way.

The ravines were muddy, and their banks slippery in consequence of the rain; we had, however, the good fortune to fall upon an Indian trace, which complied with our proper direction, and which indicated the best points at which these gullies might be passed. In its course it conducted us to a creek which was pouring down a torrent of water. Here was an encampment that had obviously been occupied within a day or two, there being fresh rinds of watermellons strewed about it.

One of the party, on attempting to cross this creek, was thrown into the water, in consequence of his horse having plunged suddenly beyond his depth; he, however, avoided being carried down with the rapid current by seizing the depending bough of a tree; the horse also was fortunately saved. By taking a different direction we all passed over without further casualty. But we were unable to trace any farther the party that we thus ascertained to have so recently preceded us, their footsteps being here entirely obliterated by the rain.

At the distance of sixteen miles, we encamped at an early hour on the bank of the river, and sent out hunters, who, however, after examining the vicinity, returned unsuccessful. Our three meals were, therefore, again, by stern necessity, reduced to a single frugal one, and our table, the soil, was set with a few mouldy biscuit crumbs boiled in a large quantity of water, with the nutricious addition of some grease.

Julien, who had been despatched for the peace flag, which was casually left at a ravine, to our great satisfaction returned with a skunk, or pole-cat, that he had fortunately killed. This we determined to preserve for a feast to-morrow.

21st. One of our horses strayed away last night, and could not now be found; we, therefore, set out without him, and as usual without breakfasting. The Indian trace was again discovered, and pursued about nine miles to the dining place at noon. Here we were obliged to have recourse for food to a little treasured store of dried bison meat, which when all issued, amounted to the pittance of two ounces per man; this added to the *soup maigre* of the skunk, and a half pint of the crumbs of bread, afforded a tolerably good though far from abundant meal.

Proceeded on under an extreme atmospheric temperature of ninety degrees. Several deer were seen, but they proved to be so shy, that our hunters, perhaps through over eagerness, did not succeed in approaching them within gun-

shot. After accomplishing a distance of ten miles we pitched our camp on the river bank. Here the stream turns rather
abruptly to the east, after having preserved a southerly and
south of west direction for a considerable distance. A copious stream of water, called Neshetongo, or Grand Saline, flows into the river at this point, nearly opposite to our
camp.

Supped on a few bread crumbs boiled in water. A black
wolf, the first seen since our departure from the Missouri,
made his appearance in the distance.

22nd. Three of the horses having strayed, detained us
until eight o'clock, when a fall of rain commenced, which
continued during the morning, and wet us thoroughly to the
skin. A few hostile Indians, aware of our condition, might,
perhaps, have disappointed our hopes of a safe return to the
settlements, inasmuch as the rain had rendered our arms
and ammunition completely unfit for use, and left us defenceless.

A note, like that of the prairie dog, for a moment induced
the belief that a village of the marmot was near; but we were
soon undeceived by the appearance of the beautiful Tyrannus *forficatus* in full pursuit of a crow. Not at first view
recognizing the bird, the fine, elongated tail plumes, occasionally diverging in a furcate manner and again closing
together to give direction to the aerial evolutions of the bird,
seemed like the extraneous processes of dried grass, or twigs
of a tree, adventitiously attached to the tail, and influenced
by currents of wind. The feathered warrior flew forward to
a tree, from whence at our too near approach he descended
to the earth at a little distance, continuing at intervals his
chirping note. This bird seems to be rather rare in this
region, and as the very powder within the barrels of our
guns was wet, we were obliged to content ourselves with
only a distant view of the bird.

The river margin, on which we held our course, has

narrow and fertile, supporting a tolerably thick growth of mossy cup oaks, with walnut, cotton-wood, elm, and much underwood, through which it is sometimes rather difficult to force a passage. The river is now more serpentine in its course, than it was remarked to be nearer the mountains; but it is here wide, and still thickly studded with sand bars.

One of the hunters rescued the body of a small fawn from the wolves, that had killed and embowelled it. This afforded us all a good dinner; and as we had, in the morning, drawn upon our almost exhausted store of sweet corn for a gill to each man, as a breakfast, we are to-day comparatively well fed.

Near our evening encampment were the remains of a large Indian hunting camp.

Our distance to-day nineteen miles.

On the following day we set out again fasting, and pursued our journey over a beautiful, open, level bottom. The bluffs on our left, of but moderate height, were partially clothed with oaks, and the river on the right skirted with the cotton tree. But a single ravine crossed our morning route. At eleven o'clock the mercury in the thermometer indicated 93 degrees.

At the distance of about two miles from our resting place of noon, we again halted, and pitched the tents in anticipation of a violent storm, as a nimbus of an unusually menacing aspect, was imposingly announced by wind and thunder, and seemed rapidly approaching from the south. In order to make amends for this delay, the hunters were sent out to endeavour to procure some food. But as the storm passed round, they were soon recalled, bringing with them the seasonable supply of four turkeys. On the subsequent part of the day we passed over a small stream, which we call Bitter-apple creek, with but a slow moving current, of the width of about ten yards, and three feet deep. Its bed was so muddy, that two of the pack-horses were mired, but were finally brought safely out. We then ascended into the prairie, where after labouring over an almost continual succession of ravines, we passed down to the river bank, and encamped for the night, having travelled about 20 miles. Numerous deer were seen to-day, but they were very shy.

The last Bitter-apple vine that occurred on the expedition was seen to-day. We were once again saluted by the notes of the Blue jay, and the Pine warbler, (Sylvia *pinus*) also occurred.

24th. As the high prairies offered almost continually a succession of steep and rugged ravines, which called for too much exertion from our horses to pass them, it was determined to endeavour to force our way through the undergrowth of the bottom. This we found to be now so intricate, that in many places it was really difficult to force a passage through the intertwined briars, and climbing plants. Our progress was however, at length altogether interrupted by a deep and miry slough of the river, over which no ford could be found. Fortunately, however, the sandy bed of the river itself offered a sufficiently firm footing to enable us to pass round the obstacle. Tired of the brambles, we again sought the prairie, and ascending an elevated hill, enjoyed a fine view of the river in its meanders, to a great distance, but the place of destination, Belle Point, which we now all anxiously looked out for, was not yet in sight.

A journey of 9 3·4 miles brought us to a large stream of clear water, but hardly perceptible current, passing over a bed of rock and mud; the banks were steep and high, and afforded us a very pleasant resting place during the presence of the mid-day heats. A flock of paroquets flew over our heads, uttering their loud note, with their usual loquacity. The kingfisher was flying from one withered support to another over the surface of the creek, and occasionally darting into the water in pursuit of some little scaly victim; and a large white crane, (Ardea *egretta*, Wilson,) stalked, with slow and measured strides, in the shallows of the creek. A Glass snake, (Ophisaurus *ventralis*) approached us, and was captured.

In the afternoon, small cumulus clouds arose in the horizon, and we again put forward, under a temperature of 95 degrees. Three miles farther, a large ravine occurred, containing much water in the deeper parts of its bed, but dry at intervals; it is wooded as far as we can trace it with the eye, and in the season of floods it must discharge a large volume of water at its confluence, which is distant about five miles from the creek crossed this morning.

We passed by several singular, natural elevations, with conical summits, and halted early to hunt, for which purpose four men were sent out, who returned with two turkeys, which furnished a very light supper.

25th. Remained encamped, in order to give the hunters an opportunity to procure some game. We had nothing for breakfast or dinner, and as our meals a few days past, have been few and light, we have become impatient under the pressure of hunger; a few fresh water muscles, (Unio) and two or three small fishes, and a tortoise, which had been found in the mud of the ravine, were roasted and eaten, without that essential condiment, salt, of which we had been for some time destitute. The hunters so anxiously looked for, at length returned, bringing but three ducks, (Anas *sponsa*) one of them had shot down three deer, but they all escaped.

As we have no idea of our distance from Belle Point, and know not what extent of country we are doomed to traverse in the state of privation to which we have of late been subjected, we have selected from our miserable horses, an individual to be slaughtered for food, in case of extremity of abstinence, and upon which, although very poor, we cannot forbear to cast an occasional wishful glance.

Bijeau, before he parted from us, urged by his wishes for our safety, drew for our information, a sketch of the country over which we had to pass, as far as he had travelled in that direction, on a former occasion, which sketch was terminated by two large streams, entering the river near to each other, and diverging in the opposite direction. As the remarkable relative course of these two streams as represented by Bijeau, corresponded to sufficient exactness with the representation of the Verdegris and Grand rivers, which terminated the sketch which Major Long drew to depict the country from Belle Point upwards; we believed that by joining the two sketches, we had a complete view of the country before us as far as the settlements. Bijeau's sketch proved to be a pretty faithful transcript of the country as far as the two water courses that we passed on the 18th inst., which, as they terminated his map, we then supposed were of course, the Verdigris and Grand rivers. But not being able to recognise in Major Long's draft one single feature of the region we have since traversed, we finally concluded either that we had not yet arrived at the true Verdigris river, or, that we had passed by our place of destination without perceiving it. In this state of uncertainty it was determined to continue our course with as much speed as the exhausted situation of our horses would permit, with the hope of soon arriving at some settlement where we might obtain the proper direction.

The greatest heat of the day was 97 degrees. Two hunters were this evening sent forwards to encamp, and hunt early in the morning.

Another flock of paroquets were seen to-day.

26th. Penetrated through an intricate bottom of bushes interlaced by vines and briars, the timber chiefly oak. The hunters had procured nothing, but Lieut. Swift had the good fortune to kill a fine buck, and one of the hunters afterwards, a turkey. These were a happy alleviation to us, and at our noon halting place we enjoyed the rare luxury of a full meal. At this position was a large ravine containing much water, of the depth of 2 1-2 feet, and width of twenty or twenty-five yards, but without any visible current; its bed was muddy, and in some places rocky.

The journey of the afternoon was equally intricate with that of the morning; our way led along the fertile but narrow eastern margin of the ravine, or, as it would be called in the settlements of the Arkansa, *bayou;* and immediately on our left ascended the abrupt and rocky ridge of the bluff.

After a fatiguing journey of nineteen miles, we encamped on the river bank, in a fine clear bottom, surrounded semi-circularly by the forest. The plum bushes, which abound in the country through which we have for several days been travelling, are generally killed, probably by conflagration, their black and defoliated branches strongly contrasting with the verdure around them; to day, however, we met with some which had escaped uninjured, and which afforded a few ripe plums.

27th. The river bottom becoming very narrow, obliged us to ascend upon the high grounds, which we found to be little less than mountainous, often rocky and steep, and as usual, intersected by profound ravines. Mr. Swift having succeeded in killing another deer, we halted, after a journey of twelve miles, in order to jerk the meat which we now possessed, and to rest the horses, whose feet were bruised and broken by fragments of rock.

The corporal did not join us until evening. The horse which he had rode became so exceedingly feeble as to be no longer able to support the weight of his rider, who therefore dismounted, and attempted to drive him on before him. In spite of his utmost endeavours the horse proceeded so slowly that the corporal was obliged to abandon him, in order to seek our trail that he had lost on the rocks over which we had passed. Not being able to regain the trail, and supposing we had directed our course towards the river, he wandered along its margin to a considerable distance, until almost exhausted with fatigue and vexation; he at length ascended a high hill that commanded a view of the country around, and had the satisfaction to see a column of smoke rising above the forest at a distance. This sure indication he had pursued until, approaching with much caution, he was overjoyed to ascertain that his beacon was no other than the smoke from our meat drying process. Supposing that the horse would be able to travel after having rested during the night, the corporal was directed to accompany Julien to the spot where he had been left, and to bring him on, in the morning.

We availed ourselves of this leisure time to mend our horse gear, clothes, and mockasins.

In the evening a slight fall of rain took place, accompanied by thunder in the north east, which at night became heavy and loud.

28th. The horse that gave out yesterday was brought in, together with two others that had strayed, and for which we were hunting. We were now traversing an elevated and uneven ridge of country, which at many points may be safely estimated at five hundred feet above the surface of the river, and wooded to a great distance from that stream.

In the afternoon having descended to the river, we again laboured through the difficulties of dense underwood which such productive soils usually present, until towards evening, when we had the happiness to see a well worn Indian path, which had been interrupted by the river, and now took a direction towards our left. Wishing to pursue this route as well for the facility of travelling, as with the hope of soon arriving at some Indian town, we readily persuaded ourselves that it deviated from the course we were pursuing, only in compliance with the inequalities of the country. With little hesitation, therefore, we struck into the path, and night gathered around us before we threw ourselves, supperless, upon the ground to repose, after a fatiguing march

of about twenty-one miles, during which the greatest degree
of heat was 92°.

Several small flocks of the common wild-pigeons flew by
us both yesterday and to-day, in a southerly direction.

29th. After some detention in seeking a troublesome horse
that had strayed, we again proceeded forward fasting. This
abstinence, to which we have been several times subjected,
affects one of our party in a singular and uniform manner:
his voice becomes hollow-toned, and his hearing much impaired, a state that is popularly known, as he expresses it,
by the phrase of *the almonds of the ears* being *down*.

We pursued the Indian path a considerable distance this
morning, but as its course continued to diverge from the
river, and we were fearful of deviating too far, we abandoned it, and by an oblique course endeavoured to regain the
river. Here, however, the undergrowth being almost impervious, induced our return to the path, which we again attained near an Indian hunting camp of the past season, situate
in a beautiful prairie, near a gently swelling hill. Here finding a little water in a ravine puddle, we halted, and served
out a stinted ration of dried meat to each individual, instead
of dinner, which so far from gratifying, tended to stimulate
our desire for food.

Having been some days entirely destitute of tobacco in
any shape, those of the party who are habituated to the use
of it experience an additional and formidable privation. One
of the men, who was erroneously supposed to have still a
remnant of the precious stimulant in his possession, was
heard to reply to an earnest and most humble petition for
a small taste of it, or to be allowed to apply his tongue to
it, " every man chaws his own tobacco, and them that has'nt
any, chaws leaves."

During the prevalence of the greatest heat of the day,
which was ninety-four degrees, we again set forward, and
passed over a gently undulated surface supporting an open

forest of young and scrub oak, intermixed with hickory. In the course of a few miles, we arrived at the edge of this forest, which here crowned a much elevated region. It was in fact higher, in proportion to the surface before us, than any other portion of the country we had seen on this side of the mountains. The eye, from this height, roved over a vast distance of prairie, and comparatively plain, country; and it was evident that we had now passed the hilly, and even mountainous, region which we have of late been traversing. A few hills still interrupted the continuity of surface below, more particularly on the right of the landscape towards the river. Not a human being was yet to be perceived, nor a single trait indicative of their present existence. It seemed, for a moment, that our little cavalcade alone was endowed with the vital principle, and that the vegetable world held a solitary and silent dominion. Belle Point still evaded our sight; we might have passed it, or it might still have been very far before us, yet we could no longer struggle through the tangled underwood that inclosed the river, nor pick our passage amongst the loose stones of the bluffs, in order to preserve an uninterrupted view of the bank of the river, upon which that post is established. From this position the path winds rather abruptly downward, and at a little distance on the plain, conducted us through an abandoned Indian hunting camp.

The horse that gave out on Sunday, having been since both packed and rode, this afternoon sunk under his rider, to the ground, and resisted our efforts to induce him to rise. As he appeared to be entirely exhausted we reluctantly abandoned him. He had been a sprightly, handsome, and servicable animal, and was chosen from a considerable number of horses, and presented to Mr. Say, by Major O'Fallon, when at the Pawnee villages.

After a day's journey of twenty-two miles, a favorable situation for an encampment offering timely, at a site which appeared to have been occupied by a tribe of Indians, during the late winter, induced us to pitch the tents, and prepare for the night. Lieutenant Swift, whose dexterity as a marksman had previously relieved us in times of need, now succeeded in killing a turkey for our evening meal.

30th. We pursued the path about ten miles further, with the hope of its soon terminating at some Indian village; but as it continued to diverge too widely from our apparent true course, we once again relinquished it, and turned towards the river, which we expected to regain in the course of a few miles, by tracing down the opposite bank of a large ravine, which now presented itself.

At our resting place of noon the banded rattlesnake, (C. *horridus*,) occurred; and five young turkeys were procured by the hunters.

Resuming our journey, it soon became obvious that the ravine we were tracing did not discharge into the Arkansa, but into some large tributary to that river, and which from an elevated ground we could distinctly see meandering to a great distance on the left. Another Indian path was now discovered, which, by its direction seemed to comply with our proper course. It led us to recross the ravine with its most luxuriant growth of trees, bushes, and weeds. On emerging from this intricate maze, we observed a large column of smoke arising in the southeast, as if from the conflagration of some entire prairie. This occurrence, combined with the effects of a large *burning* in the vicinity of our evening encampment, that seemed very recent, and the appearance of the well-worn pathways, inspired us with a renewed expectation of soon meeting with human beings, and of arriving at some permanent Indian village.

The highest temperature of the day was ninety-five degrees. Our distance this afternoon was ten miles.

31st. We arose early, and on looking at the horses that were staked around the camp, three of the best were missing.

Supposing that they had strayed to a distance, inquiry was made of the corporal respecting them; who answered that three of the men were absent, probably in pursuit of them, and added, that one of those men who chanced to be last on guard, had neglected to awaken him to perform his duty on the morning watch. Forster, a faithful, industrious soldier, and who, in performing the culinary services for the party, had not lately been laboriously occupied, now exclaimed that his knapsack had been robbed; and upon examining our baggage, we were mortified to perceive that it had been overhauled and plundered during the night. But we were utterly astounded to find that our saddlebags, which contained our clothing, Indian presents, and manuscripts, had also been carried off.

This greatest of all privations that could have occurred within the range of possibility, suspended for a time every exertion, and seemed to fill the measure of our trials, difficulties, and dangers.

It was too obvious that the infamous absentees, Nowland, Myers, and Bernard, had deserted during the night, robbing us of our best horses, and of our most important treasures.

We endeavoured in vain to trace them, as a heavy dew had fallen since their departure, and rested upon every spear of grass alike, and we returned from the fruitless search to number over our losses, with a feeling of disconsolateness, verging on despair.

Our entire wardrobe, with the sole exception of the rude clothing on our persons, and our entire private stock of Indian presents, were included in the saddlebags. But their most important contents were all the manuscripts of Mr. Say and Lieutenant Swift completed during the extensive journey from Engineer Cantonment to this place. Those of the former consisted of five books, viz., one book of observations on the manners and habits of the mountain Indians, and their history, so far as it could be obtained from the interpreters; one book of notes on the manners and habits of animals, and descriptions of species; one book containing a journal; two books containing vocabularies of the languages of the mountain Indians; and those of the latter consisted of a topographical journal of the same portion of our expedition. All these being utterly useless to the wretches who now possessed them, were probably thrown away upon the ocean of prairie, and consequently the labour of months was consigned to oblivion, by these uneducated vandals.

Nowland, Myers, and Bernard, though selected, with others, by the officers of Camp Missouri, with the best intentions, for the purpose of accompanying our party, proved worthless, indolent, and pusillanimous from the beginning; and Nowland, we ascertained, was a notorious deserter in two former instances.

This desertion and robbery occurred at a most unfortunate period, inasmuch as we were all much debilitated, and their services consequently the less dispensable on that account, in the attentions necessarily due to the pack-horses, in driving these animals, loading and unloading them, &c.

We resumed our journey, upon our Indian pathway, in silence; and at the distance of sixteen miles we passed through the river forest, here three miles in width, and once again encamped upon the bank which overlooks the Arkansa. No trace of Belle Point, nor any appearance of civilization was yet in view. But we were all immediately struck with the change in the appearance of the water in the river. No longer of that pale clay colour to which we have been accustomed, it has now assumed a reddish hue, hardly unlike that of the blood of the human arteries, and is still perfectly opake from the quantity of an earthy substance of this tint, which it holds in suspension. Its banks and bars are formed from depositions of the same colour. This extraneous pigment has been contributed by some large stream flowing in from the opposite side, and which, in consequence of our late aberrance, we had not seen.

The hunters returned without game, but bringing us a few grapes, and some unripe persimmons, all of which were eaten.

The extreme heat of the day was ninety-five degrees, and in the evening thunder and lightning occurred in the western horizon.

CHAPTER XIV.

The party meet with Osage Indians—Some account of this nation—Manner of taking wild horses.

SEPTEMBER 1st. The hunters, who had been sent out at daylight, returned at 8 o'clock again unsuccessful, but after a journey of about three hours we had an opportunity to appease the cravings of hunger, and halted to regale ourselves on a small fawn that was shot. At three o'clock proceeded on, under the extreme atmospheric temperature of the day of ninety-six degrees, and as the current of air was scarcely perceptible, the day was, as usual, very sultry. We were, at length, very agreeably surprised by hearing an Indian whoop, in our rear, and, on looking back, a mounted Indian was observed upon a rising piece of ground, contemplating our movements. The usual ceremony of displaying our flag and deputing an individual to assure him of the pacific nature of our mission, induced him readily to approach; and after some communication he consented to encamp with us. He informed us that he was the son of Clermont, principal chief of the Osages of the Oaks, or *Osage des Chenes* of the French traders, in whose territories we then were. Their village was at the distance of about fifteen miles, but by far the greater portion of the inhabitants of it were now on their way to this river, for the purpose of hunting. They had heard the reports of the guns of our hunters, and agreeably to their custom had sent out spies, of whom he was one, to ascertain from whom the sound proceeded; that he had fallen upon our trail, and consequently had no difficulty in finding us, and was moreover glad to see us. Indeed his conduct proved that he entertained towards us the most friendly and generous disposition. He was not tardy in ascertaining our wants, nor parsimonious in his attempts to relieve them. He passed his pipe around, a ceremony which signifies just as much, amongst these people, as the drinking to friendship and good fellowship does amongst the lower classes in civilized society; but to us, who had been so long deprived of the use of tobacco, it was an intrinsic gratification. He then laid before us some fine ripe blue plums; and remarking that the small portion of fawn meat, that constituted all our store, was very lean, he said that he would soon bring some more palatable food, and leaving his pipe and tobacco-pouch on the ground, with the request that we would partake freely of both, he disappeared in the forest.

It was dusk when he returned, with a fat buck hanging in pieces from his saddle; he was accompanied by five or six young warriors. These young men had visited the opposite side of the river, where they had discovered a herd of bisons, and as they were hastening back to Clermont with the intelligence, they observed our trail, which they mistook for that of a Pawnee war party, and were exerting their utmost speed homeward when they met with our friendly Indian, who smiled as he informed us of their mistake.

The remnant of our fawn had been cooked, and was partly eaten on their arrival, when they readily accepted our invitation to partake of it. In return for which, when their meat was prepared, the whole was set before us, and they respectfully waited until we were satisfied.

We now ascertained our position with respect to the settlements. We were within about four days' march of Belle Point, and the next large stream we would cross was the Verdigris.

Previously to retiring to rest the Osages performed their vespers, by chanting, in a wild and melancholy tone, a kind of hymn to the Master of Life.

Very remote lightning in the south-eastern horizon.

2nd. Our guests awakened early, and one of them retiring a short distance from his companions, began the well known ceremony common to this nation, of crying aloud with a voice of lamentation, intended probably as an invocation to the departed spirit of a relative or friend.

Messengers were despatched before sunrise to Clermont's camp, to inform that chief of the proximity of a party of white men on this side of the river, and of bisons on the other; and soon afterwards the remainder of our guests, with the exception of one that concluded to remain with us, departed to hunt.

Other Indians, attracted by curiosity, visited us in the course of the day, one of whom informed us that three men, whose appearance corresponded with the description of our deserters, were now at the village, and that the approaching hunting party, being already apprised of their character, Clermont, who was himself with the party, had forthwith despatched an order to the village to have them detained there, until the decision of our chief respecting them should be known.

This most welcome news induced Lieut. Swift and Julien, accompanied by Clermont's brother and two or three of the young warriors who were present, to set out immediately for the village, in order to seize the recreants, and conduct them to camp. Thus we were inspired with the most sanguine expectations not only of retrieving our losses, but also of subjecting the offenders to that punishment which was their due.

In the afternoon we had the company of numerous Indians from the hunting party, and an individual that left our camp early in the morning in pursuit of the bisons on the opposite side of the river, brought a horse-load of very lean meat. Their demeanour was pacific and kind, and they appeared disposed to serve us. They brought a considerable quantity of plums of a blue colour, and exceedingly agreeable taste, which were collected from trees growing in the adjacent forest. Our cook having intimated to one of them our want of salt, he instantly mounted his horse, and after a short absence, returned with a supply. One half of the hunting party was soon afterwards observed fording the river in a long line about a mile below our camp; the other portion we were told would cross the river at some point above the camp to-morrow morning, and would act in concert with the others, so as to surround the herd of bisons that they were now going in pursuit of.

In the evening Mr. Swift returned unsuccessful. When he left us in the morning he directed his course to Clermont's camp, which he found in the prairie, near a small puddle of impure water. He was very cordially and graciously received by the chief, who invited him to partake of some food. He assured Mr. Swift of his regret at being unable to induce any of his young men to pursue our fugitives, who, as he had but then been informed, departed from the village early in the morning. This unwillingness on the part of his young men, arose from their extreme anxiety to hunt the bisons, that were at this time unusually near, an enjoyment which they would on no account relinquish. He likewise regretted that he was at present so circumstanced as to be unable to comply with his wishes, by visiting our camp. "But" said Clermont, " if your chief will visit me at my camp, which will be established near yours in the evening, I will treat him well; I will present him with as much maize and dried meat as he wants; I will moreover furnish him with young men to serve as guides, and a horse or two if he wants them, to aid in the transportation of the baggage." Lieut. Swift assured him that we were much in want of such assistance as he had proffered, and that on our arrival at Belle Point. his generosity should be requited; but the chief declared his indifference to any recompense for such services. Mr.

Swift further learned that the deserters during their short stay at the village, had traded freely for provisions, with the trinkets they found in our saddle bags, and although dressed in our clothing, they appeared to imagine themselves suspected to be not what they seemed.

This idea was, in truth, well founded, for the Indians observing that they retained their guns constantly within their grasp, even when partaking of the hospitality of the different lodges, believed them to have committed some crime or outrage in consequence of which, they regarded themselves as unsafe in any asylum.

As the camp was about to move when Mr. Swift arrived there, he now took his leave to return, but inadvertently deviating from the proper course, he struck the river several miles above our camp. Clermont, meeting with his trail, perceived at once that he had gone astray, and immediately deputed one of his sons to pilot him to our camp.

In the acceptation of these Indians, white man and trader appear to be synonymous, and many of those who visited us, importuned us much to trade for leather, dried meat, pumpkins, both dried and fresh, &c.; in exchange for which, they desired our blankets, and even the clothing from our bodies.

The superiority of the hunting qualifications of the Indians over those of our hunters, was obvious, in an instance which occurred to-day. The corporal went to the forest for the purpose of killing a deer, and it was not long before an Indian who accompanied him pointed out one of those animals in a favorable situation. The corporal fired, but thought he had missed his object. The Osage, however, insisted that the animal was mortally wounded, and advanced forward a very considerable distance, where our hunter could see nothing of the usual sign of blood, or trodden grass, and found the victim dead upon the ground. One of the party, on an another occasion, saw an Osage shoot at a deer running, and wound him, another Indian, at a short distance further, fired at the same deer, and brought him down, both, of course, with single ball.

The extreme heat of the day was 95 degrees.

3rd. Our chief, who, upon the invitation of Clermont visited the Indian camp, accompanied by Julien and Clermont's son, returned this morning with two other sons of that chief, and a handsome young squaw, wife of one of them. His reception was not equal to his anticipations; Clermont, however, and one of his sons each presented a skin of maize, but that chief could not realize the almost splendid offers he had made us of guides and horses.

Word was brought to Clermont, that the information received yesterday of our deserters having departed from the village was incorrect, and that they still remained there. This induced at once, the offer of every thing they were in possession of, with the exception of the manuscripts alone, to any persons who should bring them to our camp. With this liberal offer, Clermont himself, accompanied by Julien, set out for the village to arrest them, but on their way, a messenger whom they met, assured them, that they had actually and finally departed this morning. Thus all our hopes of recovering our lost property vanished.

The stature of the Osages that fell under our observation was by no means superior to that of the Missouri Indians, and in very many instances, their form exhibited a beautiful symmetry. They do not seem to differ in point of features or colour from the Indians just mentioned. But the custom seems to be the more general in this nation of shaving the head, so as to leave only a scalp on the back part and above, which is, as usual, ornamented with silver plates, broaches, and feathers.

Their dresses and decorations are very similar to those of the Omawhaws, Otoes, and Konzas, but from their proximity to the settlements, they are furnished with a greater proportion of manufactured articles from the whites.

Their government, so far as we could ascertain, was of the same description with that of the other nations, and their manners, though perhaps less fierce and warlike, seem to be, with the exception of their vociferous matins, not very essentially distinct.

They have the usual armature of the bow and arrow, tomahawk, war-club, and scalping knife, but a large proportion of them have fusees, and we saw but very few who bore the lance and shield. They are freely branded by the Missouri Indians with the epithet of cowards. They are at present in amity with the Sauks and Foxes, and their friendship with the Konzas, with whom they freely intermarry, seems to have been uninterrupted since the expedition of Lieut. Pike.

The horses belonging to the Osages are by much the best we have seen amongst the Indian nations, and they are kept in the best order. The Indians generally of this country, appear to be excellent connoisseurs of horses, and to perceive any defects in them with a remarkable readiness. One of Clermont's sons possessed a very fine horse, for which the Kaskaia horse was offered, but the exchange was refused.

Horses are the object of a particular hunt to the Osages. For the purpose of obtaining these animals, which in their wild state preserve all their fleetness, they go in a large party to the country of the Red, or Canadian river, where these animals are to be found in considerable numbers. When they discover a gang of horses they distribute themselves into three parties, two of which station themselves at different and proper distances on the route, which, by previous experience, they know the horses will most probably take, when endeavouring to escape. This arrangement being completed, the first party commences the pursuit in the direction of their colleagues, at whose position they at length arrive.

The second party then continues the chase with fresh horses, and pursues the fugitives to the third party, which generally succeeds in so far running them down as to noose and capture a considerable number.

The name of this nation, agreeably to their own pronunciation, is Waw-sash-e; but our border inhabitants speak of them under the names of *Huz-zaws* and *O-saw-ses*, as well as Osages. The word *Wawsashe* of three syllables has been corrupted by the French traders into *Osage*, and though the spelling of the latter has been retained by the Americans, we have still further swerved from the original, by pronouncing the word agreeably to the genius of our language.

The lodges or huts of their villages are yet covered with the bark of trees, but it is probable that they will adopt the more permanent and preferable architecture of dirt lodges, used by most of the Missouri nations.

As we proceeded to load our horses, at ten o'clock, in order to continue our journey, we perceived that several small articles, of no great value, had been pilfered from us, by our visitors. These are the only losses we have sustained from Indian theft during this protracted journey. During the stay of our party at Fort Osage, last season, Mr. Sibley, Indian factor at that place, politely furnished us with the following information respecting the Osages, being the copy of a report made by him to government in the late war with Great Britain. We present it to the reader in Mr. Sibley's own words:

" 1. The Chaneers, or band of the Arkansa—six hundred men—town situated near the mouth of the Verdigris, or branch of the Arkansa—Clermont principal chief.

" 2. The Great Osages, or White Hair's band—four hundred men—town situated near the head of the Osage River—Che-sho-hun-ga principal chief.

" 3. The Little Osages—two hundred and fifty men—town situated on the Ne-ozho, a branch of the Arkansa—Ne-zu-rus-nee principal chief.

" These tribes are at war with all their neighbours, except the Konzas, and a part of the Sauks and Foxes. With the Konzas they are, and long have been, on the most intimate and friendly terms. With the Sauks and Foxes they are at present barely at peace. All their chiefs, except Clermont, are very weak, and unpopular. Many of their great war captains are in opposition to their chief, and have powerful influence in their respective tribes; of these are, " The Duck," " Big Wolf," and " John Le Foe" of the Great Osage, " Sansoreille," " Big Soldier," and " The Soldier of the Oak" of the little Osage. Their councils are very much distracted by the jealousies and intrigues of the principal warriors, and for want of energy and decision in the chiefs. When I left them last spring, my impressions were, that the Osages were generally disposed to be at peace with us, but that they were very much dissatisfied and displeased, and losing their former unbounded confidence in us, in consequence of what they alleged to be a failure on the part of the United States to fulfil the treaty existing between them and the United States. My opportunities for observation and inquiry concerning the temper and disposition of those Indians were very good, and were not neglected; and my acquaintance with the Osages being very general, extending almost to every individual, and of long standing, upwards of eight years, enables me to speak confidently of them.

"In the year 1804 the President of the United States gave his promise to a number of Osage chiefs, then on a visit at Washington, to establish for them a trading house, on the plan authorised by a law of congress in 1806. The President repeated the same promise to another deputation of Osage chiefs then here. In 1808 the president ordered the establishment to be made, and accordingly, in October of that year, it *was* made.

" So far this was a gratuitous act of the government, but in the following month it assumed a very different character.

On the 8th of November, 1808, Peter Chouteau, the United States' agent for the Osages, arrived at Fort Clark. On the 10th he assembled the chiefs and warriors of the Great and Little Osages in council, and proceeded to state to them the substance of a treaty, which, he said, Governor Lewis had deputed him to offer the Osages, and to execute with them. Having briefly explained to them the purport of the treaty, he addressed them to this effect, in my hearing, and very nearly in the following words: " You have heard this treaty explained to you. Those who now come forward and sign it, shall be considered the friends of the United States, and treated accordingly. Those who refuse to come forward and sign it shall be considered enemies of the United States, and treated accordingly." The Osages replied in substance, " that if their great American father wanted a part of their land he must have it, that he was strong and powerful, they were poor and pitiful; what could they do? he had demanded their land and had thought proper to offer them something in return for it. They had no choice, they must either sign the treaty, or be declared the enemies of the United States."

" The treaty was accordingly signed on the same day, and so much were the Osages awed by the threat of Mr. Chouteau, that a very unusual number of them touched the pen, many of whom knew no more the purport of the act than if they had been an hundred miles off; and I here assert it to be a fact, that to this day the treaty is not fairly understood by a single Osage.

" Thus the trading house, which had been established gratuitously, in conformity with the earnest solicitations of the Osage chiefs, and repeated promises of the President, was made a part of the price of the lands acquired under that treaty by the United States. In April 1810 this treaty was ratified and confirmed by the senate, and was duly proclaimed by the President of the United States to be a law of the land. The Osages complained of the delay which took place between its signature, from which time it was binding on them, and the payment of the first and second annuities, which were not made till September 1811. The trading house was kept up, and well supplied, until early in June 1813, at which time the establishment was, by order, broken up, and has been discontinued ever since, contrary to the expectations, and entirely against the consent of the Osages, who considered the trading house as the only benefit they had acquired by the treaty.

" No complaints have been made against the Osages, from the signature of the treaty till after the trading house and garrison were withdrawn from Fort Clark; since that time a party of the Great Osages murdered one of our citizens; and the murderers were promptly demanded, agreeably to the treaty, by Governor Clark, and would have been surrendered, if Mr. Chouteau, who was sent after them, had performed his duty. Several other important things are promised the Osages in the treaty; a mill; ploughs, and other implements of husbandry; a blacksmith to mend their guns, ploughs, &c.; and block houses, to defend their towns. In short they were induced to believe, that an establishment was to be permanently kept up near their towns, which should afford them a ready market at all times for their furs and pelts, encourage and assist them in acquiring habits of civilization, and protect them from their surrounding enemies. A mill and one block house have been built at an enormous expense; and a blacksmith has been fixed; all at the town of the Great Osages. The mill I believe is of some use to those few who are near it. The blacksmith, although expensive to government, is not of the smallest service. The block house is only useful to the traders, who sometimes go to that village.

" All of them would be extremely useful, if properly placed, and taken care of, but detached as they are from the agency, and unconnected with an establishment such as was originally contemplated at Fort Clark, they are at present of very little use.

" These facts concerning the Osage treaty, are stated merely to show that we have not dealt justly with the Osages, and to infer from them, that unless immediate steps are taken, to recover that confidence and respect which those Indians once had in the United States, the inevitable consequence will be their decided and active hostility against the settlements of the Missouri, and those back of the Lead Mines. British emissaries had repeatedly attempted to engage the Osages in their service, previous to the evacuation of Fort Clark, but without effect. The leading men have often declared to me their determination " never to desert their American father, as long as he was faithful to them." At a time when we were under serious apprehensions of an attack on Fort Clark, the warriors of the Little Osages offered their services to me to defend the post. In less than two months after these declarations and offers of services, Fort Clark was evacuated, and the Osage establishment abandoned, without any notice or apology for so very extraordinary and unnecessary an act. Thus were the Osages left, I may truly say, in the arms of the British agents. How far those agents have succeeded in weaning them from their growing attachment to the United States, I am unable to say; they have had full scope for their arts, and it would be idle to suppose they have not made some progress.

" Of all the Missouri Indians, the Osages were the least accessible to British influence; from their strong attachment to the French, they had acquired a French prejudice against the English, which since my acquaintance with them has rather increased than diminished. Such are the Osages and such our relations and political standing with them.

" The Osages of the Oaks, or Clermont's band were separated from the other bands and fixed in their present situation chiefly, it is said, through the influence of Mr. Chouteau, previously to the cession of the territory to the American government. The monopoly of the Missouri trade having been granted to Mr. Manuel Lisa, by the Spanish authorities, Mr. Chouteau, a rival trader, could no longer traffick with them on the waters, or within a certain distance of the Missouri. He, therefore, managed to separate a considerable portion of the nation from the interest of his rival, and induced them to establish a town near the Arkansa, of the trade of which river he enjoyed a monopoly.

CHAPTER XV.

Verdigris river—Mr. Glen's trading house—New species of lizard—Neosho, or Grand river—Salt works—Large spider—Illinois creek—Ticks—Arrival at Belle Point.

SEPTEMBER 4th. The face of the country exhibited the same appearance as that of yesterday's journey, until we arrived at a dense forest, which we supposed to margin the *Verdigris* river, or Was-su-ja of the Osages. There being no trace to direct us, we were obliged to penetrate the intricate undergrowth as we might, and after a tedious and laborious passage of something more than three miles, we attained, probably by a somewhat circuitous route, the river which we had so long vainly sought. At our crossing place the stream was probably eighty yards wide, and one foot in depth, running with a brisk stream over a rocky bed, though above and below, as far as we examined, the depth of water is much more considerable. This river is more rapid and pellucid than any tributary we have passed on this side of the mountain streams, and during the season of floods its volume is augmented by the tribute of those ravines over which we passed on the 29th and 30th ult. Late in the afternoon we struck the Osage trace leading from their village to the trading establishment, at the confluence of the Verdigris, whither we now directed our course. Our evening encampment was at a small ravine, in which were some plum bushes, bearing fruit yet unripe, of a fine red colour, and without the slightest exaggeration, as closely situate on many of the branches, as onions when tied on ropes of straw for exportation.

Distance 17 3-4 miles. Extreme heat 90 degrees.

5th. At ten o'clock we arrived at Mr. Glen's trading house near the Verdigris, about a mile above its confluence with the Arkansa. We were hospitably received by the interpreter, a Frenchman, who informed us that Mr. Glen was absent on a visit to Belle Point. In reply to our inquiries respecting the best and shortest route to the place of our destination, two Americans who were present, assured us that there was a path the whole distance, so obvious as not to be mistaken, and that they were so much occupied as to be unable to spare any one to pilot us. Unfortunately, however, for our informant, a military cap which was discovered suspended from a beam, betrayed him to be a soldier belonging to the garrison of Belle Point, temporarily employed at this place. When asked by what right he had entered into any other engagements whilst in the service of the United States, he replied, that he had the permission of his officers, but as he could not show a *permit* he was ordered to join our suite forthwith, as a guide, and to assist with the pack horses.

The interpreter informed us, that the distance to the town of the Osages of the Oaks is about fifty-five miles; from thence to the village of the second band of Osages, called the Little Osages, residing near the Neosho, or Grand river, more than sixty miles; thence to the village of the third band, called the Great Osages, resident near the head waters of the Osage river three miles. He assured us that Clermont had then four wives, and thirty-seven children! a number doubtless unprecedented amongst the North American Indians, and which may probably be attributed to this chief by mistake. We also learned that at the distance of twenty-five miles, was a copious salt spring, lately worked with the permission of the Indians, but at present it is abandoned, and the apparatus removed. Mr. Nuttall in his interesting journal of travels in the Arkansa territory has given an excellent account of this saline. It produced agreeably to his statement, under the management of the company, 1 bushel of salt, from 80 gallons of water, and 120 bushels were manufactured in a week.

A beautiful species of lizard, (agama) is occasionally met with in this territory. It runs with great swiftness. The forms of its scales, their arrangement and proportions, considerably resemble those of *Polychrus marmorata*, with the exception of the caudal ones, the series of which are equal, and the scales near the tip of the tail only are mucronate. A band over the shoulders somewhat resembles that of *Stelio querts-paleo.**

In addition to our usual fare served upon the earth, we here enjoyed the luxury of wild honey, and Indian corn or maize bread, spread upon a table, and felt, perhaps, a little of that elation which the possession of a new garment gives to the beaux, when we found ourselves mounted on stools and benches around it.

The Sassafras, (Laurus *sassafras*) occurred this morning, and soon after our departure from the trading house we saw the Cane, (Miegia *macrosperma*) and were soon involved in a dense cane brake. Here we were hardly fanned by a breath of air, and during the prevalence of the extreme heat of the

---

* *Agama collaris*, S. *Scales* of the back, neck, and head beneath, anterior legs, and superior and posterior portions of the posterior legs small, slightly convex, mutic, rounded, or a little oblong, obsoletely arranged in transverse lines; those of the abdomen and breast larger, slightly hexagonal or quadrate, and distinctly arranged in transverse lines; those of the tail rather smaller than the abdominal ones, arranged in bands, mutic, quadrate, towards the tip of the tail oblong, carinated, and acute; front, middle of the head and vertex, and anterior portion of the inferior jaw with scales approaching the size of plates; *colour*, back, with five or six dusky broad bands, alternating with narrow, fulvous bands, which have each a series of yellow or cinereous spots; a few spots are also scattered on the dusky bands: *sides* greenish yellow; *sides of the neck* fulvous, more or less varied with brilliant vermillion red, a deep black band, and another on the shoulder, both obsolete above, and terminating near the anterior legs: *beneath* pale; *posterior thighs* with a series of pores; *eyes* silvery, pupil round, black: *tail* long, tapering: cylindrical.

Length from nose to cloaca, 4 inches. tail 5 2-5 inches.

A specimen is deposited in the Philadelphia Museum.

day, which was 96 degrees, the state of the atmosphere was extremely oppressive. A short ride brought us to the *Neosho*, or *Grand river*, better known to the hunters by the singular designation of the *Six Bulls.*

It enters the Arkansa very near to the confluence of the Verdigris, and at the ripple, which offers us a facility of crossing, is about 80 yards wide, the water clear, above and below, moving with a gentle current, and its bed and shores paved with large pebbles. At the entrance of the opposite forest, our guide, to whose tongue the direct and very obvious path was so familiar, now became bewildered, and after reconnoitring to his heart's content amongst the entangled briars, vines, and nettles, ushered us into a trace which conducted to an old Indian encampment, and terminated there. Further progress was in a great measure intercepted by the cane brake, which, not presenting any path, obliged us to break our passage with much labour. The dusk of the evening found us still pursuing a devious course through a world of vegetation, impenetrable to the eye, vainly seeking a spot upon which an encampment could be fixed; when to our unspeakable joy, and without previous intimation, the prairie of *Bayou Menard* appeared suddenly before us. The timber of these bottoms is large and various. The extreme heat of the day 96 degrees. Distance, eighteen miles.

Our pleasure at first seeing civilized white men was of no ordinary kind; it appeared as though we had already arrived at our own homes and families, in anticipation of Belle Point, which had hitherto seemed the utmost boundary, and terminus of our pilgrimage.

6th. A fine morning; and as on the days of the 1st inst. and 30th ultimo, no dew had fallen. Crossed the ravine at the head of Bayou Menard, and ascended the elevated hills, clothed with small oaks, and arrived at a branch of Green Leaf bayou, about nine o'clock, a distance of eight miles.

A slight shower of rain fell in the afternoon, and during our ride, we first observed the dog wood (*Cornus Florida;*) in the evening we arrived at Mr. Bean's salt works. These are situate on a small creek, which flows into the Illinois, about a mile below, and are at the distance of about seven miles from the Arkansa. Mr. Bean commenced his operations in the spring, and has already a neat farm house on the Illinois, with a considerable stock of cattle, hogs, and poultry, and several acres in Indian corn. Near the springs he has erected a neat log house, and a shed for the furnace, but his kettles, which were purchased of the proprietors of the Neosho establishment, were not yet fixed. He assured us that the water was so far saturated, as not to dissolve any perceptible quantity of a handful of salt that was thrown into it. On the side of a large well which he had sunk to collect the salt water, and perhaps two feet from the surface of the soil, he pointed out the remains of a stratum of charcoal of inconsiderable extent, through which they had penetrated, and which, to a by-stander was a certain proof that these springs had been formerly worked by the Indians. But as no other appearances justified this conclusion, a greater probability seems attached to the idea, that during some former conflagration of the prairies, the charred trunk or branches of a tree were here imbedded. Another agent, however, of sufficient efficacy to operate this carbonization of wood, resides in the sulphuric acid, liberated by the decomposing pyritous rocks, so abundant here.

Whilst waiting with a moderate share of patience, for our evening meal of boiled pumpkins, one of the children brought us a huge, hairy spider, which he carried upon a twig, that he had induced the animal to grasp with its feet. Its magnitude and formidable appearance surprised us. The boy informed us, that he had captured it near the entrance of its burrow, and that the species is by no means rare in this part of the country. Not having any box suitable to contain it, nor any pin sufficiently large to impale it, we substituted a wooden peg, by which it was attached to the inside of a hat. This species so closely resembles, both in form, colour, and magnitude, the gigantic bird-catching spider of South America,* that from a minute survey of this specimen, which is a female, we cannot discover the slightest characteristic distinction. But as an examination of the male comparatively with that of the avicularia, may exhibit distinctive traits, we refrain from deciding positively upon the species.

Distance, twenty-four miles.

7th. The Illinois is called by the Osages, Eng-wah-condah, or Medicine-stone creek. At our fording place, near the saline, it was about sixty yards wide, with clear water, and pebbly shores, like those of the Neosho. We proceeded on through a country wooded with small oaks, interspersed with occasional small prairies, and crossed a deep ravine, called Bayou Viande. These bayous, as they are named in this country, unlike those of the lower portion of the Mississippi river, are large, and often very profound ravines or water courses, which, during the spring season, or after heavy rains, receive the water from the surface of the prairies, and convey it to the river; but in the summer and early autumn, the sources being exhausted, the water subsides in their channels, occupying only the deeper parts of their bed, in the form of stagnant pools, exhaling miasmata to the atmosphere, and rendering their vicinity prejudicial to health.

The extreme temperature of the day was 93 degrees, but it was rather abruptly reduced by a strong wind with thunder and lightning, from the S. E. which brought up a heavy rain, that continued to drench us until the evening, when, after a ride of fourteen miles, we encamped at Bayou Salaison, or meat salting Bayou. At our mid-day refectory, we were much annoyed by great numbers of small ticks, that were excessively abundant amongst the grass, and crawl-

* *Mygale avicularia.*

ed by dozens up our leggins. Wherever they effected a lodgment upon the skin, their numerous punctures would cause an intolerable itching sensation that bid defiance to repose. In the evening, in addition to the needful process of drying our clothing and blankets, we had ample employment in scratching, and picking the pestiferous arachnides from our bodies. On entering the water for relief, the disagreeable sensation seemed to be mitigated for a time, only to be augmented on our return to the atmosphere. Mosquitoes, which were also abundant, were readily expelled from our tents by the smoke of burning wood; but the ticks, otherwise constituted, frustrated our endeavours to obtain the necessary rest and sleep during the night.

These ticks are of two different species, and in common with other species inhabiting different parts of the United States, are distinguished by the name of *seed ticks*, probably on account of their small size, when compared with others of the same genus.

The larger of the two kinds* may be compared, in point of transverse diameter, to the head of a small sized pin, but the other one is so much smaller, as to elude the sight, excepting on minute inspection.

The Cherokee Indians frequently visit this vicinity, on hunting excursions, and our guide informs us, that a hunting party of that nation is at present encamped at the mouth of this Bayou, at the distance of two and a half miles from our camp.

8th. The face of the country presents the same appearance with that we passed over yesterday, offering, in the arrange-

---

* *Ixodes molestus*. S. *Body* reddish-brown, punctured, orbicular, very slightly approaching ovate; *scutus* rounded or subangular, hardly attaining the middle of the body, and with two distant, indented, longitudinal lines; *tergum* with about four dilated black distant radii behind the middle, margin from near the middle of the side with ten or twelve impressed acute, equal, equidistant lines, which do not crenate the edge or upper surface.

Length rather more than one twentieth of an inch.

ment of forest and fertile prairie, many advantageous sites
for plantations, of which one is already established at the
confluence of Big Skin Bayou.

During the afternoon's ride the country was observed to
be more hilly. Soon after the occurrence of the greatest heat
of the day, which was 91 degrees, several showers of rain
fell, accompanied with distant thunder.

On a naked part of the soil, gullied out by the action of
torrents of water, we beheld a hymenopterous or wasp-like
insect (Sphex) triumphantly, but laboriously, dragging the
body of the gigantic spider, its prey, to furnish food to its
future progeny. We cannot but admire the prowess of this
comparatively pigmy victor, and the wonderful influence of
a maternal emotion, which thus impels it to a hazardous
encounter, for the sake of a posterity which it can never
know.

Distance nineteen miles.

9th. Pursued our journey, with every hope of reaching
the place of rendezvous appointed by Major Long, before
noon. Since passing Bayou Viande we have observed the
country, on either side of our path, to be distinguished by
extremely numerous natural elevations of earth, of some considerable degree of regularity. They are of a more or less
oval outline, and their general dimensions may be stated at
one hundred feet long, by from two to five feet in greatest
height. Their existence is doubtless due to the action of
water. Should the rivers Platte and Arkansa be deprived of
their waters, the sand islands of their beds would probably
present a somewhat similar appearance.

An Indian who observed us passing, hallooed to us from
a distance, and expecting some important communication,
we waited some time, until he came up. He proved to be a
Cherokee, dressed much in the manner of the whites, and
not a little infected with the spirit of an interrogator, common, no doubt, to those with whom he has been accustomed

to associate, and therefore probably regarded as a concomitant of civilization. We left him to his own surmises, respecting our object and destination, and soon arrived at the path which strikes off, for the river. After passing a distance of four miles through a cane brake, we arrived at a hut and small farm, belonging to a soldier of the garrison, and were shortly on the strand of the river, with the long-sought Belle Point before us. We were soon ferried over, and were kindly received on the landing by Captain Ballard and Mr. Glen. The former gentleman was at present invested with the command, in consequence of the temporary absence of Major Bradford on a visit to St. Louis. His politeness and attention soon rendered our situation comfortable, after a houseless exposure in the wilderness of ninety-three days.

The greatest heat of the day was 91 degrees, and distance travelled nine miles.

The Arkansa, below the great bend, becomes more serpentine than it is above, and very much obstructed by sand bars and islands, either naked or clothed with a recent vegetation; they are but little elevated above the surface of the water, and are covered, to some depth, during the prevalence of floods in the river. At Belle Point, and some distance above, these islands almost wholly disappear, but the sandy shores still continue, and are, as above, alternately situated on either side of the river, as the stream approaches or recedes from the opposite river bottoms. The colour of the water was now olive-green. All the red colouring matter, with which it is sometimes imbued, is contributed by streams entering on the southern side. The current of the Arkansa is much less rapid than that of the Platte, but the character of those two rivers in a considerable degree corresponds, in their widely spreading waters of but little depth, running over a bed of yielding sand. The rise of the waters at Belle Point takes place in the months of March and early April, with a less considerable freshet in July and August. But to this place navigation is seldom practicable for keel boats, from the month of August to February inclusive, though the autumnal freshet of October and November frequently admits their passage.

CHAPTER XVI.

Journey from Belle Point to Cape Girardeau—Cherokee Indians—Osage War—Regulators—Settlements of White River.

THE site of Fort Smith was selected by Major Long, in the fall of 1817, and called Belle Point in allusion to its peculiar beauty. It occupies an elevated point of land, immediately below the junction of the Arkansa and the Poteau, a small tributary from the southwest. Agreeably to the orders of General Smith, then commanding the 9th military department, a plan of the proposed work was submitted to Major Bradford, at that time, and since commandant at the post, under whose superintendence the works have been in part completed, not without some deviation from the original plan. The buildings now form two sides of a hollow square, terminated by strong block houses at the opposite angles, and fronting towards the river.

The hill, which forms the basis of the fort, is of a dark gray micaceous sandstone, in horizontal laminæ, and rises about thirty feet above the water. The country back of the fort, has an undulating surface, gradually ascending as it recedes, being covered with heavy forests of oak, tulip-tree, sassafras, &c. Towards the south and southeast, at no great distance, rise the summits of the mountainous range already mentioned. The Sugar-loaf and Cavaniol mountains, the former being one of a group of three similar conic summits, are visible from some points near Fort Smith. The Poteau, so called by the French, from the word signifying a post or station, rises sixty or seventy miles southwest of Belle Point, opposite to the sources of the Kiamesha, a branch of Red river. Nearly the whole of its course is through a hilly or mountainous region, but it is one so sparingly supplied with water, that the Poteau, within two miles of its confluence with the Arkansa, is in the dry season, no more than a tri-fling brook. In an excursion which we made from Fort Smith, we ascended the Poteau about a mile and a half, where we observed an extensive bed of bituminous clay slate, indicating the neighbourhood of coal. Tracing this slate to the south and east, we found it to pass under a very consi-derable sandstone hill. Several circumstances induce us to believe, that it rests on a sandstone similar to that at the fort; attentive examination will show, that these rocks have a slight inclination towards the east, and if the bituminous slate in question had been supported by compact limestone, as has been conjectured,* it is highly probable this rock would have emerged near where the sandstone appears at Belle Point. We make this remark, because, although we have often seen both limestone and bituminous clay slate, in various parts of the Arkansa Territory, it has never been our fortune to meet with them in connexion.

A few rods above this bed of bituminous shale, we cross-ed the Poteau almost at a single step, and without wetting the soles of our mockasins, so inconsiderable was the quan-tity of water it contained. The point between the confluence of the Poteau and the Arkansa, is low and fertile bottom land, and like that on the opposite side of the river, covered with dense and heavy forests of cotton-wood, sycamore, and ash, intermixed with extensive and impenetrable cane brakes. In these low grounds the beautiful papaw tree, whose lus-cious fruit was now ripe, occurs in great abundance. It rises to the height of thirty or forty feet, and its trunk is some-times not less than a foot in diameter.

* Nuttall's Travels into the Arkansa Territory, p. 144.

Grape vines, several scandent species of smilax and cissus, and an undescribed vine, allied to menispermum, are so intermixed with the sturdy undergrowth as to render the woods almost impassable. Paths have been opened by the people of the garrison, where they have been found necessary, by cutting away the canes and small trees, but they may be said to resemble subterranean passages, to which the rays of the sun never penetrate. We found the air in these, and indeed in every part of the heavy forests, stagnant, and so loaded with the effluvia of decaying vegetable substances, as to be immediately oppressive to the lungs. After spending an hour or two in an atmosphere of this kind, we found ourselves perceptibly affected with languor and dizziness.

The gardens at Fort Smith afforded green corn, melons, sweet potatoes, and other esculent vegetables, which to us had, for a long time, been untasted luxuries. It is probable we did not exercise sufficient caution, in recommencing the use of these articles, as we soon found our health beginning to become impaired. We had been a long time confined to a meat diet, without bread or condiments of any kind, and were not surprised to find ourselves affected by so great and so sudden a change. It may be worth while to remark that we had been so long unaccustomed to the use of salt that the sweat of our faces had lost all perceptible saltness, and the ordinary dishes which were brought to our mess table at the fort appeared unpalatable, on account of being too highly seasoned.

In a region of extensive river alluvion supporting, like that of the Arkansa, boundless forests, impervious to the winds and the rays of the sun, it is not surprising that a state of the atmosphere unfavorable to health should exist. Intermitting, remitting, and continued billious fevers prevail during the summer and autumn; and in many instances terminate fatally. Among recent settlers the want of the most common comforts, of the advice and attendance of skilful physicians, and above all the want of cleanliness, and the destructive habits of intemperance, are causes operating powerfully to produce and aggravate these diseases. The settlements about Fort Smith were sickly, and we saw numbers with that peculiar sallowness of complexion which accompanies those chronic derangements of the functions of the liver so often the consequence of billious fevers. It is obvious that the causes of the acknowledged sickliness of the recent settlements in the south and west are, in a great measure local, and unconnected with the climate. By the increase of settlements, and the progress of cultivation, they will be in part removed.

Fort Smith was garrisoned by one company of riflemen, under the command of Major Bradford. Among other important designs contemplated in the establishment of this post, one was to prevent the encroachments of the white settlers upon the lands still held by the Indians. Some of the most fertile portions of the Arkansa territory are those about the Verdigris, Skin Bayou, Illinois, Six Bulls, &c., in which some unauthorised settlements were heretofore made, but have recently been abandoned, in compliance with the requirements of the commandant at Fort Smith.

The opportunity offered by a few days' residence at Fort Smith, was seized for the purpose of ascertaining, by several successive observations, the latitude and longitude of the place. The results of several observations of the sun's meredian altitude, and of lunar distances, taken, between the 14th and 19th of September, give for the latitude of Belle Point 34° 50′ 54″, and for the longitude 94° 21′ west of Greenwich.

On the 19th Captain Bell left the fort to proceed on his way to Cape Girardeau, accompanied by Dougherty and Oakley, two of the engagees, whose services were no longer required. On the 20th Dr. James and Lieutenant Swift departed in company with Captain Kearney, who had visited the post in the discharge of his duties as inspector and paymaster. It was the design of this party to descend the Arkansa to the Cherokee agency, and to proceed thence to the Hot Springs of the Washita.

On the 21st the party, now consisting of Maj. Long, Messrs. Say, Seymour and Peale, accompanied by Wilson, Adams, Duncan and Sweney, the other soldiers being left at the fort, commenced the journey towards Cape Girardeau. We took with us five horses and five mules, two of the latter being loaded with packs. Capt. Ballard kindly volunteered his services as guide, and attended by a servant, accompanied us the first day's journey on our march.

Our route lay on the south side of the Arkansa, at considerable distance from the river and led us across two small creeks, one called Massern, or Mount Cerne and the other the Vache Grasse.* The latter stream has a course of several miles, but during the dry season discharges very little water. The small path we followed, lay, for the most part, through open woods of post oak, blak jack, and hickory, occasionally traversing a narrow prairie. In these open plains, now covered with rank grass and weeds, we discovered here and there some traces, such as a skull or hoof of a bison, indicating that the exclusive possession of man to these regions, had been of a very recent date.

It was near five o'clock when we arrived at the solitary cabin of a settler, and though we found no inhabitant about the place, we halted and encamped near the spring. Our horses were scarce unsaddled, when a man, who seemed to be the occupant of the house came up, and informed us that half a mile further on our way, we should find a house and good accommodation. Accordingly we again mounted our horses,

---

* The word Masserne, applied by Darby as a name to the hills of the Arkansa territory, near the boundary of Louisiana; by Nuttall to the mountains at the sources of the Kiemesha and the Poteau, is supposed to be a corruption of *Mont cerne* the name of a small hill near Belle Point, long used as a look-out post by the French hunters.

and rode forward to Mr. Billingsly's, where we met a very hospitable reception. As the night approached, we observed that several young women and men, the sons and daughters of the family disappeared, going to the cottages of the neighbors (the nearest of which seemed to be the one we had passed) to spend the night, that they might leave their beds for us.

Some feather beds having been given up by their ordinary occupants, expressly for our use, we could not well avoid accepting the accommodation thus offered; but, instead of proving an indulgence, we experienced from them more inconvenience that gratification. We spent an unquiet and almost sleepless night, and arose on the following morning unrefreshed, and with a painful feeling of soreness in our bones, so great a change had the hunter's life produced upon our habits. Those of the party who spread their blankets, and passed the night on the floor of the cabin, rested much more pleasantly.

On the succeeding morning Capt. Ballard returned to Belle Point, and we resumed our journey, accompanied by one of the sons of our landlord, who undertook to guide us on our way, until we should fall in with a path which we might continue to follow. We passed through a hilly country, crossing two creeks, heretofore called the middle and lower Vache Grasse. At the distance of four or five miles from the Arkansa, on each side, the country is broken and mountainous, several of the summits rising to an elevation of near two thousand feet above the surface of the water. Several trees, which stood near our path, had been in part stripped of their bark, and the naked trunks were marked with rude figures representing horses, men, deer, dogs, &c. These imperfect paintings done with charcoal and sometimes touched with a little vermillion, appeared to be historic records, designed to perpetuate or at least to communicate the account of some exploit in hunting, a journey, or some similar event.

A little before sunset we arrived at a settlement on the stream called Short Mountain Bayou. The little cabin we found occupied by two soldiers belonging to the garrison, who were on their return from the settlement, at Cadron, whither they had been sent with letters, on our arrival at Fort Smith, Cadron being the nearest post town. We had expected letters from our friends, by the return of the express, but were disappointed.

The soldiers informed us that the house, in which they had quartered themselves for the night, had been for a week or two deserted, since its proprietor had died, and his wife, who was sick, had been removed to the nearest settlement. The place is called the Short Mountain Settlement, from a high ridge of sandstone, a little to the northwest, rising in the form of a parallelogram to an elevation, according to our estimate, of about twelve hundred feet; its sides are abrupt, and in many places, particularly towards the summit, perpendicular. The summit is broad and nearly tabular, being covered with small trees, among which the red cedar, or some other evergreen tree predominates.

The plantation is somewhat elevated on a rocky eminence, at a little distance from the creek, but it is surrounded on all sides, save one, by the heavily wooded low grounds, in which we are to look for the causes whose operation have made it so soon desolate. Short Mountain Bayou, if we may judge from the depth and width of its channel, and the extent of its low grounds, is a large stream, or rather one which drains an extensive surface, but at this time it exhibited a succession of green and stagnant pools, connected by a little brook, almost without any perceptible current. On the surface of these pools, we saw the floating leaves of the nymphæa, kalmiana, some utricularias, and other aquatic plants.

23d. After leaving the wide and fertile bottoms of the Short Mountain Bayou, our path lay across high and rocky hills, altogether covered with woods. The upland forests are almost exclusively of oak, with some little intermixture of hickory, dogwood, and black gum. They are open, and the ground is in part covered with coarse grasses.

At noon we arrived at the Cherokee settlement on Rocky Bayou, and were received with some hospitality at the house of the Metiff Chief, known by the name of Tom Graves. Though entirely an Indian in his character and habits, he has the colour and features of an European, and it was not without some difficulty, we could be made to believe that he was in reality, allied by birth to the people among whom he holds the rank of a chief. His house, as well as many we passed before we arrived at it, is constructed like those of the white settlers, and like them, surrounded with enclosed fields of corn, cotton, sweet potatoes, &c., with cribs, sheds, droves of swine, flocks of geese, and all the usual accompaniments of a prosperous settlement.

Graves, our landlord, though unable to speak or understand our language, held some communications with us by means of signs, being occasionally assisted by a black girl, one of his slaves who interpreted the Cherokee language. He told us among other things that the Osages do not know how to fight, that the Cherokees were now ready to give up the Osage prisoners, if the Osages would deliver into their hands the individuals, who had formerly killed some of the Cherokees, &c. He has shown his admiration of military prowess, by calling one of his children Andrew Jackson Graves. He treated us with a good degree of attention, and showed himself well acquainted with the manner of making amends by extravagant charges. Our dinner was brought in by black slaves and consisted of a large boiled buffaloe fish, a cup of coffee, corn bread, milk, &c. Our host, and his wife of unmixed aboriginal race, were at table with us, and several slaves of African descent were in waiting. The Cherokees are said to treat their slaves with much lenity.

The band of Cherokees now residing on the Arkansa have recently removed from the east side of the Mississippi. They are almost exclusively agriculturists, raising large crops of corn, and cotton enough for clothing their families, which they manufacture in their own houses.

After dinner we proceeded a few miles, taking with us one of Graves' sons, as a guide, who lead us to a place affording good pasture for our horses. Here we encamped.

24th. From the settlement of the Cherokees at Rocky Bayou, our route lay towards the east across a succession of rocky hills sparingly wooded with oak, intermixed with the cornus florida, attaining an unusual magnitude.

As we descended towards the Arkansa, we perceived before us the cabins and plantations of another settlement of Cherokees. Passing near a wretched and neglected tenement, we observed a white man who appeared to be the occupant, and called upon him to direct us to the place, where, as we had been told, the river could be forded. It was not until we had repeated our request several times, that he seemed disposed to give any attention. He then approached at a snail's pace, and sitting down upon the ground, drawled out his direction, terminating each word with a long and hearty yawn. The depression and misery, which seemed written on his features, and the sallowness of his complexion, convinced us that disease, as well as native indolence had some share in occasioning the apparent insolence he had shown, and cured us of any wish we might have felt to reproach him.

Following a winding pathway, which led through deep tangled thickets, and heavy cane brakes, we arrived at the ford, and crossing without difficulty, halted at the settlement of Walter Webber a young chief of the Cherokees. Here we found the gentlemen of our party who had left the garrison before us.

The chiefs of the Cherokee nation had called a grand

council, to meet at Point Pleasant, the day after our arrival there, to adopt measures to forward the negotiations for peace with the Osages, with whom they had been at variance for many years.

The origin of the quarrel existing between these two powerful and warlike nations, is by some referred to the period of the American Revolution, when the Osages killed a number of refugees, who had fled to them for protection. Among these were some Cherokees, some Indians of mixed breed, and it is said some Englishmen, to whom the success of the American arms rendered unsafe a longer residence in the country then occupied by the Cherokee nation. Whether the outrage thus alleged against the Osages, was in fact committed, it is not at this time easy to determine. It appears, however, agreeably to the information we have been able to collect, that of late years the Cherokees have, almost uniformly been the aggressors, while the abuses of the Osages, so loudly complained of, both by the Cherokees, and the whites have been acts of retaliation. A large number of Cherokees now live on the south side of the Arkansa, upon lands claimed by the Osages, and all the Cherokees of the Arkansa, are in the habit of hunting and committing other depredations on the Osage hunting grounds.

In 1817, the Cherokees with a number of Delawares, Shawnees, Quapaws, and eleven American volunteers, the whole amounting to about six hundred men, made an irruption into the territory of the Osages, having previously taken measures to quiet the suspicions of their enemies by occasional messages, professing a peaceable disposition on their part. When they had arrived near the village, they sent a deputation to the Osages, concealing at the same time their numbers, and their hostile intention, and inviting Clermont, the chief, to a council, which they proposed to hold at a little distance from the town. Clermont being absent on a hunt, with the young men of his village, an old Indian, and one in high standing with his people, was appointed to act in his stead, and commissioned to conclude a peace with the Cherokees, according to the wish they had expressed by their messengers. But what was his surprise when, on arriving at the spot, designated as that at which the council was to be held, instead of a few chiefs and old men, as had been represented, he found himself surrounded by the whole armed force of the Cherokees. He was seized and put to death on the spot. The design of this act of perfidy, had been to effect the destruction of Clermont the bravest and most powerful of the Osages. The Cherokees then proceeded to the attack of the town, where on account of the absence of the efficient men they encountered little resistance. A scene of outrage and bloodshed ensued, in which the eleven Americans are said to have acted a conspicuous and a shameful part. They fired the village, destroyed the corn and other provisions, of which the Osages had raised a plentiful crop, killed and took prisoners between fifty and sixty persons, all old men, women, and children.

Four of these prisoners, who had been since held in captivity by the Cherokees east of the Mississippi, had been brought to Point Pleasant by a Metiff, called capt. Rogers, and a consultation was now to be held concerning the manner of restoring them to the Osages.

In the winter of 1817—18, some of the leading men of both nations had been summoned to a council at St. Louis, by Gov. Clark, for the purpose of negotiating a peace. By the treaty then made, the Cherokees had agreed to relinquish the prisoners in question, in consideration of which they were to be allowed the privilege of hunting in the country north of the Arkansa, as high as the Grand river, or Six Bulls, and on the south side as high as they pleased. The stipulated surrender of the prisoners not having been made, a party of Osages, who were hunting on Red river, some time in the ensuing winter fell in with three Cherokee hunters whom they murdered by way of retaliation. This circumstance tended to widen the breach between them, till at length both parties were resolved on war, which was for the present prevented, by the interference of governor Miller, and by the check imposed by the presence of an armed force at Belle Point, on the frontiers of the two nations. At the time of our visit, it was hoped the influence of governor Miller would effect the establishment of a permanent peace.

The first of the ensuing month, (October,) had been appointed for the surrender of the prisoners, and governor Miller was said to be then on his way to Belle Point, to ensure the fulfilment of the conditions stipulated between the contending parties. The Osages were to give up the men concerned in the murder on Red river, in exchange for the women and children then prisoners with 'the Cherokees.*

The Cherokees were taught the culture of cotton many years since by governor Blount of North Carolina, who offered them a stipulated price for all they would deliver at the trading house. They were for several years paid regularly for their cotton, but the factor at length refusing any longer to receive it, they complained to governor Blount, who advised them to manufacture it into clothing for their own use, which they consented to do, on condition of being furnished with a person to give the requisite instructions. They now raise considerable quantities of cotton, and many of them are comfortably clad in garments of their own manufacture.

The introduction of a considerable degree of civilization among the Cherokees, has been attended with the usual consequence of inequality in the distribution of property, and a larger share of the evils resulting from that inequality, than are known among untutored savages. Encroachments upon the newly established rights of exclusive possession have

* A treaty of peace was concluded between the Osages and Cherokees at Belle Point in August, 1822. *Arkansa Paper.*

been frequent, and have rendered the numerous class of the poor among the Cherokees, troublesome neighbours—both to the wealthy of their own nation, and to those of the white settlers in their vicinity, who have any thing to lose. But wealth seldom finds itself destitute of the means of protection. Three bands of regulators, or troops of light horse as they are sometimes called, are maintained among the Cherokees, consisting each, of ten men well armed and mounted, and invested with an almost unlimited authority.*

A few days previous to our arrival at Point Pleasant, a young man had been apprehended by one of these bands of regulators, on suspicion of horse theft. On examination, the supposed delinquent proved stubborn and refractory, whereupon, the captain ordered the infliction of fifty lashes, and this not seeming to produce the desired effect, an additional fifty was commenced, when the culprit confessed himself guilty, and disclosed the whole transaction in which he had been concerned.

We were called upon for advice in the case of the Osage prisoners, a young woman and three children labouring under an attack of intermitting fever. The young woman we found sitting upon the floor in a little cabin near the trading house, and crying bitterly, not more as we were informed, on account of ill health, than of her reluctance to return to the Osages. She had been long among the Cherokees whose customs she had adopted, and among whom she had formed attachments.

Tikatok's village, which we passed on the 25th, is situa-

* Mr. John Rogers a very reputable and civilized Cherokee, told me that one of the regulators happening to have a relation, who had been repeatedly guilty of theft, and finding him incorrigible, he destroyed his eye-sight with a penknife, saying " As long as you can see you will steal, I will therefore prevent your thefts by the destruction of your sight." Nuttall's Travels into the Arkansa Territory, page 135., to which work the reader is referred for an interesting sketch of the history, and of the present condition of the Cherokees. We are unwilling to dwell longer on a subject which has been so frequently discussed.

ted on the Illinois Bayou about seven miles above Point Pleasant. It consists of no more than five or six cabins, but is the residence of the venerable Tikatok, who, since the death of Tallantusky in 1817, has been considered as the principal chief of this portion of the Cherokee nation. He has been a distinguished benefactor to his people, and is familiarly known by the name of " The Beloved." The Cherokees, who live at and about this village, and those settled at a distance from the Arkansa, generally, are less subject to fevers than those who reside in the river bottoms. At a little distance above the village we left the Illinois, and proceeded across the wilderness towards Little Red river on our route to Cape Girardeau. Two or three wretched cabins only on the whole route, and two or three scattered plantations occupied by Cherokees, occur in the country between Point Pleasant and Little Red river, where we arrived on the 28th. This river has a deep rocky channel, sixty or one hundred yards in width at the point where we crossed it, which is distant about eighty miles from its confluence with White river. It had at this time scarcely a perceptible current, and in many places might be crossed on foot without wading. It is however, like most of the rivers of this region, liable to great and sudden floods which in several instances, have drowned the cattle, and destroyed and swept away the crops of those who were settled along its banks. From the marks left by the last flood upon the banks, we perceived that the range from high to low water, could not be less than sixty feet.

From Stanley's settlement on Little Red river, it is about thirty-six miles, northeast to Harding's ferry on White river. Here are numerous settlements of whites, but notwithstanding the country is hilly, and profusely irrigated, with numerous rapid streams, the inhabitants have almost without exception, a sickly appearance. Harding's ferry is about four hundred miles distant from the confluence of White river and the Mississippi. White river is navigable for keel boats at high water to this place, and during a considerable portion of the year, they may ascend one hundred miles farther. It is here about three hundred yards wide; the water is remarkably clear, and flows with a moderate current over a gravelly or stony bed.

Near Harding's ferry on the south side of White river is the Chattahoochee mountain, of about two thousand feet elevation, somewhat surpassing any other point in its vicinity. The top of this mountain marks the north-eastern angle of the Cherokee boundary, as established by general Jackson's treaty. The eastern boundary of the tract ceded by that treaty to the Cherokees, runs in a straight line from the top of the Chattahoochee, to the mouth of *Point Remove*, or Eddy Point creek, which enters the Arkansa about 30 miles above the Cadron. This line coincides nearly with the eastern limit of the mountainous region. Many small portions of valuable land are included in the territory lately ceded to the Cherokees, but by far the greater part is mountainous and barren, and unfit for cultivation.

White river has its sources in the Ozark mountains near the 94th degree of west longitude, and about the 36th north latitude, in the same district from which descend on the southwest the Illinois river of Arkansa, and on the north the Yungar fork of the Osage. The average direction of its course is nearly due east, parallel to the Arkansa, crossing about four degrees of longitude to its confluence with Black river, in latitude 35° 15′, then turning abruptly south, it flows through one degree and fifteen minutes of latitude to its bifurcation, and the confluence of its eastern branch with the Mississippi in 34° north.

Below the point where it receives the Black river from the north, and even at the Chattahoochee mountains, near one hundred miles above that point, White river is little inferior, either in the width of its channel, or in its volume of water, to the Arkansa under the same meridian.

When we have had occasion to mention among the people of White river, that we had crossed the Arkansa at the Rocky Mountains, more than one thousand miles to the west, the question has been repeatedly put to us, "Where did you cross White river?" Those who have known only the lower portions of both rivers, consider them as nearly of equal length, and as rising near each other, whereas the entire extent of country drained by White river compared to that of the Arkansa is as one to six nearly.

Three miles above its confluence with the Mississippi, White river divides into two branches, the lesser of which, turning off at right angles, flows southwest with a current sometimes equal to three miles per hour, and falls into the Arkansa at the distance of four and an half miles. It is said the current flows through this communication alternately to and from the Arkansa, according as the water in that river, is higher or lower than in White river.

Major Long entered the Arkansa through this "cut off" on the 13th of October 1817, and it has been passed more recently by Mr. Nuttall* in 1819. In both these instances, the current flowed from White river towards the Arkansa. The mouth of that branch of White river, which communicates immediately with the Mississippi, is situated fifteen miles above the mouth of the Arkansa,† and is about two hundred yards wide. The current is very gentle, and the water deep. Though perfectly transparent, it is of a yellowish colour. The banks are low and subject to periodical inundations. The soil near the mouth of White river, is an intermixture of clay and fine sand, the clay predominating, and the whole of a reddish tinge.

* Nuttall's Travels, p. 65.

† The confluence of White river with the Mississippi, has been said to be situated fifty miles above the mouth of the Arkansa; it has also been asserted that its bifurcation is at "about thirty miles above its junction with the Mississippi." See Schoolcraft's view of the Lead Mines of Missouri, pp. 248, 253. There is, however, little reason to fear that errors of this sort, upon a subject so familiarly known, will obtain general currency. In the same work the length of White river is said to be thirteen hundred miles.

Numerous settlements have heretofore been formed on
the lands contiguous to White river; and several in the portion above the Chattahoochee mountain on the south side;
but all these lands having by treaty been surrendered to the
Cherokees, many whites have been compelled to withdraw,
and leave their farms to the Indians. A small portion only,
of the lands granted to the Cherokees, by the treaty is adapted to the purposes of settlements. Some of the tributaries of
White river have extensive and fertile bottoms, but the
greater part of the country watered by this river is mountainous, and unfit for cultivation; at M'Neil's ferry, where
the road from Little Rock on the Arkansa, to Davidsonville
in Lawrence county, crosses White river, the bottoms are
wide and as fertile as any of those on the Arkansa. Here
the miegia and the pawpaw attain their greatest perfection,
and the soil is found well adapted to the culture of corn,
cotton, and tobacco. At the point formed by the confluence
of White and Black rivers, is a portion of land of a triangu-
lar form, and bounded by sides about fifteen miles in extent, which, in the excellence of its soil, as we were informed by the surveyors, is surpassed by none in the western
country. There are considerable portions of the upland soil
of White river, where the profuse supply of streams and
springs of excellent water, the elevation and comparative
healthfulness of many situations, and the vicinity of navigable rivers and other local advantages, make amends for
the want of exuberant fertility in the soil. The same remark is applicable to the country south of the Arkansa,
where are extensive tracts of hilly and rocky soils, which
seem admirably adapted to the culture of the vine and the
olive. In every part of the Ozark mountains there are vallies, and small portions of land within the hills, having a
deep and fertile soil covered with heavy forests of oak, ash,
hickory, and in some places with the sugar maple, and
abounding in excellent water. The labor of a few years,

will be sufficient to convert these tracts into productive farms, but the inconvenience resulting from the difficulty of communication and access to the different parts of the country, will for a long time retard their settlement.

In several parts of the Arkansa territory, we were shown dollars which were believed to have been coined in some of the upper settlements of White river, and it has been currently reported, that mines of silver exist, and are wrought there. It appears, however, upon examination, that much spurious coin is here in circulation, and it is probable that the White river country, owes its present reputation for mineral wealth, to the successful labors of some manufacturer of imitation dollars.

Since the time of De Soto, it has been confidently asserted by many who have written concerning Louisiana, that mines of gold and silver exist in that part of the country of which we are speaking. In an old map by Du Pratz, a gold mine is placed somewhere near the confluence of the Illinois and the Arkansa, a silver mine on the Merameg, and he says, " I myself saw a rivulet whose waters rolled down gold dust.* We are informed by Schoolcraft, that granite exists about the sources of the St. Francis, which are situated near those of White river, p. 213. Of the extent and character of this formation of granite we have not yet been able to form any definite ideas. It is however by no means improbable that to its plates of yellow and white mica we are to look for the origin of the fabulous accounts of the precious metals in those regions. Like the country of the gilded king, the El Dorado of South America, it is probable the gold and silver mines of the Arkansa territory will recede before the progress of examination, first into the wildest and most inacces-

* " The mine of Merameg, which is silver, is pretty near the confluence of the river which gives it name, which is a great advantage to those who would work it, because they might easily by that means have their goods from Europe. It is situate about five hundred leagues from the sea.'
Du Pratz's Louisiana, p. 294, vol. I.

sible parts, and at length, disappear entirely. We by no means intend to assert that the region in question will not prove of immense importance on account of its mineral treasures. Valuable mines of lead and iron are certainly frequent in many parts of it, and we can assign no reason why silver, and other metals should not be found in the argillite with quartzy veins, and in the other rocks of the transition period which are known to exist in these mountains. We only intend to give it as our opinion, that there has as yet been no foundation in actual discovery for the belief that such mines do exist.

The bed of White river, at the place where we crossed it, is paved with pebbles and fragments of a yellowish-white petrosiliceous stone, intermixed with rounded masses of transparent quartz, and sometimes with pieces of chalcedony. Its water is uncommonly transparent, and this, with the whiteness of its bed, and the brisk motion of the current, gives it an aspect of unusual beauty. The banks are high, and in many places not exposed to inundation. Dense and heavy forests of sycamore and cotton-wood stretch along the river, disclosing here and there at distant intervals, the solitary hut, and the circumscribed *clearing* of the recent settler. Some, who have been no more than two or three years resident upon their present farms, and who commenced in the unbroken forests, have now abundant crops of corn and pumpkins, with large fields of cotton, which is said to equal in quality that of the uplands of Georgia and Carolina.

Few attempts have hitherto been made to cultivate any grain except Indian corn, though the soil is thought to be in many places well adapted to wheat, barley, oats, &c.

The maize cultivated in the Arkansa territory, and in the southern and western states generally, is the variety called the gourd seed, having a long and compressed kernel, shrivelled at the end when fully ripe, and crops are not uncommon, yielding from sixty to ninety bushels per acre.

In all the uplands, the prevailing growth is oak. At the time of our journey the acorns were falling in such quantities, that the ground for an extent of many acres was often seen almost covered with them. Many recent settlers, indulging the disposition to indolence, which seizes upon almost every man who fixes his residence in these remote forests, place as much dependence upon the crop of mast as on the products of their own industry. Vast numbers of swine are suffered to range at large in the forests, and in the fall of the year when they have become fat by feeding on the acorns, they are hunted and killed like wild animals, affording to the inhabitants a very important article of subsistence. It is remarked also, that the venison becomes fat somewhat in proportion as acorns are abundant. Turkies, which are still vastly numerous in the settlements of White river, feed upon them, but are said to grow poor in consequence.

Sweet potatoes grow in great perfection in many parts of the Arkansa territory, and are but too much cultivated and eaten, their constant use as an article of food, being little beneficial to health. The common, or *Irish potatoe*, as it is here universally called, succeeds but indifferently, and few attempts are made to cultivate it.

A few of the roads which traverse the country from the Mississippi to the upper settlements of Red river and the Arkansa, have been sufficiently opened to admit the passage of waggons. On these are seen many families migrating from Missouri to Red river, and from Red river to Missouri.

The first settlements in the wilderness are most commonly made by persons to whom hardihood and adventure have become confirmed, and almost indispensable habits, and who choose to depend upon the chase, and the spontaneous products of the unreclaimed forest, rather than submit to the confinement and monotony of an agricultural life. They are therefore, of necessity, kept somewhat in advance of those settlers who intend a permanent residence in the situations they first occupy. Removing from place to place with their cattle, horses, and swine, they confine themselves to one spot no longer than *the range* continues to afford a sufficient supply of the articles most necessary to life. When the canes are fed down and destroyed, and the acorns become scarce, the small cornfield, and the rude cabin are abandoned, and the *squatter* goes in search of a place where all the original wealth of the forest is yet undiminished. Here he again builds his hut, removes the trees from a few acres of land, which supply their annual crop of corn, while the neighbouring woods, for an extent of several miles, are used both as pasture and hunting grounds. Though there is in this way of life an evident tendency to bring men back to a state of barbarism, we have often met among the rudest of the squatters with much hospitality and kindness. Near White river, we called at a house to purchase food for ourselves, and our horses, but having no silver money our request was refused, although we offered the notes of the Bank of Missouri, then in good credit. In a few miles we arrived at another cabin, where we found every member of the numerous family sick with the ague and fever, except one young girl. But here they were willing to furnish every refreshment their house afforded. There were at this time very few houses, particularly in the settlements about White river, which did not exhibit scenes of suffering similar to those in the one, of which we were now the reluctant guests. We have seen some instances, where of a family of eight or ten, not a single individual was capable of attending to the services of the household, or of administering to the wants of his suffering relatives. In these instances, we thought it better to pitch our tents at a little distance, and intrude ourselves no farther, than was necessary to procure corn, and other indispensable supplies.

On the evening of the 30th we halted at a little rivulet called Bayou Cura. The dwelling of our landlord consisted.

as is commonly the case in the new settlements, of a single
room, with beds in two or three of the corners. We were
cordially invited to make use of the beds, though it would
have been at the expense of rendering it necessary for our
host, his wife, and daughters, to sleep upon the floor of the
same room. We accordingly spread our blankets and deposited ourselves around the hearth, while the family occupied their usual stations.

On the first of October we arrived at the ford of Strawberry river, a tributary entering the *Big Black* not far from
the confluence of the latter with White river, and about fourteen miles beyond, at the ford of Spring river, a parallel
stream. Both these are rapid and beautiful rivers, possessing all the peculiarities as to the abundance, transparency,
and purity of their waters, usually observed in those rivers
which traverse elevated and mountainous districts. The
entire length of Spring river is said to be but about one hundred and forty miles, yet in the quantity of water which it
discharges, it more than twice exceeds the Canadian, having
a course of more than nine hundred miles. It is said to have
its principal source in a spring of uncommon magnitude.
Spring river unites with another, called Eleven Point, near
the little town of Davidsonville, the seat of justice for Lawrence county, and flows thence nearly due east two or three
miles, to its junction with Big Black. The country around
Davidsonville is hilly, having a deep and fertile primary
soil, and abounding in heavy forests. The sources of Eleven
Point, we have been told, are in eleven large springs, and
are near those of Spring river.

To those who have been long accustomed to the thirsty
regions of the Missouri, the Platte, and the upper Arkansa,
it is somewhat surprising to meet in tracts having nearly the
same elevation, and resting to a great extent on rocks of a
similar character, so great a number of large streams crowded into such narrow compass.

Is it not probable that a large portion of the water falling in rains upon the extensive plains at the eastern side of the Rocky Mountains may sink through the loose and porous soil, till at length meeting with some compact stratum, it may be collected into rills, and even considerable streams, which, descending through subterranean channels in the direction of the general inclination of the country, at length meet with the nucleus of the Ozark Mountains, traversing the secondary strata, like a mineral dyke, and are consequently made to appear in the form of large springs? Whether any cause of this kind operates to supply the unusual profusion of water, with which this hilly tract is irrigated, must be for others to decide. The fact is an established one.

Black river originates in an elevated part of the Ozark Mountains, between 37° and 38° north latitude, and between 90° and 91° west longitude. From the same tract descend, on the north, the waters of the Merameg, on the northeast those of Big river, on the east, and south, those of the St. Francis and Black rivers, and on the west those of the Osage and the Gasconade. By an examination of the map which accompanies this work it will be seen that the direction of the water courses clearly indicates the existence of an elevated ridge, running from the confluence of the Missouri and Mississippi, on the northeast to the junction of the Arkansa, and the Canadian on the southwest. On the north-western side of this ridge, we observe the Osage, the Grand river, the Verdigris, and even the Arkansa, inflected from that due eastern course which the tributaries of the Mississippi and Missouri, on the west, incline to pursue; and coming near its base we find the Illinois river of the Arkansa, and the Yungar fork of Osage, running in opposite directions, and nearly at right angles, to the general course of the Canadian, the Arkansa, the Main Osage, and the Konzas. The Illinois, and the great eastern tributary of the Osage receive numerous streams from the western slope of the Ozark

Mountains, but they traverse a region hitherto very imperfectly known. It appears, however, that these two rivers drain all the north-western side of the mountainous range in question. Black river runs nearly parallel, that is from northeast to southwest, along the south-eastern side of the range. Its sources are in the district of the Lead Mines, and at no great distance from those of the Merameg and the St. Francis. Its course is at first S. E. about sixty or one hundred miles, then turning to the southwest, it receives in succession from the south-eastern side of the mountains the Little Black, the Currant, Thomas' river or fork, Eleven Point, Spring, and Strawberry rivers, uniting at length with White river, in latitude 35° 15′. As far as is hitherto known it receives no considerable tributary from the east. About the sources of Black river reside the Peola or Peoria Indians, who are said to number about fifty warriors. Parallel to this river, and from twenty to sixty miles distant, on the east, is the St. Francis, a larger river, but one in many respects resembling Black river. It rises in the highlands about one hundred miles to the westward of St. Genevieve, in Missouri, and receiving before it leaves the hills Bear creek, Castor, White water, and numerous other streams, it descends toward the southeast, soon entering the extensive swamp which stretches from New Madrid, on the Mississippi, along the base of the mountains to the Arkansa. We have been informed, by some of the inhabitants of the counties of Cape Girardeau and Madison, that in this swamp the St. Francis is so much obstructed with rafts, and so lost among islands, that its course can with difficulty be traced. It is well known that in the lower part of its course it is so obstructed by a large raft as not to admit the passage of the smallest boats. Its confluence with the Mississippi is about three hundred and five miles below the Ohio, and eighty above the mouth of White river. Running parallel, both to the Mississippi and White river, and at no great distance from either, the St. Francis can have no very large tributaries; indeed we know of none, on either side, which deserve the name of rivers. We have no very definite information respecting the great swamp in which the St. Francis is said to lose itself soon after leaving the hills. The accounts of the hunters, and of some settlers, who have seen it, agree in representing it as almost impassable, covered with heavy forests of cypress, and wholly unfit to become the residence of men. This swamp, and the country about the sources of Black river and the St. Francis, appear to be near the centre of the region so powerfully affected by earthquakes in the year 1811. The fertile lands on the upper branches of the St. Francis are not very extensive, and are all more or less subject to inundation, by the sudden overflowing of the streams. On this account they cannot be considered as of great value for agriculture, but the wealth which this region possesses in its mines renders it one of the most important parts of the Mississippi valley.

On the 8th we arrived at Jackson, the seat of justice for the county of Cape Girardeau, and after St. Louis and St. Charles, one of the largest towns in Missouri. It lies about eleven or twelve miles northwest of the old town of Cape Girardeau on the Mississippi, and is surrounded by a hilly and fertile tract of country, at this time rapidly increasing in wealth and population. Jackson is what is called a *thriving village*, and contains at present more than fifty houses, which though built of logs seem to aspire to a degree of importance unknown to the humble dwellings of the scattered and solitary settlers, assuming an appearance of consequence and superiority similar to that we immediately distinguished in the appearance and manners of the people. Our horses having never been accustomed to such displays of magnificence signified great reluctance to enter the village. Whips and heels were exercised with unusual animation, but in a great measure without effect, until we dismounted, when by dint of coaxing, pushing, kicking, and whipping, we at length urged our clownish animals up to the door of the inn.

Fifteen miles north of Jackson, on a little stream called Apple creek, reside about four hundred Indians, mostly Delawares and Shawnees. At the time of our visit, the head of a Shawnee, who had been concerned in the murder of a white woman, was seen elevated on a pole by the side of the road leading from Jackson to the Indian settlement of Apple creek. It was related to us, that the crime, for which this punishment had been inflicted, was committed at the instigation of a white man. The murderer was demanded of the Shawnees by the people of Jackson, and being at length discovered by the Indians, and refusing to surrender himself, he was shot by his own people, and his head delivered up agreeably to the demand.

It is painful to witness the degradation and depression of a people once powerful and independent, still more so to see them submitting to the wanton and needless cruelties of their oppressors. We have not been informed by what authority the punishment, above mentioned, was inflicted upon a whole community for the crime of one of its members, and we are sorry to have occasion to record a circumstance so little honourable to the people of Missouri.

A miserable remnant of the Shawnee, Delaware, and Peola tribes, with a few Chickasaws, and Cherokees, were at this time scattered through the country, from the Mississippi, at the mouth of Apple Creek, westward, to the sources of Black river. They were, however, soon to remove farther west, and many of them were already on their way to the country about the upper branches of White river, where, by becoming intruders upon the territories of the Cherokees, it may be expected that their speedy and entire extinction will be insured.

The road from White river joins that from the upper settlements on the St. Francis, at some distance beyond Jackson.

Castor and White Water are two beautiful streams, traversing the country west of Jackson. They run towards the south, and soon after their confluence, enter the great swamp through which they find their way to the St. Francis.

The district of the Lead Mines, situate near the sources of the Merameg, the Gasconade, and the St. Francis, has been repeatedly described. The best accounts of it are in the works of Bradbury, Brackenridge, Stoddart, and Schoolcraft.* To those accounts we have to add a few observations respecting the rocks and soils of the region, a considerable part of which we have seen, and examined as attentively as circumstances would admit. But as discussions of this kind have little interest for the general reader, we propose to give a place in the sequel to such remarks as we have had the opportunity to make, connected with the mineralogy of this interesting region.

* Bradbury's Travels in the interior of America, p. 258. 2nd Edition; Brackenridge's Views of Louisiana, p. 256. Baltimore edition; Stoddart's Sketches of Louisiana, p. 390. Schoolcraft's View of the Lead Mines of Missouri, *passim*; but the details of mineralogy and geology in those works, appear to us deficient in accuracy.

CHAPTER XVII.

Hot Springs of the Washita—Red river—Exploring Expedition of 1806—Arrival at Cape Girardeau—Dissolution of the party.

WE must now return, to give a hasty account of an excursion from Point Pleasant, in the country of the Cherokees, to the Hot Springs of the Washita.

On the morning of the 25th our little party, consisting of Captain Kearney, Lieutenant Swift, and myself, having taken leave of our companions, recrossed the Arkansa from Webber's, and proceeded on our journey without a guide.

Having mistaken the route we had been directed to follow, we were bewildered during a considerable part of the day, wandering about through a fertile country without settlements, and covered with dense forests.

Towards evening we arrived at a settlement of Cherokees, where we engaged a guide to conduct us to the trace leading to the Springs. For this service we paid him two dollars. We encamped in an open forest of oak, where we found a sufficient supply of grass for our horses. The next day we commenced our ride at an early hour, our route lying nearly due south, at right angles to the general direction of the Arkansa. As we receded from the river we found the country to become broken and rocky, but no part of it higly elevated. The hills range from N. E. to S. W.; their sides are sometimes nearly naked, but more commonly covered with small and scattered trees. Several kinds of oak, and the Chinquapin (Castanea *pumila. Ph.)* attaining the dimensions of a tree, are met with in the sandstone tracts

We distinguish here in the uplands two varieties of soil. That just mentioned, based upon a compact, hard sandstone, and bearing forests of oak; and another resting upon a white petrosilicious rock, with fragments of which it is much intermixed. This latter is often covered with pine forests. The most common species, the yellow pine (P. *resinosa*) attains unusual magnitude; the P. *rigida* and some other species occur, but are not frequent. We also observed several species of vaccinium, the Mitchilla, the Kalmia *latifolia*, Hamamelis *virginica?* Cunila *mariana*, and many other plants common to this region, and the Alleghany mountains.

No settlements occur betweeen those of the Cherokees, about Dardeuai Eye, on the Arkansa, and the Hot Springs. The blind path, which we followed, traverses a rugged and mountainous region, having considerable resemblance, except in the want of parallelism in the ranges, to the sandstone portions of the Alleghanies. As the weather was rainy we felt some inconvenience from encamping without tents.

On the 28th we arrived at the Hot Springs. The country near these, on the north and northwest, is high and rocky. The sandstone, which extends from the Arkansa to within a few miles of the Springs, becomes, toward the south, something inclined, and apparently of more ancient deposition, until it is succeeded by a highly inclined argillite. Both these rocks are traversed by large veins of white quartz. Their inclination is towards the south, and that of the argillite at a great angle. In some localities it is but indistinctly slaty in its structure, and its laminæ are nearly perpendicular. It contains extensive beds of a yellowish-white, silicious stone, often somewhat translucent, and resembling some varieties of hornstone. Its fracture is a little splintery, and sometimes largely conchoidal. It is of a close texture, but the recent surface is generally destitute of lustre. This rock affords the stones called Washita oil stones. It may with propriety be denominated petrosilex. This name is, however, to be understood as having the application given it by Kirwan, who uses it to designate the fusible varieties of the hornstone of Werner, and not the several varieties of compact feldspar, to which it has been sometimes applied. In passing from the Hot Springs, northeast to the Lead Mine country, about the sources of the Merameg, this rock is found to be intimately connected, and to pass by minute and imperceptible gradations into the flint rock of that district, which is decidedly secondary, and of contemporaneous origin with the compact limestone. About the Hot Springs, it is not distinctly stratified, but occurs in very extensive masses, sometimes forming the body of large hills, and is marked by perpendicular seams and fissures, often placed very near each other.

The Hot Springs of the Washita are in north latitude 34° 31' and west longitude, 92° 50' 45"* near the base of the south-eastern slope of the Ozark mountains, and six miles north of the Washita. They have been erroneously represented as the principal sources of that river, which are more than one hundred miles distant.

We have been informed, that these remarkable springs were unknown even to the American hunters, until the year 1779. At that time, it is said, that there was but one spring discharging heated water. This is described as a circular orifice, about six inches in diameter, pouring out a stream of water of the same size, from the side of a perpendicular cliff, about eight feet from its base. At another place, near the top of the mountain, which rises abruptly towards the east, the heated water is said to have made its appearance near the surface of the ground, in a state of ebullition, and to have sunk and disappeared again upon the same spot. It is probable these representations are in a great measure fabulous. All we are to understand by them, is, that the gradual

* Hunter and Dunbar.

augmentation of the thermal rocks, which are constantly forming about the springs, has changed the position, and perhaps increased the number of the orifices.

These springs were visited by Hunter and Dunbar in 1804, and the information communicated by them, as well as much derived from other sources, together with an analysis of the waters, has been placed before the public by Dr. Mitchell.* They have been subsequently examined by Major Long, in 1818, from whose notes we derive the greater part of the information we have to communicate respecting them. They are about seventy in number, and rise at the bottom, and along one side of a narrow ravine, separating two considerable hills of clay slate. A small creek enters the ravine from the north by two branches, one from the northwest, and the other from the northeast, flowing after their union, nearly due south, and blending with the water of the springs, increasing rapidly in size, and acquiring so high a temperature, that at the time of our visit the hand could not be borne immersed in it. After traversing from north to south, the narrow valley containing the springs, this creek meanders away to the southeast, and enters the Washita at the distance of eight or ten miles. All the springs are within six hundred yards below the junction of the two brooks, and all except one, on the east side of the creek.

We subjoin some particulars observed by Major Long at the time of his visit in 1818.† During the winter, the steam which rises from the springs is condensed to a white vapour, which is often visible at a great distance.

The water is limpid and colourless, and destitute, when cooled of either taste or smell, and according to the analysis of Dr. Mitchell purer than ordinary spring water. It how-

---

* See the New York Medical Repository.

† On the first of January, 1818, the thermometer in the air, at sunrise, stood at 24°, at 2. P. M., 49°, at sunset, 41°.
Immersed in the water of the creek, below the Springs, at 61°, above 46°

ever deposites, as it comes in contact with the air, a copious
sediment which has gradually accumulated until it has become an independent rock formation of considerable extent.
This rock appears to consist of flint, lime, and a little oxide
of iron. It is often of a porous or vessicular texture, and

Temperature in Spring, No. 1. being the lowermost on the creek, 122°.
Water discharged: 4 gallons per minute.

"   No. 2. A few feet from No. 1. 104°, discharging
1 gallon per minute.

"   No. 3. Twenty-five yards from the last, 106°, discharging 2 gallons per minute.

"   No. 4. Six yards above the last, 126°, discharges
2 gallons per minute.

"   Of a spring issuing from the ground, at a considerable distance up the side of the hill, 64°.

"   Nos. 5, 6, and 7, 126°, 94°, 92°. These rise very near
each other, the warmest being more elevated than
the rest. They discharge about 8 gallons per minute.

"   No. 8. Issuing from the ground, fifty feet above the
level of the creek, uniting, as it rises with another,
at 54°. Temperature of the mixture, 128°. Discharge of the two, ten gallons per minute.

"   No. 9. Rising in the point of a small spur, sixty
feet above the level of the creek, 132°. Discharges
two gallons.

"   No. 10. Forty feet above the creek, 151°. Discharges
ten gallons. Green bushes in the edge of this,
which is the hottest spring.

"   No. 11. Three feet above the Creek, 148°, discharging twelve gallons.

"   No. 12. Thirty yards above the last, 132°. Discharging twenty gallons.

"   Nos. 13, 14, 15, Near the last; 124, 119, 108°. Discharging 4 gallons each.

"   No. 16.   do   122°. Discharging 3 gallons.

"   No. 17. The uppermost on the creek, 126°.

"   Nos. 18. 126°, 19, 128°, 20, 130°, 21, 136°, 22,
140°.

All these are large springs, and rise at an elevation of at least one hundred feet above the creek. In the same area are several others, and what
is more remarkable, several cold ones. In many of the hot springs I observed bubbles rising in rapid succession, but could not discover any perceptible smell from them. Not only confervas and other vegetables grow
in and about the hottest springs, but great numbers of little insects are
seen constantly sporting about the bottom and sides.

The entire quantity of water flowing in the Creek, after it receives the
water of the Hot Springs, may be estimated at from 900 to 1000 gallons per minute.

the amygdaloidal cavities are sometimes empty, and sometimes contain very delicate stalactites. Hæmatitic iron ore occurs disseminated in every part; also extensive caverns sometimes filled with a bright red metallic oxide. Dr. Wilson, who has been some time resident at the springs, informed us, that the continued use of the water occasions salivation, from which it has been commonly inferred that it contains mercury in solution.

The time of our visit to the springs being one of very unusual drought, the quantity of water was somewhat less, and the temperature higher than ordinary. The time required to boil eggs as much as they usually are for the table, was fifteen minutes. In the same time, a strong cup of coffee was made, by immersing our kettle in one of the springs.

A number of baths have been made, by forming excavations in the rock, into which the hot water is constantly flowing. By cutting off, or increasing the supply, the temperature can be regulated at pleasure. Over some of these are built small log cabins, and in the neighbourbood are twenty or thirty huts, occupied at some seasons of the year by persons who resort hither for the benefit of the waters.

Three miles northeast from the Hot Springs is a large fountain of water of the ordinary temperature, forming the source of the small stream already mentioned, as flowing down from that direction. It rises from the summit of a little knoll six or eight feet in diameter, and divides into two streams, one of which flows towards the east, the other towards the west. Both, however, unite at the base of the knoll, and the brook flows thence southwest, between two petrosilicious hills, to its confluence with another from the northwest, to form the Hot Spring creek. The quantity of water discharged by this spring can scarcely be less than from eighty to one hundred gallons per minute. Immediately on the south rises a considerable hill, and the elevation of the spring itself, above the level of the highest of the thermal springs is thought to be not less than one hundred and fifty feet. The water is transparent, but has a perceptible metallic taste, and deposites upon the stones over which it flows a copious, rust-like sediment. The Spring is known in the neighbouring settlements as the " poison spring," a name which we were told it had received from the following circumstance, said to have taken place many years since. A hunter, who had been pursuing a bear, and was much exhausted with heat and fatigue, arrived at this spring in the middle of the day, and finding the water cool and not unpleasant to the taste, he drank freely of it, but immediately afterward sickened, and died. His death was occasioned, probably, not by any deleterious quality in the water, but by the disease commonly induced by drinking too largely of cold water when the body is heated. The neighbouring inhabitants, however, imputed the hunter's death to some supposed poisonous property in the spring. Not long afterwards, a discontented invalid residing at the Hot Springs, came to a resolution of putting a period to his own life. This he concluded to bring about by drinking the water of the Poison Spring. He accordingly repaired to it, and after drinking as much as he was able, filled his bottle, and returned home. Instead of dying, as he had expected, he found himself much benefited by his potation. Notwithstanding this discovery of the sanative quality of the water, the spring still retained its former name; it is now used without apprehension, and is much resorted to by people who visit the Hot Springs.

About two miles to the northeast of this spring, a little to the left of the road leading to the settlement of Dardenai, is the principal quarry from which the Washita oilstones are procured. It is near the summit of a high and steep hill, composed of the petrosiliceous rock already mentioned. The oil stones are found in the perpendicular seams or fissures of the rock, from which they are detached with little difficulty,

having as they are dug from the quarry, nearly the requisite
shape and size. They are then carried by hand, or thrown
to the foot of the precipice, whence is an easy transportation
of ten or twelve miles to the Washita. By this river they
descend to New Orleans, and some have been carried thence
to New York, where they are known as the *Missouri oilstones*. These stones are said not to be inferior in quality
to the oilstones from Turkey.

In the immediate neighbourhood of the Hot Springs, we
observed a number of interesting plants. The American
holly, [Ilex *opaca*,] is frequent in the narrow vallies within
the mountains. The leaves of another species of Ilex, [I.
cassine, the celebrated *Cassine Yaupon*,] which grows about
the Springs, are there used as a substitute for tea.

The Angelica tree, [Aralia *spinosa*, Ph.] is common along
the banks of the creek, rising to the height of twelve to fifteen feet, and bending beneath its heavy clusters of purple
fruit. The Pteris atropurpurea, Asplenium melanocaulon,
A. ebenum, and other ferns are found adhering to the rocks.
In the open pine woods the Gerrardia *pectinata*, considered
as a variety of G. *pedicularia*, is one of the most conspicuous
objects.

The sources of the Washita, are in a high and broken
part of the Ozark Mountains in north latitude 34° 15',
and between 93 and 94° west longitude, and sixty or an
hundred miles southwest of the settlement of Cadron on the
Arkansa. From the same mountainous district, descend towards the northeast the Petit Jean, and Le Feve, tributaries to the Arkansa; on the northwest the upper branches of
the Poteau, on the southwest the Kiamesha, and on the
southeast the Mountain, Cossetot, Rolling, and other streams
discharging into the Little river of Red river. The principal
source of the Washata is said to lie very near that of the
Fourche Le Feve, and to descend towards the west from
the same hill, out of which flow the upper branches of the

Le Feve towards the east. These particulars are, however, of little importance except as serving to illustrate the character of that portion of the country. The whole region is strictly mountainous, and its numerous streams are rapid and serpentine, winding their way among abrupt and craggy hills, so thinly covered with pine and post oak, that the sober gray of the sandstone, is often the prevailing colour of the landscape. The hills at the sources of the Poteau and the Kiamesha abound in clay slate, and a slaty petrosilex destitute of organic remains.*

It is remarked by the hunters, that the most remote and elevated sources of all the rivers of this region, are in, or near, extensive woodless plains. As far as this is the case, it would seem to prove that the existing inequalities of the surface, have been produced almost entirely by the currents of water wearing down, and removing continuous portions of the horizontally stratified rocks. In districts where secondary rocks only are found, as in the country of the Ohio, there appears little difficulty in attributing this origin to all the hills, and even in the mountainous tract under consideration as the most recent rocks, and those of horizontal stratification, occupy the highest portions of the hills, we may perhaps be allowed to suppose, they formerly covered a much greater extent of country than at present, overlaying those portions of rocks of more ancient deposition, which now appear upon the declivities of the mountains. It cannot escape the remark of any person, who shall visit the range of country which we call the Ozark mountains, that the direction of the ridges (particularly of those where sandstone is the prevailing rock,) conforms to the course of the principal streams. None of the tributaries to the Washita above the Hot Springs, have hitherto been explored. The Little Missouri and the Fourche au Cado, enter it in suc-

* Nuttall's Travels, p. 150.

cession from the west, in the course of a considerable bend
which it makes to the south, after receiving the waters of
Hot Spring creek. These two streams are mostly in a
mountainous country, though some fertile lands, and some
settlements occur on each. On the Little Missouri, Hunter and Dunbar, found the maclura, a tree confined to fertile
soils. The first considerable stream entering the Washita
from the north is the Saline, rising in three principal branches, twenty or thirty miles northwest of the Hot Springs.
The road from Dardenai to the Springs, crosses these
streams near their sources in an extremely rugged and mountainous region. The Saline, like the Washita itself in this
part, and the other tributaries already enumerated, is liable
to great and sudden floods, and also to great depression in
seasons of drought. Originating in a mountainous tract,
and in the continuation of the range so profusely supplied
with springs in the country about the sources of White river,
we might expect the Washita would be fed by numerous
and unfailing fountains. It appears, however, to derive the
greater part of its supplies from the water of rains, and consequently to rise and fall according to the time of year, and
the state of the weather. At the point where Major Long
crossed it on the 31st December 1817, six miles southwest
of the Hot Springs, the river was one hundred and fifty
yards wide, about four feet deep, and running with a rapid
current.

In the latter part of October 1820, at the time of our journey, the Washita at Keisler's settlement, about fifteen miles
below the springs, was something less than one hundred
yards in width, flowing in a deep and unequal channel over
a bed of clay slate. The water is here ten or fifteen feet
deep in many places, and the current scarce perceptible. As
we looked down upon the river from the elevated banks, it
appeared like a quiet lake, and the unusual blackness of the
waters suggested the idea of its great depth. Little groups

of naked rocky islands were disclosed here and there in different parts of the channel. On examination we found the apparent dark colour of the water, to depend upon the complexion of the rocks which form the bottom and sides of the bed, they being principally a dark coloured argillite, and not only these; but the small fragments of quartz and other whitish stones, had acquired from lying in the water a peculiar tinge of dark brown. We expected to find an incrustation covering the surface of these stones, but upon examination, the colouring matter seemed inseparably blended with the rock itself. The water seen by transmitted light, was entirely transparent, and had no perceptible saltness to the taste.

At a distance of five or six miles eastward from the Hot Springs, on the road leading towards the town of Little Rock, on the Arkansa, commences a tract of land having a fertile soil, and a beautiful situation, and extending to the Washita. Some parts of this region afford exceptions to the remark generally applicable to the Arkansa territory, that the best soils are found in the alluvion of the rivers. Some extensive districts of primary soil along the base of the mountains are of a quality rarely surpassed in fertility, bearing heavy forests of oak, ash, and sugar maple, which attain here to greater size than we have seen in other parts of the United States.

We arrived about sunset on the 28th at Keisler's plantation, where we made application for permission to spend the night. This was readily granted, though as is often the case, in such remote and solitary habitations, the house was not in the most complete readiness for the accommodation of travellers. A quantity of Indian corn, was immediately gathered in the adjoining field, a part of it was given to our horses, and a part prepared for our own supper.

During the *green corn season*, which is a time of jubilee and rejoicing among the agricultural Indians, and scarce less so with many of the white settlers, those who live remote from corn mills, use no other bread than such as we now saw prepared within the space of an hour, from the standing corn. Such ears are selected as are fit for roasting, and the corn grated from the cob, by means of the side of a tin lanthron, or some portion of an old coffee pot punched full of holes. In this state it forms a soft paste, which, with the addition of a little salt, is spread upon a heated stone, or an iron pan, and baked before the fire.

The *Cove* is a valley commencing among the mountains, at no great distance to the east of the Hot Springs, and containing a small rivulet, which enters the Washita six or eight miles below Keisler's. This valley is bounded towards the west by loamy hills, disclosing at intervals, cliffs and ledges of clay slate and petrosilex. In the lowest part of this valley at a place called Roark's settlement, we discovered a bed of granite, forming the basis of a broad hill which rose by a very gradual ascent towards the east. We were directed to the examination which brought us acquainted with the existence of this rock, by the representation of Roark, that in his cornfield not far from the house, was a bed of plaister of Paris. Being conducted to the spot, we found a quantity of loose granitic soil, that had been raised from a shallow excavation, and was intermixed with numerous large scales of talc. The examination had been carried a few feet below the surface, and had terminated upon the granite in question, abounding in shining scales of talc and mica, which had been mistaken for plaister. Having collected several beautiful masses of an aggregate of feldspar, talc, and quartz, we returned to the house where our breakfast was in preparation. Being informed by our landlord, that blue vitriol, native copper, and other interesting minerals, had been formerly discovered near the sources of the little brook that ran past the house, we delayed our journey for some time, that we might continue our examination. In following the brook towards its sources, we were much gratified in finding an extensive bed of native magnet, which seemed to be embraced in the granite. Not far distant the same rock contained large masses of pyrites, and of bluish green mica. In these we readily perceived the blue vitriol, and native copper, mentioned by our host. In some places we found the bed of the brook paved almost exclusively, with detached schorls. We collected also several other interesting imbedded minerals. More extensive examinations will hereafter show this spot to be one, among the most interesting in America, to a mineralogist. The great depth of soil resting upon this formation of granite, prevented our examining it at as many points as we could wish, also from ascertaining to our satisfaction its extent, and its connexion with the neighbouring rocks. It appears, however, at several points in an area of fifteen or twenty acres, and always in place. We saw not a single boulder or detached mass at any distance. This may be owing in part to the perishable structure of the granite, and in part to its being surrounded on all sides by more elevated rocks of slate or sandstone. On the summit of the hill a grave had been recently dug. In the granitic soil which lay about it, we saw many fragments of pyrites, also uncommonly large and beautiful laminæ of talc, intermixed with scales of mica. These two minerals are, we think rarely found in such intimate connexion, yet retaining so perfectly their distinctive characters, as in the instance under consideration. The talc sometimes forms an integrant part of the granite and we have seen it blended with mica in the same specimen.

The road leading towards the Little Rock, on the Arkansa, passes from the granite of the Cove over a coarse hard sandstone, embracing beds of conglomerate or pudding stone, and in many respects closely resembling some of the varieties of the old red sandstone of the Alleghany mountains. Towards the east the surface of the country rises gradually, and the sandstone, without giving place to any other stratum, becomes more micaceous and slaty, and at length assumes all the characters of a sandstone accompanying coal.

In the afternoon of the 29th, we arrived at Lockhart's settlement on the Saline Fork of the Washita. The soil of some of the bottom lands along this stream is not inferior to any we have seen west of the Mississippi. It is well watered, and abounds in excellent timber. Pine and oak are intermixed with the ash, hickory, and sugar maple. Here are some well cultivated gardens, and extensive plantations of corn, cotton and tobacco. Mr. Lockhart and his family, who are emigrants from North Carolina, consider the climate more agreeable than that of the country they came from, and have continued during a residence of several years to enjoy good health. We could not fail to attribute this remarkable exemption from disease, in a great measure, to the regularity, neatness, and good order of their domestic economy.

30th. In crossing some broken ridges of sandstone which occupy the high and uninhabited tract between the vallies of the Arkansa and Washita, we followed the obscure path communicating between the settlements on the Saline and the town of Little Rock. As we were descending from one of these ridges, our attention was called to an unusual noise, proceeding from a copse of low bushes on our right, at a few rods from the path; on arriving at the spot we found two buck deer, their horns fast interlocked with each other, and both much spent with fatigue, one in particular being so much exhausted as to be unable to stand. As we perceived it would be impossible they should extricate themselves, and must either linger in their present situation until they died of hunger, or were destroyed by the wolves, we despatched them with our knives, not without having first made an unavailing attempt to disentangle their antlers. Leaving their bodies in the place where we had killed them, we called at the cabin of a settler, which we found within a few miles, and requested him to go back and fetch the venison for the use of his family. From the occasional occurrence of the skulls of deer and elk with the horns interlocked with each other, and from the fact above mentioned, it appears that the contests of these animals, at the season of their orgasm, often prove fatal to both parties. From the form of their horns, and the manner of fighting, it seems probable they must often be entangled with each other, and when this is the case both fall an easy prey to the wolves.*

The Saline has an entire length of about one hundred and fifty miles, running all the way nearly parallel to the Washita, to its confluence near the latitude 33° north. After entering the state of Louisiana, the Washita receives from the east, the Barthelemi, the Bœuf, the Macon, and the Tensa, all of which having their sources near the west bank of the Mississippi, may be considered as inosculating branches of that river, since at times of high floods they are fed from it. The western tributaries are the Saluder, Derbane, and Ocatahoola, deriving their sources from a spur of the Ozark mountains, which in the northern part of Louisiana divides the broad alluvial valley of Red river from that of the Mississippi. About twenty miles southwest from the confluence of the Tensa, Washita, and Ocatahoola the latter expands into a considerable lake, and sends off a branch to Red river. Indeed the Washita might, without great impropriety, be considered as entering the Mississippi at the point where its waters unite with those of the Ocatahoola and Tensa. The periodical inundations cover the country westward to this point, and even in times of low water the channels communicating with the Mississippi are numerous. From this point there is an uninterrupted connection through

* From the observations we had the opportunity of making, it appears that numbers of male bisons, particularly such as have become enfeebled by age, perish annually in the terrible conflicts of their rutting season. We have sometimes seen the horns of the younger bulls splintered almost to the roots; and have met with great numbers of carcasses of such as had apparently been killed in battle.

a system of lakes and water courses stretching along parallel to the Mississippi, about thirty miles distant, and communicating through the river and lake Atchafalaya with the Gulf of Mexico, at a point more than one hundred and fifty miles west of the principal *debouchure* of the Mississippi.

The Red River of Louisiana enters the Mississippi from the west in north latitude 31° 5′, and in 16° 35′ west longitude from Philadelphia.* From the Mississippi to the mouth of Black river, (as the Washita is called below the confluence of the Ocatahoola and Tensa,) is twenty-six miles by water. The aggregate width of Red river, for this distance, is from three hundred to three hundred and fifty yards. The depth of the water in summer varies, according to the actual measurements of Messrs. Freeman and Humphrey, from eighty-four to forty-two feet; the range from extreme high to low water is from twenty-five to thirty feet, and the banks are elevated from fourteen to twenty-five feet above the surface of the river at low water. At no great distance on each side is a second alluvial bank, rising a few feet higher than the immediate bank of the river. Back of this the surface is raised nearly to *high water mark*, but descends gradually towards the lakes and swamps which occur along both sides of the valley of the river. In the wet season the lower part of Red and Black rivers are lost in an extensive lake, covering the country from the Mississippi westward near one hundred miles, to the settlement of the Avoyelles. The distinction made by Du Pratz between the country on the south and that on the north side of Red river, appears to be strictly applicable only to the part lying below the point where Red river enters the immediate valley of the Mississippi.†

* Ellicot: 31° 1′ 15″ according to Mr. De Ferrer.

† " The south side of this river, quite to the rapid part, is entirely different from the opposite side; it is something higher, and rises in proportion as it approaches to the height I have mentioned; the quality is also very

Above Black river the bed of Red river immediately contracts to one hundred and twenty yards, which is its average width from this point to the Rapids, seventy-two miles above. The current becomes, in a corresponding degree, more rapid, running with a velocity of from two and an half, to three miles per hour, at a moderate stage of water, in the early part of summer. The average depth in this section is stated at from eighteen to twenty feet, at a time when the water is twenty-one feet below its maximum of elevation. The banks are generally bold and steep, on one side or the other, and often on both. The bottom lands are level, and exceedingly fertile, but bear the marks of periodical inundation. The forests of the lower section of Red river differ little from those of the Mississippi and the Arkansa. White gum, cotton-wood, pecan, locust, white oak, mulberry, sycamore, hackberry, and cypress, occupy the low grounds, while the low and scattered hills are covered with pine, intermixed with a small proportion of oak and hickory. The only portion of the low lands in any sort fit for cultivation is a narrow strip immediately on each bank, commencing a little above the mouth of Black river, and enlarging upwards; but even here the settler is not secure, as uncommon swellings of the river, sometimes lay the whole under water. Aside from this the extreme insalubrity of the air, occasioned by the vicinity of extensive swamps, stagnant ponds, and lagoons, tends greatly to retard the progress of settlements in this quarter.

At the Rapids the river spreads to three hundred yards in width. The banks are thirty feet high, and never overflowed. Here has for many years been a settlement. The

different. This land is good and light, and is disposed to receive all the culture imaginable, in which we may assuredly hope to succeed. It naturally produces fruit trees and vines, in plenty; it was on that side, muscadine grapes were found. The back parts have neater woods and meadows, intersected with tall forests. On that side the fruit trees of the country are common, and above all the hickory and walnut trees, which are sure indications of good soil." Du Pratz's Louisiana, p. 166.

soil of the neighbouring country is extremely fertile. A bed
of soft sandstone, or indurated clay, crosses the river, causing a fall of ten feet in fifty yards. " This stone, when exposed to the air, becomes as hard as freestone, but under
water it is found as soft as chalk: a channel could with very
little labour or expense be cut through any part of the bed
of the river, and need not be extended more than two hundred yards. It is believed that twenty men, in ten days,
with mattocks only, could, at low water, open a channel sufficiently wide and deep for all the barges that trade in this
river to pass with safety and ease.* Three quarters of a
mile above this rapid is another very similar in extent and
magnitude.

Thirty miles above the Rapids we find the river divided
into two beds, each having a high bold bank. The right
channel contains about one-third of the volume of water of
the whole river. They separate from each other four or five
miles below Natchitoches, and unite again here, forming an
island sixty miles long and five wide. The right branch is called by the French " Rigote de Bon Dieu," and the other Old
river. Another island, commencing one-fourth of a mile below Natchitoches, extends parallel to that above mentioned
thirty-four and an half miles: this is about four miles wide.
The current in all the branches which lie between these islands and the main shore is rapid, but not equally so. The
description already given of the valley of the river is applicable to this portion. On each side the surface descends
from the river, terminating in a line of pools and cypress
swamps, which extend along the base of the bluffs. Settlements were here somewhat numerous in 1806. The small
cottages are placed near the bank of the river, and the cultivated lands extend back but a little distance. " The inhabitants," says Freeman, " are a mixture of French, Spanish,
Indian, and Negro blood, the latter often predominating.

* Freeman's MS. Report to Wm. Dunbar, Esq.

The separation of the water of the river into three distinct branches, each confined within high and steep banks, raised twenty and even thirty feet above the medium elevation of the water, and their reunion after traversing severally an extent of sixty and thirty miles, might, at first view, appear a matter of curious inquiry, but, upon the slightest investigation, it will be discovered, that this whole country, adjacent to the river, has been *made* or raised to its present elevated position by frequent inundations and deposition from the water. This evidently appears from the great quantities of timber frequently seen as you ascend the river, deposited as low as low-water mark under steep banks of different heights, from twelve to thirty feet.

Red river takes its name from the colour of its water, which is, in time of floods, of a bright red, and partakes more or less of this colour throughout the year, as is also the case with the sands of its bed. There can be no doubt the colouring matter, on which this tinge depends, is derived from the red sandstone of the salt formation already described, although no person qualified to give a satisfactory account of the country, has hitherto traced Red river to that formation. We propose to add some brief notices of this important river, derived from the unpublished materials of the exploring party sent out by the government of the United States in 1806, also from the notes of Major Long, who visited the upper settlements in 1817, not neglecting such additional information, from the works of Darby and others, who have written of Louisiana, as may appear of importance.

Red river was explored at a very early period by the French, but their examinations appear to have extended no farther than to the country of the Natchitoches and the Cadoes* and, although subsequent examinations have a little

* In 1700, M. De Bienville ascended the Red river to the country of the Natchitoches and Yatasse Indians, but could find no Spanish esta-

enlarged the sphere of our acquaintance with its upper branches, we are still unfortunately ignorant of the true position of its sources.

Three years after the cession of Louisiana to the United States, a small party known by the name of the "Exploring Expedition of Red river," and consisting of Captain Sparks, Mr. Freeman, Lieutenant Humphrey, and Dr Custis, with seventeen private soldiers, two non-commissioned officers, and a black servant, embarked from St. Catharine's landing, near Natches, on board several barges and small boats, with instructions to ascend Red river to its sources. On the 3rd of May, 1806, they entered Red river, expecting to be able to ascend with their boats to the country of the Pawnee Piqua Indians. Here it was their intention to leave their boats, and packing their provisions on horses, which they should purchase of the Pawnees, they were to " proceed to the top of the mountains," the distance being, as they believed, about three hundred miles.

On the 19th May, they arrived at Natchitoches, distant from the Mississippi 184 miles 266 perches, measured by log line and time. At this place they delayed some days, and having received information that their advance would be opposed by the Spaniards, they resolved to increase the strength of their party by retaining a detachment which had been ordered by the secretary of war to join them at Nachitoches, " for the purpose of assisting the exploring party to ascend the river to the upper end of the great raft, and to continue as far afterward as might appear necessary, to repel by force any opposition they might meet with."

Accordingly twenty men were selected from the garrison at Natchitoches, and, under the command of Lieutenant Duforest, joined the exploring party.

---

blishment in that quarter. The Yatasse village was about forty miles northwest of the present town of Natchitoches in the settlement of Bayou Pierre.

Darby on the authority of La Harpe.

They were now thirty-seven in number, aside from the officers, and were furnished with a supply of flour sufficient for nine months' provision. On the 2nd June, they left Natchitoches and proceeded towards their destination. The journal of their tour, by Mr. Freeman, which has been obligingly put into our hands by Gen. D. Parker, is extremely circumstantial, and embraces much valuable information. We make use of it without particular reference whenever we have occasion to speak of that part of Red river explored by the party. On the 7th of June, they were overtaken near a small village of Natchitoches and Paskagoulas, by an Indian guide and interpreter, whom they had hired at Natchitoches. He brought a letter from Dr. Sibley, the Indian agent, giving information that a considerable body of Spanish troops were already on their march from Nacogdoches, with a design to intercept the exploring party. At the distance of one hundred and two miles above Natchitoches, they left the bed of the river turning out through one of those numerous communications called bayous, which connect the principal channel with those lateral chains of lakes, pools, swamps, and marshes, which extend along the sides of the valley. Their design, in leaving the river, was to avoid that singular obstruction to the navigation, called the Great Raft, having been informed by Mr. Toolan, an old and respectable French inhabitant, that it would be impossible for them to pass through it. They had already encountered three similar obstructions, through which they had made their way with extreme toil, by loosening and floating out, the logs and trunks of trees, that had been piled upon each other in such numbers as to fill the bed of the river from the bottom, usually at the depth of thirty feet, and rising three or four feet above the surface of the water.

The Bayou Datche, as the part of the river is called into which they entered, conducted them to a beautiful lake

called Big Broth.*   It is thus described by **Mr Freeman.**
" This beautiful sheet of water extends from the place we
first entered it seventy miles in a north-westerly direction,
and, as far as we saw it, is beautifully variegated with handsome clumps of cypress trees, thinly scattered in it. On the
right hand side it is bounded by high land, which ascends
from the surface of the water, and at the distance of one
hundred yards, is elevated about forty feet, and covered
with forests of black oak, hickory, dogwood, &c. soil good
second rate. It is bounded on the left by a low plain, covered with cypress trees and bushes. The depth of water is
from two to six feet. High-water mark ten feet above the
present level of the surface. It is called by the Indians *Big
Broth*, from the vast quantities of froth seen floating on its
surface at high water. We passed out of this large lake by
very difficult passes through bayous into another very handsome lake of about a mile wide, called Swan lake, and so on
through long crooked bayous, lakes, and swamps, full of dead
standing timber."

Having made their way for many days along this chain of
lakes, they were at length anxious to return to the river.
After searching some time for a passage, and finding their
pilot incapable to direct them, they resolved to wait while
they could send messengers by land to the Coashatay village,
and procure a guide. The return of this messenger brought
them some information calculated to aid in extricating themselves from the labyrinth of lakes in which they were bewildered, also the promise of the Coashatay chief, that he
would join the party himself and conduct them to the river.
This promise, however, it was not his intention to fulfil. The
party, therefore, on the 20th June, resumed their search for
a passage, returning some distance on their route. On the
25th, they discovered a narrow and obstructed channel,

* Lake Bistineau.

through which, after removing several rafts, trees, &c., they found their way into the river. Thus, after fourteen days of incessant fatigue, toil and danger, doubt and uncertainty, they at length gained the river above the Great Raft, contrary to the decided opinion of every person who had any knowledge of the difficulties they had to encounter.

The distance from Natchitoches to the point where the party entered Red river above the Great Raft is two hundred and one miles by the meanders of their route. Above the raft the river is two hundred and thirty yards wide, thirty-four feet deep, and has a very gentle current. The banks are ten or twelve feet high. On the north side the lands rise considerably, at a little distance, and are covered with heavy forests of oak, poplar, and red cedar.

At the Coashatay village,* about twenty miles above the

---

* The latitude of this point, acccording to the observations of the Exploring party, has been ascertained by Lieutenant Graham.

	deg. m. s.
Coashatay village, June 27th, 1806. Observed the double meridian altitude of star Antares (α Scorpii)	62 30 25
Index error of sextant,	2 1-2
	2) 62 30 22 1-2
	31 15 11 1-4
Correction for refraction,	1 33 1-4
True meridian altitude of star Antares	31 13 38
	90
Meridian zenith distance, do.	58 46 22
Declination of Antares for reduced time,	25 59 20 S.
Latitude,	32 47 02 N.

	deg. m. s.
June 30th. Double meridian alt. Antares	62 31 20
Index error	1 05
	2) 62 30 15
	31 15 07 1-2

Great Raft; the commander of the exploring party received information by an express, from the chief of the principal village of the Cadoes, which is thirty miles farther to the west, " that about three hundred Spanish dragoons, with four or five hundred horses and mules were encamped near that village with the design to prevent the further advance of the Americans." The Coashatay and Cado Indians of

		deg. m. s.
		31 15 07 1-2
Correction for refraction,	. . .	1 33 1-2
True meridian alt. Antares,	. . .	31 13 34
		90
True meridian zenith distance do.	: .	58 46 26
Declination of Antares for June, 1806, .	.	25 59 20 S.
Latitude	. . . .	32 47 06 N.

At the same place (Coashatay village.)

		deg. m. s.
July 1st, 1806. Double meridian alt. Antares,	.	62 31 45
Index error of sextant,	. . .	1 05
		2) 62 30 40
		31 15 20
Deduct for refraction	. . . .	1 33
True meridian alt. Antares,	. . .	31 13 47
		90
True meridian zenith distance do.	. .	58 46 13
Declination of Antares for red. time,	. .	25 59 20 S.
Latitude,	. . . . .	32 46 53 N.

Latitude of Coashatay village.

		deg. m. s.
By observation, June 27th, 1806	. .	32 47 02 N.
" " 30th, "	. .	32 47 06
" · July 1st, "	. .	32 46 53
Mean latitude,	. . . . .	32 47 00 1-3 N.

this part of Red river are agricultural and half-civilized, like the Cherokees.

On the 1st of July, a messenger arrived at the encampment of the party, near the Coashatay village, giving information of the near approach of the Cado chief, with forty young men and warriors of his village. About noon they made their appearance on the opposite bank of the river, and kept up for a few minutes an irregular firing by way of salute. This was returned both from the camp and the village in a manner highly gratifying to the Cado party. The customary ceremonies used in meeting Indians being past an exchange of complimentary speeches followed.

The Cado chief expressed great uneasiness on account of the Spaniards who were encamped near his village. Their commandant had been to see him, had taken him by the hand, and asked him if he loved the Americans; he answered, he did not know what to say, but if the Spaniards wished to fight the Americans, they might go down to Natchitoches, and fight them there, but they should not shed blood in his territories. He said he was pleased with what he had heard respecting the designs of the exploring party, he wished them to go on and see all his country, and all his neighbours. " You have far to go, and will meet with many difficulties, but I wish you to go on. My friends, the Pawnees, will be glad to see you, and will take you by the hand. If you meet with any of the Huzaas [*Osages*] and kill them, I will dance for a month. If they kill any of your party, I will go with my young men and warriors, and we will be avenged for you." The soldiers belonging to the expedition having paraded in open order and single file, the forty young Cadoes commenced on the right of the line, and marching towards the left, shook each man by the hand in the most earnest manner. When their leader had reached the other extremity of the line, they instantly placed themselves in a corresponding line about three paces distant, and their partizan or principal warrior, delivered a short address to the sergeant.

" Here we are," said he, " all men and warriors. Shaking hands together, let us hold fast, and be friends forever." It was said by the interpreter, he prefaced his observation by saying he was glad to see that his new brothers had the faces of men, and looked like men and warriors.

After a delay of a few days, the Cado chief professing the most friendly disposition towards the exploring party, withdrew with his young men, to his own village. On the 11th July, the officers of the party having as yet no certain knowledge of the designs of the Spaniards, re-embarked on board their little fleet, and began to ascend Red river, from the Coashatay village, having engaged the Cado chief to watch the motions of the Spanish troops, and to give timely notice of any thing interesting to the expedition. The river above the Coashatay village became very crooked and wide, and the water was so low that the boats were often aground, though they drew no more than from sixteen to twenty inches of water.

On the 26th July, in the afternoon, three Indians appeared on the sand beach, who were found to be the runners sent from the Cado chief, agreeable to previous engagement. They brought information that the Spaniards had returned to Nacogdoches for a reinforcement, and new instructions; that six days since, they had arrived at the Cado village, about one thousand strong; that they had cut down the U. S. flag in the Cado village, and had said it was their intention to destroy the exploring party. They had taken from the Cado village, two young men to conduct them to a handsome bluff, a few miles above, where they were now encamped, to await the arrival of the party. The Indian messengers, and the Cadoes who had remained, appeared much alarmed, and entreated the commanding officer to return, saying, if they met the Spaniards, not one would come back alive. The distance to the Spanish camp was three days' journey. On the following day, the party made a deposite of some of their most important papers, with a small stock of ammunition, provisions, and astronomical instruments, in a retired place, that they might not be entirely destitute of resources after the contemplated rencontre with the Spaniards should have taken place. At sunset, on the 28th July, as they were about to encamp, they heard several guns ahead of them, which left no doubt that they had arrived near the Spanish camp. On the ensuing morning, Capt. Sparks, Mr. Freeman, and a favorite Indian, walked before the boats, along the sand beach, with their guns in their hands. The Indian discovering some tracks, ran hastily among the bushes on the bank, and then returning, made signs that the Spaniards were there. The party was now halted, the arms examined, and put in readiness for immediate action; then all went on board the boats, and continued their ascent, as if they had known nothing of the Spanish troops. The advanced guard, which the Indian had discovered, consisted of twenty-two men, stationed a mile and a half below the encampment of the main body. On seeing the boats, they fled instantly, and hid themselves in the woods, leaving behind their clothes and provisions.

On turning the next bend, they had a beautiful view of the river, for about a mile. The banks were steep on both sides, and level sand beaches occupied about one half the bed of the river. On one of these, at the distance of half a mile, they discovered a sentinel, and soon afterwards, saw a detachment of horse gallop from thence, through the small cotton-wood bushes, near the next bend of the river, and shortly after return to their former station. As it was now the middle of the day, the Exploring party halted, according to custom, and kindled fires to prepare their dinner.

About half an hour after they had halted, a large detachment from the Spanish camp were seen riding down the sand beach, enveloped in such a cloud of dust, that their numbers could not be accurately estimated. The soldiers belonging to the exploring party were directed to take possession of a thick cane brake on the immediate bank of the river, at a short distance above the boats, to be in readiness should there be occasion to attack the advancing party on their flank. A non-commissioned officer and six men were sent still further up the river, and ordered to be in readiness to assail the Spaniards in the rear.

The advancing party of horse came on at full speed, disregarding the first challenge of the two sentinels stationed at some distance in advance of the boats. When the sentinels cried *halt* the second time, they cocked their pieces, and were in the act of presenting them, when the Spanish squadron halted, and displayed on the beach, about one hundred and fifty yards distant. Their officers moved slowly forward and were met by Captain Sparks, whom the Spanish commandant politely saluted, and a parley ensued, which continued about three quarters of an hour. The Spaniards being greatly superior in numbers, and expressing a determined resolution to fulfil their orders, which were to prevent, at all hazards, the farther progress of the Exploring expedition, the officers of that party reluctantly consented to relinquish their undertaking. The spot where this interruption took place, is two hundred and thirty miles, by water, above the Coashatay village, consequently, six hundred and thirty-five miles above the mouth of Red river. Below this point the river and country lose in a great measure, the peculiar characters which belong to the region of recent alluvial lands within the valley of the Mississippi. The swamps and bayous are less frequent, the forests more open, the trees smaller, and the soil less fertile. Open meadows are more frequent here than below. A portion of Red river above, between this point, and the upper settlements, is but imperfectly known.

The average direction of Red river, as far as it has been hitherto explored, from the confluence of the Kiamesha in latitude 33° 30′ to its junction with the Mississippi in 31° 5′ is from northwest to southeast. Above the Kiamesha, it is supposed to flow more directly from west to east. The streams tributary to Red river are comparatively small, and few in number. Above the Washita, already mentioned, the principal are the Little river of the south, and the Little river of the north, both entering near the north-western angle of the state of Louisiana, and both hitherto, little known. The next in order is the Kiamesha, rising in the Ozark mountains, opposite the Poteau, and entering Red river about one thousand miles from the Mississippi. The Kiamesha has been explored from its sources to its mouth, by Major Long, who first visited it in 1817. The country about the sources of this river is mountainous, being broken into numerous irregular heaps and ridges of an old ferruginous sandstone, with its stratifications highly inclined towards the south. The timber in the mountainous country is the yellow pine, intermixed with red, white, and mountain oak, the small chesnut, the American box, or hop hornbeam, [Ostrya *virginica*] the red cedar, &c. In the low lands towards Red river, all the forest trees common to the valley of the Arkansa are found with the addition of the maclura, which is now so rare about the Arkansa that it can scarce be said to make a part of the forests there. Extensive prairies exist on the lower part of the Kiamesha, some of which command delightful views of the surrounding country. Before you lies the great valley of Red river, exhibiting a pleasing variety of forests and lawns; beyond are the summits of the Ozark mountains, imprinting their broad outline upon the margin of the sky.

At the mouth of the Kiamesha, Red river is about two hundred yards wide. Its course is serpentine, forming points alternately on the right and left, terminating in sand bars, covered with red mud, or clay deposited from the water of the river. In its lowest stage the river may be forded at any place, so that a person may pass along the bed as in the Canadian, by travelling on the sand bars, and occasionally crossing the water between them.

The soil and climate of Red River are said to be peculiarly adapted to the culture of cotton. The crop sometimes yields twenty-five hundred pounds of seed cotton per acre, and this of a quality inferior to none except the Sea island.

Of the Vaseau or Boggy bayou, and the Blue River, two considerable streams tributary to Red river next above the Kiamesha, we have little information. They appear to enter like what are called the north and south forks of the Canadian, near the foot of the western slope of the Ozark mountains. Above these, the principal tributary is the Faux Ouachitta, or False Washita, from the north, which has been described to us by Mr. Findley, (an enterprising hunter, whose pursuits often led him to visit its banks,) as bearing a very near resemblance to the Canadian river of the Arkansa.

We are as yet ignorant of the true position of the sources of Red river, but are well assured the long received opinion that its principal branch rises " about thirty or forty miles east of Santa Fe" is erroneous.

Several persons have recently arrived at St. Louis in Missouri, from Santa Fe, and among them, the brother of Capt. Shreeves, who gives information of a large, frequented road, which runs nearly due east from that place, and strikes one of the branches of the Canadian, and that at a considerable distance to the south of this point in the high plain, is the principal source of Red river. His account confirms an opinion which we had previously formed, namely, that the branch of the Canadian explored by Major Long's party in August, 1820, has its sources near those of some stream, which descends towards the west, into the Rio del Norte, and consequently that some other region must contain the head of Red river. From a careful comparison of all the information we have been able to collect, we are satisfied that the stream, on which we encamped on the 28th July, is the Rio Raijo of Humboldt, long mistaken for the source of the Red river of Natchitoches, and that our camp of Aug. 1st was within forty or fifty miles east from Santa Fe. In a region of red clay and sand, where all the streams have nearly the colour of arterial blood, it is not surprising that several rivers should have received the same name, nor is it surprising that so accurate a topographer as the Baron Humboldt, having learned that a *red river* rises forty or fifty miles east of Santa Fe, and runs to the east, should conjecture it might be the source of the Red river of Natchitoches. This conjecture, (for it is no more) we believe to have been adopted by our geographers, who have with much confidence made their delineations, and their accounts correspond to it.

In relation to the climate of the country on Red river, we have received little definite information. The Journal of the Exploring Expedition contains a record of thermometric observations for thirty-six days, commencing with June 1st 1806, and extending to July 6th. These were made between Natchitoches and the Coashatay village, and the temperature, both of the air and the water of the river, are noted three times a day, at 6 A. M., and 3, and 9 P. M. They indicate a climate extremely mild and equable. The atmospheric temperature ranges from $72°$ to $93°$ Fah., that of the water from $79°$ to $92°$. The daily oscillations of the mercurial column are nearly equal, and the aggregate temperature rises slowly and uniformly towards midsummer.

From Lockhart's settlement on the Saline river of Washita to Little Rock, on the Arkansa, is about twenty-five miles. As we approached the Arkansa, we found the country less broken and rocky than above. The soil of the uplands is gravelly, and comparatively barren, producing almost exclusively scattered forests of oak, while along the streams are small tracts of extremely fertile bottom lands. In some of the vallies the cypress appears, filling extensive swamps, and imparting a gloomy and unpromising aspect to the country.

This tree is well known in all the southern section of the United States to indicate a low and marshy soil, but not universally one which is irreclaimable. It is rarely if ever met with north of the latitude of 38°. In many respects, particularly in the texture, firmness, and durability of its wood, and in its choice of situation, it resembles the white cedar* of the northern States, but far surpasses it in size, being one of the largest trees in North America. " There is," says Du Pratz, " a cypress tree at Baton Rouge, which measures twelve yards round, and is of prodigious height." In the cypress swamps few other trees, and no bushes, are seen; and the innumerable conic excrescences called knees which spring up from the roots, resembling the monuments in a church yard, give a gloomy and peculiar aspect to the scene. The old error of Du Pratz, with regard to the manner of the reproduction of the cypress, is still maintained with great obstinacy by numbers of people who never heard of his book.

" It renews itself," says he, " in a most extraordinary manner. A short time after it is cut down, a shoot is observed to grow from one of its roots, exactly in the form of a sugar loaf, and this sometimes rises ten feet high before any leaf appears; the branches at length rise from the head of this conical shoot." p. 239.

We have often been reminded of this account of Du Pratz by hearing the assertion among the settlers, that the cypress never grows from the seed. It would appear, however, that he could have been but little acquainted with the tree, or he would have been aware that the conic excrescences in question spring up and grow during the life of the tree, but never after it is cut down.

At Little Rock, a village of six or eight houses, we found several of the members of a missionary family destined to

---

* Thuja *occidentalis*, L.

the Osages. They had exposed themselves during the heat of summer to the pestilential atmosphere of the Lower Mississippi and Arkansa; and we were not surprised, when we considered their former habits, to find they had suffered most severely from their imprudence. They had all been sick, and two or three of their number had died; the survivors we understood were on the recovery. They had been some time at Little Rock, the water in the Arkansa having fallen so low as to render their further ascent impracticable.

The village of Little Rock occupies the summit of a high bank of clay slate, on the southwest side of the Arkansa. Its site is elevated, and the country immediately adjoining in a great measure exempt from the operation of those causes which produce a state of the atmosphere unfavorable to health. It is near the commencement of the hilly country, and for a part of the year will be at the head of steam boat navigation on the Arkansa. The country in the rear of the projected town is high, and covered for the most part with open oak forests.

3rd. We left Little Rock at an early hour, taking the road towards Davidsonville. This led us, for about four miles, through the deep and gloomy forests of the Arkansa bottoms. Here we saw the Ricinus *palma christi* growing spontaneously by the road side, and rising to the height of twelve or fourteen feet. We arrived at Little Red river by about nine o'clock, the distance from the Arkansa being not more than eight or nine miles. In the high and rocky country about White river, we fell in, with the route which had been pursued by Major Long and his party, and following this we reached Cape Girardeau a few days after their arrival. The distance from Belle Point to Little Rock, by the way of the Hot Springs, is two hundred and ten miles, from Little Rock to Cape Girardeau, three hundred, in the whole five hundred and ten miles.

Major Long's notes of a tour in the Arkansa Territory

contain tables of meteorological observations, showing the variations of temperature from September 30th 1817 to January 31st 1818. The country, in which these observations were made, is that between the Arkansa, at Fort Smith, and the Red river, at the mouth of the Kiamesha, about the Hot Springs of the Washita, and the settlement of the Cadron. Here we find, in the month of January, the mercury at zero, and shortly after at 58°, a degree of cold that would not discredit the climate of Moscow, and a rapidity of change and violence of vicissitude comparable with the ever varying temperature of the Atlantic States. We might expect in the latitude of 34°, and in a region placed along the southwestern slope of a moderately elevated range of mountains, a mild and uniform climate. But almost every portion of the territory of the United States seems alike exposed to the influence of the western and north-western winds refrigerated in their passage over the wide and frozen regions of the Rocky Mountains, and rushing down unobstructed across the naked plains of the great desert, penetrating quite to the Atlantic coast.

We have reason to believe that the opinion of M. Volney, respecting the comparative temperature of the regions east and west of the Alleghany mountains, has been somewhat too hastily adopted. Our limited observations have led us to suspect that at equal elevations, the aggregate temperature, if any thing different, is by no means more mild or equable on the western side of the mountains, in the valley of the Mississippi, than on the Atlantic coast, and in confirmation of this opinion we are happy to cite the authority of Mr. Darby, whose opportunities for observation have been much greater than ours, he having spent sixteen years in the valley of the Mississippi. Some passages in the work of Baron Humboldt seem at variance with the prevailing opinion which he has adopted from Volney and Barton, of the greater mildness of the climate of the western parts of the Mississippi country. " The proximity of Canada, the great breadth of the new continent towards the north, the mass of snows with which it is covered," says he, " occasion in the Mexican atmosphere frigorifications by no means to be expected in these regions."* By the inspection of the tables of thermometric observations annexed to this volume it will be seen that the extremes both of cold and heat are greater at Council Bluff than at Germantown in the vicinity of Philadelphia.

It is proper to remark that the winter of 1817-18 was considered one of unusual severity in the Arkansa Territory. From the account of Hunter and Dunbar it appears that in December 1804 the weather was much milder in the same portion of country. An alligator was seen, in December, many miles above the entrance of the Saline Fork, and even at the Hot Springs many plants were in flower, and the ground in the woods had considerable appearance of verdure.

On the 12th October, the Exploring party were all assembled at Cape Girardeau. Lieutenant Graham with the steam boat Western Engineer, had arrived a day or two before from St. Louis, having delayed there, some time subsequent to his return from the Upper Mississippi. In the discharge of the duties on which he had been ordered, lieutenant Graham and all his party, had suffered severely from bilious and intermitting fever.

A few days subsequent to our arrival at Cape Girardeau, the greater number of those who had been of the party by land, experienced severe attacks of intermitting fever, none escaped except Capt. Bell, Mr. Peale, and Lieut. Swift. Maj. Long and Capt. Kearney, who had continued their journey immediately towards St. Louis, were taken ill at St. Genevieve, and the latter was confined some weeks. The attack was almost simultaneous in the cases of those who re-

* New Spain, p. 58, Vol. I.

mained at Cape Girardeau, and it is highly probable, we had all received the impression which produced the disease nearly at the same time. The interruption of accustomed habits, and the discontinuance of the excitement afforded by travelling, may have somewhat accelerated the attack. We had observed that we had felt somewhat less than the usual degree of health, since breathing the impure and offensive atmosphere of the Arkansa bottoms about Belle Point, and there, we have no doubt the disease fastened upon us. In every instance, we had the opportunity of observing, the attack assumed the form of a daily intermittent. The cold stage commenced with a sensation of languor and depression, attended with almost incessant yawning, and a disinclination to motion, soon followed by shivering, and a distressing sensation of cold. These symptoms pass off gradually, and the hot stage succeeds. The degree of fever is usually somewhat proportioned to the violence of the cold fit, the respiration becomes full and frequent, the face is flushed, the skin moist, and the patient falls into a heavy slumber; on awaking after some time, extreme languor and exhaustion are felt, though few symptoms of fever remain. This routine of most uncomfortable feelings commencing at nine or ten in the morning, occupied for some time, the greater part of our days; late at evening, and during the night we suffered less.

Intermitting fevers are of such universal occurrence in every part of the newly settled country to the west, that every person is well acquainted with the symptoms, and has some favorite method of treatment. A very common practice, and one productive of much mischief, is that of administering large draughts of whiskey and red pepper, previous to the accession of the cold stage. Applications of this kind may sometimes shorten the cold fit, but the consequent fever is comparatively increased, and the disease rendered more obstinate. The Peruvian bark is much used, but often so injudiciously as to occasion great mischief.

Cape Girardeau, formerly the seat of justice, for a county of the same name, is one of the oldest settlements in Upper Louisiana, having been for a long time the residence of a Spanish intendant or governor. Occupying the first considerable elevation on the western bank of the Mississippi, above the mouth of the Ohio, and affording a convenient landing place for boats, it promises to become a place of some little importance, as it must be the *depot* of a considerable district of country, extending from the commencement of the Great Swamp, on the southeast, to the upper branches of the St. Francis. The advantages of its situation must be considered greater, than those of the settlements of Tyawapatia and New Madrid, which are not sufficiently elevated. It is near the commencement of the hilly country extending up the Mississippi, to the confluence of the Missouri, northwest to the Gasconade and Osage rivers, and southwest to the province of Texas. Two or three miles below Cape Girardeau the cypress swamps commence, extending with little interruption far to the south.

The town comprises at this time about twenty log cabins, several of them in ruins, a log jail, no longer occupied, a large unfinished brick building, falling rapidly to decay, and a small one, finished and occupied. It stands on the slope and part of the summit of a broad hill, rising about one hundred and fifty feet above the Mississippi, and having a deep primary soil, resting on horizontal strata of compact and sparry limestone. Near the place where boats usually land, is a point of white rock, jutting into the Mississippi, and at a very low stage of water, producing a perceptible ripple. It is a white sparry limestone, abounding in remains of Encrini, and other marine animals. If traced some distance, it will be found to alternate with the common blue compact limestone, most frequently seen in secondary districts. Though the stratifications of this sparry limestone are horizontal, the rock is little divided by seams and fissures, and would undoubtedly afford a valuable marble, not unlike the *Darling* marble quarried on the Hudson.

The streets of Cape Girardeau are marked out, with formal regularity, intersecting each other at right angles, but they are now in some parts so gullied and torn by the rains as to be impassable, in others, overgrown with such a crop of gigantic vernonias and urticas, as to resemble small forests. The country back of the town is hilly, covered with heavy forests of oak, tulip tree, and nyssa, intermixed in the vallies with the sugar tree, and the fagus sylvatica, and on the hills with an undergrowth of the American hazle, and the shot bush or angelica tree. Settlements are considerably advanced, and many well cultivated farms occur in various directions.

Two or three weeks elapsed previous to Major Long's return from St. Louis, when, notwithstanding his ill health, he left Cape Girardeau immediately, as did Capt. Bell, both intending to prosecute without delay, their journey to the seat of government.

About the first of November, Messrs. Say, Graham, and Seymour, had so far recovered their health, as to venture on a voyage to New Orleans, on their way home. They left Cape Girardeau in a small boat, which they exchanged at the mouth of the Ohio for a steam boat, about to descend. Mr. Peale, who had escaped the prevailing sickness, accompanied them. On his way down the Mississippi, Mr. Say observed the new animal described in the subjoined note.*

---

* Genus. *Scincus,* Daud.

S. *lateralis.* Say. Light brown above; a lateral blackish line; about six scales behind the *head* wider than the others.

Body above light brownish, with small black spots or abbreviated lines, sides with a dilated black vitta which commences at the nostril, passes through the eyes, is varied with pale spots and abbreviated longitudinal lines, is paler towards its inferior edge and obsolete behind; *scales* smooth; *tail* longer than the body, with very numerous, obsolete, small longitudinal spots; superior and inferior series of scales beyond the middle transversely widened into plates; *head* with the rostrum rather short; immediately behind the plates of the head are about six scales larger than

Dr. James and Lieut. Swift only, were left with the steam boat Western Engineer at Cape Girardeau. Lieut. Swift had received instructions, as soon as the water should rise sufficiently, to proceed with the boat to the falls of Ohio, where it was to remain during the winter.

Early in November, the frosts had been so severe at Cape Girardeau, that the leaves were fallen, and the country had assumed the aspect of winter. On the 9th at four P. M. the shock of an earthquake was felt. The agitation was such as to cause considerable motion in the furniture, and other loose articles in the room where we were sitting. Before we had time to collect our thoughts, and run out of the house, it had ceased entirely; we had therefore no opportunity to form an opinion of its direction. Several others occurred in the time of our stay at the Cape, but they all happened at night, and were all of inconsiderable duration. "Shakes," as these concussions are called by the inhabitants, are, in this part of the country, extremely frequent, and are spoken of as matters of every day occurrence.

Several ladies and gentlemen, passengers on board a steam boat ascending the Mississippi in 1820, went on shore near New Madrid. In one of the houses, which they entered, they found a small collection of books. As they were amusing themselves with the examination of these, they felt the whole house so violently shaken, that they were scarce able to stand upon their feet. Some consternation was, of course,

---

the remaining cervical ones; *legs* spotted with pale; *beneath* greenish-white;

Total length	4 inches.
Tail	2 2-5

Occurred during our passage down the Mississippi to New Orleans, and proved to be specifically indentical with specimens which I formerly collected in Georgia and East Florida. Daudin describes no species with which it can be confounded, if we except his *S. laticeps*, from which apparently kindred species it differs in being totally destitute of any thing like bands. The large scales behind the head are very similar to the subcaudal scales of a Coluber.

The largest individual I have seen, was less than five inches long—a specimen is deposited in the Philadelphia Museum.

felt, and much terror expressed. " Don't be alarmed" said
the lady of the house, " it is nothing but an earthquake."

Several houses in and about Cape Girardeau, have formerly been shaken down, forests have been overthrown,*
and other considerable changes produced by their agency.
Their effect upon the constantly varying channels and bars
in the bed of the Mississippi, must doubtless be very considerable.

These concussions are ordinarily felt through a great extent of country, from the settlements on Red river, and the
Washita, to the falls of Ohio, and from the mouth of the
Missouri to New Orleans. Their great extent, and the
very considerable degree of violence with which they affect
not only a large portion of the valley of the Mississippi, but
of the adjacent hilly and mountainous country, appear to us
most clearly to indicate a cause far more efficient, and deep
seated than " the decomposition of beds of lignite or wood
coal, situated near the level of the river, and filled with pyrites," according to the suggestion of Mr. Nuttall.†

From the beginning of the year 1811 till 1813, a vast extent of the earth lying between 50 and 45° of north latitude,
limited by the meridian of the Azores, the range of the Alleghanies and the Green Mountains of Vermont,‡ the valley
of the Missouri, the cordilleras of New Grenada, the coasts
of Venezuela, and the Volcanoes of the smaller West India
islands, was shaken at the same time by commotions attributed to subterranean fire.§ The destruction of Carraccas in
1811, and of other towns along the south-western shores of

---

* The forest adjoining the settlement at Little Prairie below New
Madrid, presents a singular scene of confusion, the trees standing inclined
in every direction, and many having their trunks and branches broken.
See *Mississippi Navigator*, p. 180.

† Travels into the Arkansa Territory, p. 53.

‡ Several of the earthquakes of 1811, were distinctly felt at Middle-
bury in Vermont, on the shores of Lake Champlain, and at many other
places along the northwestern side of the Alleghany Mountains.

§ See Humb. Pers. Nar. vol. 4. p. 8.

the Mexican gulf, was simultaneous with the agitations of the earth so severely felt at New Madrid, Cape Girardeau, the rapids of the Ohio,* and among the Otoes and other tribes on the Missouri.† At the time of the appearance of a new island, which was called Sabrina, in the volcanic group of the Azores, the smaller West India Islands, though at the distance of several hundred leagues, experienced frequent earthquakes. More than two hundred shocks were felt, from May 1811 to April 1812, in the island of St. Vincent. This was the time of those incessant agitations in the valley of the Mississippi, the Ohio, and the Arkansa, and in all the western parts of the United States.

It has been repeatedly asserted, that volcanic appearances exist in the mountainous country between Cape Girardeau, and the Hot Springs of the Washita, particularly at the latter place; but our observation has not tended to confirm these accounts, and Hunter and Dunbar, who spent some time at the Hot Springs, confidently deny the existence of any such appearances in that quarter. Reports have been often circulated, principally on the authority of hunters, of explosions, subterranean fires, blowings and bellowings of the mountains, and many other singular phenomena, said to exist on the Little Missouri of Washita, and in other parts of the region of the Hot Springs; but it is easy to see that the combustion of a coal bed, or something of equal insignificance, may have afforded all the foundation on which these reports ever rested. But though no traces of existing or of extinct volcanoes, should be found in any part of the country affected by these earthquakes, it is not, therefore, necessary, to go in search of causes like those which, in other parts of the earth, are believed to produce similar effects.

On the morning following the earthquake above men-

---

* Bradbury's Travels, p. 208. 2d. Edit.
† See p. 272. vol. 1. of this work.

tioned, a fall of snow commenced, and continued during the day; towards evening, it fell mixed with hail and rain, and covered the ground to the depth of about six inches.

The rain continued for some days, the mercury ranging from 40° to 48° and 50°, a temperature and state of weather as little grateful to an ague-shaken invalid as any can be. The snow, which fell on the 10th, remained on the ground until the 18th, when it had nearly disappeared, and a succession of bright days followed. The air was now filled with countless flocks of geese, sand-hill cranes, and other migratory birds on their passage to the south. The migrations of the Ardea *canadensis* afford one of the most beautiful instances of animal motion we can any where meet with. These birds fly at a great height, and wheeling in circles, appear to float without effort, on the surface of an ærial current, by whose eddies they are borne about in an endless series of revolutions. Though larger than a goose, they are seen to rise to so great an elevation, as to appear like points, sometimes luminous, and sometimes opake, as they happen to intercept or reflect the rays of the sun, but even from this height their shrill and incessant clamour may be heard.

While at Cape Girardeau, we were induced, from motives of curiosity, to attend at the performance of some ceremonies by the negroes, over the grave of one of their friends, who had been buried a month since. They were assembled round the grave where several hymns were sung, an exhortation was also pronounced by one who officiated as minister of the gospel, who also made a prayer for the welfare of the soul of the deceased. This ceremony, we are told, is common among the negroes in many parts of the United States; the dead are buried privately, and with few marks of attention; a month afterwards, the friends assemble at the grave, where they indulge their grief, and signify their sorrow for the deceased, by the performance of numerous religious rites.

On the 22nd November, having been informed the Ohio

had risen several inches, Lieutenant Swift determined to leave Cape Girardeau with the steam-boat on the following day. Dr. James had so far recovered as to be able to travel on horseback, and immediately set forward on the journey to the Falls of Ohio, intending to proceed, by the nearest route across the interior of Illinois.

The immediate valley of the Mississippi, opposite the little village of Bainbridge, ten miles above Cape Girardeau, is four miles wide, exclusive of the river, which washes the bluffs along the western side. Upwards it expands into the broad, fertile, and anciently populous valley, called the American bottom. On the east it is bounded by abrupt hills of a deep argillaceous loam, disclosing no rocks, and rather infertile, bearing forests of oak, sweet gum, tupelo, &c. The road crossing the hilly country between the Mississippi and the village of Golconda on the Ohio passes several precocious little towns, which apppear, as is often the case in a recently settled country, to have outgrown their permanent resources. The lands, however, are not entirely worthless, and on some of the upper branches of the Cache, a river of the Ohio, we passed some fertile bottoms, though they are not entirely exempt from inundation at the periodical floods. The compact limestone about Golconda contains beautiful crystals of fluate of lime. Sulphuret of lead also occurs in that vicinity, as we have been informed, in veins accompanying the fluate of lime.

On arriving at Golconda, Dr. James had become so much indisposed, by a recurrence of fever and ague, as to be unable to proceed. This circumstance, with others, induced Lieutenant Swift to leave the steam-boat for the winter at the mouth of Cumberland river, twenty miles below. After a delay of a few days, the latter continued his journey towards Philadelphia on horseback.

Having thus traced the progress of the Exploring party to the place of their final separation, we shall here add some discussions concerning the topography and the mineral geography of the countries west of the Alleghany mountains, of a more general description than seemed compatible with the humble style of a diary, which we thought convenient to retain. The following paper from Major Long, comprises moreover, many observations made on various journies previous to those detailed in the foregoing account, and in parts of the country remote from those traversed by the Expedition.*

* Most of the collections made on this expedition have arrived at Philadelphia, and are in good preservation. They comprise, among other things, more than sixty prepared skins of new or rare animals, which have been deposited in the Philadelphia Museum; several thousand insects, seven or eight hundred of which are probably new: five hundred have already been ascertained to be so, and have been described.

The herbarium contains between four and five hundred species of plants, new to the Flora of the United States, and many of them supposed to be undescribed.

Many of the minerals, collected by Mr. Jessup, were left at Smithland, Ky. A suite of small specimens, adapted to the illustration of the geology of the country from the Alleghanies to the Rocky Mountains has been received.

A collection of terrestrial and fluviatile shells was also made. Of these more than twenty new species have already been described and published. The organic reliquiæ collected on the voyage from Pittsburgh to St. Louis, have not yet been received in Philadelphia, but are daily expected.

The sketches executed by Mr. Peale amount to one hundred and twenty-two; of these twenty-one only were finished, the residue being merely outlines of quadrupeds, birds, insects, &c.

The landscape views, by Mr Seymour, are one hundred and fifty in number: of these, sixty have been finished.

We take this opportunity to express our acknowledgments of the politeness of Messrs. Price and Morgan, who have kindly franked the transportation of our collections from New Orleans to this city.

END OF THE NARRATIVE.

CHAPTER XVIII.

General description of the country traversed by the Exploring Expedition, extracted from a report of Major Long to the Hon. J. C. Calhoun, Secretary of War, dated Philadelphia, January 20th, 1821.

THE region to which the attention of the expedition has been directed, occupies a respectable portion of the immense valley situated between the Alleghany and Rocky Mountains, and lies between thirty-five and forty-two degrees of north latitude, and eighty and one hundred and six degrees of west longitude from Greenwich, embracing an extent of about five hundred miles in width from north to south, and one thousand three hundred miles in length from east to west. As might be expected in a region of this extent, a great diversity of surface is presented to view, exhibiting all the varieties, from the most level and unbroken, to the most rugged and mountainous aspect. The most broken parts of this region, are those situated along the Ohio, from its source to its confluence with the Mississippi, and on the west of the Mississippi, between Red river and the Arkansa, and between the latter and the Missouri, extending westward about four hundred miles from the Mississippi. The whole region, in a geological point of view, is constituted of three varieties of formations, which characterize the surface throughout, viz. transition, secondary, and alluvial. A tract, however, of considerable extent, including the Hot Springs of the Washita, and extending northeastwardly to the Lead Mines back of St. Genevieve, has by some been considered as primitive; but it is believed that the rocks discoverable therein, are not of a character to warrant such a decision.

In order to give a more distinct conception of the country or region under consideration, it may be regarded as divisible into the following sections, viz. 1st. the country situated between the Ohio river and the Alleghany Mountains; 2nd, the country situated between the Ohio, Mississippi, and the lakes; 3d, the country situated between the Mississippi and Missouri rivers; 4th, the country situated between the Red and the Missouri rivers, west of the Mississippi, and east of the meridian of Council Bluff; and 5th, the country between the proposed meridian and the Rocky Mountains.

I.—*Of the country situated between the Ohio river and the Alleghany Mountains.*

The country on the south side of the Ohio, including the northerly parts of Pennsylvania, Virginia and Tennessee, together with the whole of Kentucky, abounds in hills elevated, in the vicinity of the Ohio, from four to eight hundred or a thousand feet above the water table of the river, and rising many hundred feet higher, in the neighbourhood of the Alleghany Mountains. This section is watered by many streams of considerable magnitude, tributary to the Ohio, the most important of which are the Monongahela, Kenhawa, Great Sandy, Licking, Kentucky, Salt, Greene, Cumberland, and Tennessee. Most of these rivers are navigable for keel-boats, and many of them for steam-boats, some hundreds of miles, during the boating season, which generally commences about the 20th of February, and terminates early in June. Occasional freshets contribute to render them navigable during short portions of the other months of the year, but no reliance can be placed on periodical returns of freshets, excepting those of the spring season. Upon these rivers are extensive and valuable tracts of bottom land, covered with deep and heavy forests, and possessed of a soil adapted to the cultivation of all the variety of vegetable products, common to the various climates in which they are situated. The highlands back of the bottoms, although variegated with hills and vallies, alternating with each other in quick succession, are generally possessed of a surface susceptible of being tilled, and in many instances, of a soil equally rich and prolific, with that of the bottoms. In many parts of the country, however, the hills are abrupt and stony, to such a degree as renders them unfit for tillage. The average produce per acre, upon the farming lands of this section may be estimated at the following rates, viz. Indian-corn or maize, forty bushels, wheat twenty-two, rye twenty-six, oats thirty-five, barley thirty, tobacco from twelve to fifteen hundred weight, and cotton from five to seven hundred weight. In regard to the products last mentioned, viz. cotton and tobacco, it should be observed, that they are cultivated only in the southwesterly parts of this section, and that oats and barley are seldom cultivated, except in the upper or northeasterly parts.

Of the population of this section, if we except the towns

and villages and their immediate vicinities, as also a large portion of country surrounding Lexington, Kentucky, and another of considerable extent, including Nashville, Tennessee, it is yet but thinly inhabited, affording room for a population far more numerous and more widely diffused. There are extensive tracts of country between the Alleghany mountains and the Ohio, as yet almost entirely destitute of inhabitants, the most considerable of which are situated in the vicinity of the mountains, also the country generally between Tennesse river and the Mississippi. As this section of country is pretty generally well known, the foregoing *outline* of its topography will suffice.

II.—*Of the country situated between the Ohio, Mississippi, and the Lakes.*

The section of country next in the order proposed, is situated north of the Ohio river, and comprehends the states of Ohio, Indianna, and Illinois. This section may be subdivided into three orders or varieties of country, which merit a separate consideration, viz. the hilly, the plain or rolling, and the valley country.

1. The hilly country like, that south of the Ohio, exhibits a very uneven surface, variegated with hills and dales, irregularly distributed, and occupying about one-third part of the section under consideration. This portion of the country, is of an oblong form, extending in a direction nearly parallel to that of the Alleghany mountains. It is limited on the southeast by the Ohio river, and on the northwest by an imaginary line, commencing on the Mississippi near the Grand Tower, and running in a direction nearly east-northeast, till it approaches the easterly part of Lake Erie. On the east it mingles with the hilly country, comprehended in the back parts of Pennsylvania and New York. In short, the whole region, situated between the Alleghany mountains and the imaginary line above specified; or, in other words, the country through which the Ohio and its tributaries, except the Wabash, have their courses, may be arranged under this head. The hills, throughout the whole, are very similar in respect to their altitudes, multiplicity, and conformation.

Although the hilly country, north of the Ohio, is in many places rugged and broken, yet a large portion of it is susceptible of cultivation. No high mountains are to be seen; the hills usually rise from six to eight hundred feet above the common level, or about one thousand feet above the water tables

of the principal rivers, and invariably present rounded summits. Interspersed amongst the hills, are numerous fine tracts
of arable land, which may, in general, be alleged of the vallies
of the numerous rivers and creeks by which the country is
watered. The soil upon the hills is generally productive, except where the surface is rocky, and the declivities abrupt,
which is more particularly the case in the vicinity of rivers,
where the high lands are divided into numerous knobs, being
cut by deep ravines, with abrupt and precipitous banks.

The hilly country having been generally esteemed more
healthy than either of the other varieties, above mentioned,
has acquired a more numerous population than the latter.
As yet, however, no part of this section has its full comple-
ment of inhabitants, if we except as before, the numerous
towns and villages, and their immediate neighbourhoods. In
regard to the products of agriculture, the same remarks that
have been made concerning the section south of the Ohio,
are equally applicable to the country under consideration,
with the exception that cotton is cultivated only in the southwesterly extreme of this section, and tobacco is raised for
domestic uses only.

The most considerable rivers intersecting this section of
country, are the Muskingum, Scioto, Big Miami, and Wabash, all of which in the spring season, are navigable two or
three hundred miles from their mouths. The vallies of these
rivers, give place to many extensive and fertile bottoms,
well adapted to cultivation, and producing the necessaries of
life in great abundance and variety.

2. *The Plain or Rolling country* is separated from that last
under consideration, by the imaginary line above mentioned.
It is not to be inferred, however, that the junction of these
two regions, is distinctly marked by any characters whatever, by which the line can be traced with precision, but that
a gradual change of aspect is observable in travelling from
one variety of country to the other, and that the general direction of the line indicated by this change, is that specified
above. The other boundaries of this variety are the Mississippi on the west, and the Lakes Erie, and Michigan, and the
Fox and Wisconsan rivers, on the north and east. This variety
of country, although not entirely destitute of hills, is almost
throughout the whole extent, possessed of an undulating or
rolling surface, rising into broad and gentle swells in some
parts, and subsiding into extensive flats or plains in others.
The vallies of numberless water courses, bounded by abrupt

bluffs or banks, afford some diversity to its aspect; and the bluffs in particular, of the principal streams, being cut by numerous ravines, contribute in many places to give the surface a hilly and broken appearance. Although no part of this region can with propriety be denominated hilly, especially when compared with the portions of country above considered, yet upon the Wisconsan, Fox, the head-waters of Rock and Melwakee rivers, the country is considerably diversified with hills, or rather swells and vallies. The only hills worthy of particular notice, not only in this variety, but in the whole section under consideration, are the Ocooch and Smoky mountains, which are broad and elevated ridges, rather than mountains. The former is situated about twelve miles north of the Wisconsan, one hundred miles above its mouth, and the latter about forty miles south of the portage between the river just mentioned, and Fox river of Green Bay. The rivers of most note within this region, are the Wabash above the hilly country, before described, the Kaskaskias, Illinois, Rock and Wisconsan, tributary to the Mississippi, the Fox of Green Bay, the St. Joseph of Lake Michigan, and the Maumee and Sandusky tributary to Lake Erie. These rivers are all navigable for boats of ten to fifteen tons burden, when swollen by spring freshets, but during the greater part of the summer and fall, they have not a sufficient depth of water to be navigable for boats of burden, and in winter their navigation is entirely obstructed by ice. The spring freshets, consequent to the melting of the snow and ice, usually take place in the month of March, the southerly streams being open for navigation much earlier than those in the north.

The *Prairies* or *Savannas* east of the Mississippi, are mostly situated in this particular region, occupying at least three-fourths of it. These are waving or flat tracts of country of greater or less extent, separated from each other by narrow skirts of woodland situated upon the margins of rivers and creeks. They are generally possessed of a rich soil, yielding a spontaneous growth of grass and other herbage of a luxuriant appearance. They are well adapted to the cultivation of corn, wheat, rye, barley, oats, &c., of which they yield plentiful crops.

The prevailing opinion, in regard to this portion of the country, viz. that it is unhealthy, appears too well founded to admit of refutation. The causes that contribute to render it so, are very obvious. A large proportion of the prairies, are so flat, that much of the water deposited upon them by showers, remains stagnant upon the surface, till it is carried off gradually by evaporation, which renders the atmosphere humid and unhealthy. The vegetable mould of which the immediate surface is composed, and the abundance of vegetables that spring and decay upon the ground, contribute largely to render these exhalations more deleterious. Although there are but few swamps or mashes, and very rarely pools of stagnant water to be met with in this region, still, the general water-table of the country is so little inclined, that the streams, having but a moderate descent, are uniformly sluggish, often exhibiting the appearance of a succession of stagnant pools. The consequence is, that the vegetable matter they contain, instead of being carried away by the strength of the current, is deposited upon the bottoms and sides of the channels, and while in its purtrescent state, serves to augment the quantity of noxious effluvia with which the atmosphere is charged.

The population of this region, compared with its extent, is very limited; and, with the exception of a few villages, the settlements are very scattering. Large portions of it, embracing the northerly parts of Indiana and Illinois, are almost entirely destitute of inhabitants. Many parts of the country must remain uninhabited for many years to come, on account of the scarcity of timber, and other deficiencies, such as the want of mill-seats, springs of water, &c., which are serious blemishes in the character of a large proportion of the country. There are however, numerous and extensive tracts within this region, possessed of a rich soil, and in other respects well adapted for settlements, and presenting the strongest inducements for emigrants to occupy them.

3. The country of the third order, agreeably to the subdivision above given, viz. the valley country, is situated upon the rivers, and is included within the hilly and plain countries above described. The tracts belonging to this order, usually denominated bottoms, are altogether alluvial, being composed of alternate layers of sand and soil, deposited from the water of the rivers upon which they are respectively situated. The alluvion thus deposited, having once constituted a part of the surface of the countries drained by the water courses tributary to the rivers along which the deposit has been made, it will readily be inferred that the fecundity of the vallies will, in some measure, correspond with that of the countries whence their alluvion was derived. Accordingly, we find the bottoms more or less productive, in proportion to the fertility of the regions in which the rivers take

their rise and through which they flow. In the valley of the Ohio, the quality of the soil appears to improve, from its source downward. The alluvion of which it is composed, is supplied by the Alleghany and Monongahela rivers, which have their origin and courses in a hilly and mountainous country, possessed in general of a sandy surface. The alluvion supplied by other tributaries, entering the Ohio at various points between its source and its mouth, is of a better quality, being composed principally of argillaceous and calcareous earth, which are prevailing ingredients in the soil of the country drained by those tributaries.

It should be remarked, however, in relation to all the varieties of alluvia, that they are partially composed of the fine particles of decayed vegetable matter, with which the water drained from the surface of the ground is invariably charged. This property, in alluvial deposits, often prevails to such a degree as to render soils apparently sandy and sterile, remarkably productive. The alluvial bottoms throughout the United States afford innumerable examples of this fact. The fertilizing principle is no doubt partially contained in the slimy deposits left upon the surface of the ground after an inundation, essentially contributing to the fecundity of the soil.

The most extensive tract of valley country east of the Mississippi, is that situated within the bluffs of this river, usually denominated the American bottom, extending from the mouth of the Ocoa or Kaskaskias river, northwardly to that of the Missouri. This spacious bottom, although at present elevated much above the range of the highest freshets, is nevertheless alluvial. Its length along the Mississippi is about eighty, and its average breadth about four miles. It is generally destitute of a timber growth, except along the margin of the river, upon which is a skirt of woodland extending almost from one end of the tract to the other. The alluvion of the American bottom is composed of the rich mud brought down by the turbid Missouri, united with an abundance of vegetable matter yielded by the waters of the Upper Mississippi, which also characterizes the bottoms of this extensive river, from the Missouri downward to its mouth. Upon this bottom are situated the town of Kaskaskia, the villages of Prairie de Rocher, Harrison, Prairie du Pont, Cahokia, and Illinois, together with many other settlements.

On the same side of the river another large tract of valley

land, called the Mississippi bottom, commences a few miles
below the mouth of the river Kaskaskias, and extends downward along the Mississippi between fifty and sixty miles,
having an average width of about three miles. This tract,
in regard to soil and aspect, is of a character similar to that
of the American bottom, except that the former is more plentifully stocked with timber.

Besides these, there are numerous other bottoms on the
Mississippi, within the limits prescribed for this report, all
of which are composed of a rich alluvion. Those in particular, situated below the confluence of the Mississippi and
Missouri, are possessed of a soil exceedingly luxuriant, being composed, as before observed, of the rich and fertilizing
mud deposited from the water of the Missouri. Most of
them are covered with deep and heavy forests of timber, accompanied with a luxuriant under growth of vines, shrubs,
grass and other herbage.

The bottoms of the Wabash, Kaskaskias, Illinois, and
Rock rivers, are also made up of a rich alluvion of sand and
loam, containing a large proportion of vegetable mould.
Their surfaces, like those of the Mississippi bottoms, are generally flat, exhibiting tabular elevations or benches, formed
by the washing of the rivers at different periods. Large
tracts of prairie land are to be met with upon them, but for
the most part, the proportion of woodland is amply sufficient
to supply the adjacent country with timber and fuel.

The vallies of these rivers differ from that of the Ohio,
not only in having a greater width, but also, in being limited
on both sides by bluffs stretching along their whole length,
and maintaining nearly a parallel direction; whereas the valley of the Ohio is bounded by aprupt hills, irregularly disposed, in some instances, protruding far into the valley, like
promontories, and in others, retiring from the river and affording room for bottoms of pretty large extent.

The Ohio bottoms are uniformly clad in deep forests, except where these have been removed by settlers—no prairies
worthy of notice making their appearance.

The valley country, from the circumstances already detailed in allusion to the country constituting the second variety, is almost without exception unhealthy. But, at the
same time, it appears evident that this evil gradually decreases in proportion to the increase of population, and the
consequent advancement of agriculture; for the products of
the soil, which the bottoms yield in the greatest profusion,

instead of being left to wither and decay upon the surface, are necessarily consumed in the subsistence of man and beast, in consequence of which, one of the most fruitful causes of pestilential effluvia, viz. vegetable putrefaction is in a very considerable degree, removed.

The prevailing timber growth of the region, comprehending the two sections of country already described, is exhibited in the following list of trees, viz. cotton wood, willow, sycamore, black walnut, pecan, coffee tree, sweet and sour or black gum, red and water elm, hackberry, blue and white ash, linden, yellow and white poplar, catalpa, black and honey locust, buck eye, bur oak, white and black oak, mulberry, box elder, white dogwood, sugar tree, white maple, wild cherry, red oak, hickory, iron wood and hop hornbeam. The foregoing constitute the principal timber growth of the valley country, and are* to be met with more or less frequently throughout the whole of it. Red beech is abundant in some parts of the valley of the Ohio, and in those of many of its tributaries. It abounds also in the northerly parts of the states of Ohio and Indiana. Post oak, black-jack, and several other varieties of the oak, also, chesnut, white and shell-bark hickory, persimmon, &c. are sometimes found in the bottoms, but are more prevalent upon the hills and high lands. Pitch pine abounds in many parts of Ohio and Indiana, and generally in the neighbourhood of the Alleghany mountains. White pine occasionally makes its appearance in the northerly parts of Ohio. Red cedar is found in a great variety of places throughout the country, but nowhere in great abundance.

The under-growth of the several tracts of country above considered, includes a great variety of shrubs, vines, brambles, grasses, and other herbage, to be enumerated in a Botanical catalogue daily expected from Dr. James.

The most valuable timber trees are the white, post, and bur oaks, the white and blue ash, the shell bark hickory, the black walnut, the cherry, the locust, chesnut, poplar, mulberry, birch, cottou wood and linden. The two last mentioned are seldom used when other kinds of timber are to be had. The cotton wood is not only the most abundant timber growth upon the bottoms, but is more widely diffused than any other, and in many places, is the only variety of forest trees that makes its appearance, which, however, is more particularly the case westward of the Mississippi.

III.—*Of the country situated between the Mississippi and Missouri rivers.*

We next proceed to a consideration of the country west of the Mississippi, and shall begin with that situated between this river and the Missouri. This section contains no mountains, or indeed hills of any considerable magnitude. The term *rolling* appears to be peculiarly applicable in conveying an idea of the surface of this region, although it is not entirely destitute of abrupt hills and precipices. The aspect of the whole is variegated with the broad vallies of rivers and creeks, and intervening tracts of undulating up-land, united to the vallies by gentle slopes. Its surface is chequered with stripes of wood land situated upon the margins of the water courses, and dividing the whole into extensive parterres. If we except those parts of the section that âre contiguous to the Mississippi and Missouri, at least nineteen-twentieths of the country are completely destitute of a timber growth.

Within the vallies of these two rivers are extensive tracts of alluvial bottom, possessed of a rich soil. The bottoms of the Missouri, in particular, are probably inferior to none within the limits of the United States, in point of fertility. Those of the Mississippi are very rich, but do not exhibit symptoms of so great fecundity as the former. The bottoms of both, on ascending the rivers, become more sandy, and apparently less productive.

The bottoms of the Missouri are, for the most part, clad in a deep and heavy growth of timber and under-brush, to the distance of about three hundred and fifty miles above its mouth. There are, however, prairies of considerable extent occasionally to be met with on this part of the river. Higher up the prairies within the river valley, become more numerous and extensive, till at length no woodlands appear, except tracts of small size, situated at the points formed by the meanders of the river.

The bottoms on the Upper Mississippi, (that part of the Mississippi situated above its confluence with the Missouri being distinguished by this appellation) contain less wood land in proportion to their extent, than those of the Missouri. The prairies upon this river also become more numerous and extensive as we proceed upward.

The interior of the country situated between the vallies of these rivers, presents, as before remarked, a rolling aspect, inclining to hilly and broken, in some parts, but generally variegated with gentle swells and broad vallies. Within this section are numerous small rivers and creeks, with vallies of a character similar to that of the Mississippi or Missouri, but not so fertile. These vallies expand to a great width, compared with the magnitude of the streams upon which they are situated, but are not bounded by abrupt bluffs, like those of the two rivers just mentioned. They are generally covered with a luxuriant growth of grass and other herbage, and occasionally present copses of wood land of moderate extent. The timber growth of the bottoms is similar to that of the Mississippi bottoms, cotton wood, blue and white ash, hackberry, black walnut, cherry, mulberry, hickory and several varieties of the oak being the prevailing timber trees. The hills or high lands are in some instances covered with a scrubby growth of timber and furze, consisting of post oak, black jack, hazle, green briar, &c.

The soil of this section is probably equal if not superior to that of any other tract of upland of equal extent, within our territory. But the scarcity of timber, mill-seats and springs of water, defects that are almost uniformly prevalent, must for a long time prove serious impediments in the way of settling the country.

The population of this section of country is located almost exclusively within the vallies of the Mississippi and Missouri, and in their immediate neighbourhoods; extending upward along the former about one hundred and sixty, and along the latter, about three hundred and twenty miles above their confluence. The most populous parts of the country, are the county of St. Charles, situated near the junction of these two rivers, Cote Sans Des-sein and its vicinity—that part usually denominated the Boon's Lick country, extending from the mouth of Osage river upward, along the Missouri to the river Charaton, and the country on the Mississippi, including the Salt river settlements, which have become numerous and pretty widely diffused.

Along the vallies, both of the Mississippi and Missouri, there are still innumerable vacancies for settlements, holding forth inducements for emigrants to occupy them, equally as strong, as any of the positions already selected. The inhabited portions of this section have, in many instances, proved unhealthy, owing, in all probability, to the same causes that have been herein assigned, in relation to the country east of the Mississippi, which operate with equal force and effect upon the inhabitants of this section.

IV.—*Of the country situated between the Missouri and Red Rivers, west of the Mississippi, and east of the Meridian of the Council Bluff.*

Although no precise limits can be assigned as the western boundary of this section, yet the meridian above proposed, may be regarded as a line of division between two regions differing in their general character and aspect. It is not pretended that the immediate course of the line is marked by any distinct features of the country, but that a gradual change is observable in the general aspect of the two regions, which takes place in the vicinity of the proposed line. The assumed meridian is in longitude ninety six degrees west, nearly, and crosses the Platte a few miles above its mouth—the Konzas near the junction of its principal forks—the Arkansa about one hundred miles above the Verdigris or seven hundred miles from its mouth—the Canadian, about one hundred and fifty miles from its mouth, and the Red river about one hundred and fifty miles above the Kiamisha river.

The section of country under consideration, exhibits a great variety of aspect, the surface being diversified by mountains, hills, vallies, and occasional tracts of rolling country. Within the section is an extensive tract of bottom land, deserving of a particular consideration. It is situated on the Mississippi, commencing a few miles below the Ohio, and extending downward to Red river, uninterrupted by hills or high lands, and subject in many places to inundation from the freshets of the Mississippi. The bottom contains many large swamps, rendered almost impenetrable by a dense growth of cypress and *cypress-knees*, (the latter of which are conical excrescences springing from the roots of the cyprus, and shooting up in profusion, to the height of from one, to eight or ten feet.) The most extensive of these swamps commences near the head of the bottom, and passes southwestwardly, back of New Madrid, the Little Prairie, St. Francisville, &c. and terminates near the village of the Post of Arkansa. The Great Swamp, the name by which this extensive morass is designated, is about two hundred miles in length, and is of variable width, from five, to twenty or thirty miles. The timber growth of this and of the other swamps, which are of a similar character, but inferior magnitude, consists principally of cypress, of a superior quality. But the difficulty of removing it renders it of little value to the country. Within the bottom are also numerous lakes, lagoons, and marshes, once, no doubt, parts of the bed of the Mississippi, or of some of its tributaries that have their courses through the bottom. Notwithstanding the general depression of this bottom, it contains many 'insulated tracts of considerable extent, elevated above the range of the highest floods. The bottom, almost throughout its whole extent, supports a dense and heavy growth of timber of an excellent quality, together with a luxuriant undergrowth of cane brake, vines, &c.

It may not be improper to remark in this place, that great havoc is annually made amongst the timber of this tract, by lumber and fuel-mongers, who furnish the New Orleans market with large supplies of these articles, particularly of the former.

The bottom is bounded on the west by a chain of heights corresponding to the river bluffs on other parts of the Mississippi, but not arranged in so regular a manner. These are the commencement of a part of the hilly country hereafter to be considered. The most considerable rivers that flow through the bottom, and pour their tribute into the Mississippi, are the St. Francis, the Big Black, and White Rivers, which are confluent, the Arkansa, Washita, and Red rivers.

There are also a few other bottoms on the west side of the Mississippi, of moderate size. The largest of them are Tywapata, and Bois-broule, situated a little above the mouth of the Ohio.

The hilly and mountainous country commences immediately west of the Mississippi bottom, and extends westwardly about four hundred miles. Although the terms *hilly* and *mountainous* are expressive of the general character of the country, yet the following portions of this section may be enumerated as exceptions; viz. a tract of country comprehending St. Louis, Belle Fontaine, Florissant, and extending south-westwardly so as to include the Lead-Mine tract, Belle View, &c. This tract, (which embraces the most populous part of the Missouri territory) may be denominated rolling, or moderately hilly. Considerable portions of the country situated between the Arkansa and Red rivers, particularly in the vicinity of the latter, are also of this character. On the Arkansa, above Belle Point, is an extensive tract of a similar description, as also many tracts of inferior size, on the north side of Arkansa, between the village of the Post, and the Cadron settlements. On the south side of the Missouri is also an extensive tract of rolling country, commencing at the river Le Mine, six miles above Franklin, and extending upward along the Missouri, with occasional interruptions, to the Council Bluff. Such is the extent of this tract, that it comprises almost the whole of the country situated between the assumed meridian line and the Missouri, from Fort Osage, upward. On the head waters of the Osage river, and on those of its principal tributaries, the country is said to be of a similar character also. To these may be added large portions of country situated on the Verdigris river, upon the Arkansa above Grand river, and upon the Canadian from its mouth upward, to the distance of about two hundred miles. The tracts here designated, exhibit broad and elevated swells of land, separated from each other by deep and spacious vallies.

These portions of country are chequered with woodlands and prairies, in many instances alternating with each other in due proportion for the accommodation of settlers with farming and woodlands. On the Missouri, above Fort Osage, and on the Osage river, however, the proportion of woodland is very inconsiderable, and the timber it affords, of a scrubby character. The prairies here, as on the north of the Missouri, occupy at least nineteen-twentieths of the whole surface. Some portions of the Red river country are also deficient in the quantum of woodlands attached to them; but in general it may be observed, that the more southerly regions are better supplied with timber than those farther north. The growth of the woodlands interspersed among the prairies, is mostly post oak, hickory, black-jack, and white oak upon the high lands, and cotton wood, sycamore, black and white walnut, maple, bur-oak, and several other trees common to the western bottoms, in the vallies. The bow-wood, or as it is sometimes called the Osage Orange, is found upon the southerly tributaries of the Arkansa, and upon the Red river, and its tributaries. This tree is deserving of particular notice, in as much as it affords a timber extremely compact and elastic—its trunk and roots may prove very useful in dying yellow, and its fruit of importance in medicine.

The residue of this section, with the exception of the river bottoms and tracts of valley land scattered in various directions throughout the whole, is extremely hilly, broken, and mountainous, the hills and mountains rising from five to fifteen hundred feet above the water table of the country in which they are situated. They are exceedingly numerous, and are divided into a multiplicity of knobs and peaks, having rounded summits, and presenting perpendicular cliffs and abrupt precipices of transition sandstone. Their surfaces generally are covered with rocks of this description, or flinty fragments strewed in profusion upon them. The growth upon them is almost exclusively pitch pine, cedar, scrubby oaks, hickory, haw, and bramble; the poverty of the soil in some instances, and the scarcity of it in others, excluding the more luxuriant vegetable productions common to the more level country in their vicinity.

The groupe of mountains situated between the Arkansa and Red rivers, gives rise to the following streams, all of which are sufficiently copious for mill-seats, and abound in cascades and falls, well adapted to such purposes, viz. the Blue-water, Kiamisha, and Little rivers, the Mountain, Rolling, Cossetot, and Saline forks of Little river, all of which are tributary to Red river; the Little Missouri, Cadeau, Washita, and the Saline, all confluent; the Mamelle, Le Fevre, Petit Jean, and Poteau, tributary to the Arkansa, besides numerous creeks of less note.

The hills and mountains between the Arkansa and Missouri are equally prolific in water courses. The most considerable of these are the Verdigris, Neosho or Grand river, Illinois, together with the Frog, Mulberry, White-oak, Spadra, Pine, Illinois, Point remove, and Cadron creeks tributary to the Arkansa, the Little Red, and White rivers confluent streams; the Strawberry, Spring, Eleven Point, Currant, Little, and Big Black, all confluent and tributary to White river, which enters the Mississippi about thirty miles above the mouth of the Arkansa. The St. Francis and the Merameg have their sources in this broken region also, and discharge themselves into the Mississippi. Of the vallies of the rivers last enumerated, viz. those north of the Arkansa and tributary to the Mississippi, it is observable, that they are uniformly possessed of a rich soil, but owing to the excessive floods occasionally brought down through them from the hills and mountains, their cultivation is very precarious. The valley of White river, and those of some few others, are in many places elevated above the reach of the highest freshets, and are not altogether subject to this inconvenience, but for the most part, they are liable to be annually swept by overwhelming freshets, which prostrate fences, buildings, and every artificial structure that opposes their march. Even a fall freshet has been known to inundate plantations situated within the vallies, to the depth of eight or ten feet. These floods are generally very sudden as well as excessive, to such a degree, that on some occasions, the water has risen in the course of one night, more than twenty feet. By the sudden rises of the water, the planter, who in the evening thought his family and possessions secure from harm, has been compelled, the next morning, to embark with his family, in a canoe, to save themselves from impending destruction, while his habitation, fields, cattle, and all his effects are abandoned to the fury of the torrent.

The streams rising in the same hilly country and tributary to the Missouri are the following, viz. the Bon Homme Creek, the Gasconade, the Osage and its tributaries, the Le Mine, the Blue-water, and several streams tributary to the Konzas river. Upon some of these, as the Bon Homme, Gasconade, and upon some few creeks beside, mills have been constructed, at which much of the lumber of the St. Louis market is sawed.

This section as yet is but very partially populated, although the inhabitants in some portions of it, are considerably numerous. The most populous part of the section is the country situated immediately below the mouth of the Missouri, including the town of St. Louis, and the villages of Florissant and Carondelet, Herculaneum, St. Genevieve, Bainbridge, Cape Girardeau, Jackson, St. Michaels, and the country in their vicinity, the Lead Mine tract, including Mine a Berton, Potosi, and Belle View, are considerably populous. The settlements in these places, however, if we except the sites occupied by the towns and villages just enumerated, are still very scattering, and but a small proportion of the land susceptible of agriculture is yet under cultivation. Besides these, there are numerous other settlements, and several small villages within this part of the Missouri territory, distributed in various directions, and constituting a very scanty population. They are scattered along the Missouri, from its mouth, to Fort Osage, a distance of more than three hundred miles, on the Gasconade, Merameg, St. Francis, Big Black, and several of its tributaries.

Within the Arkansa territory there are but few villages, and the settlements are yet very scattering. The principal villages are the Post of Arkansa, situated about sixty miles above the mouth of the river, Davidsonville on Black river, near the mouth of Eleven Point river, a small village at the commencement of the high lands on the Arkansa, at a place called the Little Rock, about two hundred miles from the mouth of the river, selected as the seat of government for the territory. Besides these, there are a few other inconsiderable villages on the Arkansa river, as also several of small size situated in the country between the river just mentioned and Red river; the most considerable of which are at Pecan Point, Mount Prairie, Prairie D'Inde, &c. These villages contain but very few houses, and those generally of a rude structure, a circumstance attributable only to the infancy of the territory. The settlements of the territory are scattered along the Arkansa, from the White river Cut-off, (a channel uniting these two rivers at the distance of thirty miles above the mouth of the former, and three miles above that of the latter,) to Belle Point, a distance of about four hundred miles. On Little Red, White, and Strawberry rivers, are many scattering settlements, as also on the Washita, Cadeau, Little Missouri, and the several forks of Little river. The settlements upon Red river extend upward to the Kiamisha, a distance of about one thousand miles from its mouth, following the meanders of the river.

The settlements of the section under consideration, are most numerous in those parts represented in the foregoing description as being variegated with prairies and woodlands alternating with each other. In the valley of the Arkansa, however, which is generally clad in rich forests and luxuriant *cane brakes,* prairies are seldom to be met with, and settlers have had recourse to *clearing* the land necessary for their plantations.

In addition to the white settlements above pointed out, there are numerous villages and settlements of the Cherokee Indians, extending along the Arkansa, from the mouth of Point Remove creek, upward, to Mulberry river, a distance of about one hundred miles. These settlements, in respect to the comforts and conveniences of life they afford, appear to vie with, and in many instances even surpass those of the Americans, in that part of the country.

There are a few villages of the Quawpaws, or Arkansaws, and Chocktaws, situated on the south side of the Arkansa river, below the high lands. They are not numerous, subsist principally upon game and Indian corn of their own raising, and have ever been friendly to the whites. Upon the river St. Francis are a few settlements of the Delawares and Shawnees, dispersed remnants of those unfortunate nations. The several bands of the Osage nation resident upon

the Verdigris and upon the head waters of Osage river, also the Konzas Indians, living upon the river bearing their
name, are included within this section of the country.

In regard to climate, this region, as it expands through
more than eight degrees of latitude, may be expected to afford a considerable variety, and the position is sufficiently
verified by the commencement and progress of annual vegetation. The change of climate is also indicated by certain
peculiarities observable in the vegetable products of different parts of the country. For example, vegetation begins at
least a month earlier in the southern, than in the northern
extreme of the region. The Spanish moss disappears northwardly of the thirty-third degree of north latitude. Cotton
and indigo cannot be cultivated to advantage in a latitude
higher than thirty-six degrees, and the cane brake is seldom
found north of 37 1-2 degrees.

In regard to the salubrity of the climate, there is also a
diversity, depending upon local circumstances rather than
upon the temperature of the weather. A luxuriant soil yielding its products to decay and putrify upon the ground, also stagnant waters, flat lands, and marshes, in which the river vallies of this region abound, cannot fail to load the atmosphere with pestilential miasmata, and render the country
unhealthy, wherever these occurences are to be met with.
But it is presumed that the causes of disease will gradually
be exterminated, as the population of the country increases.

Of the rivers of this region, there are many that are navigable for keel-boats of several tons burden, but all of them
have more or less obstructions from shoals and frosts at different periods. The Arkansa, which in point of magnitude
and extent, deservedly ranks second amongst the tributaries
of the Mississippi, (the Missouri being the first) is navigable
to the mouth of the Neosho, or Grand river, a distance of
about six hundred miles. In this part of the river, however,
the navigation is liable to obstructions, for want of a sufficient
depth of water, during a period of two and a half or three
months commencing in July. Occasional obstructions are
also imposed by ice forming in the river, during the winter
season, but these are seldom of long continuance, the winters
being usually short and mild. As the freshets of the river
seldom continue more than a few days at a time, and are usually attended by sudden rises and falls of the water, boats of
moderate draft and burden only, are suited to its navigation. The Arkansa is navigable at all seasons for boats of this

description, about two hundred miles, which comprehends the distance by the meanders of the river, from the Mississippi to the commencement of the high lands. Above the mouth of the Neosho, it spreads to a much greater width than below, and the water is more extensively diffused over its bed, which renders the shoals more numerous and the navigation more precarious. This part of the Arkansa, cannot indeed be considered navigable, even for perogues of a large size, except during the short period of a freshet, which is seldom long enough to complete a voyage of one hundred miles ascending and descending.

The Red river is navigable during most of the year, to the Great Raft, about five hundred miles from its mouth. At this place its navigation is effectually obstructed, except in a high stage of water, when keel-boats of ten or fifteen tons burden, may pass it through devious channels, or bayoux, and ascend several hundred miles above. That part of the river situated above the Raft, however, like the upper part of the Arkansa, is rendered impassable for boats of burden, by shoals and sandbars in a moderate stage of water.

The Washita, tributary to Red river, is navigable many miles. That part of it particularly, situated within the valley of the Mississippi, and denominated Black river, admits of constant navigation for boats of burden. The Little river, which is also tributary to Red river, together with its Forks heretofore enumerated, are navigable in high water. White river is navigable, in a moderate stage of water, between three and four hundred miles;—also the Big Black, its principal tributary, and several branches of the river last mentioned, viz. the Strawberry, Currant, Eleven Point, and Spring rivers. The St. Francis is blocked up near its mouth, and rendered impassable for boats of every description, by rafts of logs and drift wood, completely choaking the channel of the river, and in many places occupying the whole of its bed, for the distance of several miles together. The Merameg, is also navigable many miles, in a moderate stage of water.

The Gasconade, Osage, and Konzas rivers, are navigable in the spring season, but their navigation seldom extends far inland from their mouths, being obstructed by shoals or rapids.

Of the rivers tributary to the Missouri, it is remarkable, that their mouths are generally blocked up with mud, consequent to the subsidence of the summer freshet of that river, which usually takes place in the month of July. The reason is obvious. The freshets of the more southerly tributaries are discharged early in the season, and wash from their mouths the sand and mud, previously deposited therein, leaving them free from obstructions. These freshets having subsided, the more northerly branches discharge their floods, formed by the melting of the snow at a later period. The Missouri being swollen thereby, backs its waters charged with mud, considerable distances up the mouths of the tributaries before alluded to. The water here becoming stagnant, deposits its mud, and the tributaries having no more freshets to expel it, remain with their mouths thus obstructed, till the ensuing spring.

The lower part of the Canadian river, although it is included within the section under consideration, will be described in the sequel of this report, in connection with the rest of that river.

Of the animals found in the several sections of country above described, there are a great variety in almost every department of Zoology. But as most of them are common in other parts of the United States, they need not be enumerated here.

V. *Of the country situated between the Meridian of the Council Bluff, and the Rocky Mountains.*

We next proceed to a description of the country, westward of the assumed meridian, and extending to the Rocky Mountains, which are its western boundary. This section embraces an extent of more than four hundred miles square, lying between ninety-six and one hundred and six degrees of west longitude, and between thirty-five and forty-two degrees of north latitude.

Proceeding westwardly from the meridian above specified, the hilly country gradually subsides, giving place to a region of vast extent, spreading towards the north and south, and presenting an undulating surface, with nothing to limit the view or variegate the prospect, but here and there a hill, knob, or insulated tract of table land. At length the Rocky Mountains break upon the view, towering abruptly from the plains, and mingling their snow capped summits with the clouds.

On approaching the mountains, no other change is observable in the general aspect of the country, except that the isolated knobs and table-lands, above alluded to, become more frequent and more distinctly marked,—the bluffs by which the vallies of water courses are bounded, present a greater abundance of rocks,—stones lie in greater profusion upon the surface,—and the soil becomes more sterile. If, to the characteristics above intimated we add that of an almost complete destitution of woodland, (for not more than one thousandth part of the section can be said to possess a timber growth,) we shall have a pretty correct idea of the general aspect of the country.

The insulated tracts herein alluded to as table lands, are scattered throughout the section, and give to the country a very striking and wonderful appearance. They rise from six to eight hundred feet above the common level, and are surrounded, in many instances, by rugged slopes, and perpendicular precipices, rendering their summits almost inaccessible.—Many of them are in this manner completely insulated, while others are connected with the plains below, by gentle acclivities leading from their bases to their summits, upon one side or other of the eminence. These tracts, as before intimated, are more numerous, but less extensive in the vicinity of the Rocky Mountains, than they are, further eastward;—and in the former situation they are more strikingly characterized by the marks above specified, than in the latter.

The geological formations that present themselves along the declivities of these heights, are principally horizontal strata of secondary sandstone and breccia or pudding stone, alternating with each other. Clinkstone prevails upon the surface of them in many places, but in general the superior strata are rocks, of the description just before mentioned. These tracts are denominated tabular, not from any flatness of surface, by which they are characterized, but from their appearance at a distant view, and from the horizontal disposition of the stratifications imbedded in them. Their surfaces are usually waving, and in some instances rise into knobs and ridges, several hundred feet high. Many of them are clad in a scrubby timber growth of pitch pine, red cedar, scrubby oaks, &c. while others exhibit a bald or prairie surface.

By far the greater proportion of this section of country is characterized by a rolling and plain surface, which may be alleged, not only of the space included within the limits first assigned, but of extensive portions of country north and south of it. Although the elevated table lands, a description of which has just been given, are situated within this region, they occupy but a small proportion of it. In addition to these inequalities in the surface of the country, there are numerous mounds or knobs of various magnitudes, and occasional swells of greater or less extent, which contribute to give a pleasing variety to the prospect. The country is also divided into extensive parterres by the vallies of rivers and creeks, which are usually sunk one hundred and fifty or two hundred feet below the common level, and bounded in some places by perpendicular precipices, and in others by bluffs or banks of gentle slopes.

Immediately at the base of the mountains, and also at those of some of the insular table-lands, are situated many remarkable ridges, rising in the form of parapets, to the height of between fifty and one hundred and fifty feet. These appear to have been attached to the neighbouring heights, of which they once constituted a part, but have at some remote period, been cleft asunder from them, by some extraordinary convulsion of nature, which has prostrated them in their present condition. The rocky stratifications, of which these ridges are principally composed, and which are exactly similar to those of the insulated table-lands, are distinctly marked, and have various dips, or inclinations, from forty-five to eighty degrees.

Throughout this section of country the surface is occasionally characterized by water-worn pebbles, and gravel of granite, gneiss, and quartz, but the predominant characteristic is sand, which in many instances, prevails almost to the entire exclusion of vegetable mould. Large tracts are often to be met with, exhibiting scarcely a trace of vegetation. The whole region, as before hinted, is almost entirely destitute of a timber growth of any description. In some few instances, however, sandy knobs, and ridges make their appearance, thickly covered with red cedars of a dwarfish growth. There are also some few tracts, clad in a growth of pitch pine, and scrubby oaks; but in general, nothing of vegetation appears upon the uplands, but withered grass of a stinted growth, no more than two or three inches high, prickly-pears profusely covering extensive tracts, and weeds of a few varieties, which, like the prickly-pears, seem to thrive best, in the most arid and sterile soils.

In the vicinity of the Rocky Mountains, southwardly of the Arkansa river, the surface of the country, in many places, is profusely covered with loose fragments of volcanic rocks. On some occasions, stones of this description are so numerous, as almost to exclude vegetation. A multiplicity of ridges and knobs of various sizes, containing rocks of this character, also make their appearance. All these formations seem to be superincumbent upon horizontal strata of secondary sand stone. But, the volcanoes whence they originated, have left no vestiges by which their exact locality can be determined. In all probability they were extinguished, previously to the recession of the waters that once inundated the vast region between the Alleghany and Rocky Mountains.

Of the rivers that have their courses through this section, those of most note are the Platte, the Konzas and its forks, the Arkansa, and the Canadian tributary to the Arkansa. The Platte rises in the Rocky Mountains, and after an easterly course of about eight hundred miles, falls into the Missiouri, at the distance of about seven hundred miles from the Mississippi. It derives its name from the circumstance of its being broad and shoal; its average width being about twelve hundred yards, exclusive of the islands it embosoms, and its depth in a moderate stage of water, so inconsiderable, that the river is fordable in almost every place. The main Platte is formed of two confluent tributaries of nearly equal size, called the North and South Forks, both of which have their sources, considerably within the range of the Rocky Mountains. They unite, about four hundred miles westward from the mouth of the Platte, having meandered about the same distance eastwardly from the mountains. Besides these the Platte has two tributaries of a respectable size, the one called the Elk Horn, entering a few miles above its mouth, and the other the Loup Fork, entering about ninety miles above the same place. The vallies of the Platte and its several tributaries are extremely broad and in many places, possessed of a good soil. They gradually become less fertile, on ascending from the mouths of the rivers on which they are situated, till at length they exhibit an arid and sterile appearance. The alluvion of which the bottoms are composed, contains a large proportion of sand, which, added to the nitrous and saline matter blended with it, occasions frequent appearances of complete barrenness. Magnesia also appears to be a component part of the soil, a quality invariably derogatory to the fertility of any soil. The valley of the Platte, from its mouth to its constituent forks, spreads to the width of ten or twelve miles, and forms a most beautiful expanse of level country. It is bounded on both sides by high lands, elevated twenty-five or thirty feet above the valley, and connected therewith by gentle slopes.

The river in several places, expands to the width of many miles, embosoming numerous islands, some of which are broad and considerably extensive, and all of them covered with a growth of cottonwood and willows. These are the only woodlands that make their appearance along the river; and in travelling westward, these become less numerous and extensive, till at length, they entirely disappear. Copses and skirts of woodland again present themselves in the neighbourhood of the mountains, but they are of small magnitude, and the trees they furnish, are of a dwarfish growth. For a distance of nearly two hundred miles, commencing at the confluence of the North and South Forks, and extending westwardly toward the mountains, the country is almost entirely destitute of woodland, scarcely a tree, bush, or even a shrub making its appearance.

The Platte is seldom navigable except for skin canoes, requiring but a moderate depth of water, and for these, only when a freshet prevails in the river. No attempts have ever been made to ascend the river in canoes, for any considerable distance, the prevalence of shoals and the rapidity of the current discouraging such an undertaking. The bed of the Platte is seldom depressed more than six or eight feet below the surface of the bottoms, and in many places even less—and spreads to such a width, that the highest freshets pass off, without inundating the bottoms, except in their lowest parts—the rise of the water on such occasions being no more than five or six feet.

In order to account in some measure for the diversity of soil observable in the vallies of most of our western rivers, it may not be improper in this place, to assign one of the principal causes that operate in producing this effect. The alluvial deposits of which the river bottoms are formed, consist of particles of mud and sand more or less minute. The coarser and more ponderous particles are of course first deposited, while the finer are transported by the current to a greater distance, and deposited nearer the mouths of the rivers. Thus it happens, that the bottoms situated nearest to the sources of the western rivers, are sandy, and contain but a small proportion of vegetable mould, while those nearer their mouths, are generally furnished with a rich and fertile loam.

The Konzas or Konzays, as it is pronounced by the Indians, is made up of two considerable streams, heading in the plains between the Platte and Arkansa rivers, called the Republican and Smoky Hill forks. Tributary to the former of these, are the Solomon's and Saline forks, of less magnitude, rising also in the same plains. The Konzas is navigable only in high freshets for boats of burden, and on such occasions not more than one hundred and fifty or two hundred miles, the navigation being obstructed by shoals. The character of this river and its several branches is similar to that of the Platte and its tributaries. Woodlands are seldom to be met with, except in narrow skirts and small copses along the water courses. Much of the country situated upon its forks, is said to be possessed of a good soil, but is rendered uninhabitable for want of timber and water. The bottoms are possessed of a light sandy soil, and the uplands are in many places characterized by aridity and barrenness. The surface, for the most part, is rolling, but in some instances inclines to hilly.

That portion of the Arkansa included within the section under consideration, has a bed or channel varying in width from four hundred yards to more than a mile, exclusive of islands. In the neighbourhood of the mountains its width does not exceed fifty or sixty yards, gradually growing wider in its progress downward. Its valley, for a distance of more than one hundred miles from the place where it issues from the mountains, contains a considerable timber growth, principally of cotton wood, in skirts bordering upon the river, which occasionally embosoms islands clad in the same kind of growth. Every appearance of timber, however, is lost on a farther progress eastward, and nothing is presented to variegate or adorn the prospect inland, but a broad expanse of waving prairies.

Proceeding eastward along the river, its valley gradually widens, and the bluffs or banks by which it is bounded, become less elevated and abrupt. The bottoms rise but a few feet above the water level of the river, but the freshets having a broad bed like that of the Platte, to expand upon, seldom rise so high as to inundate the bottoms. This part of the Arkansa, as before hinted in the former part of this report, cannot be considered as navigable except for boats of light burden, during the prevalence of a freshet. In a very low stage the river is said to disappear in many places, the whole of its water passing off through the immense body of sand of which its bed is composed.

The Arkansa having a direction nearly east and west, has no great variety of climate to traverse in its course from the mountains to the Mississippi. Consequently there is no successsion of thaws taking place upon the river, calculated to

maintain a freshet for any great length of time. The freshets are occasioned by a simultaneous melting of the snow
throughout the whole extent of the river, and by showers of
rain, which falling upon a rolling surface, is quickly drained
off, and causes sudden, but seldom excessive rises in the
river. We have witnessed in the Arkansa, no less than three
rises and falls of the water, in the course of two weeks.

The most considerable streams tributary to this part of the
Arkansa, are the Negracka or Red Fork, and the Newsew-
ketonga, or Grand Saline on the South, and the Little Arkansa and Stinking Fork on the north side. The Negracka
rises within a short distance of the mountains, and after
meandering eastwardly between four and five hundred miles,
unites with the Arkansa at the distance of about nine hundred miles from the mouth of the latter. The Newsewke-
tonga has its source in the plains between the Arkansa and
Canadian rivers, and unites with the Negracka about one hundred and fifty miles below the Negracka. The head waters
of the Little Arkansa take their rise near the Smoky Hill
fork of the Konzas, and are discharged into the Arkansa,
about eight hundred and sixty miles above its mouth. The
Stinking Fork rises amongst the head waters of the Neosho,
and enters the Arkansa, about eight hundred miles from its
mouth. Besides these, there are many other streams of
smaller size, entering on both sides of the river.

The Canadian rises at the base of the Rocky Mountains,
and after a meandering course of about one thousand miles,
enters the Arkansa at the distance of about five hundred and
fifty miles from the mouth of the latter. This river has generally been represented upon the maps of the country as
having a north-easterly course, whereas its source is nearly
in the same latitude as its confluence with the Arkansa, consequently its general course is nearly east. In its course, it
forms an extensive curve to the southward, leaving a broad
space between it and the Arkansa, in which several streams,
many hundred miles in length, tributary to both of these rivers, have their origin and courses.

This river has a broad valley, bounded by bluffs from two
to five hundred feet high, faced with rocky precipices, near
its source, and by abrupt declivities, intersected by numerous
ravines, lower down. It has a spacious bed, depressed but
a few feet below the bottoms, and exhibiting one continued
stratum of sand through the greater part of its length. It is
the channel through which the water of a vast extent of

country is carried off, yet, during most of the summer season, it is entirely destitute of running water throughout a large proportion of its extent, a circumstance in proof of the aridity of the region drained by it. Fifty miles above its mouth, it receives at least two-thirds of its water from its principal tributary, denominated the North Fork. This fork rises between the Arkansa and Canadian, and ·has a meandering course of about eight hundred miles. Six miles above the fork just mentioned, another tributary enters the Canadian, called the South Fork, about half as large as the other. Notwithstanding the supplies afforded by these two tributaries, the Canadian has not a sufficiency of water in summer, to render it navigable even to their mouths. At the distance of twenty miles above its mouth, a chain of rocks, (slaty sand-stone) extends across the bed of the river, but occasions no considerable fall. A little above the entrance of the South Fork, is another of the same description, forming rapids of moderate descent, not more than four hundred yards in length. With these exceptions, the bed of the river presents no rocky formations *in place*, for more than four hundred miles from its confluence with the Arkansa. About three hundred and fifty miles from that point, beds of Gypsum or Plaster of Paris begin to make their appearance, in the bluffs fronting upon the river, and upon the declivities of the highland knobs. A great abundance of this article is to be met with, not only upon the Canadian, but also upon the upper part of the Arkansa. The hills in which it is imbedded, are composed of ferruginous clay and fine sand of a deep red complexion. Hence the Arkansa derives the colouring matter that gives to its waters their reddish hue.

The bottoms of the Canadian, in the neighbourhood of its mouth, are possessed of a soil exceedingly prolific, but like those of the other rivers of this region, the more remote their situation from the mouth of the river, the more sandy and sterile is their appearance. Its valley is plentifully supplied with timber of an excellent quality, for a distance of about two hundred miles, on the lower part of the river, and the highlands for nearly the same distance are agreeably diversified with prairies and woodlands. This portion of the river is situated eastward of the assumed meridian, and the country upon it has already been partially described in a former part of this report.

The woodland growth upon the lower part of the Canadian, consists of cotton wood, sycamore, white, blue and black ash, swamp cedar, red elm, coffee tree, yellow wood, sugar tree, box elder, white and black walnut, wild cherry, mulberry, &c. in the river valley, and hickory, white and post oak, black-jack, black oak, &c. upon the adjacent uplands. On a progress westward, the most valuable of the timber trees above enumerated, disappear, till at length occasional groves of cotton wood, mingled with mulberry, red elm, and stinted shrubbery of various kinds, constitute the only woodlands of the country. On this occasion, it may be observed, that the cane or reed, the pea vine, pawpaw, spice wood, hop vine, and several other varieties of shrubs and vines, common only to rich soils, are no where to be found within this section, or westward of the proposed meridian.

The country of the Canadian, above that just mentioned, or that portion of it west of the assumed meridian, appears to be possessed of a soil somewhat richer than the more northerly parts of the section, but exhibits no indications of extraordinary fecundity in any part of it. Proceeding westward, a very gradual change is observable in the apparent fertility of the soil, the surface becoming more sandy and sterile, and the vegetation less vigorous and luxuriant. The bottoms appear to be composed, in many places, almost exclusively of loose sand, exhibiting but few signs of vegetation. Knobs, and drifts of sand driven from the bed of the river by the violence of the wind, are piled in profusion along the margins of the river, throughout the greater part of its length. It is remarkable, that these drifts are, in many instances, covered with grape vines of a shrubby appearance, bearing fruit in the greatest abundance and perfection. The vines grow to various heights, from eighteen inches to four feet, unaccompanied in some instances by any other vegetable, and bear a grape of a dark purple, or black colour, of a delicious flavour, and of the size of a large pea, or common gooseberry.

The waters of this section, almost in every part of it, appear to hold in solution a greater or less proportion of common salt and sulphate of magnesia, which, in many instances, render them too brackish or bitter for use. Saline and nitrous efflorescences frequently occur upon the surface, in various parts of the country—and incrustations of salt of consideracle thickness, are to be found in some few places south of the Arkansa river. As to the existence of rock salt in a mineral state, some doubts are to be entertained, if the decision is to rest upon the character of the specimens exhibited as proofs of the fact. The several examples of this formation, that we have witnessed, are evidently crystalline salt, deposited by a regular process of evaporation and crystallization, and formed into concrete masses or crusts upon the surface of the ground.

Indications of coal are occasionally to be seen, but this mineral does not probably occur in large quantities. The geological character of this section, is not such as to encourage the search for valuable minerals. A deep crust of secondary sand stone, occasionally alternating with breccia, with here and there a superstructure of rocks of a primitive type, are the principal formations that present themselves.

Of the animals of this region, the buffaloe or bison ranks first in importance, inasmuch as it supplies multitudes of savages not only with the principal part of their necessary food, but also contributes to furnish them with warm clothing. The flesh of this animal is equal if not superior to beef, and affords not only a savoury but a wholesome diet. A large proportion of this section, commencing at the assumed meridian, and extending westward to within one hundred miles of the Rocky Mountains, constitutes a part only of their pasture ground, over which they roam in numbers to an incredible amount. Their range extends northwardly and southwardly of the section, as far as we have any particular account of the country. The animal next in importance is the wild horse, a descendant, no doubt, of the Spanish breed of horses, to which its size, form, and variety of colours, show that it is nearly allied. In regard to their contour, symmetry, &c. they afford all the varieties common to that breed of horses. They are considerably numerous in some parts of the country, but not abundant. They are generally collected in gangs, but are sometimes solitary.

Grizzly or white bears are frequently to be seen in the vicinity of the mountains. They are much larger than the common bear, endowed with great strength, and are said to be exceedingly ferocious. The black or common bears, are numerous in some parts of the country,—but none of these animals are found remote from woodlands, upon the products of which, they depend in a great measure for their subsistence.

The common deer are to be met with in every part of this section, but are most numerous in the vicinity of woodlands. The black-tailed, or mule deer, is found only in the neighbourhood of the mountains. Hilly and broken lands seem to afford them their favourite pasture ground.

The elk is also an inhabitant of this section, but is not to be found remote from woodlands. The cabrie, wild goat, or as it is more frequently called, the antelope, abounds. It associates with the buffaloe, and is one of the most common occupants of the plains, from which it retires only in quest of water.

Wolves are exceedingly numerous, particularly within the immediate range of the buffaloe. Of these there are many varieties, distinguishable by their shape, size and colour.

The marmot, commonly called the prairie dog, is more abundant throughout this section than any other quadruped. They live in villages scattered in every direction, and thickly inhabited; a single village, in some instances, occupying a tract of ground three or four miles in extent. Their habitations are burrows, three or four inches in diameter, situated at the distance of fifteen or twenty paces asunder. Their habits and manners, in other respects, are peculiarly interesting. They subsist on vegetables—their flesh is similar to that of the ground-hog, and their hair equally as coarse.

The beaver, otter, mink, and muskrat, are numerous upon the rivers, creeks, and rivulets issuing from the mountains, and generally upon those whose vallies are supplied with woodland.

Badgers, raccoons, hares, pole-cats, porcupines, many varieties of squirrels, panthers, wild cats, lynxes, and foxes of several species, are also inhabitants of this section. Besides these, the country affords a great variety and abundance of reptiles and insects, both venemous and harmless.

Of the feathered tribes, no very great variety is observable. The turtle dove, the jay, the barn swallow, the quail, (partridge of the middle states) the owl, whip-poor will, and lark, which seem more widely distributed over the territory of the United States than any other birds, are found here. Several varieties of the hawk, containing some new species, the bald and gray eagle, the buzzard, raven, crow, fish crow, magpie, turkey, two or three varieties of the grouse, pheasant, pigeon, many varieties of the sparrow and fly catcher, the whooping or sand-hill crane, curlieu, sand-piper, together with a variety of other land and water fowls, are more or less numerous in this region. It is remarkable, that birds of various kinds, common to the sea coast, and seldom found far in the interior, pervade the valley of the Mississippi, to a great distance from the Gulf of Mexico, and frequent the regions adjacent to the Rocky Mountains.

In regard to this extensive section of country, we do not hesitate in giving the opinion, that it is almost wholly unfit for cultivation, and of course uninhabitable by a people depending upon agriculture for their subsistence. Although tracts of fertile land, considerably extensive, are occasionally to be met with, yet the scarcity of wood and water, almost uniformly prevalent, will prove an insuperable obstacle in the way of settling the country. This objection rests not only against the immediate section under consideration, but applies with equal propriety to a much larger portion of the country. Agreeably to the best intelligence that can be had, concerning the country both northward and southward of the section, and especially to the inferences deducible from the account given by Lewis and Clark, of the country situated between the Missouri and the Rocky Mountains, above the river Platte, the vast region commencing near the sources of the Sabine, Trinity, Brasis, and Colorado, and extending northwardly to the forty-ninth degree of north latitude, by which the United States territory is limited in that direction, is throughout, of a similar character. The whole of this region seems peculiarly adapted as a range for buffaloes, wild goats, and other wild game, incalculable multitudes of which, find ample pasturage and subsistence upon it.

This region, however, viewed as a frontier, may prove of infinite importance to the United States, inasmuch as it is calculated to serve as a barrier to prevent too great an extension of our population westward, and secure us against the machinations or incursions of an enemy, that might otherwise be disposed to annoy us in that quarter.

The Indians of the section last described, whose numbers are very limited, compared with the extent of country they inhabit, will be considered in the sequel of this report.

VI.—*Of the Rocky Mountains.*

This range of mountains has been distinguished by a variety of appellations, amongst which the following are the most common, viz. Rocky, Shining, Mexican, Chippewyan, Andes, &c. The general course of the range is about N. N. W. or S. S. E. Its breadth varies from fifty to one hundred miles. They rise abruptly out of the plains which lie extended at their base on the east side, towering into peaks of great height, which renders them visible at the distance of more than one hundred miles eastward from their base. They consist of ridges, knobs and peaks, variously disposed, among which are interspersed many broad and fertile vallies. The more elevated parts of the mountains are covered with perpetual snows, which contribute to give them a luminous, and at a great distance even a brilliant appearance, whence they have derived the name of the Shining mountains.

Between the Arkansa and Platte, on a small creek tributary to the former, is situated a high part of the mountains, denominated the " Highest Peak," on many maps of the country, and said to be more elevated than any other part, within the distance of one hundred and fifty, or two hundred miles. This peak, whose summit has been accounted inaccessible, was ascended by a detachment of the Expedition, conducted by Dr. James, from which circumstance it has been called James' Peak. Its elevation above the common level, ascertained by a trigonometrical measurement, is about eight thousand five hundred feet. But, the correctness of the statement, that it is higher than any other part of the mountain within the distance above mentioned, is questionable. Judging from the position of the snow near the summits of other peaks and ridges at no great distance from it, a much greater elevation is apparent.

The mountains are clad in a scattering growth of scrubby pines, oak, cedar, and furze, and exhibit a very rugged and broken aspect. The rocky formations embodied in them, contrary to the opinion generally received, are uniformly of a primitive character, consisting of granite, gneiss, quartz, rocks, &c. It should be remarked, however, that a deep crust of secondary rocks, the same as the stratifications of the plains before mentioned, appears to recline against the east side of the mountains, extending upward from their base, many hundred feet.

At the base of James' peak above designated, are two remarkable springs of water, considerably copious, and strongly impregnated with fixed air. At the place also where the Arkansa issues from the mountains, are several medicinal springs, on the north side of the river, rising in a small area at the base of the mountain. These springs were discovered by captain Bell, and in consequence we have taken the liberty to call them Bell's springs. They are six in number, one of which is strongly impregnated with fixed air, another with sulphuretted hydrogen, and the rest, with salt and sulphur—the water of all being more or less chalybeate.

VII.—*Of the Indians inhabiting the section of country last described.*

This country is exclusively inhabited by savages, no other beings of the human family having fixed their abode within it. They consist of the following tribes and nations, whose numbers, places of residence, and mode of life, will be subjects of consideration as far as our knowledge of them extends.

The Otoes, or, as they are called in their own language, the Wah-tooh tah-tah, reside in a permanent village of dirt or earthen lodges, on the south bank of the river Platte, about fifty miles from its confluence with the Missouri, and thirty miles south westwardly from the Council Bluff. The principal remnant of the old Missouries, who have become extinct as a nation, have their residence with the Otoes. In the course of the last winter, whilst these Indians were absent from their village, on their winter *hunt,* their town was partly burnt by the Sauks, which misfortune induced them to take up a temporary abode upon Salt river, a few miles from their former residence. But it was generally supposed that they would return again, and rebuild their town. The name of their principal chief is Shongo-tonga, or Big Horse. Probable number of lodges, one hundred—of persons, fourteen hundred. The Otoes and Missouries are esteemed a brave people, and are friendly towards the Americans. They are at war with the Sauks, Foxes, Sioux, Osages, Iatans, and other Indians west of the Missouri. A small band of the Iaways resided for some time with these Indians, but not being able to harmonize with them, lately returned to their old village on the river De Moyen, of the Mississippi. Their principal chief, usually called Hard Heart, being dissatisfied with the conduct of his tribe, remains with the Otoes.

The Omawhaw, or as it is commonly written, the Maha nation, exultingly boast that they never have killed an American. On the contrary, they have ever been very friendly, and still hold the Americans in the highest estimation. Under the influence of their present principal chief, Ongpatonga, or the Big Elk, they never go to war except in the pursuit of a predatory war party, in consequence of which, the traders have given them the reputation of being cowardly. But the history of this people shows that they have been as ambitious of martial renown, and have acquired as large a share of it as any of their neighbours. They formerly resided in a village of dirt lodges, upon Omawhaw creek, a small stream entering the Missouri about two hundred miles above the Council Bluff, but they have recently abandoned it, and are about building a town on Elk Horn river. Their number of souls is about fifteen hundred.

The Poncahs have their residence in a small village of dirt lodges, about one hundred and eighty miles above Omawhaw creek. This tribe have a common origin with the Omawhaws, and speak the same language. Their principal chief is called *Smoke Maker*. Their number is about two hundred souls.

The tribes above enumerated, evidently sprung from the same common stock, the language of all being radically the same. They have a tradition that their fathers came from beyond the lakes.

The Pawnees are a race of Indians distinct from the preceding, their language differing radically from that of the Indians alluded to. The Pawnees consist of three distinct bands, that have their residence at present, on a branch of the river Platte, called the Loup Fork, about sixty miles from the mouth of the latter, and between one hundred and eight, and one hundred and fifteen miles westward from the Council Bluff. The three bands are distinguished by the appellations of the Grand, the Republican, and the Loup Pawnees. The two former acknowledge a common origin, but the latter deny having any natural affinity with them, though their habits, language, &c. indicate the same ancestry. They live in three villages, included within an extent of about seven miles, on the north bank of the Loup Fork, all compactly built.

The village of the Grand Pawnees, is situated immediately on the bank of the river, and contains about one hundred and eighty earthen lodges, nine hundred families, or three thousand five hundred souls. The name of the principal chief of this village, is Tarrarecawaho, or Long Hair.

The village of the Republican Pawnees, is situated about three miles above that of the Grand Pawnees—contains about fifty lodges, two hundred and fifty families, or one thousand souls. The name of their principal chief is Fool Robe, who is very much under the influence of Long Hair. This band separated many years since from the Grand Pawnees, and established themselves upon the Republican Fork of the Konzas river, where they were visited by Pike, on his tour westward. They seem to be gradually amalgamating with the parent stock, and their village wears a declining aspect.

The village of the Loup Pawnees, or Skere, as they call themselves, is situated four miles above that last mentioned, immediately on the bank of the river. It contains about one hundred dirt lodges, five hundred families, or two thousand souls—making an aggregate of six thousand five hundred souls, belonging to the three villages. The name of their principal chief, is the Knife Chief. A few years since, the Loup Pawnees had a custom of annually sacrificing a human victim to the Great Star, but this was abolished by their present chief, aided by the noble daring of his gallant son. They appear unwilling to acknowledge their affinity with the other Pawnees, but their language being very nearly the same, proves them to be of the same origin.

Although these bands are independent of each other in all their domestic concerns, government, &c. yet, in their military operations they generally unite, and warfare becomes a common cause with them. Their arms are principally bows and arrows, lances, war clubs, and shields, with some few fire arms. They are expert horsemen, but generally fight on foot. They are more numerous, and accounted more formidable in warfare than any other combination of savages on the Missouri. Their confidence in their own strength, gives them a disposition to domineer over their weaker neighbours. They are at war with the Osages, Konzas, Sioux, Iatans, Kaskaias, Kiaways, Shiennes, Crows, &c.

The several tribes above described, cultivate maize or Indian corn, pumpkins, beans, water melons, and squashes.— They hunt the bison or buffaloe, elk, deer, beaver, otter; the skins of which, they exchange with the traders for fusees, powder and lead, kettles, knives, strouding, blankets, beads, vermillion, silver ornaments, and other trinkets. They prefer the Mackinaw guns, blankets, &c., and will give a higher price for them, knowing that they are greatly superior to those furnished by American traders.

The Konzas and Osages, both of which reside in the vicinity of the meridian assumed as the eastern boundary of this section, may here be admitted to a more particular consideration than that already allowed them in this report. The Konzas Indians reside in a village of earthen lodges, situated on the north side of the river, near the mouth of Blue Earth creek, entering the river about one hundred miles from its mouth. Their village consists of about one hundred and thirty lodges, and contains about fifteen hundred souls. This tribe was formerly very troublesome to our traders, frequently robbing them of their goods, but since the establishment of the upper posts on the Missouri, they have become very friendly. They are at war with most of the other tribes and nations herein enumerated, except the Osages and Otoes, with the last of whom they have lately made peace, through the agency of Major O'Fallon, Indian agent for the Missouri. Several Indians of the Missouri tribe reside with them.

The Osages are divided into three bands or tribes, called the Grand Osage, the Little Osage, and Clermo's band. The two former of which reside in permanent villages, situated on the head waters of Osage river, and the last, upon the Verdigris, about sixty miles from its confluence with the Arkansa. According to Pike, whose estimate of their numbers is probably near the truth, the Grand Osages amount to one thousand six hundred and ninety-five. The Little Osages to eight hundred and twenty-four, and Clermo's band to fifteen hundred souls, making an aggregate of about four thousand. These Indians are not accounted brave by those inhabiting the country to the north and east of them, but are the dread of those west and south of them. Although they have occasionally been chargeable with depredations committed against the whites, they have been provoked to the perpetration of them, by aggressions or trespasses on the part of the latter, or else the depredations have been committed by malcontents of the nation, who will not be governed by the council of their chiefs. These Indians hold the people and government of the United States in the highest estimation, and have repeatedly signified their strong desire, to be instructed by them in the arts of civilization. The United States have purchased from them large and valuable tracts of country for mere trifles,— which the Osages have been the more willing to relinquish, under the prospect and encouragement given them, that the Americans would become their neighbours and instructors. They are in a state of warfare with all the surrounding tribes and nations of Indians, except the Konzas. It is said that they are about forming an alliance with the Sauk and Fox Indians of the Mississippi, and that the latter are preparing to remove to their country. They have recently driven the Pawnees of Red river from their place of residence, and compelled them to seek an abode upon the head waters either of the Brassis or Colorado.

The Konzas and Osages, are descendants from the same common origin, with the Otoes, Missouris, Iaways, Omawhaws, and Poncahs, to which may be added the Quawpaws, and several other tribes not mentioned in this report. The languages of all of them are radically the same, but are now distinguished by a variety of dialects.

VIII.—*Of the Arrapahoes, Kaskaias, Kiaways, Iatans, and Shiennes.*

These nations have no permanent residences or villages, but roam sometimes in society and sometimes separately, over a large portion of the section of country last described. They hunt the bison principally, and migrate from place to place, in the pursuit of the herds of that animal, upon the flesh of which they chiefly subsist. Being thus accustomed to a roving life, they neglect the cultivation of the soil, and subsist almost exclusively upon animal food. They formerly carried on a limited trade with the Spaniards of Mexico, with whom they exchanged dressed bison skins for blankets, wheat flour, maize, &c., but their supplies of these articles are now cut off, by a war which they are at present waging against that people. They also, at distant periods, held a kind of *fair*, on a tributary of the Platte, near the mountains, (hence called Grand Camp Creek) at which they obtained British merchandize from the Shiennes of Shienne river, who obtained the same at the Mandan village, from the British traders that frequent that part of our territory. Last winter, they traded a great number of horses and mules, with a party of white men, who had ascended Red river, but whence the party came could not be ascertained: it, however, appeared probable that they were citizens of the United States, or possibly freebooters from Barrataria.

The Shiennes associated with those wandering tribes, are a small band of seceders, from the nation of the same name, residing upon Shienne river. They are said to be daring and ferocious. They are, however, kept under restraint by the energy and firmness of their chief. The *Bear's Tooth*, who is the principal chief of the Arapahoes, and the head chief of all these nations, possesses great influence over the whole. His mandates, which are uniformly characterized by discretion and propriety, are regarded by his subjects as inviolable laws.

The Kaskaia and Kiaway languages are very difficult to acquire a knowledge of. Our interpreter, who had lived several years with them, could only make himself understood by the language of signs, with the aid of a very few words of the Crow language, which many of them appeared to understand. Indeed many of the individuals, of these different nations, seemed to be ignorant of each other's language, for when they met, they would communicate by means of signs, with now and then an oral interjection, and would thus maintain a conversation apparently without the least difficulty or misapprehension.

These nations are at war with all the Missouri Indians, as far down as the Osages, who are also included amongst their enemies, and it was rumoured that hostilities had recently commenced between them and the Shiennes, upon the river of the same name.

Their implements of war, consist of the bow and arrow, the lance, war-club, and shield. They usually fight on horseback, and as horsemen, display great skill and activity.

Their habitations are leather lodges, which serve them as tents on their march, and dwellings at the places of their encampment.

Widely diffused as these Indians are and never embodied, it is impracticable even to conjecture their numbers, with any degree of probable accuracy. They roam, not only throughout the section above specified, but extensively, within the range of the Rocky Mountains.

The foregoing remarks concerning the Indians of this part of the country, have been made, for the most part, agreeably to the suggestions of Mr. Say, whose attention was particularly directed to researches of this nature. But having been robbed of his notes upon the customs, manners, traditions, &c. of the western Indians, by the men, who deserted from captain Bell's party, he could give no farther account of them, than what his recollection could supply. Of the Konzas, Otoes, Pawnees, and other Indians near the Council Bluff, his notes are considerably extensive, but the vessel on board of which they with other articles, were shipped from New Orleans, having been obstructed in her passage up the Delaware by ice, we have not yet received them.

IX.—*Observations embracing several traits of character common to the Indians of the western country.*

An accurate and extensive knowledge, of the numerous tribes and nations of Indians living within the United States territory, can only be attained by a long residence with them. They are seldom communicative, except upon subjects intimately connected with their personal experience or present interests, and welfare. In regard to matters of an abstract or metaphysical nature, their ideas appear to be very limited; at any rate very little is known of their sentiments upon subjects of this kind, owing probably, in a great measure, to the inability of the persons usually employed as interpreters, to converse intelligently concerning them. The delicate trains of thought and reflection, attributed to them by writers, who have attempted to enlarge our acquaintance with the Indian character, usually have their origin in the ingenuity of the writers themselves. The exploits of their war parties, and particularly those of individuals, are often recounted, but are seldom transmitted to succeeding generations, unless they are characterized by some signal advantage to the tribe or nation to which the party or individual belongs. Hence, their history is very defective, affording but few incidents, and characterized by no regular series of events. In regard to the population and strength of the several tribes and nations, also the ages of individuals, no precise statements can be made; all the information given under these heads is almost without exception, conjectural. In relation to subjects of this kind, the Indians are either ignorant or wilfully silent, and deem it an impertinent curiosity that prompts a stranger to the investigation of them.

Notwithstanding these obstacles in the way of acquiring authentic and credible information concerning the savages, yet there are certain traits in their general character, that are observable in a partial acquaintance with a variety of tribes and nations, and upon these the following remarks are grounded.

They are, almost without exception, addicted to habits of extreme indolence; self-preservation, self-defence, and recreation, being their usual incitements to action. The laborious occupations of the men, consist almost exclusively in hunting, warfare, and tending their horses. Their amusements are principally horse-racing, gambling, and sports of various kinds. The cultivation of corn and other vegetables, the gathering of fuel, cooking, and all other kinds of domestic drudgery, is the business of the women, the men deeming it degrading to their dignity, to be occupied in employments of this kind. Their religion consists in the observance of a variety of rites and ceremonies, which they practise with much zeal and enthusiasm. Their devotional exercises consist in singing, dancing, and the performance of various mystical ceremonies, which they believe efficacious in healing the sick, frustrating the designs of their enemies, and in giving success to any enterprise in which they may be embarked.

Amongst all the tribes of the west, secret associations or councils are common, the proceedings of which are held sacred, and not to be divulged, except when the interests of the people are thought to require a disclosure. To these councils, which they denominate medicine, or rather magic feasts, none are admitted but the principal men of the nation, or such as have signalized themselves by their exploits in battle, hunting, stealing horses, or in any of the pursuits accounted laudable by the Indians.

They appear to have no laws, except such as grow out of habitual usages, or such as are sanctioned by common consent; and the execution of these seems to be vested entirely in the chiefs and warriors, who are allowed to use the utmost severity, in enforcing order and subordination.

In all their acts of devotion, as also on all occasions where their confidence is to be won, or their friendship to be plighted, the smoking of tobacco seems to be invariably regarded, as an inviolable token of sincerity. They believe in the existence of a Supreme Being, whom they denominate "Master of Life," or "Good Spirit," but, of his attributes, their ideas are vague and confused.

They are, generally, in the habit of offering in sacrifice, a portion of the game first taken in a hunting expedition, a part of the first products of the field, and often a small portion of the food provided for their refreshment. In smoking they generally direct the first puff upward and the second downward to the earth, or the first to the rising and the second to the setting sun, after which they inhale the smoke into their lungs, and puff it out through the nostrils, for their own refreshment.

They have some indistinct notion of the immortality of the soul, but appear to know no distinction of heaven or hell, Elysium or Tartarus, as the abode of departed spirits.

The arts of civilized life, instead of exciting their emulation, are generally viewed by the Indians as objects unworthy of their attention. This results as a natural consequence, from their habits of indolence. They are aware that much labour is requisite in the prosecution of them, and being inured, from their infancy to look upon manual labour of every description, as a drudgery, that pertains exclusively to the female part of their community, they think it degrading to the character of men, to be employed in them. Hunting, horsemanship, and warfare, are the only avocations in which their ambition or sense of honour, prompts them to engage.

Their reluctance to forgive an injury, is proverbial. "Injuries are revenged by the injured; and blood for blood is always demanded, if the deceased has friends who dare to retaliate upon the destroyer." Instances have occurred where their revenge has become hereditary, and quarrels have been settled long after the parties, immediately concerned, have become extinct.

Much has been published in relation to the high antiquity of Indian traditions, of those particularly which relate to their origin, and their religion. But from the examples afforded by the several nations of Indians resident upon the Mississippi and its waters, but little proof is to be had in favour of the position. It is not doubted, that the immediate objects of their worship, have been held in reverence by their predecessors, for a long succession of ages; but in respect to any miraculous dispensations of Providence of which they have a traditional knowledge, their ideas are at best exceedingly vague and confused, and of occurrences recorded in sacred history, they appear to be entirely ignorant. The knowledge they have of their ancestry is also very limited, so much so, that they can seldom trace back their pedigree more than a few generations, and then know so little of the place whence their fathers came, that they can only express their ideas upon the subject in general terms, stating, that they came, "from beyond the lakes, from the rising or setting sun, from the north or south," &c. In some instances, where their term of residence in a place has evidently been of short duration, they have either lost, or conceal their knowledge of the country whence their ancestors came, and assert that the Master of Life created and planted their fathers on the spot where they, their posterity, now live. They have no division of time except by years, seasons, moons, and days. Particular periods are distinguished by the growth and changes of vegetables, the migrations, incubations, &c. of birds and other animals.

Their language is of two kinds: viz. verbal and signal, or the language of signs.

The former presents a few varieties marked by radical differences, and a multiplicity of dialects peculiar to individual tribes or nations descended from the same original. The latter is a language common to most, if not to all of the western Indians, the motions or signs used to express ideas, being, with some slight variations, the same amongst all of them. Nearly allied to the language of signs, is a species of written language which they make use of, consisting of a few symbolical representations, and of course, very limited and defective.

The figures they make use of have but a faint resemblance to the object described, and are rudely imprinted upon trees, cliffs, &c. by means of paints, charcoal, and sometimes by carving with a knife or other edged tool, and are significant of some movement, achievement, or design of the Indians. A variety of figures of this description are to be seen upon the cliffs, rocks, and trees, in places held sacred, and frequently resorted to by the Indians, but of their import, little is known. Many of these symbols are made by the magicians, or men of Medicine, and are probably of sacred or devotional import.

Much intrigue, cunning, and artifice, are blended with the policy of the Indians, and judging from the usual practice, it is a favorite, and well-approved maxim with them, that "the end sanctifies the means." In an interview with strangers, it appears to be their first object, to ascertain their motives, and the objects of their visit, and after regarding them for some time without a show of curiosity, a variety of interrogatories are proposed, in order to satisfy themselves upon these points. This they appear to do with the view also of scrutinizing into the character and disposition of their guests. In the course of the conversation they become more and more familiar and impertinent, till at length, their familiarity is succeeded by contempt and insult. Thus, from the coldest reserve, they are in a short time, impelled by curiosity, and a propensity to abuse, where they are not in some measure compelled to respect, to the commission of outrages, even without the slightest provocation. This kind of treatment, however, is easily obviated at the commencement of an interview, by resisting every advance made by the Indians towards familiarity, and by uniformly opposing firmness and reserve to the liberties they are disposed to take.

These attributes of the Indian character manifest themselves not only in the well known sratagems they adopt in warfare, but in the management of their domestic concerns, in which rivalships of one kind or other are engendered; parties are formed, and pretenders arise, claiming privileges that have been withheld from them, and placing themselves at the head of factions, occasionally withdraw from the mother tribe. Thus new tribes are formed and distributed in various directions over the country, with nothing to mark their genealogy but the resemblance of their language to that of the parent stock, or of other Indians that sprung from the same origin.

The chiefs or governors of tribes, have their rank and title by inheritance; yet in order to maintain them, and secure themselves in their preeminence, they are under the necessity of winning over to their interests the principal warriors and most influential men of their tribe, whose countenance and support are often essential to their continuance in authority.

In conciliating the friendship of these, the chief is often compelled to admit them to participate in the authority with which he is invested, and to bestow upon them any effects of which he may be possessed. Thus it often happens, that the chiefs are among the poorest of the Indians, having parted with their horses, clothes, trinkets, &c. to ensure the further patronage of their adherents, or to purchase the friendship of those that are disaffected.

The situation of principal chief is very frequently usurped during the minority of the rightful successor; or wrested from an imbecile incumbent by some ambitious chief or warrior. In this case, the ascendency obtained over the nation by the usurper is gradual, and depends upon the resources of his own mind, aided by his reputation for generosity and valour.

The condition of the savages is a state of constant alarm and apprehension. Their security from their enemies, and their means of subsistence, are precarious and uncertain, the former requiring the utmost vigilance to prevent its infraction, and the latter being attended with no regular supplies of the necessaries of life. In times of the most profound peace, whether at their villages or on a hunting expedition, they are continually on the alert, lest they should be surprised by their enemies. By day scouts are constantly kept patroling for a considerable distance around them, and by night sentinels are posted, to give notice of the approach of strangers.

When they engage in a *hunt*, they generally abandon their villages, old men, women and children joining in the enterprize, through fear of being left at home without the strength

of their nation to protect them. On their march they endeavour to make as great a display of force as practicable, in
order to intimidate any of their enemies that may be lurking
to spy out their condition. With this view, they are careful
to pitch their lodges or tents at the places of their encampment, in such a manner, and in such numbers, as to give the
impression at a distance, that they are numerous and formidable. We have witnessed a hunting party on their march,
consisting of not more than one hundred persons, including
men, women, and children, yet at their encampment, more
than thirty lodges were pitched, each of which would ac-
commodate at least, twelve adult persons.

It is an opinion generally credited, that the Indians are
possessed of strong natural appetites for ardent spirits, but
there is at least room to doubt of its being well founded.
That their appetites for them are often strong and ungovern-
able, is very certain, but they may be considered as factitious
rather than natural, having been created by occasional indulgences in the use of intoxicating liquors. Instances are
not rare, in which Indians have refused to accept liquor
when offered them. After a long abstinence from food, any
thing calculated to allay the cravings of the appetite is eagerly swallowed; and on such occasions, nothing perhaps
produces such an effect more speedily, than spirituous liquor.
Indians, while lounging about a trading establishment, are
often destitute of food for a considerable time, and can obtain no other kind of refreshment from the trader but liquor,
which is bestowed partly in exchange for commodities they
may have to dispose of, and partly by way of encouraging
them to return to him with the products of their next hunt.
A small draught, on such occasions, produces intoxication,
and the sudden transition from a state of gnawing hunger
to that of unconcerned inebriety, cannot fail to make them
passionately fond of a beverage that can thus change their
condition so much to their immediate satisfaction. In their
use of ardent spirits, the Indians appear to be less captivated
with their taste than with their exhilarating effects. The
quality of liquor is not a subject of discrimination with them;
provided it has sufficient strength to inebriate, they are satisfied, let its character in other respects be what it may. Having contracted the habit of intoxication, they seldom appear
thankful for liquor unless it has been bestowed in such quantities as are sufficient to produce that effect.

In the indulgence of their appetites, they display but few,

or no traits of epicurism, choosing those kinds of food that are most nutritive, without regarding their taste, or flavour.

In the preservation of their food no pains are taken to render it savoury or palatable, their object is solely to reduce it to a state of security against putrefaction. They make no use of spices or other aromatics, either in preserving or cooking their food. Even salt is not considered as an essential, and is seldom used as an appendage in their cookery. This article is only prized by them on account of its usefulness for their horses. In regard to their choice of food, however, and manner of cooking it, the small variety within their reach, and the impracticability of obtaining condiments of different kinds, perhaps renders them less particular in these respects, than they would be under different circumstances. It cannot be supposed that they are entirely insensible to dainties of every description, on the contrary, they appear remarkably fond of sugar and saccharine fruits.

They appear to have a natural propensity for the fumes of tobacco, which they invariably inhale into the lungs, and eject through the nostrils. They make no use of this article except in smoking, which is an indulgence of which they are exceedingly reluctant to be deprived. When they cannot obtain tobacco, they use as a substitute the dried leaves of the sumac, the inner bark of the red willow dried, and the leaves and bark of a few other shrubs, the fumes of which are less stimulating, but equally as palatable as those of tobacco.

The Indians under consideration know not the use or value of the precious metals, except as trinkets or ornaments for their dress. They use wampum, and in some few instances, shells of a small size, and of a particular character, as a substitute for money. But, in general, furs, peltries, horses, and various articles of dress, at standing or fixed rates of barter, are the immediate objects, both of internal and external trade.

They do not hold their property in common, but each individual enjoys the fruit of his own toil and industry. They are accounted more or less wealthy, according to the number of horses they are possessed of, and the style in which they are able to dress.

Polygamy is common amongst them, every man being allowed to have as many wives as he can maintain. Marriages are binding upon the parties only as long as they think proper to live together, and are often contracted for a limited term particularly specified. Females, during the periods of their catamenia, are excluded from society, and compelled even to sleep apart from their families, in small tents or lodges constructed for their use.

Dancing is common amongst them, both as a devotional exercise, and an amusement. Their gestures on both occasions are similar, except that on the former they are accompanied by solemnity, and on the latter by cheerfulness, and are characterized by extraordinary uncouthness rather than by gracefulness. No ribaldry, however, or tricks of buffoonery are practised on these occasions; on the contrary, their deportment is uniformly accordant with their ideas of decorum. This exercise is invariably accompanied by singing, or a kind of chanting, in which the women, who are generally excluded from a participation in the former, perform their part. Their music consists in a succession of tones, of equal intervals, accompanied by occasional elevations and depressions of the voice. The modulations with which it is variegated, are by no means melodious; the voices of all the chanters move in unison, and appear to utter the same aspirations. The same series of sounds appears to be common to the chanting of all the tribes.

The foregoing are among the most common features in the general character of the western Indians. Although in a region so extensive as that inhabited by them, and amongst so great a variety of tribes and nations, a considerable diversity of character is to be expected and admitted, yet it is believed that the traits above considered are common to the whole as a race of barbarians. And, although the shades of barbarism in which they are enveloped, uniformly exclude the light of civilization, yet it is not to be presumed that they are equally dark and malignant in all cases.

IX.—*Of the Mississippi, Missouri, and Ohio rivers.*

I trust it will not be deemed improper on this occasion, to offer a few remarks upon the character of these rivers, embracing more particularly the condition of their navigation.

The causes heretofore alleged as giving occasion to a diversity of soil within the vallies of the western rivers, have an effect also in giving character to their channels or beds. For example, the banks near the mouths of the rivers, being composed of a fine, unctuous, and adhesive alluvion, are less liable to crumble and wash away, and constitute a more permanent barrier to resist the force of the current than those higher up, that are composed of coarser materials. In consequence, the beds of the river are rendered narrower and deeper towards their mouths than at greater distances above them. This is more particularly the case with the Mississippi, Red, Arkansa, and some others, whose beds or channels gradually dilate and become more shoal, on ascending from their mouths. Thus it happens, also, that the navigation of the Mississippi has fewer obstructions between Natches and its mouth, than above, this part of the river having so great a depth of water, that snags, bars, &c. are sunk below the reach of every kind of water craft employed in its navigation. From Natches upward, to its confluence with the Missouri the river presents impediments that become more and more numerous and difficult to pass. Still, however, the main channel, though intricate in many places, affords a sufficient depth of water in all stages for boats of five or six feet draft to ascend to the mouth of the Ohio. From this point to the Missouri, a distance of more than two hundred and twenty miles, the navigation is partially obstructed during a very low stage of the water by shoals, so that it is navigable only for boats of moderate burthen, requiring but about three feet of water. At the distance of about thirty miles above the mouth of the Ohio, there are two rocky bars extending across the Mississippi, called the Big and Little Chains, which in the deepest channel across them afford no more than five or six feet of water, in a low stage, and occasion a great rapidity of current. The Mississippi is usually at its lowest stage about the middle of August, the summer freshet of the Missouri having subsided previously to that time. It usually continues in this stage till it is swollen by the fall freshet of the Ohio, after which it subsides again and remains low during the winter. The distance from New Orleans to the mouth of the Missouri, is estimated at about twelve hundred miles. Its current in the main channel of the river is supposed to have an average velocity of 3 3-4 miles per hour in a moderate stage of the water, but when the river is high its velocity is considerably accelerated. Its water is turbid, being charged with a fine argillaceous mud, of a light colour, derived exclusively from the Missouri.

The Missouri is a very wild and turbulent river, possessing the ruder features of the Mississippi, but destitute of the gentleness characteristic of the latter in many places. The obstructions to the navigation of the Missouri, although they are of the same character with those of the Mississippi,

are far more numerous and formidable than those of the latter. The channel is rendered exceedingly intricate by means
of sand-bars and islands, and the navigation, in many places,
is very hazardous on account of the multiplicity of rafts,
snags, sand-bars, &c., with which the channel is beset. No
part of the river is exempt from these obstructions, for any
great distance, particularly when the water is low.

As this river in connection with some of its principal tributaries, traverses a considerable variety of climates, embracing more than ten degrees of latitude, a series of spring freshets invariably takes place, maintaining an elevated stage of
water, from the breaking up of winter, early in March, to the
middle, and sometimes the last of July, when it is terminated
by the summer freshet yielded by the most northerly of its
tributaries. During this period, there is a sufficient depth of
water to admit boats of almost any burden; but during the
residue of the year, it can hardly be called navigable, except
for boats, drawing no more than twenty-five or thirty inches.
The river is usually blocked up with ice during the winter
season. The average velocity of its current in a middle
stage of water, may be estimated at four and a half miles,
and in time of a high freshet, it moves with an accelerated
velocity, equal to five or five and a half miles per hour.

The Ohio river, as before hinted, differs from those just
described, in the rapidity of its current, the width of its bed,
character of its channel, and in several other respects. But
as its general character is well known, a few remarks in relation to it, will here suffice. The obstructions to its navigation are sand-bars, some few rafts and snags, and rapids, to
which the intricacy of its channel in several places, may be
added. During a middle and high stage of water, these obstructions entirely disappear, and an accelerated current is
the only difficulty to be encountered. The average velocity
of the current in a moderate stage of water may be estimated
at two and a half miles, and in a high stage at three miles
per hour. The season in which the navigation of the Ohio
can be relied on, commences between the middle of February and first of March, and continues to the latter part of
June. A fall freshet usually takes place in October or November, and the river is again navigable for a few weeks.
During the rest of the year, boats of inconsiderable burden
meet with numerous obstructions in their progress, from the
lowness of the water, and in many places, no channel can be
found of sufficient depth to admit their passage. At the dis-

tance of about seventeen miles from its mouth, is the first serious obstruction to its navigation, consisting of a limestone bar, extending across the river, denominated the Big Chain. Three miles above is another bar of a similar description. The range of rocks, of which these appear to be a portion, seems to extend across the point of land situated between the Ohio and Mississippi, presenting itself again on the latter, at the Big and Little Chains, before mentioned. The falls of the Ohio, at Louisville, are impassable for boats of burthen, except in the higher stages of the water. Le Tart's Falls and numerous other rapids, denominated ripples, are also impassable for boats of any considerable burden, when the river is at its lowest stage. In this state the river is fordable in numberless places.

X.—*Of the Great Valley or Basin of the Mississippi.*

This vast region, embracing more than twenty degrees of latitude and about thirty of longitude, although it has been explored in various directions by men of intelligence, is yet but imperfectly known, and probably no country in the world affords a more ample or interesting field for philosophic investigation. A thorough acquaintance with its geological character, would, in all probability, lead to the most important conclusions, in forming a correct "theory of the earth," while a knowledge of its vegetable and mineral productions, may be conducive to the comforts and enjoyments of a large portion of the human family. All we shall presume to offer under this copious head, will be a few general remarks relative to the position and conformation of the valley, grounded almost exclusively upon the hydrography of the country, so far as it has come under our observations.

The valley is bounded on the west by the Rocky Mountains, on the east and southeast by the Alleghanies, and south by the gulf of Mexico. To the northward no precise limits can be assigned as its boundary. Although many have supposed that the waters of the Mississippi are separated from those running northwestwardly into the Pacific Ocean, and northeastwardly into the Atlantic, by a mountainous range of country, yet from the best information that can be had on the subject, the fact is quite otherwise. The old and almost forgotten statement of savage origin, viz, that "four of the largest rivers on the continent, have their sources in the same plain," is entitled to far more credit. The rivers alluded to are the Mississippi, the St. Lawrence, the Saskashawin, and the Oregon or Columbia river. Agreeably to the accounts of Col. Dixon, and others who have traversed the country, situated between the Missouri and the Assiniboin, a branch of Red river of Hudson's Bay, no elevated ridge is to be met with, but, on the contrary, tributaries to both these streams take their rise in the same champaign, and wind their way in various directions to their far distant estuaries. Judging from the maps that have been given of the country near the sources of the Mississippi, and of the region generally, situated northwardly of the Great Lakes, as also from the accounts of various travellers, who have penetrated many parts of those countries, the same remark appears equally applicable to a large portion of the whole. The water courses are represented as chains of lakes of various magnitude, while lakes and stagnant pools are scattered in almost every direction, without ridges or perceptible declivities, to show the direction in which they are drained. But we forbear to enlarge on this subject, and beg leave that reference may be had to Tanner's map of North America, comprehending the region of which we have been treating, as a document containing ample illustrations of our opinion. Hence it will be inferred that the valley of the Mississippi, is merely a portion of an immense region of valley or flat country, extending from the Gulf of Mexico northeastwardly to the Atlantic and northwestwardly to the Pacific Ocean.

Within the valley or region drained by the Mississippi, are situated no less than three distinct ranges of mountainous country, the localities of which we will attempt to point out. The first and most considerable, is a range of mountains, commencing within the Spanish province of Texas, and stretching in a northeastward direction, till it is terminated by the high lands on the lower part of the Missouri river. To this range we have given the name of the Ozark mountains, an appellation by which the Arkansa river was formerly distinguished, as also the tribe of Indians since denominated the Quawpaws, inhabiting near that river. Its direction is nearly parallel to that of the Alleghanies. Its peaks and ridges are less elevated, than those of the latter, and do not present the same regularity in their arrangement. The second is denominated the Black Hills, commencing on the south, or Padouca Fork of the river Platte, at the distance of about one hundred miles eastward of the Rocky Mountains, and stretching northeastwardly towards the great northerly bend of the Missouri. Of this range, very little is yet known, but the fact that there is such a range, is partially substantiated by the concurrent testimony of the traders and hunters of the Missouri, with whom it is a noted land-mark, and is more fully corroborated by the hydrography of the country, as may be shown by the map.

The third is a range of hilly and broken country, commencing on the Wisconsan, near the Portage, and extending northwardly to Lake Superior. To this range we have taken the liberty to give the name of the Wisconsan hills. The Ocooch and Smoky mountains before mentioned, are connected with this range. In its geological characters, and more especially in its metallic productions, so far as our inquiry will enable us to decide, it appears nearly allied to the Ozark mountains, and circumstances are not wanting to induce the opinion that they were once the same continuous range. Dr. James is decidedly of the opinion, that the metalliferous region of the Mississippi, which extends from Red river, to Lake Superior, in the direction of these two ranges, strongly indicates that a continuous range, as just hinted, once had an existence.

The Mississippi river may be regarded as occupying the lowest part of the valley, from its great estuary, the gulf of Mexico, to its confluence with the Missouri and Illinois. Thence to Lake Michigan, the immediate valley of the Illinois, is to be viewed as the lowest part of the great valley under consideration. This conclusion necessarily results from an attentive consideration of the characters of the three rivers just mentioned. If the inclinations of the plains down which these rivers respectively flow, be in any degree proportionable to the velocities of their currents, the plain of the Illinois will be found to have far the least inclination, inasmuch as the velocity of its current is not more than one-fourth of that of either of the others. But in order to have a more distinct view of the matter, let us assume the parallel of latitude intersecting the Illinois at its head, or point of confluence of the Kankakee and Des Plains rivers, and suppose a vertical section cut in the direction of the parallel. Such a section would intersect the Missouri at the distance of nearly seven hundred miles from its mouth, the Mississippi at about two hundred and sixty, and the Illinois at two hundred and fifty from the same point. Hence allowing that the plains of each have the same inclination, the point of intersection on the Missouri, would be at a greater elevation than that on the Mississippi, and that on the Illinois would be less elevated than either. But the difference of inclination in these plains, is manifest, not only from the comparative velocities of the several streams alluded to, but from the circumstance, that the Illinois is destitute of any considerable rapids throughout its whole course, whereas the Mississippi, in addition to a current uniformly more rapid, is hurried down the De Moyen rapids, eleven miles in length, and the Missouri, without a perversion of terms, may be denominated a rapid, throughout the distance above specified. By a similar course of reasoning, it may also be made to appear, that the assumed point of intersection on the Illinois is less elevated than any other point, in the same parallel of latitude between that river and Lake Erie, and even that it is somewhat lower than the surface of the lake itself, for the aggregate descent from the surface of Lake Michigan, to the point under consideration, is evidently greater than from the surface of the same lake, to that of Lake Erie, or in other words, the descent of the Des Plains from Chicago to its confluence with the Kankakee, is greater by a few feet, than that of the stream uniting Lakes Huron and Erie.

This view of the subject affords us a clue' whereby to ascertain, with some degree of precision, the aggregate fall of water, from the head of the Illinois to the Gulf of Mexico. Agreeably to the surveys of the great canal of New York, the elevation of Lake Erie, above tide water, is found to be five hundred and sixty-four feet. Hence we may assume, in round numbers, four hundred and fifty feet as the altitude of the head of the Illinois above the ocean.

Of the conformation of the valley in other respects, no other ideas can be advanced, but such as are suggested by a general view of the topography of the country, and especially of the courses of the principal rivers, as exhibited in the map of the country drained by the Mississippi. We will only add, that the inclined plain, constituting the western side of the valley, or in other words, the great slope, down which the Red, Canadian, Arkansa, Konzas, Platte, and other large rivers have their courses, has probably a greater general inclination, than any other side of the valley. In forming an estimate of the aggregate descent of this slope, commencing at tide water and extending to the base of the Rocky Mountains, Pike allows eight thousand feet, which probably exceeds the truth more than one half. We would substitute three thousand feet as the aggregate elevation of the base of the mountains above the Ocean, and are of the opinion that this amount rather exceeds the truth.—This altitude, added to that of James' Peak as before stated, would give for the height of that peak above the Ocean, eleven thousand five hundred feet. Comparing this altitude with that of the " inferior limit of perpetual snow," as estimated by M. D. Humboldt, for the latitude of forty degrees, viz. nine thousand eight hundred and forty-six feet above the Ocean, we find the summit of the peak one thousand six hundred and fifty-four feet higher than that elevation, and judging from appearances, this difference of altitude seemed sufficiently well marked by the distance, to which the snow extended, from the summit downward upon the sides of the Peak, to authenticate in a good degree, the calculation above stated.

CHAPTER XIX.

Observations on the geology of the country traversed by the Expedition.

THE most prominent feature of the continent of North America, is the great chain of the Rocky Mountains, evidently a continuation of the Andes of the southern hemisphere, stretching parallel to the direction of the western coast, from the Isthmus of Panama to the Frozen Ocean.* Their summits, rising far above the limit of perpetual frost, look down upon the wide plains of the Mississippi and its tributaries, unvaried except by a low range of rocky hills, commencing near the confluence of the Missouri and Mississippi, and running southwest to the Rio Del Norte. Eastward of these, the surface again subsides to a plain, stretching to the foot of the great chain of the Alleghanies. This last range, far less elevated and alpine than the Rocky Mountains, traverses the continent in a direction parallel to the Atlantic coast, from the gulf of St. Lawrence on the northeast, to the confluence of the Alabama and Tombigbee rivers, in the southwest.

The Alleghanies, unlike the Rocky Mountains, have few prominent summits; instead of conic peaks and a sharply serrated outline, they present long and level ridges, rising in no point to the inferior limit of perpetual frost, and in few instances attaining that degree of elevation which is incompatible with the growth of forests.

In many particulars, a manifest resemblance is perceived between the Alleghanies, and the comparatively inconsiderable group, which we have denominated the Ozark mountains. They are parallel in direction, making an angle of about forty degrees with the great range of the Andes. In many parts of both ranges, rocks of recent formation occupy the loftiest summits, and are based on more ancient aggregates. It is well known, that from the gneiss at Philadelphia, there is a gradual ascent across strata more and more recent, to the

---

* Mackenzie. " The *Stony Mountains*, in lat. 68° 46, lon. 122° from London are," says Hearne, " of a craggy and tremendous aspect."

ròcks of the coal formation about the summit of the Alleghany. Whether this conformation prevails in every part of the range, our examinations have not enabled us to decide. We know that some of the granitic mountains of New England, are far surpassed in elevation by the neighbouring hills and ridges of mica slate, talcose rocks, or even more recent aggregates.

In the Ozark mountains, as far as they have been hitherto explored, the granites and elder primitive rocks are found at the lowest parts, being surmounted by those of more recent formation, the newer horizontal sandstones and strata of carboniferous limestone, forming the highest summits. The reverse of this is observed in the Rocky Mountains —the granite there, far surpassing all other rocks, both in extent and elevation, and forming the central and higher portions of all the ridges; that range has therefore a character very different from the Ozark or Alleghany mountains.

It has been suggested by Major Long, that the hydrography of the upper portion of the Missouri seems to indicate the existence of a mountain range approaching that river from the southwest, near the great northerly bend in the country of the Mandans. From Lewis and Clark we have also some accounts, tending to the confirmation of this opinion. Further examination may perhaps prove that this third range, called the Black Hills, resembles, in direction and general character, the Alleghany and Ozark mountains. The Rocky Mountains have not inaptly been called the back bone of the continent; these three lateral ranges going off at angles of about forty degrees, may with equal propriety be compared to the ribs.

In latitude 38° north, the eastern base of the Rocky Mountains is in about 106° west longitude. Following the same parallel of latitude eastward, you arrive at the base of the Ozark mountains, nearly in longitude 94°; the intervening space occupying an extent of near twelve degrees of longitude, is a sterile and desolate plain, destitute of timber; scorched in summer by the reverberation of the rays of the sun,— chilled in winter by the freezing west winds from the Rocky Mountains. Though we have assumed twelve degrees of longitude as the medium width of this great plain, it is to be remarked that, to many parts of it, our examinations have not been extended. In latitude 41° no mountains, and scarce an elevation deserving the name of a hill, occurs between the western spurs of the Alleghanies and the Rocky

Mountains. But, at no great distance north of this parallel, low ranges of hills begin to appear in the region southwest of lake Michigan, and though too inconsiderable in point of elevation to deserve particular notice, they exhibit peculiar characters, which seem to designate an intimate connexion with the Ozark mountains south of the Missouri. The same succession of strata, the same alternation of crystalline beds with those of mechanical deposition, and similar deposites of metallic ores are observed here, as in the regions about the Merameg and St. Francis. A marked difference is also, as we think, to be discovered between the rocks and soils on the different sides of this range. Of this we shall speak more particularly in another place. For our present purpose, it is sufficient to assume as a boundary of the region we propose first to consider—a line running from the confluence of the Arkansa and Canadian rivers on the southwest, to the junction of the Mississippi and Wisconsan on the northeast. Assuming this as the direction of the range of the Ozark mountains, it will be perceived by examining the map, that to the northwest of this line spreads an extensive plain, reaching to the base of the Rocky Mountains. This plain has been crossed in three different places by the exploring party, as already detailed. Once in ascending by the river Platte, between latitude 40° and 41° 30'—again, in descending the Arkansa in 38°; and thirdly, by the route of the Canadian, in 34°. To the information collected in these journies, we have added a little from other sources, but the greater part of this extensive region yet remains to be explored.

Sect. I.—Secondary formations connected with the Rocky Mountains.

I.—*Of the great American Desert.*

The portion of country which we design to consider under this division, has an average width of between five and six hundred miles, extending along the base of the Rocky Mountains from north to south, as far as we have any acquaintance with that range. Consisting entirely of granitic sands, or of secondary aggregates, into which the *detritus* of that chain of primitive mountains enters in large proportion—there would be propriety in designating it by some name recognizing its relation to those mountains. It has been mentioned as the " Mexican Desert,"* a name sufficiently applicable to some portions of it, but one by no means to be extended to

---

* Nuttall's Travels, p. 120.

every part alike, as it undoubtedly occupies a very considerable portion of the interior of North America. That a similar desert region exists on the western side of the mountains, we have sufficient evidence; but whether as uninterrupted and as extensive, we have not the means of determining. The Jesuit Venegas, speaking of the early history of California, says, " Father Kino and his companions, after travelling thirty leagues from San Marcelo, came to a small rancheria, [Indian village,] and leaving on the north the great mountain of Santa Clara, whose sides for the length of a league are covered with pumice stone, they arrived at the *sandy waste* on the 19th of March."* Our information is yet too limited to justify an attempt to fix the boundaries of this desert—we therefore confine ourselves to the observations our opportunities have enabled us to make.

The channel of the Missouri near the mouth of the Platte, discloses, here and there rocks of horizontal limestone, which, from their peculiar character we are disposed to consider as belonging rather to the Ozarks, than having any direct connexion with the Rocky Mountains. These rocks appear at the lowest parts of the vallies, and are usually surmounted by extensive beds of soil, consisting principally of sand, in the most minute state of division, but intermixed with remains of organized beings, and sometimes with calcareous and aluminous earth. Proceeding westward, the sand becomes deeper and more unmixed; not a rock or a stone in place, or out of place, is to be met with, for some hundreds of miles. It is believed no rocky bluffs appear along the valley of the Platte, within three hundred miles of its mouth, though a small part of this distance on the lower portion of the river has not been explored. The surface of this sandy waste is not an absolute plain, but varied with gentle undulations, such as the draining of water for a succession of centuries, from an immense table of light arenaceous earth, may be supposed to have occasioned. The gradual intermixture of the exuviæ of animals and vegetables, with what was formerly a pure silicious sand, has at length produced a soil capable of supporting a scanty growth of grasses, now almost the only covering of these desolate regions.

About four hundred miles west of the mouth of the Platte, a low range of sandstone hills crosses the country from southwest to northeast. The strata forming these hills have no

* Venegas' History of California, vol. i, p. 305, Lond. 1759.

perceptible inclination, and present appearances, which indicate their deposition to have been nearly contemporaneous to that of many of our coal formations. It has already been suggested, that this range may probably be a continuation of the *Cotes Noire*, or Black Hills, said to contain the sources of the Shienne, the Little Missouri, and some branches of the Yellow Stone.*

Beyond these inconsiderable hills, the surface again subsides nearly to a plain. The fine and comparatively fertile sand which prevailed to the east of the range, is exchanged for a gravel, consisting of rounded granitic fragments, varying in dimensions from the size of a six pound shot to the finest sand. This great mass of granitic fragments, evidently brought down by the agency of water from the sides and summits of the Rocky Mountains, slopes gradually from their base, appearing as far as our examinations have extended, in some measure to correspond in magnitude to the elevation and extent of that part of the mountains opposite which it is placed. The minute particles derived principally from the quartzy portions of the primitive aggregates, being least liable to decomposition, have been carried to the greatest distance, and now form the soil of the eastern margin of the great sandy desert. The central portions are of a coarser sand, intermixed with some particles of feldspar and mica, and minute fragments of hornblend. Nearer the mountains, pebbles and boulders become frequent, and at length almost cover the surface of the country.

That the great Sandy Desert has resulted from the wearing down of the mountains, both before and since the retiring of the ocean, will not be thought improbable, if we consider that the materials composing both regions are similar in kind, —that the granitic soils of the plain are precisely such as would result from the disintegration of the rocks now existing in the mountains, and that the numerous deep ravines and water-worn vallies, traversing the mountains in various directions, indicate such a change as is here supposed to have happened.

It is probable many parts of this extensive desert may differ from that traversed by the Platte, in having the surface more or less covered with horizontal strata of sandstone, and conglomerate instead of loose sand and pebbles. Many appearances indicate that a formation of this kind formerly

---

* Lewis and Clark's History, vol. i, p. 133.

extended down the Platte, much farther than at present. Here, as in the great plain which extends from the base of the Uralian mountains to Petersburgh, we meet with numerous elevations or platforms, like islands in the midst of an ocean.* The summits of these *outlying hills*, are crossed at equal altitudes by corresponding strata of sandstone, and conglomerate.

From the minute account given in the narrative of the Expedition, of the particular features of this region, it will be perceived to bear a manifest resemblance to the deserts of Siberia. The soil and rocks are saline; plants allied to chenopodium and salsola are peculiarly abundant, as are the astragali and others of the legumina, while trees and forests are almost unknown.

The surface of the sandy plain rises perceptibly towards the base of the mountains, and becoming constantly more and more undulating, is at length broken, disclosing some cliffs and ledges of micaceous sandstone. Near the Platte, this sandstone occurs in horizontal strata, sometimes cut through by the beds of the streams, and forming low ridges parallel to the Rocky Mountains. Whether they continue in an uninterrupted line along the base of the mountains, we have not been able to ascertain. They are separated from the first range of primitive, by more elevated cliffs of a similar sandstone, having its strata in a highly inclined position. Behind these, occur lofty but interrupted ranges of naked rocks, destitute of any covering of earthy or vegetable matter, and standing nearly perpendicular. At a distant view they present to the eye the forms of walls, towers, pyramids and columns, seeming rather the effects of the most laborious efforts of art, than the productions of nature. When surveyed from the more elevated summits of the first granitic range, these immense tables of sandstone, standing on edge sometimes almost perpendicularly, and sometimes inclining at various angles towards the primitive, resemble the plates of ice often seen thrown into a vertical position in the eddies, and along the banks of rivers.

Climbing to the summits of such of these hills as are accessible, and crossing their stratifications towards the primitive, we observe appearances similar to those found in the vallies, when circumstances enable us to push our inquiries to a corresponding extent below the surface. Having crossed

* Pennant's Arc. Zool. vol. i, p. 158.

the up-turned margin of the whole secondary formation,* which occupies the plain, and arriving at the primitive, we find these highly inclined strata of sandstone, reposing immediately against the granite. We search in vain for any traces of those rocks distinguished by the Wernerians as rocks of the transition period. We also observe an entire deficiency of all those primitive strata which the doctrine of universal formations may have taught us to look for in approaching the granite.

The sandstone along the base of the mountains, though

* The word *formation* appears to have been ordinarily used to signify a series of rocks, formed at the same time, and in the same manner; it is therefore theoretical, and implies a falsehood. Notwithstanding these objections, it is not easy to dispense with its use. Similar complaints might be made against *stratum, bed, vein,* and numerous other words, so closely incorporated with the language of geology, that the use of them cannot be avoided. In an attempt to describe the mineral features of any country, some difficulty arises from the unsettled and progressive condition of the science of geology. A nomenclature constructed upon principles applicable to other branches of Natural History, has been extended to this. Attempts have been made to define *classes, orders, genera* and *species,* of rocks, while it must be acknowledged, that the inventors of systems have hitherto failed to point out such infallible distinctions as exist in the animal and vegetable kingdoms. Among minerals, from one extreme of the series to the other, there is a constant transition of approximating aggregates into each other. The particles of inorganic matter, exempt from the influence of those peculiar laws which regulate the forms and characters of living beings, and moving in obedience only to the impulses of attraction and affinity, arrange themselves together, not always in an invariable order, and after a permanent and unalterable type, but are variously intermixed and confounded, as circumstances may have variously influenced their aggregation. Definitions have been invented, strictly applicable to particular portions of matter, which may occur under similar circumstances, in remote quarters of the globe. Fragments of granite may be found in the Rocky Mountains of America, which could not be distinguished from the granite of Egypt, such as is seen in our collections. But when we approach the imaginary limits of the artificial divisions erected by the architects of systems, we perceive the fallacy of their distinctions, and definitions. It must be evident to any person familiar with the examination of the rocky materials composing the earth's surface, that between any two of the contiguous artificial divisions, nature has placed no definite and discoverable boundary. Granite must consist essentially of feldspar, quartz, and mica; so must gneiss and mica slate, and between the two former it is often difficult to point out the line which shall be considered as marking the termination of the one, and the commencement of the other. It will, we think, be acknowledged that not one of the names applied to rocks as constituting extensive strata, conveys of itself a definite and satisfactory idea. Hence the necessity in attempting to give a detailed account of the rocks of any particular district, to define the names in almost every instance of their application.

apparently not very recent, contains remains of marine animals and plants, and embraces some extensive beds of pudding stone. It may be remarked, that the sand and gravel composing these aggregates, have the same close resemblance to the materials of the granitic mountains, as we have already observed in the uncemented materials of the plain. Indeed, it does not seem easy to determine whether the sands, gravel stones, and pebbles, now loosely strewed over the extensive plains of the Platte and Arkansa, have been brought down immediately from the granitic mountains, whence they were originally derived, or have resulted from the disintegration of the stratified sandstones, and conglomerates deposited during a long series of ages, while the waters of the ocean rested upon the great plain, and washed the base of the Rocky Mountains. The wide and equal distribution of these sands; in other words, the very gradual slope of the debris of the mountains, would seem to countenance the latter supposition.

The position of the strata of sandstone, varies in the distance of a few miles, from nearly horizontal to an inclination of more than sixty degrees, and that without any very manifest change of character, or the interposition of any other stratum.

The laminæ most distant from the primitive, occupying the eastern sides of the first ridges, though lowest in actual position, may with propriety be considered uppermost, as resting on those beyond. At the level of the surface of the great plain, they sink beneath the diluvial deposites,* and in the neighbourhood of the river Platte, are no more seen. The uppermost are of a yellowish gray colour, moderately

* To the general covering of water-worn debris, derived from all the strata, and now extending over a great part of the earth's surface, the name *Diluvium* has been given, in allusion to that great and universal catastrophe to which its deposition has been supposed assignable. By this name, it is intended to distinguish it from the partial debris occasioned by causes still in operation, such as the slight wear produced by the present rivers, the more violent action of torrents, &c. To the latter the name *Alluvium* has been appropriated, but many authors who perhaps do not confound the two classes of phenomena, have ambiguously applied the word *alluvial* to both. In the earlier parts of this work, we have sometimes distinguished the diluvial formations as *primary soils*, which, as having less of implicit allusion to a fallacious theory, may perhaps be thought equally applicable. But, with the hope of being more easily understood, we prefer to adopt such words as have been used by good authorities. For further information concerning the use of the above words, see Conybeare and Phillips' *Geology of England and Wales, Part I. p.* 28.

fine, compact and hard, constantly varying at different points, in colour as well as most other characters. The light coloured varieties often contain small round masses, about the size of a musket ball, which are more friable than the rock itself, from which they are easily detached, leaving cavities corresponding to their own shape and dimensions. They are commonly of a dark brown colour, and of a coarser sand than that which constitutes the rock itself. They may perhaps be instances of *globular structure*, analogous to what is sometimes observed in trap rocks. Where these are found, we could never discover any of those remains of shell-fish, so distinctly seen in many of the secondary rocks.

Passing downwards, or in other words proceeding towards the primitive; across the edge of the secondary, the sandstone becomes more coarse and friable, its colour inclining more to several shades of brown and red. This variety presents small nodules of iron ore, but does not appear to contain remains or impressions of organized beings. It is also less distinctly stratified than that just mentioned, and often becomes exceeding coarse, with angular fragments intermixed, being in no respect different from the rock denominated breccia, and formerly by some geologists considered a distinct stratum.

This tract of sandstone which skirts the eastern boundary of the Rocky Mountains, and constitutes a part of that immense secondary formation which occupies the valley of the Mississippi, abounds in scenery of a grand and interesting character. The angle of inclination of the strata often approaches 90°, and is very rarely less than 45°. That side of the ridges next the primitive, appears as if broken off from a part of the stratum beyond, towering in abrupt and perpendicular precipices, sometimes even overhanging and sheltering a considerable extent of surface. The face of the stratum is usually smooth and hard, and both sides are alike destitute of soil and verdure. Elevations of this description are met with, varying from twenty to several thousand feet in thickness. Neither are they by any means uniform in height. Some of them rise probably three or four hundred feet, and considering their singular character, would appear high, were they not subjected to an immediate and disadvantageous comparison with the stupendous Andes, at whose feet they are placed. Their summits, in some instances, are regular and horizontal, and are crowned with a scanty growth of cedar and pine. Where the cement and most of the materials of the sandstone are silicious, the rock evinces a tendency to break into fragments of a rhombic form, and in this case the elevated edge presents an irregularly notched or serrated surface.

Sandstones consisting of silex, with little intermixture of foreign ingredients, are usually durable. But in the region of which we speak, the variations in the composition, cement, and character of the sandstone, are innumerable. Clay and oxide of iron entering into its composition, in certain proportions, seem to render it unfit to withstand the attacks of those atmospheric agents, whose effect is to hasten dissolution and decay. Highly elevated rocks of this description, may well be supposed in a state of rapid and perceptible change. The sharp angles and asperities of surface which they may have originally presented, are soon worn away; the matter, constantly removed by the agency of water from their sides and summits, is deposited at their feet; their height gradually diminishes, and even the inclination of their strata becomes at length obscure or wholly undiscoverable. This appears to have been a part of the process, by which numerous conic hills and mounds have been interspersed among the highly inclined naked rocks of this sandstone tract. These hills, often clothed with verdure to their summits, add greatly to the beauty of the surrounding scenery—while about the tops of the more rugged and precipitous eminences, the deep green of the small and almost procumbent cedars and junipers, with the less intense colours of various species of deciduous foliage, acquire new beauty from being placed as a margin to the glowing red and yellow seen on the surfaces of the rocks.

II.—*Sandstones of the Rocky Mountains.*

Having commenced our account of the Rocky Mountains with the consideration of that vast accumulation of rounded fragments, constituting the great desert, which may be reckoned the most recent formation, depending upon that range of mountains, we proceed to speak of the sandstones, the next member in the inverted order we have adopted. And here we take occasion to remark the peculiar grandeur and simplicity of features, which distinguish the mineral geography of this part of our continent. We have here a stupendous chain of granitic mountains many hundred miles in extent, with no stratified rocks resting about their sides except a few sandstones almost equally granitic. We discover few traces of that magnificent profusion of animal and vegetable life which in other parts of the globe has reared mountains of limestone, clay slate, and those other aggregates which consist in a great measure of the exuviæ of living beings. We shall not here be understood, to contradict an assertion before made, that the sandstones along the base of the Rocky Mountains, contain organic remains, and bear abundant evidence of having been, at a comparatively recent period, deposited gradually from the waters of the ocean.

The particular which we wish to remark, as distinguishing these mountains most strikingly from the Alleghanies, and many other ranges, is the entire want of the aggregates referred by the Wernerians to the transition period; as well as nearly all the stratified primitive rocks, and the more recent calcareous formations.*

This great range as far as hitherto known to us lies nearly from north to south. Considered topographically, the sandstone formation belongs both to the mountains and the plains; sloping down from the sides of the granite, and disappearing under the sands of the Great Desert. The western boundary of this formation of sandstone, appears to be defined, and corresponds to the side of the easternmost granitic ranges. From the Platte toward the south, it increases in width, and on the Canadian it extends more than half the distance, from the sources of that river to its confluence with the Arkansa. This sandstone formation we consider as consisting essentially of two varieties.

1st. *Red Sandstone.* This rock, which appears to be the lowest of the secondary aggregates in this part of the country, is very abundant in all the region immediately contiguous to the Rocky Mountains. We have never met with a stratum entirely similar, in the eastern part of the valley of the Mis-

---

* The highly primitive, and, if we may so speak, silicious character of the Rocky Mountains, would seem to discountenance the opinion entertained by some, that our continent has emerged from the depths of the ocean, at a period comparatively recent. The organic remains hitherto observed, in the secondary aggregates along the base of those mountains, are mostly of animals supposed to have inhabited the depths of the ocean. But if the granite of the Rocky Mountains has been *forced up* at a recent period, where are the traces of all those older secondary rocks, which should have intervened between it and the horizontal sandstones? If these mountains had formed the shores of that ocean, in which the greater part of our continent was so long immersed after the elevation of the *Old World*, we should have expected to find along their base the remains of littoral animals, and not of those which inhabited the depths of the ocean.

sissippi. It occurs at intervals along the base of the mountains reposing against the primitive rocks in an erect or highly inclined position. It varies in colour from bright brick red to dark brown, and sometimes exhibits various shades of yellow and gray. It is, however, almost invariably ferruginous, and the predominance of red in the colouring is one of its most conspicuous features.

The lowest part of the stratum has frequently least colour, and is also the most compact and hard. But this is not invariably the case, as near the Platte, that part which lies immediately on the granite, is white, and contains beds of coarse conglomerate or pudding-stone. At the lowest points, we have been able to examine, are found imbedded large oval or irregular masses of hornstone, usually of a yellowish-white or bluish colour, and near the surface of these masses are seen the few well marked organic relics, the stratum can be said to contain. Higher up, the rock becomes much softer, and usually of a browner colour. Near the upper part of the stratum, are frequently seen broad belts of a lighter colour, conspicuously marked with reticulating yellowish veins. The cross fracture of the stone is even and earthy, except in the coarser varieties. When divided in a direction parallel to that of the strata, small scales of mica are seen, but this is usual only in those parts of the stone, where natural seams or fissures existed. Small specimens from many parts of this stratum, could with difficulty be distinguished from the red sandstone, quarried at Nyac in New Jersey, and used in great quantities in the cities of New York, Albany, &c., for building.

2d. *Argillaceous, or Gray Sandstone.* Immediately above the red sandstone we have invariably found, where any rock rests upon it, a grayish or yellowish white sandstone, which we distinguish as the second variety. It most frequently contains considerable proportion of an argillaceous earth in the cement, and has a more or less slaty structure. Hence it may with propriety be denominated argillaceous sandstone. This variety being uppermost in actual position, is, perhaps, more frequently seen than the other, while at the same time it is probably less abundant.

The line of separation betwixt the two is often manifest and well defined, and in other instances they pass, by imperceptible gradations into each other. The upper or gray sandstone, is usually more compact and homogeneous, and more distinctly stratified than the red.

The precipices in both varieties, are often lofty and perpendicular, but the projections and angles of the red are more worn and rounded than those of the gray. The narrow defiles and ravines, which the streams of water have excavated, are less tortuous, when they are entirely in the gray sandstone, than in other instances. The springs of water flowing from it, are more free of mineral impregnations than such as are found in the other variety. It sometimes consists of glittering crystalline particles, but does not in this case appear to be a chemical deposite. In fine it appears under an endless variety of characters, of which it would be in vain to attempt the enumeration. Although the gray sandstone, is not invariably distinguished by the presence of an argillaceous ingredient, yet it is constantly found in connection with the soft clay slate, or bituminous shale and coal wherever these are met with. Gypsum and muriate of soda are as commonly found in or near the red variety.

These sandstones being entirely mechanical aggregates, consisting of rounded fragments of rocks, formerly constituting a part of the primitive mountains, would seem to have been deposited at a very remote period, when the waters of the primeval ocean covered the level of the great plain, and the lower regions of the granitic mountains.

Subsequent to the deposition of the horizontally stratified rocks, the position of these, in relation to the primitive, has been somewhat changed, either by the action of some force beneath the primitive rocks, forcing them up to a greater elevation than they formerly possessed, or by the sinking down of the secondary, produced by the operation of some cause equally unknown. Without supposing some change of this kind, can we account for the great inclination of the margin of the sandstone rock, which is found resting against the granite almost perpendicularly? Nearly contemporaneous to this change, was the retiring of the sea, and the consolidation of the trap rocks. The beds of loose sand and gravel, which are still accumulating, have been formed in part, from the disintegration of the sandstones, and conglomerates, partly by the action of those currents of water, which are constantly bringing down small fragments from the primitive rocks, and depositing them in the plains.

The absence of any formation of limestone, is a distinguishing characteristic of.the country under consideration. A traveller to the upper part of the Missouri mentions, " calcareous and petrosiliceous" hills, as existing in the coal districts on that river. But in ascending the Platte, from its confluence with the Missouri to the mountains, we saw not a single fragment of limestone. Small veins of carbonate of lime, crystallized in the usual form, are met with in the argillaceous sandstone of the Arkansas, also the sulphate in small quantities. Gypsum is very abundant on the Canadian river, at a distance of three or four hundred miles from the mountains. It is disseminated in veins and thick horizontal beds, in the red sandstone. The extent and thickness of these horizontal beds, would, perhaps, justify the appellation of stratum, but as gypsum is not met with in great quantities, except in connection with this sandstone, it may with propriety be considered a subordinate rock.

Rock Salt. This substance has often been said to exist in some part of upper Louisiana, in the form of an extensive stratum. We have met with salt among the natives, in masses of twenty or thirty pounds weight. The interior of these masses, when broken, presented a crystalline structure. On one of the surfaces, which had probably been that in contact with the ground or rock, on which the salt had rested, a considerable mixture of red sand was discoverable. These masses had been produced by the evaporation, during the dry season, of the waters of some small lake. The whole country near the mountains, abounds in *licks*, brine springs, and saline efflorescences, but it is in the neighbourhood of the red sand rock, that salt is met with in the greatest abundance and purity. The immediate valley of the Canadian river, in the upper part of its course, varies in width, from a few rods to three or four miles, but is almost invariably bounded by precipices of red sand rock, forming the river bluffs. In the valley between these, incrustations of nearly pure salt are often found, covering the surface to a great extent, in the manner of a thin ice, and causing it to appear, when seen from a distance, as if covered with snow.

Most of the remarkable formations of rock salt, hitherto explored and accurately described, have been found in the " red marle, or new red sandstone,"* of the English geolo-

* Conybeare and Phillipps, part 1, p. 278. The same formation was called by Bakewell, the lowest red sand rock, and by Werner " bunter sandstein," or variegated sandstone. This rock with the accompanying conglomerates and amygdaloids, is considered by Conybeare and Phillipps, as the immediate superstratum of the magnesian limestone, which rests on the great coal deposite of England; and is the lowest member of their supermedial order. Throughout its range, are found some of the

gists, called also the "older sandstone," by Frieslieben, and the "first floetz sandstone," by the Wernerians, which appears to correspond in character with the sandstone about the sources of the Canadian. Rock salt is found in connection with this sandstone at Cheshire, Northwich, and Droitwich in England; at Cardona in the province of Catalonia in Spain, and at the base of the Carpathian mountains in Moldavia and Poland. In Peru, it is accompanied by sandstone and gypsum,* and along the base of the Ural mountains, between Europe and Asia, by gypsum and red marle.† Accident or further examination, it is probable, may hereafter bring to light, those extensive beds of this substance, which

richest lands in England, consisting of a red marle, which like that of our analogous formation about the Canadian and Red rivers, is favourable to the growth of the cereal gramina, the leguminous plants, and some fruit trees. Many geologists appear to consider this stratum as exclusively the depository of the rock salt and gypsum. If this be the case, it is to be inferred that it occurs interruptedly throughout the interior of North America, from the Alleghanies to the Rocky Mountains. We have recently seen some specimens, form Lake Huron, of amygdaloidal greenstone, closely resembling that which is found associated with our muriatiferous sandstone. Some of the most copious and concentrated brine-springs in America, occur in the horizontal formations, south of Lake Ontario. Those of Salina in New York produce five hundred thousand bushels of salt annually. We stated in the first volume of this work, that the springs of Kenhawa, yield a yearly product of thirty thousand bushels of salt, and asserted inadvertently, (at page 15) that they are the most important salines in the country. The product of several establishments surpasses that of Kenhawa. The whole amount of salt manufactured annually in the United States from brine springs, is now believed to exceed a million of bushels.

* "The sandstone on the banks of Manzanares, between Cumana and and Cumanacoa, is accompanied by beds of indurated clay, containing selenite and lamellar gypsum, and resembling the muriatiferous clay of Punta Araya." See *Humb. Pers. Nar.* vol. 3. p. 11. The extensive rock salt formation of El Jereed, a part of the great Sahara, belonging to the Tunisians, is described by Shaw, as "a solid mountain of a reddish purple colour, as hard as stone." *Travels through Barbary*, page 115, in vol. 12 of Mavor's collection. The sand in the great saline desert of Persia, is of a brick red colour. Kinneir, p. 13, and Voyage of Nearchus, p. 322. The magnificent salt formation of Calla-baugh, in the kingdom of Caubul, appears from Elphinstone's description, to be connected with a stratum of red sandstone. "The road beyond the town of Calla-baugh, was cut out of solid salt, at the foot of cliffs of that mineral, in some places more than one hundred feet high above the river. The salt is hard and clear and almost pure. It would be like crystal, were it not in some parts streaked and tinged with red. All the earth, particularly near the town, is *almost blood red.*"

† *Annals of Philosophy*, vol. xviii, p. 233.

we have reason to believe, exist in the neighbourhood of the Rocky Mountains. The briny character of those great streams, the Arkansa and Red rivers, flowing over the red sandstone formation, and receiving from it the peculiar character, and colour of their waters, afford sufficient evidence of the existence of such beds, and the greatness of the quantity washed away in any given time, would lead to the conclusion, that they must be of vast extent. By the analogy of other rock salt formations, apparently similar in character, we should be instructed to search for these beds, in depressed situations and basin-shaped cavities, whose contents had not been worn down and removed by the currents of water. In England the saliferous sandstone, is locally known, as the *red dead lyer*, and is supposed to be identical with the stratum, called by the German mineralogists, the *rothe todte liegende*, and which in the north of Germany, is believed to occur over the coal, as appears from the researches of Karsten, Von Raumer, Von Buch, and Frieslieben. The same position is assigned by many of the English geologists, to their new red sandstone, while Mr. Weaver* and others, consider it inferior to the coal strata, as is the case in the country we have described.

Perhaps the most striking feature of this formation of sandstone, is the great and abrupt change in the inclination of the strata, in the parts near the granite as already described.

It may perhaps be thought possible that the gradual wearing away, by the agency of rivers, of some portions of the sandstone, may have been sufficiently extensive, to have occasioned that change of elevation of which we speak, and that those rocks now found in an inclined position, are detached portions, of what was formerly the upper part of the stratum, which having been undermined on their eastern side and supported by the granite on their western, have fallen into their present situation.

This supposition, however, seems incompatible with the vast magnitude and extent of these rocks, and entirely irreconcilable to the fact, that they dip to a great and indefinite extent below the present level, of any of the beds of the rivers.

The position of this formation, in relation to the granite, is similar to that of the sandstone of the island of Guachaco,

* Annals of Phil. Oct. Nov. and Dec. 1821.

and of the Llanos of Caraccas, resting on the granite of the Oroonoko,* in South America, also to that spoken of by Mr. Burkhardt, at the entrance of Nubia, superimposed upon the granite of Syene, to that of Aberdeenshire in Scotland,† to that of Haldon hill, overlaying the granite of Dartmoor in England,‡ to that mentioned by Mr. Schoolcraft,§ as found near Lake Superior, and probably to that of Behring's island off the coast of Kamschatska,‖ but it does not appear that those formations have the same peculiarities in regard to inclination.

If this formation of sandstone consisting of the two varieties just mentioned, ever extended across the valley of the Mississippi to the Alleghany mountains, as some might be disposed to believe, we cannot pretend to determine what was its position, relative to the immense masses of floetz, limestone, and other rocks now found in that valley. But as the red variety is still extensively disseminated and usually accompanied by those valuable substances salt and plaister, it may not be amiss, to trace as far as our examinations have enabled us to do it, the outline of the region which it occupies. As we have before mentioned, it is found in the vicinity of the river Platte, in an highly inclined position, covering a narrow margin, immediately at the foot of the Rocky Mountains. From the accounts of Lewis and Clark, we are induced to believe, that it exists under similar circumstances near the falls of the Missouri. On the Canadian, it is constantly met with from the sources of that river, on the borders of New Mexico, near Santa Fe, in 105° west, until you arrive within a short distance of its confluence with the Arkansa, in longitude 97° west. The waters of the Canadian, from flowing over the sandstone in question, acquire an intense red colour, and are so impregnated with muriate of soda and other soluble salts, as to be unfit for use. This we are credibly informed, is also the case with the waters of a number of rivers tributary to the Arkansa, above the Canadian on the same side, also with the waters of Red river. Hence the

---

* See Humb. Pers. Nar. vol. 4, p. 384 and 572, also vol. v, p. 633, Lond. Ed.

† Mac Culloch in the *Journal of Science and the Arts*, vol. x, p. 30.

‡ Conybeare and Phillipps. Part 1, p. 132.

§ Schoolcraft's Narrative, page 159.

‖ Behring's Island, says Pennant, consists of high granitic mountains, craggy with rocks and peaks, changing into freestone towards the promontories. *Arct. Zool.* vol. i, p. 219.

conclusion appears to be justified, that this rock extends from near the Arkansa on the north, to a point beyond Red river on the south, and from near the mouth of the Canadian, an unknown distance to the west. It is not unlikely, it may exist about the sources and upper branches of the Rio Colorado of California, the Red river of Santa Fe, and the other *Red rivers* of New Mexico. Near the mountains, and for a great distance to the south and east of the High Peak, it is covered by the gray sandstone.

Other secondary rocks found in different parts of the great valley of the Mississippi, will be noticed hereafter. Those above enumerated, seem to have a peculiar dependence upon the Rocky Mountains, and for this reason, we thought proper to consider them in connection with that range. They also appear in some measure independent of the other members of that great secondary formation, on the borders of which they occur.

The peculiar features of the region occupied by these rocks, have been minutely described in the narrative of our journey. It is a region destined by the barrenness of its soil, the inhospitable character of its climate, and by other physical disadvantages, to be the abode of perpetual desolation. The immense grassy plains on its southern and eastern borders, are adapted to the feeding of cattle and sheep, and it is not improbable, the countless herds of bisons and wild horses, will soon give place there, to domesticated animals. The coal, salt, plaister, and iron, which constitute the mineral wealth of this portion of the United States' territory, lose much of their value, on account of their remoteness from navigable streams. Beautiful carnelians and agates occur in the alluvial regions of the Platte and Missouri, but these will never become objects of any importance.

III.—*Floetz Trap Rocks.*

Another family of rocks of recent formation, and connected with the sandstone last mentioned, remains to be noticed.

These are rocks of basaltic conformation, belonging to the class by some mineralogists denominated superincumbent, and by many considered of volcanic origin. They present a striking contrast by their dark colour, and by the vastness and irregularity of their masses, to the smooth, light, and fissile sandstones on which they rest. Sometimes they are compact, and apparently homogeneous in their composition, in many particulars of structure, form, hardness, &c. seeming more analogous to the primitive rocks than to those re-

cent secondary aggregates with which they are associated.
In other instances, black and formless masses of porous and
amygdaloidal substances are seen scattered about the plains,
or heaped in conic piles, but having no immediate connexion with the rocks on which they rest. An extensive
formation of the rocks belonging to this class occurs along
the eastern slope of the Rocky Mountains, about the sources
of the Canadian, and the Red river of Natchitoches. Among
them we distinguish two leading varieties referrible to the
two divisons called Greenstone and Amygdaloid.

1st.—*Greenstone.* It appears in the limited district we
examined, under almost every variety of form and character
noticed by mineralogists. Sometimes it is nearly or quite
free from any intermixture of hornblend, and is of a fine
dark green colour, and closely resembles some varieties of
serpentine. Sometimes its colour is a dull gray, graduating
into brown and black of various shades and intensities. It
forms numerous conic hills of considerable elevation, scattered without order in various parts of the plain. These hills
are usually of a regular and beautiful form. The great plain
in which they stand is elevated and destitute of timber or
water, but ornamented with a carpet of thick and verdant
grasses. The hills, though steep and high, are smooth and
green to their summits; the surface on all sides being unbroken by trees or rocks, and covered with thick turf; the whole
forms a scene of singular beauty. During our journey across
the district based upon the rocks now under consideration,
we had constant occasion to admire the freshness and abundance of the grasses and other herbaceous plants. The
plains of the Platte and Arkansa we had seen, brown and desolate as if recently ravaged by fire, but here we passed elevated tracts where for many miles we could find no water
for our necessities, yet the vegetation possessed the freshness of spring in the most fertile regions. The greenstone
sometimes appears in low ridges, extending considerable distance, and sloping on both sides into the level of the plain.
In the sides of ravines and water-courses, perpendicular
precipices of considerable elevation occur, but the vallies
are usually almost filled with large broken masses, and
fragments sometimes exhibiting a prismatic form. It falls
readily into large masses, but seems strongly to resist that
progress of disintegration, which it must undergo before it
can be removed by the water. The faces of the perpendicular
precipices are often marked by distinct and large seams run-

ning parallel to each other, and at right angles with the horizon. Following the water courses, which are sunk a considerable distance below the surface, the line of separation from the sandstone, on which the greenstone rests, at length becomes visible.

2d.—*Amygdaloid.* We apply this name to a porous or vessicular rock of a very dark gray, greenish, or black colour, usually found near the greenstone, but sometimes in connexion with the sandstone. In its ultimate composition it resembles greenstone, but we have never seen in it such large fragments of feldspar and scales of mica as are observed in that rock. The amygdaloidal cavities, with which it is everywhere penetrated, are of various sizes; some of them appear like bubbles, which had been formed in a semi-fluid mass, and afterwards lengthened and variously distorted by the motions of the contiguous matter. Near the surface they contain a soft, white, or yellowish-white substance, very different from the rock itself, usually a pulverulent carbonate of lime. This gives the recent surface a mottled appearance. In surfaces which have been for some time exposed to the air this soft substance has been removed, and the pores and vessicles are empty.

Amygdaloid does not appear to occupy any very great extent of the country near the Rocky Mountains; we have not met with it imbedded in, or surmounted by any other rocks. It forms conic hills like the greenstone, which sometimes occur in deep water-worn vallies, bounded on both sides by perpendicular walls of sandstone. It is likewise seen in the high plains, sometimes in the form of narrow and crooked ridges, apparently following what were formerly the beds of small brooks. Some very high and sharp conic hills were visible to the westward, but at a great distance. Two of this kind, which stand near each other, and seem to be detached from the primitive mountains, are called the Spanish peaks, and at the end of July snow was still to be seen on them.

Where either of the two rocks last mentioned occur it is not uncommon to find detached masses of a stone somewhat resembling the pumice stone of commerce. It is usually of a faint red, or yellowish-white colour, but sometimes brown, or nearly black. It feels less harsh than the pumice stone used in the arts, and seems to consist in a great degree of clay. It appears to be entirely similar to the substance brought down the Missouri by the annual floods, and by many considered a product of pseudo-volcanic fires, said to exist on that river.

Of the extent of this formation of trap, and of the actual elevation which it attains, we have no very definite information. Some of the greenstone hills which we examined, appeared to rise nearly to the region of perpetual frost.

In the soils resting on the rocks of this formation, gravel and water-worn pebbles rarely occur, except in situations where it is easy to see they may have been derived from the underlying sandstone.

We are not disposed to enter into any discussion concerning the origin of the trap rocks. The volcanists and those who believe the trap formations to have been thrown up in a state of fusion from beneath the crust of the earth, will have a ready explanation of a fact mentioned in our journal, namely, that pieces of charred wood were found inclosed in the sandstone underlying the formation in question.

Though we sought in vain for some evidence that the rocks of this formation traversed the strata of sandstone in the manner of the whin dikes of England, we are conscious our examinations were too limited to justify us in asserting that this is not the case, nor can we adduce a single fact, from which it could be inferred, that these rocks have been deposited, like the accompanying strata of sandstone, from suspension in water. We saw no instance of their alternation with the sandstones, and no appearance of the gradual transition of these rocks into each other. The country occupied by this formation presents scenery of a very peculiar and interesting character. It is remarked by Humboldt,* that in the Canary islands, in the mountains of Auvergne, in the Mittelgebirge in Bohemia, in Mexico, and on the banks of the Ganges, and we may add, in the United States, the formation of trap is indicated by a symmetrical disposition of the mountains, by truncated cones, sometimes insulated, sometimes grouped, and by *elevated plains, both extremities of which are crowned by a conical rising*. In some of the unpublished drawings by Mr. Seymour, these peculiar features of the scenery of the floetz trap formation have been preserved.

From the account we have given of these rocks, it will be perceived, that here, as in Mansfeld, Thuringia, and the circle of Saale†, the red sandstone, the porphyritic and

* Personal Narrative, vol. i. p. 87. American Edition.

† Annals of Philos. vol. xviii. p. 248, on the authority of *Friesleben.*

amygdaloidal trap, and the coal strata, are in direct and immediate connexion, while limestones, except the sulphate, are of rare occurrence.

Recapitulation.

The Secondary Formations along the eastern base of the Rocky Mountains, are

1st.—*Red Sandstone.* Rests immediately on the granite, is rather indistinctly stratified; strata sometimes inclined, and sometimes horizontal. Abounds in gypsum, salt, and iron, but contains no indications of coal.

2d.—*Argillaceous, or gray Sandstone.* Overlays the red, conforming to it in the inclination of the strata. Occurs principally near the primitive; contains coal and iron.

3d.—*Greenstone and Graystone.** Of an imperfectly columnar structure, resting on the argillaceous sandstone.

4th.—*Amygdaloid.* Sometimes containing augit, and sometimes hornblend. Occurs with the greenstone, about the sources of the Canadian river, and constitutes, with the foregoing, the newest floetz trap formation.

5th.—*Sand and Gravel.* Resting on the sandstones, and extending over the Great Desert, but rarely found with the trap rocks.

Sect. II.—Of the Rocky Mountains.†

The principal summits of this lofty chain of mountains are visible in some conditions of the atmosphere, at the distance of one hundred and forty miles. In approaching them from the east, across the great plain, as the curvature of the surface appears to subside, peak after peak becomes visible, and at the distance of one hundred miles, the view is that of several conic summits rising, unconnected with each other from their bases. At a nearer approach, the mountain is dis-

---

* Pinkerton.

† We use this name, because it appears to be most generally adopted, and is perhaps as appropriate as any of those hitherto applied to this great and almost unknown chain of mountains. If any has a claim to be received on account of greater antiquity, it is certainly that of *Chippewyan,* used by Carver, M'Kenzie, and the earliest English writers, and far more applicable than *Missouri, Mexican, Caous, Shining, Sandy,* or any of the many other unmeaning adjuncts which have been proposed. The Indians are said to have no name for the whole range. Those parts about the sources of the Arkansa and Rio Del Norte, have been called Sierra Madre, and Sierra Vert, by the Spaniards of New Mexico.

cerned constituting an uninterrupted chain, crowned with
sharp conic summits. In one or two instances, the smooth
surface of the plain extends unbroken to the base of the granitic mountains; more commonly low parallel ridges of sandstone mark the boundary of the secondary, and the commencement of the primitive regions. It has already been remarked, that in most instances these sandstones are separated from the granite by no interposed stratum of older secondary, or transition rocks. What will perhaps be considered
an exception to this remark, is found at the point where the
river Platte descends from the mountains. Here, in the first
of the primitive ridges, the rock is an aggregate of feldspar
and hornblend. Along the eastern side of this ridge, where
the feldspar is in the greatest proportion, it is of the flesh coloured variety, most common throughout the Rocky Mountains, having its unmixed masses comparatively large and of
a cubic form. Hornblend and quartz, in small proportions,
complete the aggregate. This has the aspect and fracture of
granite, and should perhaps be considered a granite, in
which hornblend takes the place of mica. Proceeding towards the west, the proportion of feldspar decreases rapidly,
and its particles become smaller, until at length it disappears,
and the rock consists almost exclusively of hornblend.
This is of a distinctly columnar structure, and assumes all
the characters of primitive trap. It forms an abrupt spur or
ridge, crossing from north to south the narrow chasm which
contains the bed of the Platte, pushing that river a little out
of its direct course. This narrow ridge, falling off perpendicularly on both sides, may well be compared to a close line
of palisades placed within, and closing the passage which
seemed to promise an entrance into the mountains. The
drawing taken on the spot by Mr. Seymour, of which an engraving has been made for our Journal, displays some of the
prominent features of this peculiar formation. The external
characters of this rock, seem to us to indicate an origin in
no respect differing as to time and circumstances from that
of the granite.* Small specimens taken from different points,

* By adhering too scrupulously to the definitions and principles of
European authors, and which are not in all instances applicable to this
country, much confusion has been introduced into the descriptions
given by American geologists. In particular, we think that sienitic and
trap formations have been too much multiplied. If any geologist shall
hereafter attentively examine that extensive formation of rocks without
mica, and containing hornblend, which extends westward from the gra-

within a short distance of each other, would probably receive from mineralogists the different appellations of primitive, trap, hornblend rock, greenstone, sienite, &c. But, as the rock graduates by imperceptible degrees from one of these into all the rest, it probably may be found in the same way, passing into granite. It often contains quartz, but little or no mica. From the Platte southward to the High Peak, the mountains are entirely of a granite, in which the predominating ingredient is feldspar. This feldspar is usually flesh coloured, and sometimes reddish brown. Its crystalline form is often distinctly seen in masses, where small fragments of mica and quartz are intermixed. The fragments of quartz are small, and minutely blended with the other ingredients. The mica is usually black, and in small scales; it is also in small proportion, compared with the quartz and hornblend. At the foot of the High Peak, the lower region of the mountain is strewed with many small masses of rocks, among which may be found well marked specimens of gneiss, and a few of mica slate. The former of these rocks is found in place about ten miles to the west of the Peak, at the place where the Arkansa leaves the mountains; but we have no where seen mica slate, except in small detached masses. The granite, which forms the base of the Peak, is similar to that already described. By the action of atmospheric agents, it crumbles rapidly into small fragments of the size of a nut. The steepest parts of the side of the mountain are every where covered with these small and loose masses. No considerable change occurs in the geological character of the mountain, until you arrive at the base of the last cone of the Peak. Above this point no mica is found; the rock, like that of the summit of the Silla of Caraccas,* the cataracts of Atures, and many high points in the mountains of South America and Mexico, and like that of Syene in Egypt, is a granite, consisting of quartz, hornblend and feldspar, but so minutely divided, and so closely aggregated, as to appear like a homogeneous mineral. It is extremely compact and hard, and seems to bid defiance to every agent that would

nite of Lake Champlain, rising into the high mountains of Scroon, and of the tract about the sources of the Hudson, known as " Totten Crossfields patent," and which have been pronounced sienite, he will be convinced that whatever those rocks may be called, they ought to be considered as intimately connected with the granite, and as having had a similar and simultaneous origin.

* Humb. Pers. Nar. vol. iii, p. 405, and vol. v, p. 19.

work its dissolution. It is of a yellowish red, or deep flesh colour, which appears to be little altered by long exposure to the air. Above the limits of phenogamous vegetation, it is almost wholly naked—scarce a lichen or a moss is to be seen. The line which marks the termination of the region of woody plants upon the sides of the mountains, is that which, at the time of our visit, (July 14,) separated the region of frost and snow from that below. Above this line the soil is scanty, and, where not buried under the snow, covered with a beautiful carpet of herbaceous or suffruticose plants. Another zone might be distinguished above the preceding, and encircling the summit of the mountain, in which scarce any phenogamous plant is found, and but a few inconspicuous lichens. The surface is covered with large and splintery fragments of granite, which seem to have been thrown down from above, and owing to the compact and impenetrable nature of the stone, appear as if recently broken. No considerable alteration is apparent in the character of the rock, which is similar at the base and at the summit of the cone of the peak. A few fragments of perfectly transparent quartz, and some pieces of bright green feldspar, and some detached crystals of hornblend, are seen strewed about the surface.

Sect. III.—Of the Ozark Mountains.

Leaving the newest floetz trap rocks about the sources of the Canadian, and returning eastward along the great woodless plain between the Arkansa and Red rivers, we find an extensive tract occupied exclusively by the red sandstone of the salt formation. The red and somewhat argil·laceous soil, which results from its disintegration, is far more fertile than that of the gravelly plains of the Platte, being often covered with a luxuriant growth of grasses, and affording pasturage to great numbers of herbivorous animals.

About one hundred and fifty miles west from the confluence of the Arkansa and Canadian, this red sand-rock disappears, being succeeded or perhaps overlaid, by an extensive coal formation. The argillaceous sandstone of this formation assumes various characters, at different points. The Falls of the Canadian, particularly described in our narrative, are occasioned by a small ridge of fine argillaceous sandstone of a deep green colour, crossing the bed of the river obliquely. The coal-beds in this region are of great thickness, and are apparently extensive and numerous. This formation appears in a great measure unconnected with the coal strata along the base of the Rocky Mountains, and the sandstones of the two districts are often remarkably dissimilar. For these reasons, we have been induced to consider this as belonging to the group of the Ozark mountains. These we shall now proceed to describe, according to the information in our possession.

From an inspection of the map annexed to this volume, it will be perceived, that the Missouri below the mouth of the Konzas is considerably inflected to the east, to pass round the end of a range of hills, rising in the angle between this river and the Mississippi. This range increases in elevation for some distance to the southwest, its highest point being in the region near the sources of White and Osage rivers, the two most considerable streams originating in these mountains. Farther to the southwest, losing a part of its elevation, it is traversed in succession by the Arkansa and Red rivers from the west, and gives origin to the Washita, the Sabine, and some other rivers of secondary magnitude. Our acquaintance with the country between Red river and the Rio del Norte, is too imperfect to enable us to trace particularly the continuation of the Ozark mountains, which is believed to extend to that river, and to have some connexion with its great southern bend below the confluence of the Rio Conchos. We therefore confine our attention to the portion northeast of Red river.

Though no point of great elevation occurs in any part of the range, the whole is truly a mountainous region, and well entitled to a distinctive appellation. Its parallelism in general direction, to the Atlantic coast, and to the great chain of the Alleghanies, together with the character and inclination of its component strata, afford unequivocal evidence that it belongs to a system, independent of the Rocky Mountains. In several particulars, a striking resemblance is manifest between this range and the Alleghanies, and in some, as we shall notice hereafter, as strong a dissimilarity.

Near the western limits of the Coal Formation, which are also the limits of the mountainous country on the Canadian and Arkansa, compact limestone occurs for the first time, (as far as our acquaintance extends) on this side the Rocky Mountains. This formation of limestone, and the accompanying strata of argillaceous sandstone, though they do not perhaps always strictly coincide in position, may be traced far to the north, and these we consider as marking the western limits of the Ozark mountains. It is to be remarked, that in these observations we do not intend to apply this name with strict geographical precision to those portions only, which are sufficiently elevated to be called mountains, but so far to extend its signification, as to include not only the high and broken ridges, but several less elevated tracts, possessing the same peculiar mineralogical features.

The few facts and observations we have it in our power to contribute towards an account of this interesting range, were collected during a pedestrian excursion from Bainbridge on the Mississippi, through the country of the lead mines at the sources of the Merameg and St. Francis, and a journey from Belle Point, by the way of the Hot Springs of the Washita, and the upper settlements of White river, to Cape Girardeau. For some important facts we are indebted to Major Long's unpublished journals of tours in various parts of the region in question, and to Mr. Nuttall's "Travels into the Arkansa territory."

I.—*Carboniferous limestone.**

We commence with the consideration of this stratum, as it is one of frequent occurrence, and perhaps occupies a greater extent of surface than any other. It so frequently alternates with the micaceous sandstones, and with the peculiar flint rock of this district, that we have never been able to devise any theory of arrangement applicable to more than an inconsiderable extent of territory.

A few miles west of the rapids of the Canadian, a thin stratum of compact limestone of the common blue variety, and abounding in organic remains, overlays the argillaceous sandstone of the coal formation. This limestone becomes more abundant towards the south, and is the prevailing rock in the country about Red river, near the mouth of the Kiamesha.†

* Conybeare and Phillips apply this name to the limestone of the English coal measures, [p. 340. pl. 1.]. *Compact limestone* is a name obviously inapplicable to the whole series of calcareous beds, occurring in connexion with the coal.

† The valley of Red river abounds in limestone, often containing shells of oysters and other moluscous animals in a state of petrifaction. Similar shells are also seen detached, scattered in profusion over the surface of the ground, retaining their original form entire. On the Arkansa the rocks are generally sandstone, no limestone being to be found, except on the Illinois, Grand, and Canadian rivers.
Maj. Long's Ms. Journal.

Among the shells found about Red river, is one which approaches nearest to the variety of the Gryphæa *dilatata* of Sowerby, p. 149. fig. 2, but the

At Cape Girardeau, in the country a few miles in the rear of Herculaneum and St. Genevieve, and in many places throughout the district of the lead mines, a coarse crystalline limestone of a light gray colour, occurs, and is usually the lowest rock visible in those places. It is very indistinctly stratified, and has in many respects a manifest resemblance to the more crystalline varieties of primitive limestone. For such it appears to have been mistaken by Mr. Schoolcraft, who, in his work on the lead mines asserts, that the " mineral soil at Mine á Burton, and the numerous mines in its vicinity reposes on primitive limestone," p. 108. Afterwards, at p. 119, speaking of this primitive limestone, he says, " on going deeper, the rock again graduated into a compact limestone, very hard, and of a bluish-gray colour, in which were frequently found small cavities studded over with minute pyramids of limpid quartz;" and again, at the page first referred to, he informs us, " the *primitive limestone* passes into *transition* and *secondary* in various places on the banks of the Mississippi, between Cape Girardeau and St. Louis." We adduce these statements as confirming our own observation of the alternation of the *crystalline* or *sparry* limestone with the compact blue variety.

We have never met with limestone about the Lead Mines which did not contain organic remains, and the white crystalline variety abounds particularly in casts of encrinites,

lobe is far less distinct, and the shell is far more narrowed towards the hinge, and is somewhat less dilated, and much more like an ostrea. It may be called *G. corrugata*; small valve flat, and very much wrinkled, and like the other, narrowed near the hinge; the beak is short, and curved upwards and laterally, and the sulcus is very distinct. Length and greatest breadth of the small valve nearly equal, from 1 1-2 inches to 2 inches; found by Mr. Nuttall on Red river. It is in a very perfect state of preservation.

Mr. Nuttall brought also from Red river, a species of ostrea, which to the eye appears hardly changed. The anterior portions of the specimens are wanting, but the greatest breadth of the remaining portion of the largest one is nearly three inches. The hinge fosse in this species is proportionally much more contracted and smaller in every respect, than any other species of the genus we have seen. That of the specimen above mentioned, is less than 1-2 an inch. The specimens were evidently those of old shells being much thickened.

Another species of ostrea, a hinge fragment of an old and thickened individual, which appears to have been long and narrow; the hinge fosse itself is long and wide.

Length of the hinge more than 3 inches, greatest width, do. 1 inch.

SAY.

though these are not always manifest without careful examination.*

This limestone, though rather indistinctly stratified, is marked by horizontal seams, distant one or two feet, and sometimes more, from each other. Its exposed surfaces become somewhat bleached, and rough with small prominences, in which we may often distinctly trace the forms of animal remains. The recent fracture is uneven, distinctly crystalline, and much like that of many moderately fine-grained granites. Careful examination shows, that, in many instances, the most minute particles visible under a lens, have assumed the rhombic form common to the carbonate of lime. These crystalline particles vary greatly in size, and are sometimes half an inch across. In the interior of the casts of animal remains they are sometimes less distinct than in parts of the rock where no such remains are discovered.

These vast beds of sparry limestone consisting almost exclusively of deposites from chemical solution, would seem to have been formed during periods when great tranquillity prevailed in the waters of the primeval ocean, and their alternation with limestones of the common earthy variety, and with sandstones embracing fragments rounded by attrition, may be considered as proofs that those periods, whatever may have been their distinguishing peculiarities, alternated with other periods of a different character.*

This variety of limestone, is perhaps the lowest rock hitherto noticed, in the country of the Lead Mines, and it may, according to the suggestion of Mr. Schoolcraft, be considered as the basis rock in that district; but as it appears to pass through every intermediate variety into the compact blue limestone, we have hesitated to separate it from that rock, which often overlays the newest sandstones. If this view of the subject be admitted, it results, that we are to consider the whole of that part of the Ozark mountains, which contains the Lead Mines, as belonging to a coal formation.† We have met with no primitive rocks in this range

---

* The limestone of the English coal formation is observed to *be rendered highly crystalline, and unfit for lime, when in the vicinity of trap rocks.*‡ It is not improbable that future inquiries may detect rocks of this character among the carboniferous limestones of the Ozark mountains.

† The principal supply of lead used in England, is derived from the rocks of the carboniferous series, they also afford some zinc and copper, but in smaller proportion than the rocks of the transition and primitive

‡ Conybeare and Phillipps. p. 445.

north of the Arkansa Mr. Schoolcraft informs us that granite, gneiss, and mica slate, exist in Missouri, but has omitted to point out the particular localities.*

At St. Louis, Cote Sans Dessein, Isle à Loutre, and at many points on the Missouri, the limestone partakes of the character of both the varieties above described but is rarely if ever so exclusively crystalline, as in the Lead Mine district. Most of the limestones that occur immediately on the banks of the Missouri, between Franklin and Council Bluff, are crystalline, and often of a yellowish or reddish white colour.†

The horizontal limestone, near the mouth of the Ohio, is of a bluish gray colour, of a compact or fine granular structure, and contains some metallic ores, sometimes occurring in veins, which contain beautifully crystallized fluat of lime. Near some of these localities of fluat of lime, we have observed the rock itself to contain small and apparently waterworn masses of hornstone, and some fragments of a perfectly white grannular limestone.

II.—*Petrosilex.*

In the vicinity of Bainbridge, ten miles above Cape Girardeau, is a stratified gray flint rock, having an aspect and fracture very similar to the common gun flint. This rock is here an extensive stratum, and occurs in connexion with compact limestone. In tracing it towards the southwest, we have not been able to detect the slightest interruption to its continuity, through an extent of more than two hundred miles, along the central portion of the mountainous district. Towards the southwest it is found to acquire gradually a more and more primitive character, and losing near the Chattahooche mountain the accompanying stratum of compact limestone, it appears near the Hot Springs of the Washita, associated with the highly inclined argillite of that district. This rock has not, within the compass of our observation been found to exhibit traces of organic remains. Its colour seems gradually to change according to its age, or at least, with the apparent age of the rocks, associated with it. South of the Arkansa, it is of a yellowish or pearly white col-

series. Conybeare and Phillipps, pp. 335, 351. The celebrated copper mine of Ecton in Staffordshire, is situated in the limestone of the coal formation. Ibid. p. 350.

* Views of the Lead Mines, p. 92.

† Jessup's Report.

our, about White river it is a dirty yellow; and at the St. Francis, a grayish brown. A corresponding change may also be
noticed in the inclination of the strata, and in other particulars. Aside from this apparently intimate connexion,
there is a particular resemblance between the petrosilex of
the Washita and the flint rock of the Lead Mine district.
The rock in both instances falls readily into small masses of
a few ounces weight, the hills based on it are usually rounded, and often bear open forests of pine, while the timber
most frequent on the sandstone hills is usually oak.

Open woods of pine and oak occur in almost all the uplands in the Ozark mountains, and are considered unfailing
indications of a meagre and flinty soil. This flinty stratum
is extensively distributed, and deserves the particular attention of such as may hereafter visit the interesting region in
which it occurs. Our limited observations have induced us
to assign it a place, next above the limestones of the coal
series, where these are found, but we were disappointed in
not being able to trace the outcrop of any stratum, cutting it
off from the more ancient petrosilex of the Washita.

III.—*Argillaceous Sandstone.*

The sandstones of this small group of mountains, appear
under almost every variety of character, but in most of them,
as far as hitherto examined, we discover traces of coal, or of
those minerals, and those impressions of vegetables, which
usually accompany it. In the inclined sandstone near the
Hot Springs, there are, it is true, no indications of coal, and
that rock is, in every respect, similar to what are called the
transition sandstones, of the Alleghany and Catskill mountains; but by following it an inconsiderable distance, either
east or west, it is found passing imperceptibly into the coal
strata of the Poteau, and of the Little Red river of White
river. In this instance, as in that of the stratum last mentioned, we find a rock apparently possessing as much unity
as can belong to such a subject, passing from recent *secondary* through all the intermediate grades to the oldest
transition, and thus demonstrating the fallacy of the doctrines
of the original continuity and systematic succession of strata.

A conspicuous character in the sandstones, about the central and western portions of the region under consideration,
is the great proportion of mica, in large scales, which enters
into their composition. Fragments of the sand-rock, about the

mouth of the Poteau, might be mistaken for mica slate. This mica is rarely, if ever, of that dark coloured variety, which prevails in the Rocky Mountains, and in the other materials of these aggregates, we discover a manifest want of resemblance to those mountains. A very slight comparison of the secondary formations, at the base of the Rocky Mountains, with the corresponding aggregates in the Ozark range, will be sufficient to convince any one, that if they have resulted from the wearing down of primitive mountains, those mountains were very dissimilar in character.

We might have remarked, when speaking of the Rocky Mountains, the absence of any formation of talcose rocks, and indeed of magnesian fossils of any kind, and a corresponding deficiency of talcose and chloritic sandstones, among the secondary rocks at the base of that range. We no sooner arrive at the western margin of the secondary, belonging to the Ozark mountains, than we observe extensive beds of sandstone, in which the prevalence of magnesia forms a conspicuous character. The beautiful green argillaceous sandstone, at the rapids of the Canadian, has been already described, and similar beds are not uncommon in many places in the vicinity of extensive coal strata.

Another peculiar variety of sandstone, occurs in connexion with the sulphuret of lead, at the Old Mines of St. Michael and at many places thereabouts. This bears apparently the same relation to the common sandstones, as the crystalline limestone above mentioned, does to the earthy varieties, and it alternates with, and passes into the common rock, in a similar manner. Its particles are crystalline, and appear to remain undisturbed in the position in which they were originally deposited from solution in water. Nevertheless, the aggregate is manifestly secondary, and embraces, like other secondary rocks, the relics of many animals and plants.

We find also about the lead mines, a sandstone like that near Hunt-house in Godeland,* consisting of small glimmering grains of transparent quartz, and so loosely cemented as to disintegrate rapidly, forming a light gray sand. In this variety, we have sometimes observed the lead ore, either disseminated or forming horizontal veins between the laminæ of sandstone. An examination of some spots might lead to the conclusion, that the soil in which most of the lead has

---

* Tilloch's Philos. Mag. vol. li. p. 210.

hitherto been found, has resulted from the disintegration of a sandstone of this kind.

Sandstone, though often covered at the surface by compact limestone, or some other rock, is probably the stratum which occurs in greatest quantity, throughout every part of this range of mountains. It is the prevailing rock, in all the country between the Arkansa and Red rivers, from the confluence of the Mamelle westward, rising to the height of two or three thousand feet, to form the summits of the Cavanid, Sugar loaf, and Mt. Cerne and to a less considerable elevation, at the Mamelle, Magazin, Castete and Short mountains.

North of the Arkansa, it forms the body of the Chattahooche mountain, and of many nameless elevations, which diversify the surface from the sources of the Little Red river to the Mississippi. Beds of coarse conglomerate or puddingstone, are met with in many places, but these are particularly frequent in connexion with the inclined sandstones about the Washita.

IV.—*Native Argil?*

Nine miles west of Bainbridge, on the road to Jackson, and on the right bank of the Mississippi, near the head of Tiawapeti bottom, also in various other places in this vicinity, are extensive beds of perfectly white substance (apparently argil), of about the hardness of common chalk, for which it has often been mistaken.*

* See " Schoolcraft's Catalogue of Western Minerals," art. i, p. 279.

A very extensive bed of *native argil* occurs on the right bank of the Mississippi, commencing near the head of Tiawapeti bottom, at the Little Chain, about forty miles above the junction of the Ohio and Mississippi, and extending, with very little interruption, near six miles above the Grand Tower, a distance of thirty-four miles. Beyond these limits, I have not observed it. Its colour is snow white; structure, fine pulverulent; fracture, dull earthy. It is amorphous, and adheres to the tongue. It does not effervesce with acids, even in the slightest degree. The bed of argil reposes on horizontal strata of silicious sandstone, and shell limestone occurs near it. In the vein of argil, nodules and veins of flint are arranged, as to make, with the horizon, an angle of about fifty degrees. The argil has been taken to New Orleans, Pittsburgh, St. Louis, &c. in considerable quantities, being mistaken for chalk, for which substance it has been used.
                                        Mr. Jessup's MS. Report.

Flint.—This occurs in nodules and veins, in a bed of native argil, above Tiawapeti bottom. Its colours are bluish gray, and greenish black. It gives

Specimens of the substance called chalk by the inhabitants, were collected at several places between cape Girardeau and Saint Louis; also on the north side of the Missouri, on the road from St. Louis to Franklin. Some of these, which were brought to New York, have been examined by my brother, Dr. J. James, and others, and were found to consist principally of alumina, none of them occasioning the slightest effervescence with acids.

This substance, whatever it is to be considered, is distributed extensively throughout the country lying around the confluence of the Missouri and Mississippi. Some specimens have been sent from Illinois to the Lyceum of Natural History at Troy, where they are spoken of as a "lithographic carbonate of lime;" but whether any experiments have been made to ascertain their real character, we have not been informed. We have not, from our own observation, found occasion to confirm the statement, that nodules of flint are found imbedded in this substance, but we have commonly found it accompanied by the flint rock, already described, which has in many respects a manifest resemblance to the flints occurring in chalk formations. We have sought in vain for the remains of echini and other animals, so common in chalk beds.

It must remain for those who shall hereafter investigate the geology of the Ozark mountains, to assign the place, and more satisfactorily to ascertain the character of this peculiar formation. It may possibly be found to occupy a position analogous to that of the chalk formations of England and France, its magnitude and extensive distribution entitle it to consideration as a distinct stratum.

We now return to the limited formations below the carboniferous limestones. These occur principally in the southern section of the Ozark mountains.

V.—*Inclined Sandstone.*

This is first in order, below the coal series, but seems so

fire with steel; the fracture is conchoidal, and the edges are translucent. The veins of flint dip to the southeast.—*Ibid.*

Imbedded in the chalk of Cape Girardeau, are occasionally found nodules of flint, which are enveloped by a hard crust of calcareous carbonate, arranged in concentric layers. Its colour is grayish black; breaks with a perfectly conchoidal fracture; is transparent on the edges, and readily gives fire with the steel.

Schoolcraft's View of the Lead Mines, p. 180.

We have yet no satisfactory information of the existence of chalk, beyond the limits of Europe.—*Conybeare and Phillipps, p.* 67, *part I.*

intimately connected with the rocks of that series, as scarce
to require separate consideration.

VI.—*Argillite.*

Of the older secondary rocks, we have observed in the
Ozark mountains, only the inclined sandstones and conglomerates above mentioned, and a limited formation of argillite, extending a few miles around the Hot springs of Washita, and re-appearing on the Arkansa, at and above the town
of Little Rock, being usually accompanied by vast beds of
Petrosilex. This latter ought perhaps to be considered a
distinct stratum—but south of the Arkansa, we have not
been able to trace it, uninterrupted for any great distance.

Mr. Nuttall, in his valuable Journal of Travels into the
Arkansa Territory, mentions *graywacke slate* as occurring
along the Arkansa river, near Little Rock, (p. 105.) We
have observed none there, in any considerable degree similar
to the graywacke slate of the transition mountains of New
York, or even to that of the Alleghanies. We are aware,
however, that some of the aggregates which we call sandstones, have all the characters attributed to graywacke slates.
"*Graywacke is a complete sandstone,*"* and, in a district
where both are so intimately blended as in that we are considering, perhaps it is unnecessary to attempt any distinction
between them; or we may persevere in the use of the two
names, at the same time acknowledging they are both applied to the same stratum.†

The Hot Springs of the Washita issue from clay slate, and
if we may judge from the inclination of the laminæ, and the
distance at the surface from the granite of the Cove, we may
conclude that a very large mass of clay slate is interposed between the surface of the granite and the point at which the
springs rise. This, however, it is not possible to ascertain.
The hottest springs on the globe, rise from beneath or within the granite,‡ and it is not improbable this rock may approach near the surface, at many points in the Ozark mountains, where it has not yet been uncovered.

The clay slate about the Hot Springs is highly inclined,
often a good deal flinty in its composition; and, as far as we

* Jamieson in the Edinburgh Encyclopedia, Art. Mineralogy.

† Humboldt considers transition schist as the basis of the graywacke in
Spain. See Pers. Nar. vol. i, p. 47, American ed.

‡ Humboldt's Personal Narrative, vol. iv. p. 171, 195; vol. v, p. 553.

have observed, contains no remains of animals or plants. It is traversed by large upright veins, filled usually with white quartz, contrasting strongly with the dark blue of the slate-stone. The elevation of the " Hot Spring Mountain," is estimated by Hunter and Dunbar, at three hundred feet above the surface of the creek at the springs. This point is probably twenty or thirty feet above the Washita at Keisler's. North of the springs, the slate rocks rise to more considerable elevation, but it is not probable that, at any point, they rise more than one thousand feet above the Mississippi.

The high lands between the Washita and Red river, are occupied principally by sandstone; the clay slate appearing to extend in a narrow line, from northeast to southwest, which, as far as we have observed, is the direction of its strata—these, when they are not perpendicular, usually dipping to the northwest.

The country about the sources of the Washita, is represented as affording many interesting minerals, among which are enumerated " martial pyrites, large bodies of crystallized spar, and hexagonal prisms, which are known to contain no small portion of the precious metals."* If the clay slate in any part of this mountainous region should be found to be accompanied by its usual attendant, the metalliferous limestone, we should be more ready to credit the accounts of the existence of the precious metals in that quarter, as at least some of the valuable mines in America, occur in that stratum.† As yet, we have no satisfactory accounts of the occurrence of that limestone, or any of the precious metals in that part of the United States.

VII.—*Granite.*

About fifteen miles southeast from the Hot Springs, near the Washita, granite is found *in situ*. It forms the base, and, as far as we could discover, the entire mass of a small hill, but little elevated above the level of the river. We found it emerging from beneath the soil at several parts, of an area of two or three hundred acres, but had not an opportunity to trace it to any great distance, nor to observe its connexion

Stoddart's Louisiana, page 391.

† Eaton's Index to the Geology of the Northern States, page 185, second edition. The most celebrated mines of Mexico and Peru, are found in the primitive and transition schist in the trap porphyries, the graywacke, and the alpine or metalliferous limestone. See Humboldt's Pers. Nar. vol. iii, p. 525, and New Spain, vol. ii, p. 494.

with any other rock. The extent of surface which it covers, we believe, cannot be very great. This granite is very soft, and disintegrates rapidly when exposed to the air. Grayish white quartz, yellowish white feldspar, and an unusually large proportion of mica, in variously and brilliantly coloured masses, enter into its composition. These large laminæ of mica are white, pearl coloured, yellow, brown, green, and often black; and in some instances so large and numerous, as to exceed in proportion the other ingredients of the aggregate. Talc also enters in large proportion into the composition of this granite. It is indeed sometimes so abundant, as to occasion a doubt whether the whole should not be considered a bed of talc, rather than granite. This talc is in tabular masses, two or three inches in diameter, and about half an inch in thickness. Zeolite is also so abundant as to seem to take the place of the other materials of the granite. It is of two varieties, radiated and mealy. Stilbite occurs in connexion with zeolite. The bed of one of the small streams, which traverses this formation of granite, is paved with small crystals and beautiful tourmalines—that of another, with native magnet. Sulphuret of iron is disseminated in the granite. Several of the appearances presented by this interesting mass of granite, would seem to countenance the opinion that it is of secondary origin, like that mentioned by Saussure, as existing near the valley of Valorsine, at Semur in Auxois, and at the city of Lyons. In speaking of the granite at these places, he says, " It could not be doubted on seeing these heaps of large crystals, that they are the produce of the rain waters, which, passing through the granite, have dissolved and carried down these different elements, and have deposited them in these wide crevices, where they have formed new rocks of the same kind. The crystals of these new granites are larger than those of the ancient, on account of the repose which the waters enjoyed in the inside of these reservoirs."

The granite of the Washita, if it is to be considered as of secondary formation, appears to be much more extensive than any of the kind hitherto known. Many more particulars must however be ascertained, before this question can be settled. We are ignorant of the manner of its connexion with any other rock, nor do we know of any formation of primitive granite, from which it could, by the action of water, have been derived. One can have no hesitation, however, in considering the Ozark mountains a separate system within themselves, having no connexion with the Alleghanies or Rocky Mountains. The sandstones which lie about these mountains, abound much more in mica than those near the Rocky Mountains, nearly in the same proportion, as the granite of the latter has less than what is met with in the little we have seen of the former. The Ozark mountains exhibit evidence of metallic riches, far exceeding any thing that appears in the Rocky Mountains. May not an extensive range of granite, and other primitive rocks, have existed at some distant period, where the Ozark mountains now are, containing the vast quantities of the ores of lead, iron, &c. now found in rocks of recent secondary origin, and even in alluvial deposites—and may not the operations of water during many ages, when an ocean rolled over the summits of these mountains, have worn down those primitive rocks—their detritus have been deposited horizontally upon their submarine sides and summits, so that the greater part of their surfaces are now covered by secondary aggregates?

Numerous specimens of minerals, brought by Lieutenant Graham and Dr. Somerville, from the Upper Mississippi and the Illinois rivers, and others from that region, now in the possession of Dr. L. C. Beck, of St. Louis, have a peculiar resemblance to similar minerals, met with in the Ozark mountains south of the Missouri. From these resemblances, and from the corroborating testimony of all the accounts we have received concerning that country rich in mines, which lies along the eastern side of the upper Mississippi, we have been induced to believe that a continuation of the Ozark mountains, or at least, of a region similar in mineralogical features, extends from the confluence of the river Missouri northward, to the sources of the Wisconsan, and the Ontonagon of lake Superior. North of the Missouri the country is very little elevated, but aside from this it appears to possess all the peculiar features of the region we have been considering. The sandstones, the limestones and other rocks have a striking resemblance. Both regions abound in the ores of lead, and both afford copper.* We are aware that the great irregularity in the direction of the ridges accessary to this range, and in the dip and inclination of the older secondary rocks belonging to it, may be considered an objection to our idea of the connexion and continuity of the different parts, and the general direction of the group. But

---

* Copper has been found in Illinois near the sources of the Cache river.

we are by no means anxious to maintain the position we have assumed. Our examinations have been limited, and we shall rejoice in any opportunity we may have for correcting our errors, and enlarging our acquaintance with this interesting range of country.

We subjoin from Mr. Jessup's report some account of a few of the most interesting minerals hitherto observed in connexion with the rocks of this district.*

* *Fluate of Lime.*—This mineral occurs in great abundance, seventeen miles south of Shawaneetown, Illinois, on Peter's creek, and proceeding about thirteen miles in a southwest direction, it again appears on and near the surface of the ground, at the three forks of the Grand Pierre creek; maintaining the same course, it breaks out in several places for near twenty miles. This beautiful and useful species of lime, occurs at Peter's creek almost invariably in a crystallized form; the crystals are universally cubes: at the three forks of the Grand Pierre creek, it occurs in masses of several feet in diameter. Both the crystallized and massive varieties, possess almost all the shades of color that have been observed in the European specimens; viz. green, violet, blue, red, yellow, white, black, and rose colored.—This mineral varies in transparency, some specimens being perfectly limpid, others opaque. Some of the violet, and rose coloured specimens when recently fractured or pulverized, yield a strong bituminous odor, this character (which has never been observed heretofore, as belonging to this species of mineral) is perceptible only in the crystallized specimens.

The vein of fluate of lime is apparently very extensive; very few minerals have been found associated with it, at the above localities. I saw at Peter's creek a few specimens of laminated calcareous spar, and a few of sulphuret of lead. Excavations have been made by several gentlemen who reside in that vicinity, for lead, but no veins or beds of this ore have been found. From examination of the situation of those specimens which I found, and the general appearance of the vein of fluor spar, I do not think that there is a sufficiency of lead ore, to reimburse the expenses that would be necessarily incurred in mining. The accompanying rocks of the vein of spar, are compact limestone, sandstone, and oolite.

Concreted Carbonate of Lime. Variety Oolite.—This occurs on Peter's creek, seventeen miles south of Shawaneetown is associated with compact limestone, and sandstone in the gangue of the fluate of lime. It is composed of globular masses, about the size of English mustard seed, which are united by a calcareous cement; the nuclei of the globules are detached leaving a small cavity in the centre of each; its colour is yellowish white; fracture dull.

Sulphuretted Hydrogen Gas.—This gas is very abundant in the water of many of the springs and wells in Missouri territory. Its origin is probably owing to the decomposition of sulphuret of iron. Six miles west of St. Louis, is a large spring of water, strongly impregnated with this gas: its odor is perceptible to the distance of four or five hundred yards from the spring. It is reported that the water has proved beneficial in cases of cutaneous disorders and rheumatic complaints.

Red Oxide of Iron.—This occurs (though not very abundant,) in the hills near Isle a Loutre, on the Missouri river. Its texture is compact,

RECAPITULATION.

The Ozark mountains extend from the sources of the Rio Colorado of Texas, on the southwest, to the confluence of the Mississippi, and Missouri in the northeast; and are continued in a low range from this point towards lake Superior. They are widest in the southwest, and in that quarter they mingle with some low tracts of secondary sandstone, extending from near the gulf of Mexico to the base of the easternmost ridge of the Rocky Mountains. Whether any similar expansion exists at the northern extremity, or whether this range is connected as a spur to the great primitive chain supposed to occupy the region north of the great lakes, and is

fracture earthy. Its external colour is brownish red; its streak, and powder blood red. This variety of ore produces good iron, and yields from sixty to eighty per cent.

Hematilic Brown Oxide of Iron.—This variety of iron ore occurs in considerable quantity in the vicinity of the vein of fluate of lime, near Shawaneetown, Illinois. It occurs there under a number of imitative forms, such as tabular, stalactitical, nodular, botryoidal, and reniform. Its colour is blackish and yellow-brown; it is easily fused and will produce near sixty per cent. of good malleable iron.

Argillaceous Oxide of Iron.—This variety of iron ore is abundant in the western parts of Pennsylvania, and Virginia, and in Kentucky, where it is almost the only ore of iron that is worked. The principal furnaces in Pennsylvania, are in Cumberland, Northumberland and Centre counties, and on the Juniata river.

Columnar Argillaceous Oxide of Iron.—Near the confluence of the Ohio and Tennessee rivers, is a locality of argillaceous oxide of iron. It is of a columnar structure, and rises from the surface of the ground in such a manner as to have some resemblance to cypress knees. This mineral has by many, been thought of volcanic origin, at least that the cause of its peculiar form is in some measure connected with the operation of volcanic causes (James).

Sulphuret of Lead, or Galena.—This mineral is abundant in Missouri territory, about sixty miles southwest of St. Louis; but as I had not an opportunity of visiting the mines, I cannot say any thing respecting its geological situation or quantity. There are two reservations for lead, in the vicinity of the United States saline, Is. From external appearances I should judge the ore was abundant; but from the success of former diggings, and the situation of the ore, which has not as yet been found there either in beds or veins; but sparingly diffused in small masses, attached to the fluate of lime, not exceeding in weight two or three pounds; I think the quantity is inconsiderable. Every specimen of sulphuret of lead that I saw there, possessed a crystalline form.

Sulphuret of Zinc, or Blende.—Fifteen miles south of Shawaneetown reniform masses of argillaceous iron are inclosed in concentric layers of slate clay, are found in a bed of slate clay. In the argillaceous iron ore small particles of sulphuret of zinc occur. This is the only locality west of the Alleghany mountains that I have seen of this ore.

separated by a wide secondary and alluvial valley, from the Rocky Mountains is yet to be determined. This range consists of low ridges irregular in direction, rarely rising to an elevation of more than fifteen hundred, or two thousand feet, and consisting principally of secondary rocks.

The formations are,

1st, *Granite*, at the cove of the Washita.

2nd, *Argillite*, ranging northeast and southwest from Little Rock, on the Arkansa to the Hot Springs, and thence to the sources of the Kiamesha.

3d, *Transition* Sandstone*. A narrow margin following nearly the same direction on the northwest side of the argillite and usually inclining like it to the south or southeast.

4th, *Flint*, [Petrosilex]. From the Hot Springs northeast to the Mississippi, and usually forming the basis of the Pine lands.

5th, *Limestone*. Compact and sparry. Distributed in the same direction as the last, but more extensive.

6th, *Argillaceous Sandstone*. with extensive beds of coal, and abounding in mines of lead.

7. *Diluvial Deposites*. There are many extensive tracts of deep argillaceous or calcareous loam, in other instances a more meager soil has resulted from the disintegration of the sand rock.

These are the remarks we have been able from observation to make respecting the geology of a part of the United States territory, west of the Mississippi. Relating to that part of the interior of our country which lies northwest of lake Superior, and north of the sources of the Missouri, we have little satisfactory information. From the accurate and intelligent Mackenzie, we are, however, able to collect a few important and interesting particulars. This enterprising

---

* In using the word *Transition* we follow the example of such as have heretofore written concerning the geology of North America, without intending to acknowledge an adherence to the exploded, or at least unfashionable doctrines of Werner. Notwithstanding Dr. Macculloch, Mr. Greenough, Mr. Kidd, and other eminent English geologists " have brought the most satisfactory proof, that there is no such class as that called transition, by the Wernerians,"* we do not know that they have introduced any word which will in this country so readily be understood to apply to those *stratified, inclined* rocks, which formerly constituted that class.

* See a paper on *Jamieson's Manual* in the Lond. Monthly Review for April 1822 p. 386. &c.

individual it is well known, travelled from Montreal, L. C. in latitude 45° 30′, long. 74° in a north-west direction to the mouth of Mackenzie's river, lat. 69°, long. 135°, and again at a later period leaving his former route at the lake of the Hills, about midway between lake Superior, and the mouth of Mackenzie's river, he ascended in a south-west direction, the Unjigah or river of Peace, to the Rocky Mountains, and crossing them, fell upon the sources of the Tacoutche Tesse which he conceived to be the northern branch of the Columbia, but which is now known to fall into the sea, near Admiralty inlet of Vancouver in 48° north.* From him we learn that the Rocky Mountains continue in an uninterrupted chain from the sources of the Missouri, in the south, to a point beyond the 65th parallel of north latitude, near the mouth of Mackenzie's river. The river of Peace which he ascended in his journey to the western ocean, has its source in these mountains in about 55° north, nearly opposite to those of the Tacoutche Tesse. Farther towards the south are the sources of the Saskatchawin, a large river discharging itself from the northwest into lake Winnipec. The mountains in this part seem to be less elevated than those more to the south, but in other respects entirely similar. Their northern termination, according to Mackenzie's account, is in about latitude 65° north, longitude 127° 40′ west. Santa Fe in New Mexico, is in lat. 36°, long. 104° 40′. From this it will be perceived, that this great mountain range lies nearly in the direction of a straight line, which in the lower latitudes is almost parallel to degrees of longitude. We have no evidence to confirm the conjecture, which nevertheless is highly probable that the principal ridges of this range consist, through their whole extent of granite, or other primitive rocks. Considering the stupendous character, the great elevation, and uniformity of the appearance of that portion of these primitive mountains with which we are acquainted, we should be led to look for similarity of character, and similar uniformity throughout. It is commonly believed as asserted by Maclure, that "a large mass of primitive, occupies all the northern part of this Continent," and he considers the great Atlantic range of primitive, the mountains of New England, New York, and the Alleghanies, as a spur from this formation. We know not on what foundation this opinion may rest, unless it be on the account of Steinhaur,

* London Quarterly Review for March 1820.

in the Geological transactions, " that the coast of Labrador is composed of rocks of granite, sienite, schist, and serpentine;" but we see no reason to consider it an improbable one. With the northern boundary of that vast formation of secondary which certainly occupies a large portion of the interior of this continent, we are unacquainted. On the southeast, its limit is the irregular border of the transition of the Alleghanies, commencing between the Alabama, and Tombigbee rivers, and running northwest to fort Anne near lake Champlain.* From this point a narrow, and perhaps interrupted stripe of secondary extends through the valley of lake Champlain to the upper part of St. John's river. The island and mountain of Montreal, are of secondary limestone. The country also between St. John's, and La Prairie, is most probably secondary, as is much of that along the St. Lawrence below Montreal. From the termination of the transition near the confluence of the Alabama and Tombigbee, the secondary rocks continue on the southwest, sometimes concealed by the recent alluvial formations of the Mississippi valley, to the Black lake river near Natchitoches. Beyond this point, the information we have is not satisfactory. From this, turning northwest, we may for the present, consider the Red river of Louisiana, as the boundary of the secondary or rather the limit of our acquaintance with this formation.

Beyond the Ozark Mountains, the district between the Red river and the Canadian is occupied by the Red sandstone of the salt formation, which is undoubtedly to be considered secondary. How far it extends to the west beyond the sources of Red river and the Canadian, we are unable to determine. At the base of the easternmost ridge of the Rocky Mountains south of the High Peak, and at no very great distance north from Santa Fe, the boundary again becomes determinate. From this point it runs nearly north, one hundred and fifty miles, where it crosses the river Platte. From the narrative of Lewis and Clark, we are enabled to determine with sufficient accuracy that it crosses the Missouri not far from the falls, in longitude about 107° W. Beyond this point the little information we have we owe to sir Alexander Mackenzie. He informs us that great quantities of coal are found about the sources of the Saskatchawin, which lie near the Rocky Mountains, and between 50° and 55° north latitude. The coal bed which he describes, lies on the

* Maclure's Observations, p. 50.

margin of a plain extending far to the north and east. The Saskatchawin running to the east traverses fifteen degrees of longitude, and discharges its waters into lake Winnipec in latitude 53° north. Lake Winnipec is connected by the Severn and Port Nelson rivers, to Hudson's bay. A water communication interrupted by one portage extends from the Saskatchawin northwest to the Missinipi or Churchill's river, thence by the lake of the Hills, Slave lake and Mackenzie's river to the north Sea. Near the lake of the Hills, in latitude 59° Mackenzie found several brine springs. This, though not decisive evidence, perhaps justifies the conclusion that secondary rocks exist in that quarter. A view of the character and direction of the several large rivers which traverse the region about Hudson's bay, of their numerous inosculations, and the number and position of the small lakes which abound in every part of it, affords evidence, that it is an extensive plain little inclined in any direction. We think we may venture to assert, that the secondary formations extend uninterrupted along the base of the Rocky Mountains, as far as to the Saskatchawin, where coal was observed by Mackenzie. What lies beyond is as yet unknown. From this coal formation our boundary must for the present run in a direction a little south of east to Lake Superior, whence it may with a few inconsiderable interruptions follow the territorial boundary of the United States until it arrives at the forty-fifth parallel of latitude, thence by the St. Lawrence to Montreal. The slight acquaintance we have with the country north of this line, is perhaps insufficient to justify the conjecture that secondary formations occupy an extensive portion of that country. Is it improbable that formations of secondary rocks extend along the base of the Rocky Mountains through their whole course, and from them spread themselves to the east knowing no limits but the Atlantic Mountains, the shores of the Gulf of St. Lawrence, and the Northern ocean? We know that rocks of this formation exist about the Gulf of St. Lawrence, whence coal, plaister and sandstone are brought to our markets.*

This boundary of the great formation of secondary rocks

* The banks of the river Montmorenci, from the natural steps downward to the St. Lawrence, consist of a lime slate placed in horizontal strata from the depth of five to twenty-four inches, each connected by fibrous gypsum of a whitish co our. Heriot 88. The island of cape Breton abounds in sandstone, coal and plaister, *ib.* 431.—Pennant's Arct. Zool. p. 508. v. i.

which occupies so large a portion of the interior of our continent includes a vast area of surface extending through twenty-five degrees of latitude and sixty of longitude. We confine our attention to that portion of it, which the state of facts at present known, enables us to speak of with some degree of confidence. This portion may be considered as occupying the area of a large triangle, whose base is a line running from Montreal, in Lower Canada, S. W. to a point near the outlet of the river Sabine, the western boundary of the state of Louisiana. The summit would be at the sources of the Saskatchawin which are west of north from the mouth of the Sabine, and north of west from Montreal. The Rocky Mountains on the southwest, and the Alleghanies on the southeast mark the limits of the secondary in those directions. Its extent towards the north and northeast is as yet unknown.

In the wide space included within these lines, we know of but one exception to the remark, that all the rocks found in place are secondary. This is the instance of the Ozark Hills traversing the horizontal strata from southwest to northeast somewhat in the manner of a whin dike. A prominent peculiarity of this range is the prevalence among the secondary strata of crystalline substances, and what are called rocks of chemical deposition, and the alternation of these with beds and strata whose integrant particles bear evident marks of having been worn and rounded by mechanical attrition. Appearances of this kind are observed in all formations of secondary rocks, but it is believed, are in few instances, as extensive or as numerous as in this. It is well known that the ores of lead so abundant in many parts of this range occur in the uppermost strata of horizontal sandstone, or in *primary* soils superimposed upon those sandstones. It has been suggested that these ores of lead may have been brought down in the alluvion of rivers from some more ancient and elevated region,* but any one who shall examine them in connexion with the substances with which they are now found associated, will be convinced that their origin has been contemporaneous to the deposition of the sandstone. That the sparry limestones, the crystalline sandstones, and perhaps the ores of lead, (almost invariably found in the form of crystals,) have been deposited from solution in water, is highly probable, and that these depositions must have taken place in connexion with circumstances not unfavorable to animal life, is

* Maclure, p. 57.

evident as all these crystalline rocks abound in organic remains.

In attempting an explanation of these appearances, can any aid be derived from recourse to the suggestion that the *matter of these crystalline beds and strata has been ejected from beneath the crust of the earth in a state of chemical solution?* These submarine eruptions may have been numerous, and may have happened at different, and remote periods; hence the occurrence of rocks consisting of particles mechanically aggregated, in alternation with those of chemical deposition. Hence the existence of metallic ores overlying recent marine sandstones and compact limestones, for these ores in a state of solution, may have been thrown out in some of the latest eruptions.

This supposition may derive some confirmation from the well known fact that this region is still in a remarkable degree, subject to subterranean concussions and earthquakes.

Though this group of mountains has probably a nucleus of primitive rocks running through its whole extent, yet these appear but rarely at the surface. We have seen such only in the places already mentioned, and have been informed of others in Washington county, near the sources of the St. Francis, and about Lake Superior.†

From the information we have been able to collect, we are induced to believe that secondary rocks occupy the country on both sides of Red river, from its sources to its confluence with the Mississippi. If this be the case the primitive of the Ozark Mountains, must be considered a small and insulated mass.

The inequalities of surface in this great secondary formation, are considerable. It has often been called the " basin of the Mississippi," but with no great propriety, since it might with perhaps equal accuracy be called the basin of the St. Lawrence, the Saskatchawin, or Mackenzie's river. The form of that part of it which contains the Mississippi river, is, however, similar to that designated by geologists, a basin shaped cavity. As far as our acquaintance extends, it is bounded on all sides by a surface of greater elevation than itself, but whether this surface is not sometimes secondary, is doubtful. It is hazardous to infer the existence at a former period, of an insulated inland sea, from any formation of secondary rocks, without being acquainted with its whole ex-

* Bakewell. † Schoolcraft.

tent, its elevation at different points, and its connexion with other rocks. On the southeast, secondary sandstones and depositions of coal are met with in some of the most elevated parts of the Alleghany Mountains. The positive elevation of the primitive mountains of New England, is, except at a few points, scarce equal to that of the secondary in the western parts of the state of New York. From the granitic rocks, along the Atlantic coast to the secondary of the Alleghanies, is an almost uninterrupted ascent. The clay slate, and granite of the Washita, occupy nearly the lowest part of the surface of the Mississippi valley. We are as yet, destitute of barometrical, or other observations by which to determine the actual height of the secondary on the sides of the Rocky Mountains. Pike estimates the elevation of the plain at the foot of the mountains, at eight thousand feet above the level of the ocean. It is probable that this estimate of Pike's far exceeds the truth, yet any one who considers the great length and rapidity of the rivers which flow from that region, the severity of cold in winter, the rapidity with which evaporation is carried on in summer, the transparency and peculiar aspect of the sky, will be convinced that those tracts are highly elevated, and there is unquestionably good reason to believe the secondary rocks along the eastern base of the Rocky Mountains, have in many points, an elevation at least equal if not much superior to the summits of the Alleghanies. In the vertical sections delineated on the maps accompanying this work, is a line indicating the *supposed level of the primitive ocean*, at the time when the secondary depositions ceased to be formed; the line being intended to mark the greatest elevation of secondary rocks on the sides of the Rocky Mountains.

This vast formation of secondary extending, as it probably does from the Gulf of Mexico, to the northern ocean, and from the bay of St. Lawrence to the Rocky Mountains, must of necessity occupy in various parts, different and sometimes great elevations. Like other great fields of similar formation, its borders are marked by high and broken ridges which become less elevated and less frequent towards the centre. Sandstone appears to be the basis and predominating rock, occupying the borders contiguous to the primitive and transition, and passing under the more recent secondary. In this sandstone, on the outskirts of the secondary, have been found most of the extensive coal beds hitherto known, also gypsum and brine springs.

We remarked in the narrative of our expedition* that at several places in the valley of the Ohio, the water of brine springs discovered by boring through the strata to the depth of two or three hundred feet, sometimes flows up and rises considerably above the surface of the earth. We also observed that there appears reason to suspect that confined subterraneous veins of water, exist under the arid tract lying westward of the Ozark Mountains.† It is not improbable that the strata of many parts of this secondary formation towards its exterior circumference may vary from an horizontal, to an inclined position, in consequence of which the water that falls in dews and rains in the hilly districts, becoming insinuated between curved stratifications, may descend towards the centre of the formation under such circumstances as would ensure its rising to the surface through wells or bore-holes sunk sufficiently to penetrate the veins. We would recommend this suggestion to the attention of the inhabitants of those parts of the secondary basin of the Mississippi, where an abundant and unfailing supply of water is unfortunately wanting. In many parts of England, as at Adelphi, Addle-Hill, Thames Street, and New-Bond street, London; at Kensington Gravel-Pits, at Tottenham High-Cross, near Silsoe in Bedfordshire, at Cambridge, and Wimpole, in Cambridgeshire, at Alford, in Lincolnshire, at Dunce-Hill, near Hull, at Oakthorpe, in Derbyshire, and at many other places within the Chalk-Basin called the *London Vale*, water rises in the manner above alluded to, from the bottom of wells of one hundred and ten to one hundred and forty feet deep, and is applied at and above the surface of the earth to various ornamental and useful purposes.‡ It is of a better quality than that of the superficial wells which do not penetrate the stratum of tenacious clay to the sands of what is called the plastic clay formation, or to the substratum of chalk, and sometimes rises with such rapidity as to overtake the well-digger and flow over his head before he can escape.§

---

* The opinion there (p. 16. vol. i.) advanced that this effect is produced exclusively by the elasticity of subterranean gases, is probably erroneous, as the rising of the water is to be attributed to the agency of hydrostatic pressure, modified in many instances by the cause there alluded to.

† Vol. ii. p. 282.   ‡ Lond. Month. Mag. vol. liv. p. 34.

§ Conybeare and Phillipps' *Outline of the Geology of England and Wales*, part. 1. p. 35, and 88.

Horizontally stratified limestone is met with in many parts of this formation, but is most abundant in the central portions, about the beds of the great rivers, and in those parts which have the least positive elevation. Compact limestone is a name sometimes used to designate all the varieties of that rock occuring in districts of secondary, but is certainly inapplicable to the limestone about Cape Girardeau, and in many other places which is, notwithstanding, manifestly secondary. Some of the limestone northwest of the primitive, on Hudson's river, about the Catskill and Helleberg Mountains is of this crystalline variety, but abounds in marine exuviæ—That of Lake Champlain, as well as the greater part of that in the interior and western parts of the state of New York, is of the compact blue variety. From the falls of the Ohio at Louisville, to Cincinnati, a mixed kind partaking of the character of both of the before mentioned varieties, is found along the river, and for some distance on each side. This limestone is confined to a small district, and is on all sides bounded by sandstone, which rises from below it, and on which it is supposed invariably to rest.* It is an interesting subject for future inquiry, whether the red standstone which is found on the southwestern branches of the Arkansa, in a horizontal position, and which in strata, highly inclined, skirts, the base of the Rocky Mountains, extends also to distant portions of the secondary, and whether like the old red sandstone of England, Scotland, and Germany,† it is the substratum of the great western coal series.

Throughout the country adjacent to the Ohio river, the prevailing and basis rock, is a gray horizontal sandstone, often approaching in character, those varieties which contain coal. It embraces extensive beds of coarse conglomerate, and supports, or alternates with compact limestone. Here, as in many parts of the valley of the Mississippi, the limestones and sandstones, like those of Turimiquiri, and Cumanacoa, in South America,‡ alternate frequently with each other.

SECT. IV.—OF THE ALLEGHANY MOUNTAINS.

By this name we intend to designate the great range of mountains extending parallel to the Atlantic coast, from the sources of the St. John's river in New Brunswick, in the

---

* Picture of Cincinnati, p. 64.
† Annals of Philos. for Aug. 1822, p. 90.
‡ See Humb. Pers. Nar. vol. iii. p. 94.

northeast, to the confluence of the Alabama, and Tombigbee, in the southwest. An outline of the geological features of this great chain has already been traced by Maclure, and particular accounts of portions of it are to be found in the works of Eaton and others, we shall therefore confine our attention to those strata, which, forming the northwestern side of the range are most intimately connected with the great secondary formations of the west.

I.—*Granular Limestone*

Appears in every part of the United States, where it has hitherto been observed to be the uppermost in the series of primitive rocks. It is true, it is often found to graduate by minute and imperceptible shades of difference, into that which is decidedly secondary. Instances of this have been observed so frequently that the fact can be no longer questioned. This fact, and others of the same kind ought not perhaps to be considered as invalidating the received opinions with regard to the classification of rocks according to the doctrines of Werner. If a division is to be made of the rocky strata of the earth into primitive, transition, &c. it is perhaps of little importance whether the boundaries thus instituted, shall traverse beds of the same substance, or separate contiguous strata composed of different materials.

That series of rocks next in order to the primitive limestone abovementioned, has been very generally denominated the transition class. It comprehends the following strata, *metalliferous limestone, clay slate, graywacke,* and *graywacke-slate,* and *old red sandstone.* If we confine our attention to the consideration of these rocks as they exist in our own country, we shall find them appearing in their different localities under circumstances of considerable uniformity.

II.—*Metalliferous Limestone.*

The prevailing colour of this rock is blue of various shades and intensities, varying into yellow and gray. It has usually a close texture, an even, large choncoidal, or somewhat splintery fracture. In many varieties, the surface by long exposure becomes coated with an incrustation of a yellowish-white powdery matter, which adheres closely. It is frequently traversed by small recticulating veins of quartz or calcareous spar, which during the gradual decomposition of detached masses, resist the progress of disintegration, and are left standing out from the surface, giving it a chequered appearance. It is the lowest, and is considered the most ancient of the rocks containing organic remains.

Geographical Distribution.—This rock occurs extensively along all the northwestern side of the primitive of the Alleghanies. In Lower Canada and Vermont, it is accompanied by granular limestone, and granular quartz, which separate it from the mica slate and talcose rocks on the east.* It is there usually inclined towards the west at an inconsiderable angle. It is separated from the compact floetz limestone of the valley of Lake Champlain, by a stratum of old red sandstone which forms the upper part of a range of hills called in Vermont, the *Snake Mountain.* In Berkshire county, in the western part of Massachusetts, and along the eastern side of the Hudson in New York, a stratum of primitive clay-slate intervenes between this rock and the granular limestone. The New Lebanon Mountain, which is of slate, and divides the primitive limestone of Pittsfield, Richmond, Stockbridge, &c. from the transition which occurs at New Lebanon Springs, and along the western base of this range, is considered primitive.†

To the northeast of the Hudson river, the transition limestone, nowhere occupies any great extent of surface from east to west, but is a narrow strip running along the margin of the primitive, and in a few miles is succeeded either by red sandstone or clay slate resting upon it. In Vermont, in the same neighbourhood, it alternates with clay slate and supports red sandstone.

Crossing the Hudson above the Highlands, and proceeding southwest, little of this stratum is seen, in the lower part of New York, but it becomes more abundant in the western parts of New Jersey and Pennsylvania. If we suppose the whole of the Alleghany Mountains of Pennsylvania, Maryland, and the western parts of Virginia, removed to a level with the surface at the base of their eastern declivities, it is probable their foundation which would be thus exposed, would be found through their whole extent, to be of transition limestone. This rock is almost the only one which occurs between the primitive limestone about twenty miles west of Philadelphia and Harrisburgh. Cove hill, the north and south mountains, and the other eastern ridges of the Alleghany, are all based upon metalliferous limestone. It is seen

---

* See Eaton's Index, p. 183. 2d. Ed.
† Dewey, in the American Journal, p. 337.

emerging from beneath the sandstone, which forms the body of these mountains at M'Connel's Town, and in most of the vallies between the Alleghanies. We learn from Maclure, that it extends to the south and west nearly to the termination of this range of mountains at the confluence of the Alabama and Tombigbee rivers in Mississippi.

III.—*Transition Argillite.*

This name is intended to comprehend not only the common varieties of the clay slate with inclined laminæ, but also some varieties of graywacke, and the silicious slate, by some considered a distinct stratum. It is believed that throughout the range of country occupied by the several rocks here mentioned, they will be found too intimately blended, and too closely entangled with each other to allow of their being considered as separate formations.

Geographical Distribution.—The formation including the abovementioned rocks has been denominated clay slate. As far as our acquaintance has extended, it occurs in all its localities associated with metalliferous limestone, or old red sandstone. It is not to be confounded with the primitive argillite which occurs below transition limestone, and is met with in the highly primitive parts of New England, nor with the aluminous schist of the great secondary formation to the west. It is distinct from either, and in most instances its character is sufficiently marked. It occurs in the central portions of that extensive strip of transition which skirts the western margin of the primitive of New York and New England, and forms the great body of the Alleghany and Catskill Mountains. It is wider and more extensive in the north, occupying much of the surface in Vermont, the northern parts of the state of New York and Canada. In the Alleghany Mountains of Pennsylvania, Maryland, and Virginia, its beds are of great thickness, and form in some instances, the prevailing rock, being, however almost invariably overlaid by sandstone. It has in several instances been observed to contain impressions of organized beings, but these are usually those of zoophytic animals, and are exceedingly unlike those found so abundantly in the schist of coal formations. Its colours are variable, it is, however, most commonly bluish-black or dark brown. Between Albany and Pittsfield, it is met with of a green colour, and a few miles to the southeast of Whitehall, New York, it is bright red.

'The *graywacke*, which in this very general and hasty view we have considered as in part, belonging to the clay slate of transition appears to us to form the connecting link between this clay slate, and the old red sandstone. In attempting to give a more detailed account of these formations, we might perhaps speak of the graywacke, as others have done, as a distinct stratum. We have, however, usually found it so intimately blended either with the sandstone, or clay slate that, in this enlarged view, we see no necessity for a separation. We cannot agree in opinion with some who have considered the graywacke as the substratum of the great secondary formation of the valley of the Mississippi. We have found it almost invariably overlaid by an inclined sandstone separating it from the horizontal rocks towards the west. This may not be as often the case at the north as in Pennsylvania, Maryland, and Virginia. Mr. Eaton, is of opinion that " graywacke underlays all that district of country in the interior of the state of New York, which would be bounded on the north, by a line drawn from Albany, westward to the Onondaga salt springs, on the west, by a line running from the salt springs by Bath to the Pennsylvania line, on the south, by a line running thence to Newburgh, on the Hudson above the Highlands, and from thence to Albany, by a line running parallel to the river, at a few miles distance." We are informed by governor Clinton,* that coal strata exist in the western part of the state of New York, and we are induced, from the analogy of the other parts of the same great secondary formation, to believe that the brine springs of Onondaga, are situated not in graywacke, but in the sandstone of that coal formation. According to Maclure,† old red sandstone appears from under the limestone, and other strata at Lewistown, ten miles below the Falls of Niagara, and also near the salines of Onondaga, in Genessee county. " This, says he, would give some probability to the conjecture that the old red sandstone is the foundation of all this horizontal formation, and is perhaps attached to some series of rocks laying on the primitive, north of the Great Lakes."

IV.—*Transition Sandstone.*

Old Red Sandstone?—Throughout the whole extent of the transition formation, beforementioned, a sandstone occurs,

* See his Speech at the opening of the Session of 1822. Since the above was written, we have been informed that coal has been discovered in the interior of New York.
† Observations on the Geology of the United States, p. 57.

evidently belonging to the oldest depositions of that rock. It is for the most part distinctly stratified, and in all cases its stratifications are inclined. It consists of grains of quartz united by a scanty cement, and usually more or less rounded as if by attrition and the operation of currents of water. These fragments vary in magnitude from the finest sand, to boulders of several pounds weight. Among the Alleghany mountains, are many extensive beds of pudding stone, or coarse conglomerate, usually consisting of white quartzy pebbles in a cement often highly coloured by oxide of iron. It is also to be observed that this formation of transition sandstone, sometimes embraces extensive beds, whose integrant particles have by no means the appearance of having been rounded by attrition. As in the case of almost all the rocks of secondary formation, there appear to have been periods during the time of its deposition when the waters of the superincumbent ocean ceased to throw down the mechanical debris of former rocks and deposited earthy matter from a state of chemical solution.

The Alleghany mountains in New York, Pennsylvania, Maryland, and Virginia, consist principally of rocks belonging to the transition class; and among these, sandstone is perhaps of more frequent occurrence than any other aggregate. Mr. Maclure has not considered the sandstones of the Alleghany mountains generally, as belonging to the old red sandstone formation of Werner; and it must be acknowledged there is some difference at least in colour, between the ferruginous sand rock, which appears on the shore of the Tappan bay, near Nyac, and extends south and west through Newark, Amboy, and Brunswick, to Norristown in Pennsylvania; and that which forms the body of the Cove, Sideling and Alleghany ridges farther to the west. But we cannot discover so marked a difference between the sandstone of the localities last mentioned, and that which occurs about the south mountain in Pennsylvania, that at Hagarstown in Maryland, and near Harper's Ferry, in Virginia, which he considers as the *old red sandstone.* Indeed this last appears to us in almost every respect, to resemble the inclined sandstone which prevails so generally throughout the middle and eastern ridges of the Alleghany mountains in Pennsylvania, and Maryland. We have already stated the opinion in part sanctioned by the observations of Maclure, that the old red sandstone, is the substratum of the part of the secondary formation south of lake Ontario. If this be the case, what stratum, if not the old red sandstone should be seen emerging from beneath that secondary along its south-eastern margin? We will not however, contend for the name. It is sufficient for our purpose, to state that the sandstone so abundant in all the principal ridges accessary to the Alleghany on the east, has the character of a rock belonging to the transition formation of the Wernerians, that is, its strata have a somewhat regular dip and inclination, it contains no beds of bituminous coal, and few remains of animals or plants. Near the summit of the ridge called particularly the Alleghany, the change to more recent secondary begins to appear. Without the interposition of any other stratum, and without any sudden change of features, the strata of sandstone, become nearly horizontal, assuming gradually all the characters of secondary rocks. About one mile west of the summit of the Alleghany, on the road from Philadelphia to Pittsburgh, the first indications of coal are observed. In the vallies, the metalliferous limestone, and the older sandstones emerge to the light. The same thing happens in the case of Catskill, and other mountains, west of the Hudson, their bases being of transition, and their summits crossed with secondary.*

The horizontal sandstones connected with the depositions of coal, occurring along the Ohio, from Pittsburgh to the confluence of Green river, assume various characters, and often support extensive formations of compact limestone.†

* See Eaton's geological section, at page 280, of the index to the Geology of the Northern States.

† The following are descriptions of the rocks, that alternate with each other as they occur, in connexion with the coal beds at Pittsburgh, commencing with the uppermost, and proceeding in a regular gradation to the lowest that we have had an opportunity of examining.

No. 1. A loose grained argillaceous sandstone, composed of minute grains of quartz, and decomposed feldspar, united by an argillaceous cement. Its colour is yellowish gray, fracture uneven, stratifications imperfect. It contains no organic remains; depth of the bed near four feet.

No. 2. Bituminous shale; natural colour, brownish black, that of the streak, dark gray. Before the blow pipe it decrepitates, burns with a bright flame, emits a bituminous odour, and soon becomes nearly white. Its structure is slaty: no animal or vegetable remains are contained in it, small veins of clay are dispersed irregularly between the layers. Depth of the bed ten feet.

No. 3. A bed of bituminous coal, its colour is brownish black, cross fracture uneven, longitudinal slaty: fragments tabular, right angled, lustre resinous, it is semi-hard, sectile, and very brittle. Vertical and hori-

The Alleghany mountains have been long since pointed out by attentive observers, as a great natural barrier, destined finally to become the line of separation between two extensive territories; embraced within the present boundaries of the United States, but unconnected by any physical ties, sufficiently strong to ensure the permanent unity of a great empire. It is now we believe, fully ascertained (if it can ever have been doubted) that the foreign communication from almost every

zontal beds of indurated clay, containing a small quantity of bitumen, occur in the coal. Depth of the bed from two to eight feet.

No. 4. Bituminous shale. Possesses the same charcters as No. 2. Varies in depth.

꡾No. 5. Indurated clay; its colour is lead gray, fracture in situations where it has been subjected to the combined actions of moisture and the atmosphere, irregularly slatose, in others uneven. Depth of this bed seven feet.

No. 6. Argillaceous chlorite slate passing by regular gradations into argillaceous chlorite sandstone. Natural colour, yellowish green, that of the streak light gray, cross fracture uneven. Its powder is soft and slightly greasy to the touch; it contains no organic remains. The depth of this bed varies.

No. 7. Compact Limestone, intimately mixed with alumine, it contains small veins of calcareous spar dispersed throughout the mass. Veins of angular fragments of carbonate of lime, united by a calcareous and argillaceous cement, extend irregularly through the rock. The fracture in some specimens is compact and earthy, in others uneven.

No. 8. Argillaceous chlorite sandstone, consisting of minute grains of quartz, chlorite slate, and talc, united by an argillaceous cement: its colour is yellowish green: fracture uneven, the powder is soft and feels greasy to the touch, it is destitute of organic remains.

No. 9. A loose grained argillaceous sandstone, thickly interspersed with thin laminæ of talc: its colour is light gray, fracture uneven, texture loose, it is liable to disintregation.

No. 10. Argillaceous sandstone, irregularly slatose; its colour is gray, with a tinge of yellow. Nodules of clay iron stone occur in considerable quantities through the mass of rock.

No. 11. Fine grained argillaceous sandstone, composed of quartz, and magnesia, united by an argillaceous cement. Its colour is yellowish gray which by the action of the blow pipe, passes into reddish brown. This rock contains great numbers of the impressions of the phylolitus.

No. 12. Indurated clay, its colour is bluish gray, structure, slatose; fracture approaching uneven, hardness inconsiderable. Impressions of small leaves occur in this, but are not numerous. they apparently consist of one species alone.

No. 13. Compact argillaceous sandstone, composed of quartz, feldspar, and thin laminæ of talc, united by an argillaceous cement, its colour is brownish gray. Nodules of clay iron stone occur in considerable abundance in this rock, they are formed by concentric layers, around a nucleus, which is the same in composition as the mass of their bed. Their size varies from that of a nut to an apple.

Jessup's Ms. Report.

part of the vast basin of the Mississippi, will find its way to the ocean, through that river; consequently, that the centre of civilization and wealth for this great fertile valley, will be placed somewhere on the banks of the Mississippi. At the present time, for a considerable part of the year, merchant vessels of three, four, and five hundred tons burthen, propelled by steam, are arriving almost daily at the falls of Ohio and at St. Louis, in eighteen or twenty days from New Orleans. The extensive forests, and the inexhaustible mines of coal distributed along all the ramifications of this great river, ensure the continuance of the means for steam navigation, by which the productions of other countries will be circulated through every part of this extensive system of inland communication.

The great chain of the Alleghanies, spreading and becoming more elevated in the southwest, must always present an obstacle to easy and direct communication between the maritime parts of Virginia, North Carolina, South Carolina, and Georgia, and the valley of the Mississippi; unless a free intercourse is established, by means of roads and canals, which may probably be effected.

In the middle states the Hudson, the Delaware, and the Susquehanna have their sources in the great secondary formation, and traversing the whole primitive and transition of the Alleghanies, discharge their waters into the Atlantic. Vessels of several hundred tons, ascend the Hudson to Albany, on the northwestern side of the Alleghany mountains; thence, an easy communication will hereafter be established along the Great Canal and the Lakes, with an extensive portion of the Mississippi basin, north of the fortieth degree of north latitude. The facilities for transportation by this route, and the easy communication by means of the national road, and the turnpike from Philadelphia to Pittsburgh, will ensure a constant intercourse and some community of interest between the Atlantic states and the countries west of the Alleghanies.

The vallies, every where interspersed with this group of mountains, are fertile, and many of the ridges have soils, capable of supporting a scattered population. Unlike the Rocky Mountains, which must always constitute an almost impassable natural boundary, this range has no wide and desolate wastes along its base, where the permanent habitations of men can never be fixed; rising in no point to the limits of perpetual frost; its sides are always accessible, clothed usually with forests, and even its broad and level summits may, in many places, be made the residence of an agricultural people.

Nevertheless it cannot be denied, that the valley of the Mississippi, both by its geological conformation and by the germs of the civil and political constitutions already planted and taking root there, seems destined to become the seat of a powerful, and agricultural empire. The gradual destruction of the forests along the Mississippi, Missouri, and other rivers, whose banks are not permanent, will, at length, remove one of the greatest obstacles to the navigation of those rivers; but their commerce must all centre at one port, and that an inconvenient one. The attention of the people will, therefore, be directed less to their foreign relations and the maintenance of commerce, than to the development of the inexhaustible resources of their own soil.

The sickliness of the more depressed portions of the valley of the Mississippi may, for some time, retard the progressive increase of population, but cannot prevent its ultimate arrival at its maximum, which is to be limited only by the immense internal resources of the country. The ancient inhabitants of this continent, if we may judge by their remaining monuments, were most numerous in the low and fertile parts of this valley. So were the ancient Egyptians on the Delta of the Nile, and below the city of Thebes, where, as Herodotus informs us "before the time of Menes was one extended marsh;" so were the ancient Romans in the vicinity of the Pontine marshes, and the Venetians in those low and almost inaccessible swamps at the bottom of the Adriatic Gulf, to which the remnant of the Veneti fled for refuge from the fury of Attila. Unfortunately the alluvion of large and small rivers often accumulates at the mouth, and is deposited in their channels, until tracts, formerly habitable and populous, are drowned and deserted.

It may be hoped the persevering industry of men will hereafter do much towards protecting the alluvion of the lower Mississippi from the annual inundations; but as the river itself must be the only natural agent, whose operations can ever do any thing towards elevating the general surface of the Delta, and since any elevation of this surface, effected by depositions from the waters of the river, must be attended by a corresponding elevation of its bed, there appears no reason to hope, that the situation of the immediate valley of the Mississippi will ever be more favorable to human life and health than at present. Nevertheless we have seen populous cities springing up in the most depressed parts of that valley, and those, who live hereafter, will probably see there, a large portion of the population, the civilization, and wealth of America.

EXPLANATION OF THE PLATE.

In illustration of the foregoing remarks we offer two transverse sections, adapted to the scale of elevation by Maj. Long. In the delineation it will be perceived little regard has been paid to the horizontal scale. The intention being to exhibit an outline of our idea of the structure of the different groups of mountains, some wide and uninteresting plains, as that between 5° and 12° west, in the northern, and 11° and 13° in the southern section have been omitted. Particular attention has been bestowed in adapting the delineations to the scale of elevation, which, as will be perceived on inspection, is divided into three parts differently graduated.

The inclinations, indicated by the lines between the different formations, are not to be considered applicable to all the strata composing those formations, as in the instance of the coal in the southern section of the Alleghanies, the strata of sandstone and bituminous shale are nearly horizontal, but occupy the several elevations indicated by the inclined line in the section; the lines, therefore, may be considered as marking the position of formations, rather than the inclination of strata.

The inclination of the strata in the southern section of the Ozark mountains is usually towards the south, or southeast, and more irregular in direction, than in the Alleghanies.

It is proper to remark that the coal strata, in the northern section of the Alleghany mountains, are very extensive, and rise nearer to the highest elevations, than in the southern, though, in the delineation, this has not been particularly represented.

ASTRONOMICAL AND METEOROLOGICAL

RECORDS,

AND

VOCABULARIES OF INDIAN LANGUAGES,

TAKEN ON THE

EXPEDITION FOR EXPLORING

THE

MISSISSIPPI AND ITS WESTERN WATERS,

UNDER THE COMMAND OF

MAJOR S. H. LONG,

OF THE UNITED STATES' TOPOGRAPHICAL ENGINEERS,
IN 1819 AND 1820.

PHILADELPHIA:

1822.

PREFACE.

I SHALL preface this manuscript, by giving an account of the instruments with which the expedition was furnished, for making observations.

1st. A bell-metal sextant of seven inches radius, divided by the assistance of the vernier to 15″ on a silver arch, executed by Spencer, Browning and Rust, London.

2d. Another sextant of brass, five inches radius, divided on a silver arch by the assistance of the vernier to 30″; made by Cary, London. It is a convenient and portable instrument: the handle, the supporter of the telescope, and the compound microscope for reading off angles, may be detached readily, and packed in the case containing the instrument when travelling.

3d. A circle of reflection, of brass, divided on a brass limb by the assistance of the vernier to 30″, which may be subdivided by the eye to the nearest 15″. The graduated limb is twelve inches in diameter, made by Spencer, Browning and Rust, London. It is not constructed with the greatest nicety, and the larger sextant was preferred to it for Lunar distances.

4th. An artificial horizon of mercury with a glass roof, the surfaces of which were ground parallel, and then polished smooth, to prevent errors from an irregular refraction. The mercury is carried in a wooden box; and the cup for holding it, with the roof, are secured in a box together, when travelling.

5th. Another smaller roof which I had made at Engineer Cantonment, after the same plan, out of two speculum glasses for a sextant, which were provided in Philadelphia. I made use of this roof with a mercurial horizon, for observing the double altitudes of the sun and stars after I separated from Major Long at Engineer Cantonment, and found that by being cautious to bring the direct and reflected images of the object whose double altitude was observed, in contact, in the middle of the cup of mercury, it answered as well as the larger horizon and roof.

6th. An achromatic telescope of four feet in length, for observing eclipses of Jupiter's satellites; the magnifying power I used for this purpose, was about 120.

7th. A box chronometer, by Tobias and Levitt, London.

8th. A pocket chronometer cased like a common watch, by Brockbank, London.

The rates of going of both these time-pieces will be found among the Astronomical Calculations.

9th. An instrument for observing the dip of the magnetic needle, executed for the use of the Expedition, by Mr. I. Lukens of Philadelphia, after an ingenious manner. It consisted of a vertical circle of brass, graduated to half degrees, in the centre of which a needle between nine and ten inches in length, was suspended in the middle by two nicely polished points resting in sockets. It was furnished with two spirit-levels at right angles to each other, and leveling screws. In order to observe the dip, the graduated vertical circle or limb must be placed so that its plane shall coincide with that of the magnetic meridian, which is done by means of a surveyor's compass, or a common pocket compass will serve for this: the instrument is then levelled, and the dip read off on two opposite points of the limb. By revolving the instrument round on its vertical diameter, and again adjusting the levels, two other readings may be obtained on opposite points of the limb. Thus the mean of four observations may be taken for the true dip, corrected by each other for any imperceptible errors in the graduation of the limb, levelling of the instrument, or eccentricity in the fixture of the needle in its sockets. I conceive that the dip may be obtained within 5′, although the circle is only graduated to 30′.

10th. An azimuth compass with a needle and card six inches in diameter, graduated to half degrees, which might be subdivided by the eye to 10′. The magnetic variation was determined by observing with this instrument the magnetic azimuth and amplitudes of the sun.—Made by Richard Patten, New York.

11th. A common surveyor's compass, with a needle six inches long. This instrument was used in tracing the course of the Missouri, as laid down on the map of the country taken by Major Long and Lieutenant Swift.—Made by the same.

12th. A fifty feet chain, with links each a foot long, convenient for travelling.—By the same.

13th. A small theodolite, four and an half inches in diameter, graduated to 30′ by the vernier, for trigonometrical purposes.

14th. Three mountain barometers, by M. Fisher and Son. Two of them got entirely out of order in the course of our travels.

15th. Several mercurial thermometers, and one of alcohol. By the same, graduated by Fahrenheit's scale.

" 16th. Our collection of instruments also embraced several of less note, viz. six travelling compasses, several pocket compasses, a small pocket telescope by Doland, several microscopes, a measuring tape, &c. &c."

The astronomical and other calculations are divided into two parts. Part first, contains the observations which were made and calculated entirely by myself except in one or two instances. I have entered the observations of my friend Lieutenant A. Talcott of the corps of Engineers, made when we were travelling together, and have taken a mean between the results obtained by him and myself in those instances. Part second contains the observations which were made by Major Long and Lieutenant Swift after I separated from them at Engineer Cantonment, and which were afterwards calculated by me while those officers were engaged in projecting maps of the country explored by the Expedition.

All the latitudes in Part first, and all except three in Part second, are deduced from the double meridian altitudes of the sun or stars, (and in one other instance in Part second, the double meridian altitude of the moon was observed,) to which the index error of the instrument is applied, which was always determined immediately preceding or after the observation, by measuring the diameter of the sun from each side of 0, (zero,) on the limbs of the instrument, and taking half the difference of the diameters thus measured, for the index error, which was called + (plus,) and added when the excess was on the negative or right hand side of 0 on the limb of the instrument, otherwise the error was called —, (minus,) and subtracted from the observed double altitude. In Part first the refractions answering to the apparent altitudes of the objects have always been corrected for the state of the barometer and thermometer, so that if any one should choose to look them over, this correction must be found by reference to the meteorological register, which will accompany this paper. In Part second the refractions could not be corrected for the state of the atmosphere, as there was no barometer to refer to. All the observations in Part second for latitude, longitude by lunar distances, and for the correction of the time, were made with the small sextant of five inches radius.

In Part first, the observations for latitude previous to the 31st August, 1819, were made with the circle of reflection, used as a sextant. After that time they were made with the larger sextant, except those made while traversing the country in the vicinity of the Council Bluff and at the Pawnee Village, and also one made at Engineer Cantonment on the 20th March, 1820, which were made with the smaller sextant of five inches radius, it being better calculated for land excursions than the other. All the lunar distances in Part first were taken with the larger one.

The first and most important point in determining the longitude, is to have the time and the rate of the time-piece well regulated. The method I pursued for this purpose was by equal altitudes of the sun, and sometimes of the stars before and after passing the meridian. For accuracy, provided your time-piece is pretty uniform in its rate of going, whether it should gain or lose time, this method is perhaps preferable to any other that can be pursued with the use of an instrument of reflection, such as a sextant or quadrant.

In determining the longitude from lunar distances the only data have been the latitude of the place determined from observation, the observed distance of the moon from the sun or stars and the correct apparent time of observation. The true and apparent altitudes of the objects are inferred from the apparent time and latitude. In Part first the moon's horizontal parallax obtained from the nautical almanac is corrected for the spheroidal figure of the earth, and according to the latitude of the place of observation. This correction was not applied in the calculations of Part second. The difference it occasions in the result is of little moment, within what might be considered as errors of observation. In computing the right ascension and declination of the moon the equation of second difference, a correction arising from the unequal motion of the moon, has in every case been applied to the proportional part of the variation of right ascension and declination corresponding to the time from noon or midnight when the observation was made in order to get the moon's true place at the given time.

One lunar observation made at St. Louis, and three at Franklin, (Missouri,) are calculated altogether by spherical trigonometry, a method which I had practised under my instructor, the late venerable Professor Ellicott, of the Military

Academy. It is very exact but too long for usual practice. I afterwards adopted Dr. Mackay's methods, both for calculating the true and apparent altitudes of the objects, and for reducing the apparent to the true distance, which are rendered very concise by means of his table of natural versed sines.*

It is hoped that the following astronomical computations will be found to correct many errors in the geography of the country west of the Mississippi, as laid down even on some of the latest and most approved maps. On Melish's latest map of the United States and contiguous Spanish and British Provinces, (entered according to the Act of Congress, June 16th, 1820,) we find the spot where Engineer Cantonment was constructed, (three miles S. E. of the point known by the name of the Council Bluff,) laid down in 41° 42' of N. latitude, and 96° 50' of longitude W. of the meridian of Greenwich. By fourteen meridian observations of the sun and stars I obtained for the latitude of that place 41° 25' 03.9" N. and forty-two distances of the moon from the sun and stars, together with three eclipses of Jupiter's Satellites, gave me for the longitude 95° 43' 53" W. of Greenwich. The position of the mouth of the river Platte is equally erroneous in longitude, and 6' of latitude too far north, according to the same. We find on the same map, that the highest peak between the head waters of the Platte and Arkansa, is laid down in latitude 40° 42' N. and longitude 107° 20' W. whereas its position determined from the observations of Major Long and Lieut. Swift made near it, is 38° 53' N. lat. and 105° 52' W. long. But by a map of Mexico, Louisiana, Mississippi Territory, &c. by John H. Robinson, M. D. &c. &c. (published in Philadelphia in 1819,) who traversed the country with the expedition under the gallant and enterprising Pike in 1806–7, the position given this remarkable point is 41° 30' N. lat. and 111° 20' W. long. from Greenwich, which is too far north by 2° 37' of latitude, and too far west by 5° 28' of longitude!! This will show what errors travellers are liable to commit in laying down plans of countries they have explored unless they have had recourse to astronomical observations for the purpose of determining the geographical positions of remarkable points.

Considerable pains have been taken in overlooking the cal-

---

* The theory and practice of finding the longitude at sea or on land, &c. by Dr. Andrew Mackay, in 2 vols. London, 1810.

culations since they were first made. They may not yet be entirely free from inaccuracies, though it is believed that none of magnitude will be found among them.

(Signed)

J..D. GRAHAM,
Lieut. U. S. Artillery.

Philadelphia, July, 1821.

PART I.

Containing Astronomical Observations and Calculations made on the Expedition for exploring the waters of the Mississippi and country west of it, under the command of Major S. H. Long, of the United States' Topographical Engineers, in 1819 and 1820. By J. D. Graham, Lieut. U. S. Artillery.

PITTSBURGH, Pennsylvania, May 1st, 1819.

Magnetic dip, as ascertained by several observations, 78° 12'.

Observations made at Shippingsport, Kentucky.

May 20, 1819.	Dip of magnetic needle, 70° 15'	
May 21, 1819.	Meridian double altitude of sun's lower limb	143° 13' 07''
	Latitude deduced - -	38 15 23 N.

Equal altitudes of Sun to find error of Time-piece.

	Time from Noon, A. M.	Time from Noon, P. M.	Error of Time-piece.
May 21, 1819.	2ʰ 45' 32''	3ʰ 33' 51''	27' 51'' too fast.
May 22, 1819.	2 22 07 2 20 43 2 19 18	3 10 14 3 08 54 3 07 31	27' 42'' fast. Mean time.

Variation of time-piece between noon of the 21st and that of the 22d was 9'' losing. Set the chronometer on the morning of the 23d to mean time.

Camp on the Mississippi River, near the mouth of the Merameg.

June 8th, 1819.	Meridian double altitude of sun's lower limb	148° 16' 30''
	Latitude deduced - - Mouth of Merameg south of Camp	38 26 09 N. 02 30
	Latitude of the mouth of Merameg river	38 23 39 N.
June 8th, 1819.	Magnetic dip at this place -	70 00 00

B

Observations made at St. Louis, Missouri Territory.

June 15, 1819.	Meridian double altitude of sun's lower limb }	148° 54' 22''
	Latitude deduced - -	38 36 14 N.
June 16, 1819.	Magnetic dip by a mean of several experiments }	70 30

Equal altitudes of Sun to find the error of Time-piece.

	Time from Noon, A. M.	Time from Noon, P. M.	Error of Time-piece.
June 16, 1819.	4ʰ 35' 40½''	4ʰ 45' 45''	} 4' 53'' fast.
	4 34 21	4 44 25	Mean time.
	4 32 59½	Lost.	

A mean of eight Lunar distances, and the time corresponding, was found as follows.

	Time per Chronometer, A. M.	Distance of nearest limbs.	Index Error.
June 16, 1819.	6ʰ 34' 26½''	69° 51' 30½''	+ 15½''

Data resulting from the foregoing Lunar Observations.

St. Louis, June 16, 1819. In latitude 38° 36' 18'' N. and longitude about 6ʰ W. of the meridian of Greenwich, at 6ʰ 34' 26½'' A. M. civil account per chronometer, the distance of the nearest limbs of the sun and moon was observed to be 69° 51' 46'' to find the longitude.

Longitude deduced, 6ʰ 00' 25'', or 90° 06' 15'' W. of Greenwich.

Note. The chronometer run down on the night of the 16th, so that the subsequent error in time, compared with the preceding, affords no data to estimate the rate of the time-piece.

Equal altitudes of Sun to find the error of Time-piece at noon.

	Time from Noon, A. M.	Time from Noon, P. M.	Error of Time-piece.
June 17, 1819.	4ʰ 42' 23''	4ʰ 53' 49'' }	5' 20½'' fast.
	4 41 03	4 52 28	Mean time.
	4 39 42½	4 51 06½ }	

Observations at St. Louis, to ascertain the magnetic variation.

	Double altitude of Sun's upper limb.	Azimuth of Sun's centre.	Magnetic variation.
June 17, 1819.	41° 06' 45''	N. 64° 40' E. }	10° 47' 38'' E.
	41 46 00	N. 65 10 E. }	
	42 28 45	N. 65 40 E. }	

Equal altitudes of Sun to find error of Time-piece at noon.

	Time from Noon, A. M.	Time from Noon, P. M.	Error of Time-piece.
June 18, 1819.	3ʰ 37′ 36″ 3 36 15 3 34 55	3ʰ 48′ 16″ 3 46 55 3 45 35 }	4′ 46″ fast. Mean time.

Equal altitudes of Sun to find error of Time-piece at noon.

	Time from Noon, A. M.	Time from Noon, P. M.	Error of Time-piece.
June 19, 1819.	2ʰ 47′ 1$\frac{2\cdot 1}{2}$″ 2 45 50$\frac{1}{2}$ 2 44 28$\frac{1}{2}$	2ʰ 57′ 07$\frac{1}{2}$″ 2 55 46$\frac{1}{2}$ 2 54 25$\frac{1}{2}$ }	4′ 11″ fast. Mean time.
June 19, 1819.	Meridian double altitude of sun's lower limb - }		149° 08′ 45″
	Latitude deduced - -		38 36 36 N.

Equal altitudes of Sun to find error of Time-piece at noon.

	Time from Noon, A. M.	Time from Noon, P. M.	Error of Time-piece.
June 20, 1819.	4ʰ 00′ 15″ 3 58 56 3 57 35	4ʰ 09′ 30″ 4 08 10$\frac{1}{2}$ 4 06 51 }	3′ 37$\frac{1}{2}$″ fast. Mean time.
June 20, 1819.	Meridian double altitude of sun's lower limb - }		149° 11′ 25″
	Latitude deduced - -		38 36 05 N.

Latitude of St. Louis by observation of June 15			38° 36′ 14″ N.
Do. do. June 19			38 36 36 N.
Do. do. June 20			38 36 05 N.
Do. by a mean of the preceding obser- } vations - - -			38 36 18 N.

Rate of Time-piece between the 17th and 20th of June, 1819.

		Variation.
June 17, 1819. 18, 19, 20,	Fast for mean time 5′ 20″ 30‴ Do. 4 46 00 Do. 4 11 00 Do. 3 37 30	34″ 30‴ losing. 35 00 do. 33 30 do.

Note. The foregoing results show the mean rate of the time-piece, (Chronometer by Tobias & Levitt, London,) in three days to be 34″ 20‴—daily losing.

Magnetic dip at Belle-Fontaine, Missouri, June 23		70° 00′
Do. at St. Charles, Missouri, June 25		70 05

Observations at our Camp on the Missouri river.

June 28, 1819.	Meridian double altitude of sun's lower limb $\big\}$	149° 06′ 25″
	Latitude deduced - -	38 34 33 N.

Magnetic dip at Cote Sans Dessein, Missouri, July 6 - - - - $\big\}$	70° 50′

Observations made at FRANKLIN, *Howard County, Missouri.*

Equal altitudes of Sun to find error of Time-piece at noon.

	Time from Noon, A. M.	Time from Noon, P. M.	Error of Time-piece.
July 16, 1819.	4ʰ 14′ 26″ 4 13 05½ 4 11 46	4ʰ 22′ 05½″ 4 20 45 4 19 24½ $\bigg\}$	1′ 41″ 17‴ slow. Mean time.
July 16, 1819.	Meridian double altitude of sun's lower limb - $\big\}$		144° 29′ 30″
	Latitude deduced - -		38· 56 57 N.
July 17, 1819.	Meridian double altitude of sun's lower limb - $\big\}$		144 10 15
	Latitude deduced - -		38 56 45 N.

The following are means of three sets of lunar distances of Moon from Sun, taken at Franklin, Missouri.

	Time per Chronometer, A. M.	Distance of nearest limbs.	
July 16, 1819. 16, 17,	8ʰ 08′ 35½″ 8 15 52 8 29 04½	62° 23′ 11″ 62 20 52½ 50 46 18 $\bigg\}$	Index error corrected.

Magnetic dip at Franklin, July 17 - -	69° 30′

Equal altitudes of Sun to find error of Time-piece at noon.

	Time from Noon, A. M.	Time from Noon, P. M.	Error of Time-piece.
July 17, 1819.	3ʰ 03′ 38½″ 3 02 17 3 00 56	3ʰ 10′ 14½″ 3 08 53 3 07 30 $\bigg\}$	2′ 20″ slow. Mean time.
July 18, 1819.	Meridian double altitude of sun's lower limb - $\big\}$		143° 47′ 41″
	Latitude deduced - -		38 57 46 N.

Equal altitudes of Sun to find error of Time-piece at noon.

	Time from Noon, A. M.	Time from Noon, P. M.	Error of Time-piece.
July 18, 1819.	3ʰ 13′ 11½″ 3 11 50 3 10 29	3ʰ 18′ 39½″ 3 17 18½ 3 15 57	2′ 58″ slow. Mean time.

Latitude of Franklin by observation of July 16	38° 56′ 57″ N.
Do. do. do. 17	38 56 45 N.
Do. do. do. 18	38 57 46 N.
Do. do. by mean of three observations	38 57 09 N.

Observations at Franklin to ascertain the magnetic variation.

July 18, 1819.	Magnetic azimuth of sun's centre, A. M.	S. 111° 20′ E.*
	Magnetic azimuth of sun's centre, P.M. same altitude	S. 87 50 W.
	Magnetic variation deduced	11 42 E.

Rate of Time-piece, (chronometer by Tobias & Levitt,) at Franklin.

			Daily losing.
July 16, 1819.	Slow for mean time	1′ 41″ 17‴	38″ 43‴
July 17, 1819.	Do. do.	2 20 00	
July 18, 1819.	Do. do.	2 58 00	38 00

Data for the calculation of the Longitude of Franklin.

1st. July 16, 1819. At 8ʰ 08′ 35½″ A. M. civil account per chronometer, the distance of the nearest limbs of the sun and moon was observed to be 62° 23′ 11″, the latitude by observation being 38° 57′ 09″ N., longitude estimated at 6ʰ 10′ W. of Greenwich to find the true longitude.

Longitude deduced, 6ʰ 11′ 43″ or 92° 55′ 45″ W. of Greenwich.

2d. At 8ʰ 15′ 52″ A. M. per chronometer, the distance of the nearest limbs of the sun and moon was observed to be 62° 20′ 52½″ on the 16th of July to find the longitude.

Longitude deduced, 6ʰ 11′ 58½″ or 92° 59′ 37″ W. of Greenwich.

3d. July 17, 1819. At 8ʰ 29′ 04½″ A. M. per chronometer, the distance of the nearest limbs of the sun and moon was observed to be 50° 46′ 18″ to find the longitude.

Longitude deduced, 6ʰ 11′ 43½″ or 92° 55′ 52½″ W. of Greenwich.

---

* The eastern and western azimuths are both reckoned from the same point (the south,) disregarding the usual method of stating courses.

Longitude of Franklin by observation, July } 92° 55′ 45″ W.
  16, (1st set) - - - - }
Do.   do.   July 16, (2d set.)   92 59 37
Do.   do.   July 17   92 55 52½

Do. do. by a mean of the preceding observations | 92 57 05 W.

Magnetic dip at Charaton, Missouri, July 24 | 69 50

Observations at our Camp on the Missouri.

July 28, 1819.	Meridian double altitude of } sun's lower limb - }	139° 27′ 20″
	Latitude deduced - -	39 06 37 N.
July 28, 1819.	Magnetic amplitude of sun's } centre at sunset - }	W. 13° 10′ N.
	Magnetic variation deduced	11 40 32 E.
July 28, 1819.	Magnetic dip at our camp	69 45

August 1st. By a series of barometrical observations made to ascertain the height of the river Bluffs, near our camp, on the Missouri, it appears that their elevation above the *bottom* is 150 feet.

Observations made at Fort Osage, Missouri.

Aug. 4, 1819.	Magnetic dip by several experi- } ments - - }	69° 18′
Aug. 5, 1819.	Meridian double altitude of } sun's lower limb - }	135° 21′ 15″
	Latitude deduced - -	39 09 40 N.
Aug. 9, 1819.	Meridian double altitude of } sun's lower limb - }	133 08 10
	Latitude deduced - -	39 09 27 N.
Latitude of Fort Osage by a mean of the pre- } ceding observations - - - }		39 09 33½ N.

Observations made at Isle Aux Vaches, (Cow Island,) Missouri river.

Aug. 19, 1819.	Meridian double altitude of } sun's lower limb - }	126° 29′
	Latitude deduced - -	39° 24′ 47″ N.

Aug. 20, 1819.	Meridian double altitude of sun's lower limb - }	125° 48′ 30″
	Latitude deduced - -	39 25 22½ N.
Latitude of Cow Island by a mean of the preceding observations - - - }		39 25 04¾ N.
	Magnetic dip at Cow Island	69 50
Aug. 22, 1819.	Magnetic azimuth of sun's centre, A. M. - - }	S. 100° 08′ E.
	Do. do. P. M. same alt.	S. 77 00 W.
	Time elapsed between the observations - - }	9ʰ 44′
	Magnetic variation deduced	11° 32′ 37″ E.

Observations at our Camp on Missouri river.

Aug. 31, 1819.	Meridian double altitude of sun's lower limb - }	117° 25′ 00″
	Latitude deduced -	39 49 01 N.

Observations at the Missouri Fur Company's Establishment, (Fort Lisa.)

Sept. 19, 1819.	Meridian double altitude of sun's lower limb - }	99° 55′ 19″
	Latitude deduced -	41 24 13 N.

OBSERVATIONS MADE AT ENGINEER CANTONMENT, THE WINTERING POST OF THE EXPLORING EXPEDITION, IN 1819—20.

Sept. 21, 1819.	Meridian double altitude of sun's lower limb - }	98° 20′ 35″
	Index error, — 40″ latitude deduced - - }	41 25 05 N.
Sept. 22, 1819.	Magnetic azimuth of sun's centre, A. M. - - }	S. 85° 55′ E.
	Do. Do. P. M. id. alt.	S. 59 45 W.
	Time elapsed between the observations - - }	8ʰ 32′
	Magnetic variation deduced	12° 58′ 49½″ E.
Sept. 22, 1819.	Meridian double altitude of sun's lower limb - }	97 33 45

Sept. 24, 1819.	Index error, — 40″ latitude deduced - - }	41° 25′ 05½″ N.
	Meridian double altitude of sun's lower limb - }	96 00 20
	Index error, — 40″ latitude deduced - - }	41° 25 00 N.
Sept. 24, 1819.	Magnetic azimuth of sun's centre, A. M. - - }	S. 85° 40′ E.
	Do. Do. P. M. id. alt.	S. 59 30 W.
	Time elapsed between observations - - }	8ʰ 34′
	Magnetic variation deduced	12° 58′ 48″ E.

Equal altitudes of Sun to find error of Time-piece, (pocket chronometer,) at noon.

	Time from Noon, A. M.	Time from Noon, P. M.	Error of Time-piece.
Sept. 24, 1819.	3ʰ 57′ 26″	3ʰ 58′ 20″ }	8′ 35″ 30‴ fast.
	3 55 55	3 56 49	Mean time.
	3 54 23½	3 55 18½ }	

	Time from Noon, A. M.	Time from Noon, P. M.	Error of Time-piece.
Sept. 25, 1819.	3ʰ 04′ 50″	3ʰ 04′ 25½″	8′ 15″ 40‴ fast.

Sept. 25, 1819.	Meridian double altitude of sun's lower limb - }	95° 13′ 10″
	Index error, — 40″ latitude deduced - - }	41 25 09 N.

Equal altitudes of Sun to find error of Time-piece, (pocket chronometer.)

	Time from Noon. A. M.	Time from Noon, P. M.	Error of Time-piece.
Sept. 26, 1819.	3ʰ 15′ 15½″	3ʰ 13′ 48½″ }	8′ 05″ 10‴ fast.
	3 13 35½	3 12 09	Mean time.
	3 11 56	3 10 30 }	

Sept. 26, 1819.	Meridian double altitude of sun's lower limb - }	94° 26′ 40″
	Index error, — 40″ latitude deduced - - }	41 24 57 N.

Equal altitudes of Sun to find error of Time-piece, (pocket chronometer.)

	Time from Noon, A. M.	Time from Noon, P. M.	Error of Time-piece.
Sept. 27, 1819.	3ʰ 35′ 11″ 3 33 35 3 32 00	3ʰ 32′ 44½″ ⎫ 3 31 09½ ⎬ 3 29 35 ⎭	7′ 55″ fast. Mean time.
Sept. 27, 1819.	Meridian double altitude of ⎱ sun's lower limb - ⎰		93° 39′ 20″
	Index error, — 40″. Latitude ⎱ deduced - - ⎰		41 25 08 N,

Equal altitudes of Sun to find error of Time-piece, (pocket chronometer.)

By large Sextant.	Time from Noon, A. M.	Time from Noon, P. M.	Error of Time-piece.
Nov. 16, 1819.	3ʰ 12′ 53″ Lost. 3 08 47	2ʰ 53′ 28″ ⎫ Lost. ⎬ 2 49 23½ ⎭	9′ 30″ 12‴ slow. Apparent time.
By small Sextant.	Time from Noon, A. M.	Time from Noon, P. M.	Error of Time-piece.
Nov. 16, 1819.	3ʰ 02′ 35½″ 3 00 28½ 2 58 20½	2ʰ 43′ 13″ ⎫ 2 41 04½ ⎬ 2 38 57½ ⎭	9′ 29″ 40‴ slow. Apparent time.
By Circle of Reflection.	Time from Noon, A. M.	Time from Noon, P. M.	Error of Time-piece.
Nov. 16, 1819.	2ʰ 45′ 16″ 2 42 58 2 40 41½	2ʰ 25′ 51½″ ⎫ 2 23 36½ ⎬ 2 21 18 ⎭	9′ 29″ 44‴ slow. Apparent time.

Error of Time-piece, by a mean of the preceding observations. Apparent time - ⎱⎰	9′ 29″ 52‴ slow.
Do. Do. Mean time - -	5 35 00 fast.

By Circle of Reflection.	Time from Noon, A. M.	Time from Noon, P. M.	Error of Time-piece.
Nov. 24, 1819.	2ʰ 46′ 26½″ 2 44 09 2 41 48	2ʰ 28′ 58″ ⎫ 2 26 41 ⎬ 2 24 20 ⎭	8′ 34″ 15‴ slow. Apparent time.
By small Sextant.	Time from Noon, A. M.	Time from Noon, P. M.	Error of Time-piece.
Nov. 24, 1819.	2ʰ 57′ 11″ 2 52 45	2ʰ 39′ 43″ 2 35 16	8′ 34″ 25‴ slow. Apparent time.

Error of Time-piece, by a mean of the preceding $\Big\}$ observations. Apparent time, - - | 8' 34" 20''' slow.

Do.   Do.   Mean time, - - | 4 35 37   fast.

Lunar distance and time correspondent, being the mean of seven observations. The farthest limb of moon from the star α. Arietis.

	Time per pocket chronom. A. M.	Distance of Moon and Star.	Index error.
Nov. 24, 1819.	8ʰ 24' 30" Baromet. 28.66	57° 41' 45" Thermomet. 40°	+ 1' 32"

Equal altitudes of Sun to find error of Time-piece, (pocket chronometer,) at noon.

	Time from Noon, A. M.	Time from Noon, P. M.	Error of Time-piece.
Nov. 26, 1819.	2ʰ 49' 21"	2ʰ 33' 23"	4' 43" fast. M. T.

At Engineer Cantonment, in latitude 41° 25' N. and longitude by account 6ʰ 23' 04" W. of Greenwich, on the 24th Nov. 1819, at 8ʰ 24' 30" P. M. civil account per chronometer, the distance of the moon's farthest limb, and the star α. Arietis, was observed to be 57° 43' 17"; to find the longitude.

Longitude deduced, 6ʰ 23' 10", or 95° 47' 30" W. of Greenwich.

Equal altitudes of Sun to find error of Time-piece, (pocket chronometer,) at midnight.

	Time before Midnight.	Time after Midnight.	Error of Time-piece.
Nov. 26, 1819.	9ʰ 24' 56" 9 22 42½ 9 20 28½	9ʰ 10' 39½" 9 08 25 9 06 11	4' 59" 34''' fast. Mean time.

Equal altitudes of Sun to find error of Time-piece, (pocket chronometer,) at noon.

	Time from Noon, A. M.	Time from Noon, P. M,	Error of Time-piece.
Nov. 27, 1819.	2ʰ 37' 07½" 2 34 43½ 2 32 16½	2ʰ 21' 49" 2 19 24½ 2 16 57	4' 43" 10''' fast. Mean time.
Nov. 27, 1819.	Meridian double altitude of sun's upper limb -		55° 33' 40"
	Index error — 16". Lat. deduced		41 25 08 N.

Nov. 27. Index errors of sextant when glasses of different shades were used as skreens before the speculum and horizon glasses, were observed to day, as follows :

The darkest shades but one, being placed before both reflectors the index error was — 16''.

The lightest shade but one being placed before the horizon glass, and no shade before the index speculum, the index error was, + 1' 32''.

The eye glass of the telescope being shaded, and no shade before either of the reflectors, the index error was, + 17''.

On the evening of the 27th Nov. at 5ʰ 50' 46'' per time-piece, (pocket chronometer,) observed an emersion of Jupiter's first satellite. The sky very clear, and the belts of Jupiter distinct for the magnifying power of the telescope, to find the longitude.

Longitude deduced, 6ʰ 22' 43'' or 95° 40' 45'' W. of Greenwich.

Equal altitudes of Sun to find error of Time-piece, (pocket chronometer,) at midnight.

	Time before Midnight.	Time after Midnight.	Error of Time-piece.
Nov. 27, 1819.	9ʰ 33' 49'' 9 31 28 9 29 09	9ʰ 20' 09'' 9 17 49 9 15 29½	} 4' 54'' 35''' fast. Mean time.
Nov. 27, 1819.	Meridian double altitude of the star Sirius -	}	64° 15' 40''
	Index error + 17''. Lat. deduced		41 25 10 N.

Equal altitudes of Sun to find error of Time-piece, (pocket chronometer,) at noon.

	Time from Noon, A. M.	Time from Noon, P. M.	Error of Time-piece.
Nov. 28, 1819.	2ʰ 44' 30'' 2 42 12 2 39 53	2ʰ 29' 44'' 2 27 26 2 25 07	} 4' 39'' 40''' fast. Mean time.

Equal altitudes of Sun to find error of Time-piece, (pocket chrometer,) at midnight.

	Time before midnight	Time after midnight.	Error of Time-piece.
Nov. 28, 1819.	9ʰ 34' 57'' 9 32 34 9 30 13	9ʰ 21' 59½'' 9 19 38 9 17 16½	} ·5' 00'' 15''' fast. Mean time.

Equal altitudes of Sun to find error of Time-piece, (pocket chronometer,) at noon.

	Time from Noon, A. M.	Time from Noon, P. M.	Error of Time-piece.
Dec. 3, 1819.	2ʰ 31′ 15″ 2 28 44 2 26 13	2ʰ 21′ 40″ 2 19 10 2 16 37	} 5′ 23″ 24‴ fast. Mean time.

Equal altitudes of Sun to find error of Time-piece, (pocket chronometer,) at midnight.

	Time before midnight.	Time after midnight.	Error of Time-piece.
Dec. 3, 1819.	9ʰ 32′ 12″ 9 29 49 9 27 26	9ʰ 24′ 17½″ 9 21 56½ 9 19 32	} 5′ 43″ 30‴ fast. Mean time.

Equal altitudes of Sun to find error of Time-piece, (pocket chronometer,) at noon.

	Time from Noon, A. M.	Time from Noon, P. M.	Error of Time-piece.
Dec. 4, 1819.	2ʰ 40′ 28″ 2 38 03½ 2 35 42½	2ʰ 32′ 02½″ 2 29 41 2 27 15½	} 5′ 34″ 07‴ fast. Mean time.

Rate of Time-piece, (pocket chronometer,) at Engineer Cantonment, between the 24th September and the 4th December, as deduced from the preceding observations.

		Fast for mean time.				Var. for 12 hours.		
Sept. 24, 1819, at noon.			8′	35″	30‴	9″	55‴	losing.
„ 25 „	do	do	8	15	40	5	15	do
„ 26 „	do	do	8	05	10	5	05	do
„ 27 „	do	do	7	55	00	1	24	do
Nov. 16 „	do	do	5	35	00	3	42	do
„ 24 „	do	do	4	35	37	1	51	gaining.
„ 26 „	do	do	4	43	00	16	34	do
„ „ „	at midnight.	do	4	59	34	16	24	losing.
„ 27 „	at noon.	do	4	43	10	11	25	gaining.
„ „ „	at midnight.	do	4	54	35	14	55	losing.
„ 28 „	at noon.	do	4	39	40	20	35	gaining.
„ „ „	at midnight.	do	5	00	15	23	09	do
Dec. 3 „	at noon.	do	5	23	24	20	06	do
„ „ „	at midnight.	do	5	43	30	9	23	losing.
„ 4 „	at noon.	do	5	34	07			

During the time for which the rate of the pocket chronometer was determined as above shown, it was kept suspended in the cabin of the steam boat, which, during the day was kept warm by fire, generally as high as the *temperate point*, and sometimes above it. At night the temperature of the cabin was generally near the freezing point, and particularly, in the latter part of November, the thermometer varied from 2° to 22° below freezing, according to Fahrenheit's scale. The chronometer was, moreover, wound up every morning at nearly the same hour.

Dec. 9, 1819.	Meridian double altitude of sun's upper limb -	52° 08' 45''
Dec. 15, 1819.	Index error, — 45''. Latitude deduced - -	41 25 00 **N.**
	Meridian double altitude of sun's upper limb -	51 13 30
	Index error, — 30''. Latitude deduced - -	41 25 00 **N.**

Equal altitudes of Sun to find error of Time-piece, (box chronometer,) at noon.

	Time from Noon, A. M.	Time from Noon, P. M.	Error of Time-piece.
Dec. 17, 1819.	2ʰ 36' 41½'' 2 34 21	2ʰ 43' 51½'' 2 41 31	7' 21'' fast. Mean time.
Dec. 19, 1819.	Meridian double altitude of sun's upper limb -		50° 55' 00''
	Index error, — 40''. Latitude deduced - -		41 25 01 N.

Equal altitudes of Sun to find error of Time-piece, (box chronometer,) at noon.

	Time from Noon, A. M.	Time from Noon, P. M.	Error of Time-piece.
Dec. 19, 1819,	2ʰ 11' 54'' 2 09 06 2 06 20½	2ʰ 14' 05'' 2 11 21 2 08 33½	3' 52'' fast. Mean time.

Equal altitudes of Sun to find error of Time-piece, (box chronometer,) at midnight.

	Time before midnight.	Time after midnight.	Error of Time-piece.
Dec. 19, 1819.	9ʰ 33' 17'' 9 30 46 9 28 17	9ʰ 34' 25½'' 9 31 56 9 29 26	3' 02'' 22''' fast. Mean time.

Equal altitudes of the star Capella, (α. Aurigæ,) to find the error of Time-piece, (box chronometer,) at the time of the star's transit over the meridian.

	Time before transit by astronomical account.	Double altitudes of star Capella.	Time after transit by astronomical account.
Dec. 19, 1819.	6ʰ 46′ 41″ 33‴	85° 10′ 00″	15ʰ 42′ 35″ 46‴
	Error of Time-piece deduced for mean time -		5′ 06″ 47‴ fast.

These observations are a mean of nine sets of altitudes, taken under favourable circumstances.

The variation of the Time-piece, (box chronometer,) between the noon and midnight of the 19th December, by equal altitudes of the sun as above, is found to be 49″ 38‴ losing. Taking this as its rate in twelve hours, and supposing it to possess a perfectly uniform motion, by making a proportion for its error at the time of Capella's transit over the meridian, it would appear to be 3′ 05″ 33‴ fast for mean time: but its error at that time is found by observation to be 3′ 06″ 47‴, making a difference of 1″ 14‴ from a truly uniform rate in the space of 11ʰ 14′ 02$\frac{1}{3}$″ of time. This difference is not more than might reasonably be attributed to errors of observations in the two sets of equal altitudes.

Double altitudes of the star Rigel, (β. Orionis,) observed when near the meridian, together with the correct times before and after the transit—to find the latitude.

	True times before and after Rigel's transit.	Numbers from table 33d of Bowditch's Navig.	Double altitudes of Rigel.
Dec. 19, 1819.	0ʰ 07′ 10″	51.4	80° 18′ 30″
	0 5 34	31.0	80 19 45
	0 4 21	18.9	80 21 15
	0 3 20	11.1	80 22 10
	0 1 18	1.7	80 22 30
	0 0 17	0.1	80 23 00
	0 2 04	4.3	80 21 00
	0 4 46	22.7	80 21 00
	0 7 20	53.8	80 18 45
	0 8 27	71.4	80 17 00
	Mean	26.64	80 20 29$\frac{1}{2}$
	Latitude deduced		41 25 00 **N.**
Dec. 20, 1819.	Meridian double altitude of sun's upper limb -		50° 52′ 50″
	Index error —1′ 04″. Lat. deduc.		41 25 04 **N.**

Dec. 20, 1819. An emersion of Jupiter's first satellite was observed at 6ʰ 03′ 15″ P. M. per box chronometer. Some flying clouds. Sky about Jupiter clear. Error and rate of Time-piece computed agreeably to the results before stated : to find the longitude.

Longitude deduced 6ʰ 22′ 42″ 22‴, or 95° 40′ 35½″ W. from Greenwich.

Equal altitudes of Capella, (α. Aurigœ,) to find the error of box chronometer at the time of Capella's transit over the meridian.

	Time before transit by astronomical account.	Double altitudes of Capella.	Time after transit by astronomical account.
Dec. 23, 1819.	7ʰ 12′ 54″	101° 21′ 26″	14ʰ 32′ 02″
	Chronometer slow for mean time,	0	3 21

The foregoing is a mean of seven observations.

Dec. 23, 1819. An emersion of Jupiter's second satellite was observed at 6ʰ 32′ 25″ P. M. per Time-piece, (box chronometer.) Sky very clear.—Belts of Jupiter distinct. Thermometer 1° below zero, of Fahrenheit's scale. Error and rate of Time-piece to be estimated as before ;—to find the longitude.

Longitude deduced 6ʰ 22′ 33″, or 95° 38′ 15″ W. of Greenwich.

Equal altitudes of Sun to find error of Time-piece, (box chronometer,) at noon.

	Time from Noon, A. M.	Time from Noon, P. M.	Error of Time-piece.
Dec. 24, 1819.	2ʰ 40′ 13½″	2ʰ 31′ 10½″	4′ 17″ 30‴ slow. Mean time.
	2 37 48	2 28 44½	
	2 35 22	2 26 18	

Equal altitudes of Sun to find error of Time-piece,) box chronometer,) at midnight.

	Time before midnight.	Time after midnight.	Error of Time-piece.
Dec. 24, 1819.	9ʰ 33′ 42″	9ʰ 23′ 25″	5′ 09″ slow. Mean time.
	9 31 15½	9 20 59	
	9 28 49½	9 18 33½	

The following is a mean of ten lunar distances from Sun, for calculating the longitude at Engineer Cantonment.

	Time of observation, P. M.	Distance of nearest limbs.	Index error.
Dec. 24, 1919.	1ʰ 53′ 43″	101° 42′ 58″	+ 15″
	Barometer 28.85	Thermomet. 19°	

Rate and error of Time-piece to be estimated from the foregoing observations.

Longitude deduced 6^h 22′ 56″, or 95° 44′ 00″ W. of Greenwich.

Equal altitudes of Sun to find error of Time-piece, (box chronometer,) at noon.

	Time from Noon, A. M.	Time from Noon, P. M.	Error of Time-piece.
Dec. 26, 1819,	2^h 38′ 24½″ 2 35 56 2 33 27	2^h 24′ 33″ 2 22 06 2 19 36	} 7′ 42″ 14‴ slow. Mean time.

A mean of nine lunar distances from star Markab, (α. Pegasi,) for calculating the longitude.

	Time of observation per Time-piece, P. M.	Distance of Star and Moon's nearest limb.	Index error.
Dec. 26, 1819.	9^h 05′ 09″ Baromet. 28.60	54° 24′ 45″ Thermomet. 28°	+ 1′ 05″

Error and rate of Time-piece to be estimated as before.

Longitude deduced 6^h 23′ 03″, or 95° 45′ 45″ W. of Greenwich.

Equal altitudes of Sun to find error of Time-piece, (box chronometer,) at noon.

	Time from Noon, A. M.	Time from Noon, P. M.	Error of Time-piece.
Jan. 3, 1820.	2^h 46′ 33½″ 2 44 04 2 41 36	2^h 14′ 33″ 2 12 06 2 09 37	} 20′ 41″ 39‴ slow. Mean time.

A mean of six lunar distances, star Pollux, (β. Geminorum,) from farthest limb of Moon, for calculating the longitude.

	Time of observation, P. M.	Distance of Moon and Star.	Index error.
Jan. 4, 1820.	11^h 35′ 32″ Baromet. 29.05	46° 38′ 36″ Thermomet. 18°	+ 50″

Error and rate of Time-piece to be estimated from the equal altitudes next following.

Longitude deduced 6^h 23″ 34″, or 95° 53′ 30″ W. of Greenwich.

Equal altitudes of Sun to find error of Time-piece, (box chronometer,) at noon.

	Time from Noon, A. M.	Time from Noon, P. M.	Error of Time-piece.
Jan. 5, 1820.	3^h 02′ 41″ 3 00 23 2 58 06	2^h 25′ 46″ 2 23 27½ 2 21 09	} 24′ 08″ 39‴ slow. Mean time.

	Time from Noon, A. M.	Time from Noon, P. M.	Error of Time-piece.
Jan. 7, 1820.	3ʰ 06′ 40″ 3 04 24 3 02 05	2ʰ 24′ 57″ 2 22 40 2 20 23 }	27′ 23″ slow. Mean time.

On the 15th January the box chronometer ran down. In the afternoon it was again wound up and re-adjusted by a watch whose error was not known.

January 25. A trigonometrical measurement was this day made to ascertain the height of the hills near Engineer Cantonment, above the low-water mark of the Missouri.

The altitude of the highest hill, as deduced from this measurement, is 275 feet above low-water mark.

Equal altitudes of Sun to find error of Time-piece, (box chronometer.)

	Time from Noon, A. M.	Time from Noon, P. M.	Error of Time-piece.
Feb. 20, 1820.	2ʰ 51′ 44″ 2 49 55½ 2 48 06	3ʰ 43′ 56″ 3 42 09 3 40 20 }	11′ 43½″ fast. Mean time.

	Time before midnight.	Time after midnight.	Error of Time-piece.
Feb. 20, 1820.	8ʰ 19′ 40″ 8 17 51 8 16 03	9ʰ 08′ 19½″ 9 06 32 9 04 44 }	10′ 43″ 50‴ fast. Mean time.

A mean of ten lunar distances, between the nearest limbs of sun and moon, and of the times correspondent.

	Time of observation, P. M.	Distance of Sun and Moon.	Index error.
Feb. 20, 1820.	1ʰ 50′ 55″ Baromet. 28.84	88° 45′ 56″ Thermomet. 36°	— 28″

Allowance to be made for error and variation of time-piece.

Longitude deduced 6ʰ 22′ 43″ or 95° 40′ 45″ W. of Greenwich.

March 20, 1820.	Meridian double altitude of sun's lower limb, (small sextant) - - - }	96° 47′ 15″
	Index error — 4′ 07″. Latitude deduced - - }	41 25 07 N.

April 2, 1820. In order to ascertain the perpendicular fall of the Missouri in a given distance, I measured accurately on a straight

edge of the shore, two distances of 400 yards each, in the same right line, and, with a leveling instrument well adjusted and placed at the point from which the distances were measured in opposite directions, found the difference of apparent level between this middle point and the station at the end of the line looking down the river to be 3.5 inches. Then turning the instrument round and again adjusting its level, found the difference of apparent level between the middle point and the station at the end of the other line, looking up the river, to be 4.75 inches. A mean of the two gives for the difference of apparent level in 400 yards - - - - 4.125 inches.
Difference of true and apparent level, in do. .411 inches, subtractive.

Perpendicular fall of Missouri in 400 yards 3.714 inches.

The perpendicular fall of the Missouri agreeably to the foregoing estimate is 16.341 inches per mile.

The difference in the apparent levels, obtained by the two observations as above, may be attributed to the effect of terrestrial refraction, which in the first instance would have a tendency to diminish the difference of apparent level, and in the second, to augment it. It was in order to correct this effect of refraction, and also any imperceptible errors in the adjustment of the instrument, that the method was adopted of making two observations, in contrary directions, from a fixed point. The instrument made use of was provided with a spirit level 9 inches in length, and an excellent telescope which magnified about thirty times.

The observations were made after the spring flood had commenced, and when the surface of the river was thirteen feet above the low-water mark.

RESULTS OF THE OBSERVATIONS MADE AT ENGINEER CANTONMENT.

Rate of Time-piece, (box chronometer,) between the 17th *December,* 1819, *and the* 7th *of January,* 1820, *as determined by equal altitudes.*

				Variation of Time-piece for every 12 hours.
1819. Dec. 17.	Chronometer fast for mean time at noon	7' 21" 00'''		
				52" 15''' losing.
19.	Do. do. -	3 52 00		49 38 do.
,,	Do. do. at midnight	3 02 22		
				48 27 do.
23.	Do. slow for mean time at 10ʰ 56' 19½"	3 21 00		
				51 53 do.
24.	Do. do. at noon	4 17 30		51 30 do.
,,	Do. do. at midnight	5 09 00		51 04 do.
26.	Do. do. at noon	7 42 14		
1820.				48 42 do.
Jan. 3.	Do. do. do.	20 41 39		51 45 do.
5.	Do. do. do.	24 08 39		48 35 do.
7.	Do. do. do.	27 23 00		

Magnetic variation and dip at Engineer Cantonment.

Sept. 22, 1819.	The magnetic variation was observed to be -	12° 58′ 49½″	**E.**
24,	Do. do. -	12 58 48	**E.**
	Magnetic variation by a mean of the above -	12 58 48¾	**E.**

Jan. 7, 1820. Magnetic dip by several observations│ 71° 07½′

Latitude of Engineer Cantonment.

Sept. 21, 1819.	By double meridian altitude of sun - - -	41° 25′ 05″	N.
22,	Do. Do.	41 25 05½	N.
24,	Do. Do.	41 25 00	N.
25,	Do. Do.	41 25 09	N.
26,	Do. Do.	41 24 57	N.
27,	Do. Do.	41 25 08	N.
Nov. 27,	Do. Do.	41 25 08	N.
,,	By double meridian altitude of star Sirius - -	41 25 10	N.
Dec. 9,	By double meridian altitude of sun - - -	41 25 00	N.
15,	Do. Do.	41 25 00	N.
19,	Do. Do.	41 25 01	N.
,,	By double altitudes of Rigel and apparent times	41 25 00	N.
20,	By double meridian altitude of sun - - -	41 25 04	N.
March 20, 1820.	Do. Do.	41 25 07	N.
	Mean latitude deduced from the above	41 25 03.9	N.

Longitude of Engineer Cantonment from the meridian of the Royal Observatory at Greenwich.

Nov. 24, 1819.	By lunar distances from α. Arietis	95° 47′ 30″	W.
27,	By an emersion of Jupiter's first satellite - -	95 40 45	**W.**
Dec. 20,	Do. do.	95 40 35½	W.
23,	Do. of Jupiter's second satellite	95 38 15	W.
24,	By lunar distances from the sun	95 44 00	W.
26,	Do. from α. Pegasi -	95 45 45	W.
Jan. 4, 1820.	Do. from β. Geminorum	95 53 30	W.
Feb. 20,	Do. from the sun -	95 40 45	W.
	Mean of the preceding results	95 43 53	W.

Observations made at the mouth of the river Platte.

Feb. 29, 1820.	Meridian double altitude of star Sirius, (α. Canis majoris) }	65° 03′ 45″
	Index error — 4′ 10″. Latitude deduced - - }	41 03 11 N.
March 1, 1820.	Meridian double altitude of sun's upper limb - }	83 44 30
	Index error — 4′ 10″. Latitude deduced - - }	41 03 18 N.
March 2, 1820.	Meridian double altitude of sun's lower limb - }	83 25 20
	Index error — 4′ 00″. Latitude deduced - - }	41 03 16 N.
March 3, 1820.	Meridian double altitude of sun's lower limb - }	84 11 45
	Index error — 4′ 00″. Latitude deduced - - }	41 03 07 N.
Latitude of the mouth of river Platte by a mean of the preceding results - - }		41 03 13 N.

The foregoing observations were made with the sextant of 5 inches radius, and at the most northern point of the junction of the river Platte with the Missouri. The difference of latitude of the two shores is about one minute. For further remarks and observations at this place, see the Meteorological Register for the month of March.

At the mouth of Elk-horn river tributary to the Platte, the following observation was made for the latitude.

March 7, 1820.	Meridian double altitude of sun's lower limb - }	87° 00′ 00″
	Index error— 4′ 15″. Latitude deduced - - }	41 12 00 N.

On the 12th of April, trigonometrical observations were made in conjunction with Lieut. Andrew Talcott of the corps of Engineers, to ascertain the height of the bluffs near the pond on the Boyer river, 1½ miles above its junction with the Missouri. From these observations, which were made with the utmost care and precision, it appears that the elevation of the bluff above the surface of the pond is 335.29 feet. The bluff of which the height is found as above, is visible on the opposite side of the river from Engineer Cantonment, and is supposed to be the highest hill in the neighbourhood of the Council Bluff. By adding 15 feet, which is about the height of the pond above the low-water mark of the Missouri river, we shall have 350 feet for the height of the top of the bluff above the low-water mark of this part of the Missouri.

At the point where the Missouri bluffs cross the Boyer river, the following observations were made to find the latitude.

April 17, 1820.	Meridian double altitude of sun's lower limb -	117° 45' 10''
	Index error — 3' 51''. Latitude deduced - -	41 32 23 N.

By Lieut. Talcott with a theodolite of 4½ inches radius.

April 17, 1820.	Meridian altitude of sun's upper limb	59° 23' 00''
	Do. of sun's lower limb	58 50 45
	Latitude deduced - -	41 32 07 N.
Mean of the preceding observations -		41 32 15 N.

On the Elk-horn river 20'' of latitute south of the fording place on the trace from the Council Bluff to the Pownee Villages, the following observations were made.

April 21, 1810.	Meridian double altitude of sun's lower limb -	120° 43' 15''
	Index error — 3' 55''. Latitude deduced - -	41 26 16 N.

By Lieut. Talcott, at the same place.

April 21, 1820.	Meridian double altitude of sun's upper limb -	121° 41' 40''
	Index error + 2' 00''. Latitude deduced - -	41 25 58 N.
Mean latitude by the preceding observations		41 26 07 N.

Observations made at the village of the Republican Pawnees, situated on the Loup Fork of the river Platte.

April 29, 1820.	Meridian double altitude of star Polaris, (α. Ursæ Minoris)	79° 21' 45''
	Index error — 4' 00''. Latitude deduced - -	41 16 43 N.

April 29, 1820.	Meridian double altitude of star Spicæ Virginis -	77° 05' 15''
	Index error — 4' 00''. Latitude deduced - -	41 17 23 N.
Latitude of the village by a mean of the preceding observations - - - -		41 17 03 N.

Note.—The village of the Republican Pawnees, is situated between the villages of the Grand Pawnees and the Loup Pawnees, being 2¾ miles east of the latter, and 4 miles W. S. W. of the former. For a particular and interesting account of these villages, the manners and customs of their inhabitants, &c. reference must be had to the manuscripts of Capt. Bell and Dr. Say, journalists of the expedition. The latitude of one of the villages last mentioned was determined by Lieut. Talcott, at the time of our visit there with Major O'Fallon, U. S. Agent, but I did not obtain from him the result of his observations.

Observations made at the confluence of the Mississippi and Missouri rivers.

July 10, 1820.	Meridian double altitude of star Altair, (α. Aquilæ)	119° 05' 30''
	Index error + 37''. Latitude deduced - - -	38 51 37 N.
July 11, 1820.	Meridian double altitude of star Altair, (α. Aquilæ)	119 05 00
	Index error + 37''. Latitude deduced - -	38 51 52 N.
Sept. 12, 1820.	Meridian double altitude of sun's upper limb -	110 53 00
	Index error + 22''. Latitude deduced - -	38 51 37 N.
Sept 14, 1820.	Meridian double altitude of sun's lower limb -	108 17 30
	Index error + 22''. Latitude deduced - - -	38 51 30 N.
Latitude of the mouth of the Missouri by a mean of the above - - -		38 51 39

Equal altitudes of Sun to find error of Time-piece, (box chrono-meter,) at noon.

	Time from Noon, A. M.	Time from Noon, P. M.	Error of Time-piece.
Sept. 14, 1820.	3ʰ 08′ 57″ 3 07 23 3 05 49	2ʰ 48′ 59″ 2 47 25 2 45 51	5′ 07″ slow. Mean time.
Sept. 15, 1820.	3ʰ 14′ 23″ 3 12 49 3 11 16	2ʰ 49′ 43″ 2 48 09 2 46 34	7′ 08″ slow. Mean time.

A mean of seven lunar observations, distance of nearest limbs of sun and moon—taken at the mouth of the Missouri.

	Time of observa-tion, P. M.	Distance of Sun and Moon.	Index error.
Sept. 15, 1820.	4ʰ 20′ 25″ Baromet. 29.02	93° 57′ 08″ Thermomet. 72°	+ 27″

Allowance to be made for error and rate of time-piece, as usual.
Longitude deduced, 5ʰ 59′ 48″, or 89° 57′ W. of Greenwich.

The longitude of the mouth of the Missouri as above is 89° 57′ W. of Greenwich; and the longitude of St. Louis deduced from a set of lunar observations on the 16th of June, 1819, (see page 10,) is 90° 06′ 15″ W. of the same meridian. The observations at both places were made with the same instruments, and under equally favourable circumstances, they are accordingly entitled to the same weight as respects accuracy. But by a traverse of the river between the two places, a distance of 18 miles, the mouth of the Missouri is found to be only 1′ 55″ of longitude E. of St. Louis. Now by taking a mean between the two results deduced from observations, and in one case adding, and in the other subtracting 57½ = half the difference of longitude by the traverse, the following results will be obtained, entitled to double the confidence of the result of either of the lunar observations above mentioned individually considered, viz :

Longitude of St. Louis, agreeably to this estimate | 90° 02′ 35″ W.
*Do.   of mouth of the Missouri   - | 90 00 40 W.

Observations made at the confluence of the De Moyen and Mississippi rivers.

Aug. 8, 1820.	Meridian double altitude of star Altair, (α. Aquilæ) }	116° 05′ 45″
	Index error + 22″. Latitude deduced - }	40 21 43 N.

* Remarkable that the mouth of this greatest tributary in the world is just one-fourth the circumference of the earth in degrees, west of the great Greenwich observatory.

Aug. 9, 1820.	Meridian double altitude of star Altair - -	116° 05' 30''
	Index error + 22''. Latitude deduced - -	40 21 50 N.
Aug. 12, 1820.	Meridian double altitude of star Altair - -	116 05 20
	Index error + 22''. Latitude deduced - - -	40 21 55 N.
Aug. 13, 1820.	Meridian double altitude of star Altair - -	116 05 40
	Index error + 22''. Latitude deduced - -	40 21 45 N.
Aug. 14, 1820.	Meridian double altitude of star Altair - -	116 05 30
	Index error + 22''. Latitude deduced - -	40 21 48 N.
Mean latitude of the mouth of De Moyen river deduced from the preceding results		40 21 48 N.

Observations made at the confluence of the Illinois and Mississippi Rivers.

Equal altitudes of Sun to find error of Time-piece, (box chronometer,) at noon.

	Time from Noon, A. M.	Time from Noon, P. M.	Error of Time-piece.
Aug. 31, 1820.	2ʰ 40' 09'' 2 38 32½ 2 36 56	2ʰ 14' 35'' 2 12 58 2 11 21	12' 38'' slow. Mean time.
Aug. 31, 1820.	Meridian double altitude of star Altair, (α. Aquilæ)		118° 52' 30''
	Index error + 22''. Lat. deduced		38 58 19 N.

Equal altitudes of Sun to find error of Time-piece, (box chronometer,) at noon.

	Time from Noon, A. M.	Time from Noon, P. M.	Error of Time-piece.
Sept. 2, 1820.	3ʰ 15' 57'' 3 14 27 3 12 57	2ʰ 41' 18'' 2 39 48 2 38 18	16' 32'' slow. Mean time.

Equal altitudes of Sun to find error of Time-piece, at midnight.

	Time before midnight.	Time after midnight.	Error of Time-piece.
Sept. 2, 1820.	9ʰ 21′ 42″ 9 20 12 9 18 42	8ʰ 46′ 15″ 8 44 44 8 43 13½ }	17′ 42″ slow. Mean time.
Sept. 2, 1820.	Meridian double altitude of star Altair - }		118° 52′ 15″
	Index error + 22″. Lat. deduced		38 58 27 N.

Equal altitudes of Sun to find error of Time-piece, at midnight.

	Time before midnight.	Time after midnight.	Error of Time-piece.
Sept. 3, 1820.	9ʰ 00′ 08½″ 8 58 40½ 8 57 14	8ʰ 19′ 56″ 8 18 31 8 17 04 }	19′ 38″ slow. Mean time.
Latitude of the mouth of Illinois river, by a mean of the observations made at that place on the 21st of August and on the 2d of September, 1820,			38° 58′ 23″ N.

On the 3d of August, 1820, an immersion of Jupiter's third satellite was observed at 8ʰ 10′ 40″ P. M. per time-piece. Also an immersion of Jupiter's first satellite was observed at 13ʰ 16′ per time-piece—to find the longitude. Allowance to be made for the error and variation of time-piece, agreeably to the foregoing results, from equal altitudes.

Longitude deduced from the immersion of Jupiter's third satellite - - - - }	90° 15′ 30″ W.
Do. do. first do. - - -	90 20 30 W.
Mean longitude west of Greenwich - -	90 18

Observations made at Cape Girardeau, on the Mississippi.

Oct. 15, 1820.	Meridian double altitude of sun's upper limb - }	88° 33′ 30″
	Index error + 23″. Lat. deduced	37 18 48 N.
Oct. 16, 1820.	Meridian double altitude of sun's lower limb - }	86 45 15
	Index error + 23″. Lat. deduced	37 18 37 N.

Oct. 18, 1820.	Meridian double altitude of sun's lower limb -	85° 17' 40''
	Index error + 23''. Lat. deduced	37 18 31 N.
Latitude of Cape Girardeau by a mean of the above observations - - -		37 18 39 N.

I had, about the middle of October, observed a series of equal altitudes of the sun for determining the error and rate of the chronometer, with a view to ascertain the longitude by the eclipses of Jupiter's satellites, several of which I found would occur during my stay at this place. I had on the nights of the 14th and 20th prepared the telescope to observe emersions of the first and second satellites, but had the mortification to be baffled in my designs in both instances by Jupiter's becoming obscured by clouds before the time for the emersions to take place. For some time after my arrival here, I was unable to make observations of any kind, owing to the debilitated state to which I was reduced by a severe attack of bilious remitting fever, which harassed me the greater part of two months previous.

From astronomical observations made by the late professor Andrew Ellicott, in 1796-7, connected with others which were afterwards made by Don Jose Joaquin de Ferrer, a Spanish astronomer, the longitude of the confluence of the Ohio and Mississippi rivers is fixed at 5^h 55' 38''.1 or 88° 54' 31½'' W. of Greenwich ;* and by a traverse of part of the Mississippi made by Major S. H. Long of the United States' Topographical Engineers, in 1817, Cape Girardeau is laid down 22' 28½'' W. of the mouth of the Ohio. By connecting the positions in longitude of these two points, we shall obtain for the longitude of Cape Girardeau 89° 17' W. of Greenwich, which probably deserves as much confidence as a single observation made at the Cape would be entitled to.

Observations for Latitude made in the old Spanish Fort at Natchez.

Nov. 20, 1820.	Meridian double altitude of sun's upper limb -	77° 52' 20''
	Index error — 4'. Latitude deduced - -	31 33 45 N.

The position of this place, both in latitude and longitude was accurately determined by the late professor Ellicott in 1797-8, while acting as our commissioner for determining the boundary between the United States and the Spanish Possessions in North America. By twenty-three observations of the zenith distances of three stars made with a zenith sector, the face of the sector being sometimes to the east and sometimes to the west, he obtained for the latitude 31° 33' 48'' N. It is perhaps the best method of testing the accuracy of in-

---

* Ellicott's Journal, p. 119, Philadelphia, 1803.

struments, to make observations with them at places whose positions have been carefully determined by experienced and eminent observers; and when we find a coincidence in the results, it tends to increase our confidence in the observations we may have made with the same instruments on other occasions. So near a coincidence, however, as exists between the latitude as stated above, and that deduced from professor Ellicott's observations, must be considered in some measure as fortuitous. So correct a result could not, under the most favourable circumstances, be expected from a single observation with a sextant whose graduations were limited to half-minutes of a degree.

END OF PART I.

PART II.

Containing the Calculations of Observations made by Major Long and Lieutenant Swift, on a tour from the Council Bluffs on the Missouri river, westward along the river Platte to its head waters in the Rocky Mountains,—thence southwardly to the head waters of the Arkansa and Canadian rivers,—and down said rivers to Belle Point, performed in 1820, under the command of Major S. H. Long, of the United States' Topographical Engineers.

Note.—The instruments used in making the following astronomical observations, were a portable sextant of 5 inches radius, graduated by the assistance of the vernier to 30″, made by Cary, London, accompanied by a mercurial artificial horizon with a glass frame, and an excellent patent-lever watch, by Robert Roskell.

Camp on the river Platte, at the fording place of the Pawnee Indians, twenty-seven miles below the confluence of the North and South, or Padouca Forks.

June 20, 1820.	Meridian altitude of sun's lower limb - -	72° 23′
	Extent of horizon, (a level sheet of water) -	700 yards.
	Height of observer's eye above horizon - - -	3½ feet.
	Index error — 4′ 15″. Latitude deduced - - -	40° 59′ 15″ N.

Equal altitudes of Sun to find error of Watch.

	Time from Noon, A. M.	Time from Noon, P. M.	Error of Watch.
June 20, 1820.	2ʰ 32′ 26″ 2 29 36	2ʰ 32′ 34″ 2 29 46	1′ 15″ fast. Mean time.

Camp on the Platte, thirty-two miles below the point where it issues from the Rocky Mountains.

| July 4, 1820. | Meridian double altitude of star Antaris, (α. Scorpii) | 48° 10′ 00″ |
| | Index error — 3′ 45″. Latitude deduced   -   -   - | 39° 57′ 40″ N. |

Observations made on the River Platte, seven minutes of latitude south of the Camp of July 4th.

Equal altitudes of Sun to find error of watch, at noon.

	Time from Noon, A. M.	Time from Noon, P. M.	Error of Watch.
July 5, 1820.	2ʰ 30′ 19″ 2 28 57 2 27 30	2ʰ 21′ 17″ 2 19 55 2 18 22	} 8′ 41″ slow. Mean time.

A mean of eight lunar distances from sun and times correspondent, to find the longitude. Latitude by account 39° 50′ 40″ N. Assumed longitude 7ʰ 01′ W.

	Time per Watch, A. M.	Distance of nearest limbs.	Index error.
July 5, 1820.	7ʰ 33′ 07″	56° 09′ 26″	— 4′

Daily variation of watch 1′ 41″ losing.

Longitude deduced, 7ʰ 01′ 23″, or 105° 20′ 45″ W. of Greenwich.

Camp at the base of the Rocky Mountains.

July 8, 1820.	Meridian double altitude of Antares - - }	49° 17′ 30″
	Index error — 3′ 45″. Latitude deduced - - }	39 23 52 N.
July 9, 1820.	Meridian double altitude of Antares - - }	49 18 15
	Index error — 3′ 45″. Latitude deduced - - }	39 23 29 N.
	Mean latitude of the camp	39 23 40 N.

At our camp on Boiling-spring Creek, at the distance of about 25 miles from James's Peak, (the same designated by Pike as the highest peak,) trigonometrical observations were made for determining the height of the peak above the level of the adjacent country. A base of 1048½ feet was accurately measured, and angles taken at its extremities, to ascertain another side of the triangle, to serve as a base to determine the height of the mountain. The angles at the extremities of the primary base, corrected for the index error of sextant, were 104° 32′ 15″ and 65° 28′ 45″—and the extent of the secondary base as found by calculation, 133372.5 feet. The angles taken at the extremities of the secondary base, included between that line and the lines of vision, to an object distinctly visible at the summit of the peak, were 96° 21′ 15″ and 81° 17′ 45″, corrected as above. The angle of elevation of the top of the peak, observed at the extremity of the secondary base, most remote from the peak, was 3° 41′ 15″, corrected also for index error of sextant. The final result of these observations, gives for the height of the peak above the plain in which the observations were made, 8507½ feet.

In order to ascertain with precision, the angle of elevation of the summit of the peak, an artificial horizon of water was employed, and the double angle of elevation observed. The angle of elevation as it stands corrected for refraction, is 3° 39′ 26″. The estimate as above gives the height of the peak above the true level of the place of observation, no correction having been made for the spherical figure of the earth.

Allowing the perpendicular fall of the river Platte, from the mountains to its mouth, to be on an average nineteen inches per mile, (which appears reasonable from the rapidity of its current compared with that of the Missouri,) the fall of the Missouri from the place where it receives the Platte to its mouth, to be 16 inches per mile, which agrees with the result from *leveling* at Engineer Cantonment—and that of the Mississippi from the mouth of the Missouri to the Gulf of Mexico to be 12 inches per mile, it would give for the height of the Platte at the base of the mountains, say at the place of the above observations, 3000 feet above the level of the ocean, and consequently the height of James's Peak would be 11507½ above the same level.

This mountain was clothed in snow for a considerable distance below its summit, when the exploring party visited it, in the middle of July, and at the same time they experienced excessive heat at its base.

Observations made on the Arkansa, at our camp, situated about twenty-five miles below the point where the river issues from the mountains.

Equal altitudes of Sun to find error of watch, at noon.

	Time from Noon, A. M.	Time from Noon, P. M.	Error of Watch.
July 17, 1820.	3ʰ 27′ 17″ 3 25 58 3 24 36	3ʰ 08′ 35″ 3 07 15 3 05 54 }	15′ 03″ slow. Mean time.
July 17, 1820.	Meridian double altitude of } Antares - - } Index error — 3′ 22″. Latitude } deduced - - }		51° 28′ 38 18 19 N.

A mean of eight lunar observations. Distance of nearest limbs of sun and moon for calculating the longitude.

	Time per Watch, P. M.	Distance of Sun and Moon.	Index Error.
July 17, 1820.	3ʰ 26′ 49″	84° 08′ 30″	— 3′ 22″

Assumed longitude 7^h 01' west.   Allowance to be made for error and rate of time-piece, as before.

Longitude of Camp deduced, 7^h 02' 39'', or 105° 39' 45'' W.

Camp on the Arkansa, two miles below the river St. Charles, or third fork of Pike.

July 19, 1820.	Meridian double altitude of Antares - -	51° 36' 00''
	Index error — 3' 22''. Latitude deduced - -	38 14 18 N.

Camp on the Arkansa, at the place where the Exploring Party was divided into two detachments.

Equal altitudes of Sun to find error of watch, at noon.

	Time before Midnight.	Time after Midnight.	Error of Watch.
July 21, 1820.	8^h 39' 58'' 8 38 38 8 37 18	8^h 17' 50'' 8 16 30 8 15 10	17' 19'' slow. Mean time.

A mean of eight lunar distances and times correspondent,—nearest limb of moon from star Spicæ Virginis.

	Time per Watch P. M.	Distance of Moon and Star.	Index error.
July 21, 1820.	9^h 40' 54''	51° 45' 47''	— 3' 30''

Variation of watch 47'' per 12 hours losing.   Error of watch to be estimated.   Longitude by account 6^h 58' W.   Lat. determined by subsequent observations.

Longitude of Camp, 6^h 55' 05'' or 103° 46' 15'' W. of Greenwich.

Equal altitudes of Sun to find error of watch, at noon.

	Time from Noon, A. M.	Time from Noon, P. M.	Error of Watch.
July 22, 1820.	2^h 58' 21'' 2 56 59 2 55 36	2^h 34' 09'' 2 32 47 2 31 23	18' 06'' slow. Mean time.
July 22, 1820.	Meridian double altitude of Antares - - -		51° 40'
	Index error — 3' 30''. Latitude deduced - - -		38 12 22 N.

Camp on the Canadian River of August 6th.

Aug. 6, 1820.	Meridian altitude of sun's lower limb - - -	71° 52′
	Extent of natural horizon, or sheet of water - -	82 yards.
	Height of observer's eye above horizon - - -	38 inches.
	Index error of sextant -	— 3′
	Latitude deduced - -	35° 16′ 19″ N.

Camp on the Canadian River of August 22d.

| Aug. 22, 1820. | Meridian double altitude of moon's lower limb - | 72° 18′ 15″ |
| | Index error — 4′ 00″. Latitude deduced - - - | 35 26 29 N. |

Camp on the Canadian River of August 31st.

Equal altitudes of Sun to find error of watch, at noon.

	Time from Noon, A. M.	Time from Noon, P. M.	Error of Watch.
Aug. 31, 1820.	3ʰ 27′ 43″	2ʰ 23′ 40″	31′ 52½″ slow. Mean time.
	3 26 21	2 22 18	
	3 24 55	2 20 57	

Altitudes of Sun and times correspondent, to find the Latitude.

	Times per Watch, A. M.	Double altitudes of sun's upper limb.	Index error.
Aug. 31, 1820.	10ʰ 29′ 20″	121° 18′ 00″	— 4′
	10 30 24	121 32 00	Error and variation of watch to be allowed.
	10 32 05	121 52 30	Lat. by account
	10 33 12	122 06 30	34° 57′ N.
	10 34 13	122 17 30	
Mean	10ʰ 31′ 51″	121° 49′ 18″	
Latitude of Camp deduced from the above			34° 57′ 35″

A mean of seven Lunar distances, and times correspondent—nearest limbs of Sun and Moon.

	Time per Watch, A. M.	Distance of Sun and Moon.	Index error.
Aug. 31, 1820.	7ʰ 32′ 06″	77° 50′ 15″	— 4′

Allowance to be made for error and variation of watch. Longitude by account, 6ʰ 26′ W.

Longitude deduced, 6ʰ 26′ 12″, or 96° 33′ 00″ W. of Greenwich.

Camp on the Canadian river, fifteen miles above its mouth.

Sept. 9, 1820.	Meridian double altitude of sun's lower limb	120° 13′ 00″
	Index error — 4′. Lat. deduced	34 50 15 N.

Observations made on the Arkansa river, at Fort Smith, Belle Point, situated at the confluence of the Arkansa and Poteau rivers.

Sept. 14, 1820.	Meridian double altitude of sun's lower limb -	116° 22′ 00″
	Index error — 4′. Latitude deduced - -	34 51 07 N.
Sept. 15, 1820.	Meridian double altitude of sun's lower limb -	115 36 00
	Index error — 4′. Latitude deduced - -	34 51 00 N.
Sept. 16, 1820.	Meridian double altitude of sun's lower limb -	114 50 30
	Index error — 4′. Latitude deduced - -	34 50 35 N.
	Mean latitude of Belle Point	34 50 54 N.

Equal altitudes of Sun to find error of watch, at noon.

	Time from Noon, A. M.	Time from Noon, P. M.	Error of Watch.
Sept. 15, 1820.	3ʰ 41′ 21″ 3 38 35	3ʰ 36′ 32″ 3 33 46	2′ 47″ fast. Mean time.

A mean of seven lunar distances and times correspondent—nearest limbs of Sun and Moon.

	Time per Watch, P. M.	Distance of Sun and Moon	Index error.
Sept. 15, 1820.	3ʰ 55′ 46″	93° 59′ 30″	— 4′

Allowance for error of watch as usual. Longitude by account, 6ʰ 18′ west of Greenwich.

Longitude of Belle Point deduced from the foregoing data, 6ʰ 17′ 24″, or 94° 21′ 00″ west of Greenwich.

END OF PART II.

A TABLE OF LATITUDE AND LONGITUDE.

Embracing the deductions recorded in the foregoing account of Astronomical Observations and Calculations.

Places of Observation.	Latitude N.	Longitude W. from Greenwich.	Longitude W. from Washington City.
Shippingsport, Ky. - -	38° 15′ 23″		
Camp on Mississippi, June 8	38 26 09		
Mouth of Merameg river	38 23 39		
St. Louis, Missouri - -	38 36 18	90° 02′ 35″	13° 02′ 35″
Camp on Missouri river, June 28	38 34 33		
Franklin, Missouri - -	38 57 09	92 57 05	15 57 05
Fort Osage, Missouri -	39 09 33		
Cow Island, Missouri river	39 25 05		
Camp on Missouri river, Aug. 31	39 49 01		
Fort Lisa, Missouri Fur Co.'s } Establishment - - }	41 24 13		
Engineer Cantonment -	41 25 04	95 43 53	18 43 53
Mouth of river Platte -	41 03 13		
Mouth of Elk-horn, tributary } to Platte - - - }	41 12 00		
Boyer river at commencement } of High Lands - - }	41 32 15		
Elk-horn river, near Pawnee } Trace - - - }	41 26 07		
Village of Republican Pawnees	41 17 03		
Mouth of Missouri river -	38 51 39	90 00 40	13 00 40
Mouth of De Moyen river -	40 21 48		
Mouth of Illinois river -	38 58 23	90 18 00	13 18 00
Cape Girardeau, Mississippi river	37 18 39	89 17 00	12 17 00
Spanish Fort at Natchez -	31 33 45		
Camp on the Platte, July 4	39 57 40		
Do. do. July 5	39 50 40	105 20 45	28 20 45
Camp at the base of the Rocky } Mountains, July 8 - - }	39 23 40		
1st. Camp on Arkansa, July 17	38 18 19	105 39 45	28 39 45
Camp on Arkansa, July 19	38 14 18		
Camp where Exploring Party } separated - - - }	38 12 22	103 46 15	26 46 15
Camp on Canadian river, Aug. 6	35 16 19		
Do. do. Aug. 22	35 26 29		
Do. do. Aug. 31	34 57 35	96 33 00	19 33 00
Do. do. Sept. 9	34 50 15		
Belle Point, Arkansa Territory	34 50 54	94 21 00	17 21 00

Erratum under Astronomical Records.

Page xxix, line 7 from bottom, after *latitude* insert *of Fording place.*
    Do.   16   do.   for 1810 read 1820.
Page xxxiii, line 19 from top, for *August* read *September.*
Page xxxix,   12   do.   for *noon* read *midnight.*

METEOROLOGICAL REGISTER.

Preliminary Explanations.

THE observations on the modifications of the clouds were particularly detailed in the Journal by Mr. Say, who being often remote from the party on detached expeditions, the phases observed by him cannot always be considered as precisely corresponding with those that occurred where the observations noted in the remaining columns of the tables were made by Lieut. Graham. As they would occupy too much space, if introduced into the body of this work agreeably to the manuscript notes, it was judged proper to modify and condense them into the smallest possible space. With this view, the nomenclature of Messrs. Howard and Forster has been adopted, and is now inserted in the meteorological tables, under the indications of the following abbreviations, viz.

S	-	Stratus.
C	-	Cirrus.
Cs	-	Cirrostratus—the addition of a full point, thus Cs. shows that this cloud was almost or entirely universal; and a comma, thus, Cs, indicates its partial occurrence. The same observations also relate to the signs for the following clouds.
Cm	-	Cumulus.
Cml	-	Cirrocumulus.
Cms	-	Cumulostratus.
Cmc	-	Cumulocirrostratus.
Ns	-	Nimbus.

But as the particular varieties of appearance which these respective clouds exhibited, could not be indicated in the allotted columns of the tables, they are altogether omitted. The column headed with the word *courses* indicates the points of the heavens from which the clouds proceed; thus | C. | S.W. | shows the occurrence of the Cirrus form of clouds proceeding from the south-west.

The letter L. sometimes inserted in the column of remarks on the state of the weather, indicates *lightning*; T. *thunder*, and R. *rain*.

Observations, by means of the Cyanometer, on the colour of the atmosphere, were also made, three times each day, by Mr. Graham; but as the instrument became imperfect in consequence of the fading of its colours, from the necessary exposure to the action of light, they have been rejected.

No record was made of the humidity of the atmosphere, as the Hygrometer provided for the use of the Expedition, proved entirely useless.

Simultaneous meteorological observations were made at Germantown, near Philadelphia, by Mr. Reuben Haines; from which the average temperature of that place during several months has been deduced and inserted for the sake of comparison, in the following tables.

Observations on the state of the weather were regularly made during the whole term of the expedition, but being too voluminous to be inserted in the work, it was thought best to select those of an entire year and reject the remainder.

Day of Month.	Temperature.	MORNING. Wind.	Temperature.	MID-DAY. Wind.	Temperature.	EVENING. Wind.	Mean Temp.	Mean Temp. at Germantown.	REMARKS.
1	68	N. W.	76	N. N. W.	77	W.	73	—	
2	65	Calm	77	W. N. W.	75	N. W.	72	—	
3	65	Calm	82	S. E.	80	S. S. E.	75	—	
4	72	Calm	83	Sy.	81	S.	78	68	
5	73	S.	85	S. E.	83	Sy.	80	—	
6	73	Calm	85	S. E.	84	E. S. E.	80	79	
7	79	S. W.	85	S. W.	84	Sy.	82	79	
8	78	S. S. W.	83	S. S. W.	83	S.	81	—	Windy during the day
9	75	S. W.	85	S. W.	80	W. S. W.	80	—	
10	68	S. E.	83	E. S. E.	75	S. E.	75	71	
11	64	S. S. E.	76	W. N. W.	72	N. W.	70	69	Thunder shower before day-light this morning
12	66	N. N. E.	73	N. N. W.	73	N. N. W.	70	69	
13	68	Calm	78	S. S. E.	72	S. S. W.	72	—	
14	72	S. E. by E.	81	S. by E.	80	S.	77	65	
15	77	S. by E.	84	E.	75	S.	80	—	Violent thunder gust commenced at 6 P. M. and continued till 7.
16	72	S. E.	84	Calm	86	Calm	77	71	Sultry
17	80	Calm	87	Calm	86	Calm	84	76	Sultry
18	80	Calm	86	N. W. by N.	81	N. W.	82	79	Light breezes. Thermometer at 88½ at 11 o'clock, A. M.
19	69	N. E. by N.	74	N. by E.	73	N. by E.	72	78	Light breezes
20	66	W. S. W.	81	W.	80	Calm	75	68	Light breezes
21	70	S. W.	83	N. W.	83	N. by W.	78	71	Light breezes
22	70	E. by S.	83	E. N. E.	84	Calm	79	—	Light breezes
23	72	Calm	82	E. S. E.	82	S.	78	—	Light breezes
24	71	Calm	84	Calm	86	S. W.	80	70	Light showers of rain in the afternoon
25	75	Calm	85	N. E.	86	N.	82	69	Thermometer at 88 at 5 P.M. Light breezes. L. in evening
26	77	N. W.	84	S.	87	W. N. W.	82	68	Light and variable breezes
27	70	N. W. by N.	84	N. N. E.	86	N. N. E.	80	73	Light breezes
28	75	Calm	83	S. by W.	86	E.	81	76	Light breezes
29	71	Calm	88	N. W.	89	N.W. by W.	82	—	Strong breezes
30	74	N. W.	81	W. N. W.	78	S. W. by S.	77	77	Strong gales of wind last night and also during this day

BAROMETER.			MODIFICATIONS AND COURSES OF CLOUDS.					
			MORNING.		MID-DAY.		EVENING.	
Morning.	Noon.	Evening.	Clouds.	Courses.	Clouds.	Courses.	Clouds.	Courses.
29.40	29.26	29.32						
29.36	29.17	29.31						
29.41	29.26	29.20						
29.32	29.16	29.17						
29.25	29 10	29.18						
29.29	29.15	29.16						
29.24	29.19	29.19						
29.20	29.15	29.16						
29.18	29.20	29.15						
29.28	29.21	29.20						
29.15	29.16	29.18						
29.36	29.27	29.28						
29.40	29.26	29.20						
29.29	29.16	29.15						
29.21	29.22	29.23						
29.26	29.21	29.18						
29.22	29.17	29.14						
29.16	29.13	29.14						
29.29	29.27	29.14						
29.35	29.22	29.20						
29.21	29.16	29.11	Fair	—	Cs, Cms,	—	—	—
29.22	29.19	29.13	Cs,	—	Cs. Cm,	—	Cs.	—
29.20	29.17	29.09	Fair	—	Cms.	—	Cms,	—
29.24	29.18	29.14	Fair	—	Ns,	—	Ns,	—
29.25	29.20	29.19	Fair	—	Cms,	—	Cm, Cml,	—
29.25	29.15	29.15	Fair	—	Cms, Cs,	—	—	—
29.29	29.09	29.10	—	—	—	—	—	—
29.15	29.08	29.06	Fair	—	Cml,	—	Fair	—
29.04	28.90	28.87	Cs.	—	Fair	—	Cml,	W.
29.00	28.99	29.00	Fair	—	Cm.	—	Cm, Cm,	—

Day of Month	MORNING		MID-DAY		EVENING		Mean Temp.	Mean Temp. at Germantown.	REMARKS
	Temperature	Wind	Temperature	Wind	Temperature	Wind			
1	69	Calm	83	W. S. W.	83	Calm	78	—	Fresh gales in middle of the day
2	71	Calm	74	W. by S.	80	N. E. by N.	75	—	Fresh gales in middle of the day
3	67	N. N. W.	80	N. W. by N.	78	N. E. by E.	75	70	Fresh and variable brs.—night fair
4	64	N. N. W.	81	E. S. E.	77	E. S. E.	74	70	Fresh breezes
5	65	S. E. by E.	80	E. by N.	79	E. N. E.	74	69	Light breezes
6	76	Calm	81	W. S. W.	84	E. N. E.	80	69	Freq. showers of R. during the day
7	72	E. N E.	86	N.W.by W.	86	S. E. by E.	81	65	Hard shower this forenoon
8	76	Calm	90	S. W.	88	E. N. E.	84	67	Light brs.—mackarel sky in even.
9	78	E. N. E.	83	S. W. by. S.	85	S. W.	82	77	Hard shower this forenoon. L. in the evening
10	80	W. S. W.	85	N. W.				79	Rained greater part of forenoon
11	71	N. E.	85	N. W. by N.	82	S. W.	79	80	Fresh breezes this afternoon, N. N. W. horizon red after twilight. Lightning. Storm of wind
12	76	Calm	87	N. W.	81	N. W. by N.	81	79	Lightning in the evening
13	79	S.	85	W.	86	Calm	83	81	Thunder shower and heavy wind from N. W. about 1 o'clock this morning—rain 1½ inches
14	77	W. S. W.	81	N. E.	82	Calm	80	78	Thunder showers and heavy wind this morning about 1 o'clk. rain ½ inch—noon L. ¼ inch rain
15	75	W. S. W.	84	W. N. W.	82		80	81	Very light breezes
16	69	W. N. W.	77	N. W.	76	N. N. W.	74	78	Very light breezes
17	54	N. N. E.	73	S. S. E.	72	N. W.	66	73	Very light breezes. Stratus at night.
18	54	N. W.	73	E. by N.	74	N. N. W.	67	70	Pleasant wea. Even. S. in N. E.
19	54	N. W.	75	E.	76	S. S. E.	68	72	Pleasant weather
20	64	S. E.	80	W. N. W.	73	E. by S.	72	72	Light breezes
21	68	E. by S.	75	E. by S.	70	S. S. E.	71	72	Light breezes
22	70	E.	80	S. by. W.	77	S. E.	75	75	Fresh breezes. T. storm in even.
23	68	Calm	73	S. S. E.				75	Several showers of rain to-day. L. incessant in the evening
24	72	Calm	83	S. E.	82	N. E.	79	75	Fr. brs. T. storm with R. in even.
25	72	N.W. by N.	83	N. N. E.	80	N. by W.	78	76	Fresh breezes. Light rain this morning. L. in the evening
26	65	Calm	83	N.	72	W.	73	76	Fresh breezes
27	64	N. W.	84	S. S. E.	75	E. S. E.	74	76	Thick fog over the river this morn.
28	69	E.	86	S. by. E.	84	N. E.	79	78	Strong breezes in the afternoon Evening L. and shower at night
29	72	E. N. E.	88	S .W. by S.	80	S.	80	77	Strong breezes
30	74	W. S. W.	89	E. S. E.	83	S. E. by E.	82	82	Moderate brs. Noon T. Even. L.
31	72	N. E. by N.	86	N. N. W.	82	E. by N.	80	86	Moderate breezes

Remarkable Phenomena.—On the 7th, 170 miles from mouth of Missouri river at 9 o'clock P. M. discovered a comet bearing nearly N. W. Observed its distance from North Star be 49° 38′.—8th, 57 minutes past 8 P. M. observed distance of comet from North Star 46′, bearing at same time N. 43°, W. Altitude 7°.

BAROMETER.			MODIFICATIONS AND COURSES OF CLOUDS.					
			MORNING.		MID-DAY.		EVENING.	
Morning.	Noon.	Evening.	Clouds.	Courses.	Clouds.	Courses.	Clouds.	Courses.
29.09	29.00	29.00	Cms,	—	Cml,	—	Cs.	—
29.16	29.18	29.18	Cs.	—	Cs.	—	Cs.	—
29.33	29.20	29.20	Cs,	—	Cs,	—	Cs,	—
29.39	29.20	29.20	Cm,	S.	Cm, & C,	S.	C, & Cs,	—
29.25	29.08	29.07	Cmc.	—	Cm, Cms, Cs,	S. E.	Ns,	—
29.07	29.05	29.06	Ns.	—	Ns,	—	Cms,	—
29.12	29.00	29.02	Cms, & Cs,	—	Cs, & Cms,	—	Cm, & Cs,	—
29.04	28.96	28.96	Cs,	E.	Cm. & Cs.	—	Cml,	—
29.04	29.00	28.98	Cs.	—	Cs. Cms,	—	Ns, Cms,	N. W.
28.99	29.05		Ns.	—	Cms.	—	Cs.	—
29.18	29.10	29.04	Cs.	S. W.	Ns.	—	Ns.	—
29.00	28.97	29.04	Ns, Cs,	S. W.	Cs.	—	Ns.	N.
29.07	29.00	29.03	Cs, Ns,	NW., NE.	Cms, Ns.	S. W.	Ns, Cs,	E.
29.03	29.13	29.13	Cs,	—	Ns.	—	Ns,	N. N. E.
29.22	29.21	29.23	S.	—	Cs, Cm,	—	Cs,	—
29.27	29.27	29.25	C, Cs,	W. N. W.	Cms,	—	Cs,	—
29.34	29.31	29.31	Cms,	—	Cms.	—	Cs,	—
29.34	29.34	29.31	S	—	Cs,	—	Cs.	—
29.34	29.34	29.34	Cmc.	—	Cs.	—	Cs.	—
29.34	29.30	29.24	Cs.	—	Cm, Cs,	—	Cs.	—
29.21	29.15	29.15	Ns.	—	Ns, Cm,	S. W.	—	—
29.06	28.97	28.97	Ns.	S.	Cms, Cml,	—	Ns	S. W.
29.00	29.00		Ns.	—	Cs, Cml,	N. W., S.	Cm, Ns,	S. S. W.
29.02	29.10	29.12	Cm, Cs,	—	Cms, Cs,	N. N. W.	Ns,	—
29.16	29.17	29.16	Cms,	N. N. W.	Cm,	N. N. W.	C,	N. W.
29.20	29.20	29.13	C, Cml,	—	Fair	—	Fair	—
29.13	29.13	29.06	S.	—	Fair	—	Fair	—
29.10	29.10	29.06	C,	—	Cms,	—	Cms,	—
29.12	29.06	29.03	C,	N.	Cs, C,	—	Cs, Cms,	—
29.08	29.01	29.00	Ns.	—	Cms, Cml,	S. W.	Cms, Cs,	—
29.00	28.90	28.88	Ns	—	Cms. Cs	N.E.,S.W.	—	—

17th—Franklin, Missouri—Magnetic intensity 26 oscillations per minute.
28th—At our Camp—Magnetic intensity 25 oscillations per minute.

Day of Month	Temperature	MORNING Wind	Temperature	MID-DAY Wind	Temperature	EVENING Wind	Mean Temp.	Mean Temp. at Germantown	REMARKS.
1	72	N. W.	85	N.	82	S. E.	79	88	
2	69	Calm	78	E. by S.	74	E. by S.	73	86	
3	68		82	S. W.	74	W. by S.	74	78	Frequent showers of rain, 1-8 of an inch rain since yesterday morn.
4	73	S.	84	S.	78	W.	78	76	Frequent showers of rain, ½ an inch of rain since yesterday morning
5	68	S. S. W.	86	W.	76	S. W.	76	75	Light sprinkles of rain
6	71	W.	88	W.	80	W.	79	75	Cloudy all day
7	71	S. W.	84	W. S. W.	81	W. S. W.	78	79	Light sprinkles of rain last night and this afternoon
8	71	Calm	84	N. E.	80	S. W. by S.	78	82	Sprinkles of rain this forenoon
9	70	S. S. W.	88	Calm	84	Calm	80	80	Sultry
10	70	S. S. E.	88	S.	84	E. S. E.	80	82	Sultry. Light. in S. E. this evening
11	72	E. N. E.	90	S. S. E.	85	E. S. E.	82	79	Pleasant brs. L. in N. this evening
12	72	Calm	92	W.	85	E. N. E.	83	81	Fresh breezes. Lightning in N. W.
13	75	Calm	91	S. W.	86	S. S. E.	84	82	Fresh breezes. Night meteors shooting to the north
14	77	Calm	93	S.	87	S.	85	82	Fresh breezes. No dew
15	76	S. E.	92	S.	86	S. S. W.	84	79	Light breezes. No dew.
16	76	Calm	90	Calm	87	N.	84	72	Light breezes. Shower of rain in the morn. No dew in the even.
17	74	E. N. E.	90	N. E.	86	N. N. E.	83	79	Light breezes
18	73	W. S. W.	86	Calm	81	E. N. E.	89	72	Light brs. noon. Rain in the E.
19	74	Calm	83	E. N. E.	80	E. N. E.	79	74	
20	76	S. S. E.	85	E.	81	E.	80	76	
21	68	Calm	84	W. N. W.	78	N. W.	76	77	Hard shower of rain from North— 3-16 of an inch of rain
22	61	N. W.	76	N. N. E.	68	N. N. W.	68	78	Windy
23	50	W.	72	Calm	67	N. W.	63	70	
24	54	S. S. E.	73	S. S. E.	70	S. S. E.	65	66	Windy
25	60	S. E.	83	S. S. E.		S. S. E.		62	Strong gale of wind during the day
26	68	S.	86	S. S. E.	80	S. S. E.	78		Strong gale of wind. Evening, rain
27	71	E.	70	N.	69	N.	70	64	Strong gale of wind. Morn. rain
28	50	N. W.	79	N. W.	66	E. N. E.	65	65	Strong gale of wind
29	50	N. N. E.	75	E. S. E.				70	Fresh breezes
30	50	E. S. E.	84	S. S. W.	71	S. W.	68	69	Fresh breezes
31	62	S.	93	W. S. W.	84	S. W.	79	71	Windy

Remarkable Phenomena.—On the evening of the 2d, when the moon was about ⁛ above the horizon, brilliant rays of light appeared very distinctly to proceed from a poï⸳ 5° or 6° to the north of the moon. Same phenomenon on the evening of the 3d.

BAROMETER.			MODIFICATIONS AND COURSES OF CLOUDS.					
			MORNING.		MID-DAY.		EVENING.	
Morning.	Noon.	Evening.	Clouds.	Courses.	Clouds.	Courses.	Clouds.	Courses.
28.87	28.77	28.74	Ns.	N. E.	Cml.	N. E.	Cs.	—
28.72	28.68	28.68	Ns.	—	Ns.	—	Ns.	—
28.68	28.70	28.74	Ns.	—	Ns.	—	Ns.	—
28.79	28.77	28.77	Ns.	E.	Cm,	—	C, Cs.	—
28.83	28.80	28.80	—	—	—	—	—	—
28.86		28.85	Cs.	—	Cs.	—	Cs.	—
28.90	28.82	28.82	Ns.	—	Cs.	—	Cms.	—
28.82	28.74	28.74	Ns.	—	Cs.	—	Cms.	—
28.75	28.74	28.74	Cs, Cms,	—	Fair	—	Cm,	—
28.80	28.80	28.80	Fair	—	Cm.	S. S. W.	Fair	—
28.86	28.86	28.78	Fair	—	Cm,	S. S. W.	C, Cs,	—
28.84	28.80	28.74	Cs.	—	Cs, Cms,	—	Cs,	—
28.77	28.70	28.70	Cm, Cs,	—	Cm,	—	Cm, Cs,	—
28.70	28.63	28.62	—	—	—	—	—	—
28.62	28.60	28.57	—	—	—	—	—	—
28.57	28.63	28.64	Ns.	N. W.	Ns.	—	Ns, Cs,	—
28.66	28.66	28.66	Cs,	—	Cs, Cml,	S.W.,N.E.	—	—
28.70	28.67	28.67	Cs,	—	Cs, Cm,	S.W.,N.E.	Ns.	E.
28.74	28.74	28.74	Ns.	—	Cms.	N. E.	—	—
28.80	28.75	28.68	Fair	—	Cm, Cs,	—	C.	—
28.68	28.63	28.66	Ns.	—	Ns.	—	—	—
28.84	28.85	28.88	—	—	—	—	—	—
29.18	28.85	28.85	Cs.	—	—	—	—	—
28.85	28.77	28.77	Cs.	—	—	—	—	—
28.83	28.65	28.65	C,	—	C,	E.	C,	E.
28.72	28.66	28.63	Cs,	—	Cs, Cm,	S. W.	Ns.	—
28.63	28.75	28.75	Ns.	N. W.	Cs, Cm,	W., N. W.	—	—
28.94	28.78	28.79	Fair	—	Cs.	—	—	—
29.00	28.84		—	—	—	—	—	—
28.97	28.67	28.54	—	—	—	—	—	—
28.57	28.44	28.45	Cs,	—	Fair	—	Fair	—

Fort Osage, August 4th, magnetic intensity 26½.
Fall of rain on the 26th instant 3-16ths of an inch—27th ½ an inch.

Day of Month.	Temperature.	MORNING. Wind.	Temperature.	MID-DAY. Wind.	Temperature.	EVENING. Wind.	Mean Temp.	Mean Temp. at Germantown.	REMARKS.
1	75	N. W.	92	S. S. E.	88	S. W.	85	75	Windy
2	75	N. W.	88	E. S. E.	74	Calm	79	78	Light breezes. Lightning in S. W. at midnight
3	63	S. S. E.	90	S. W.	78	S. W.	77	80	Hard thunder shower from W. S. W. this afternoon, lightning in N. W. in the evening
4	76	S. W.	90	S. S. E.	82	S. S. E.	82	78	Some rain last night
5	71	N. N. W.	70	N. N. W.	71	N. N. W.	70	79	Rain and lightning last night, and a shower at noon
6	66	S. E.	84	N. W.	72	N. W.	74	79	Thunder storm from S.E. last night, and another from N. W. this afternoon, and during part of the night, with rain, and some hail in the night
7	70	N. W.	85	E. S. E.	78	N. N. W.	77	80	Violent thunder storm from N. N. W. with a little hail this afternoon
8	65	N. E.	85	E. S. E.	76	E. S. E.	75	80	
9	65	E. S. E.	92	S. E.	75	S. E.	74	77	Thunder in the W. and some appearance of rain this afternoon—evening lightning in the N.
10	70	Calm	87	S. S. E.	80	S. E.	79	70	
11	72	Calm	77	S.	76	S. E.	75	65	Frequent light sprinkles of rain to-day, rain in the morning
12	74	S. S. E.	82	S.	76	Calm	77	68	
13	62	N.	74	N. N. W.	67	N. N. W.	67	62	Very windy and squally all day
14	50	W.	69	E. N. E.	60	E. N. E.	59	59	Cool breezes. S. from river at night
15	50	S. W.	74	S. S. W.	68	S. S. W.	64	64	Remarkably clear sky all this day
16	56	N. E.	78	S.	71	S.	68	65	Remarkably clear sky all this day
17	55	S.	85	E. N. E.	78	E. N. E.	72	65	Remarkably clear sky all this day
18	58	Calm	90	S. E.	75	S. E.	74	66	
19	56	N. N. W.	84	S. E.	72	S. E.	70	66	
20	58	S. E.	70	S. E.	69	S. S. W.	65	60	Night S. from the river and nimbus in N. W. horizon
21	56	E. S. E.	80	E. S. E.	74	S. E.	70	56	Fresh gales of wind
22	60	E. S. E.	76	S. E.	72	Calm	69	62	Atmosphere thick and smoky
23	54	N.	64	N. N. W.	58	N. W.	58	68	Windy
24	41	N.	64	N.	55	Calm	53	68	Windy
25	34	Calm	70	Calm	59	Calm	54	66	Frost last night
26	45	S. E.	82	S. E.	71	S. E.	66	62	⎫
27	54	Calm	80	S. E.	67	S. E.	67	61	⎪ Atmosphere very smoky, occasioned by the neighbouring prairies being on fire
28	54	E. S. E.	77	S. E.	70	S. E.	67	60	⎬
29	54	E. S. E.	85	S. E.	80	S. E.	73	60	⎪
30	62	Calm	86	N. W.	73	N. W.	73	66	⎭

Note. The Expedition arrived at ENGINEER CANTONMENT, their wintering post, on the 17th instant.

BAROMETER.			MODIFICATIONS AND COURSES OF CLOUDS.					
			MORNING.		MID-DAY.		EVENING.	
Morning.	Noon.	Evening.	Clouds.	Courses.	Clouds.	Courses.	Clouds.	Courses.
28 45	28.40	28.40	C,	—	C, Cm,	—	Cs,	—
28.41	29.20	29.20	Fair	—	Fair	—	Fair	—
28.70	28.47	28.47	C, Cs,	S. W., W.	Cs.	N. W.	Ns.	S. W.
28.47	28.47	28.47	C,	S. W.	Fair	—	Cs,	W.
28.63	28.58	28.58	Cs. Cml,	W., N.W.	Ns.	S. E.	Ns.	S.
28.58	28.50	28.50	Cs. Cml,	N. W., S.	Cs,	—	Ns.	—
28.50	28.44	28.44	Ns,	—	Cm.	—	Ns.	—
28.56	29.60	29.60	Fair	—	Fair	—	Cs,	—
28.65	28.55	28.55	C, Cm,	—	C, Cm,	—	Ns,	—
28.68	28.68	28.68	Fair	—	Cm,	--	Cm, Cs,	—
28.66	28.66	28.63	Ns.	--	Ns.	—	Ns.	—
28.63	28.64	28.64	Ns.	—	Ns	—	Fair	—
28.76	28.84	28.84	Ns.	—	Cs	→	Fair	—
29.10	28.92	28.86	Fair	—	Cm,	—	Fair	—
28.92	28.70	28.68	Fair	—	Fair	—	Fair	—
28.75	28.64	28,65	Fair	—	Fair	—	Fair	—
28 75	28.60	28.60	Fair	→	Fair	—	Fair	—
28.60	28.50	28.50	Fair	—	Cs,	N. W.	Fair	—
28.70	28.68	28.68	Fair	—	Fair	—	Fair	—
28.80	28.70	28.70	S, Ns,	--	S, Cml,	—	S.	—
28.70	28.54	28.54	S, Cs,	—·	Cs,	N. W.	Cs,	—
28.56	28.46	28.56	C, C,	—	Cs,	—	Cs,	N. W.
28.66	28.66	28 66	Cs,	N. W.	Cs,	N W.	Fair	—
28.78	28.57	28.57	Fair	--	Fair	—	S,	—
28.80	28.54	28.54	Fair	—	Fair	—	Fair	—
28.50	28.37	28.37	Fair	—	Fair	—	Fair	—
28.37	28.43	28.43	Fair	—	Fair	—	Fair	—
28.70	28.64	28,64	Fair	—	Fair	—	Fair	—
28.65	28 50	28.50	—	—	—	—	—	—
28.50	28.54	28.50	Cs,	--	Fair	—	Cs,	N. W.

September 3d, fall of rain 7-8 inch—4th, 1-8 inch—5th, 5-8 inch—7th, 3-8 inch—8th, ·8 inch.

Day of Month.	MORNING.		MID-DAY.		EVENING.			AT ENGINEER CANTONMENT.
	Temperature.	Wind.	Temperature.	Wind.	Temperature.	Wind.	Mean Temp.	Mean Temp. at Germantown.
								REMARKS.
1	46	Calm	86	N. W.	74	N. W.	68	65	Atmosphere thick with smoke
2	50	Calm	73	E.	65	E.	62	—	Atmosphere thick with smoke
3	54	S. E.	75	S. E.	72	Calm	67	—	Atmosphere thick with smoke
4	64	E. S. E.	90	S. E.	86	S. E.	80	56	Atmosphere thick with smoke
5	72	S. E.	88	S. S. E.	82	S. S. E.	80	60	Windy and squally. Atmosphere thick with smoke
6	68	S. E.	71	S. E.	47	N. W.	62	66	Light rain this morning
7	36	N. W.	39	N. W.	38	N. W	37	66	Windy.
8	32	N. W.	38	N. W.	36	N. W.	35	67	A little ice and snow last night. Windy and light snow this even.
9	31	N. W.	48	N. W.	44	N. W.	41	70	Frost last night—windy to-day
10	38	S. E.	68	N. N. W.	55	N. N. W.	53	58	Windy
11	35		56	E. S. E.	52	E. S. E.	47	53	Light sprinkles of rain to-day
12	43	Calm	53	N. E.	49	Calm	48	54	Fresh breezes of wind all this day
13	28	Calm	57	S. E.	47	Calm	44	46	Frost last night
14	42	S. E.	70	S. E.	62	Calm	58	47	
15	44	N. N. E.	58	N. N. E.	53	N. W.	51	52	
16	30	N. W.	53	N. W.	42	W.	41	57	Frost last night
17	26	S. E.	59	E. S. E.	51	S. E.	45	49	Frost last night—water also froze in a vessel left out
18	43	N. N. W.	57	W. N. W.	53	W. N. W.	51	46	Windy
19	49	N. W.	53	N. W.	45	N. W.	46	46	High wind this day
20	29	Calm	53	N. W.	45	W. N. W.	42	47	Hail last night
21	28	Calm	49	S. E.	46	S. E.	41	48	Heavy frost last night
22	38	Calm	74	Variable	65	N. W.	59	42	High wind this afternoon. Fog on the river this morning
23	40	N. W.		N. W.		N. W.		46	High winds
24		N. W.		N. W.		N. W.		48	High winds
25		S. S. W.		S. S. W.		S. S. W.	·	39	High winds
26	29	Calm	56	S. E.	54	S. E.	46	42	
27	32	Calm	59	Calm	56	Calm	49	50	
28	32	Calm	68	S. S. W.	66	S. S. W.	55	53	
29	39	Calm	61	N.	57	N.	51	52	Frost last night, smoky atmosphere to-day
30	31	Calm	52	S. E.	54	S. E.	45	52	Atmosphere filled with dense smoke
31	50	N. W.	77	N. W.	61	N. W.	62	43	Atmosphere filled with dense smoke

Remarkable Phenomena.—The Aurora Borealis appeared in N. N. E. at 8 o'clock on the evening of the 12th, near the horizon, and continued but a short time.

The atmosphere has been very thick with smoke during this month generally, occasioned by the burning of the *prairies*. This appearance has generally been near the horizon, but

BAROMETER.			MODIFICATIONS AND COURSES OF CLOUDS.					
			MORNING.		MID-DAY.		EVENING.	
Morning.	Noon.	Evening.	Clouds.	Courses.	Clouds.	Courses.	Clouds.	Courses.
28.73	28.54	28.56	Cml,	N. W.	Fair	—	Fair	—
28.74	28.62	28.62	Fair	—	Fair	—	Fair	—
28.54	28.45	28.38	Fair	—	Fair	—	Fair	—
28.38	28.28	28.28	Fair	—	Fair	—	C,	S. W.
28.38	28.35	28.35	Cml,	—	Cm,	—	C,	—
28.40	28.33	28.40	Ns.	S. W.	Ns.	—	Ns.	—
28.70	28.80	28.87	Ns.	—	Ns.	—	Ns.	—
28.96	28.94	28.94	Ns.	—	Ns.	—	Ns.	—
28.88	28.83	28.72	Fair	—	C,	—	Fair	—
28.71	28.66	28.67	C,	—	C, Cml,	—	Ns.	—
28.88	28.88	28.96	Fair	—	Ns.	—	Ns.	W. N. W.
29.21	29.20	29.23	Ns.	—	Cs,	N. W.	Cml,	—
29.45	29.28	29.25	Fair	—	Fair	—	Fair	—
29.16	28.90	28.83	Fair	—	Fair	—	Fair	—
28.69	28.64	28.65	C,	N.	Cml,	—	Cml,	—
28.87	28.78	28.78	Fair	—	Fair	—	Fair	—
28.90	28.75	28.75	Fair	—	C,	W.	C,	N. W.
28.64	28.61	28.61	C,	N. W.	Cm,	N. W.	Ns,	N. W.
28.76	28.76	28.76	Cm,	N. W.	Cm,	N. W.	Ns.	—
28.95	28.95	29.00	Cm,	—	Cm,	—	Cm.	—
29.16	29.00	28.88	Cs,	N. W.	Cs,	N. W.	Fair	—
28.66	28.35	28.45	C.	N. W.	C,	—	Fair	—
28.78			C,	—	C,	—	C,	—
			Cs.	—	C,	—	C,	—
			C,	—	Fair	—	Fair	—
28.92	28.88	28.90	C,	N. W.	C,	—	Fair	—
28.94	28.88	28.88	C,	N. W.	C,	N. W.	C	N. W.
28.96	28.73	28.67	Fair	—	Fair	—	Fair	—
28.83	28.74	28.69	—	—	—	—	—	—
28.88	28.73	28.64	—	—	—	—	—	—
28.48	28.48	28.48	C,	N. W.	C,	N. W.	C,	N. W.

at some times, particularly in the latter part of the month, the whole of the sky has been obscured by smoke, bearing much resemblance in the morning, when there was little wind, to a thick fog.

6th—Fall of rain 3-16ths of an inch.

Day of Month.	MORNING.		MID-DAY.		EVENING.		Mean. Temp.	Mean Temp. at Germantown.	AT ENGINEER CANTONMENT.
	Temperature.	Wind.	Temperature.	Wind.	Temperature.	Wind.			REMARKS.
1	52	N. W.	63	N. W.	54	N. W.	56	—	Windy and boisterous
2	33	S. E.	65	Var.	60	N. W.	52	50	Strong winds. Gust at 2 P. M.
3	44	N. W.	54	N. W.	53	N. W.	50	49	Windy
4	32	Calm	64	N. W.	58	N. W.	51	47	Windy
5	44	S. E.	54	S. E.	57	S. E.	51	44	Windy. Atmos. dense with smoke
6	46	N. W.	50	N. W.	47	N. W.	47	43	Very windy and boisterous
7	30	S. E.	54	S. E.	56	S. E.	46	50	Windy
8	47	S. E.	68	S. E.	56	S. E.	57	—	Light wind. Atmos. very smoky
9	30	Calm	40	N. W.	44	N. W.	38	47	Light wind. A little rain at evening, with thunder and lightning
10	57	S.	58	S.	54	S.	56	48	Rainy until noon
11	56	Var.	53	S.	52	S.	47	49	Light brs. Atmosphere very clear
12	38	N. W.	40	N. W.	36	N. W.	38	56	A little rain last night
13	38	S. E.	41	S. E.	43	S. E.	40	50	Fresh breezes
14	38	S. E.	64	Calm	48	Calm	50	41	Mild weather
15	45	S. E.	56	S. E.	50	N. W.	50	37	Mild. At sunset wind N. W.
16	33	Calm	52	N. W.	50	N. W.	45	50	Frost last night. Light winds
17	34	S. E.	46	S. E.	43	Calm	41	59	Frost last night
18	24	Calm	42	Sy.	43	S. E.	36	47	Heavy frost last night
19	44	S. E.	61	Sy.	61	Sy.	55	43	Moderate wind
20	39	N.	43	N.	41	N.	41	—	Windy
21	36	S. E.	38	S. E.	39	S. E.	37	47	Rain before daylight
22	40	N. W.	42	N. W.	40	N.	40	38	Rain last night
23	37	E.	39	S. E.	42	S. E.	39	46	Rain last night. Ground covered with sleet in the morning
24	35	W.	43	W.	44	W.	40	—	Rainy last night
25	36	S. E.	39	S. E.	43	S. E.	39	48	Heavy frost last night. Lit. rn. even.
26	18	N. W.	22	N. W.	23	N. W.	21	48	Snow 1-8 in. Little ice in river
27	10	Calm	20	S. E.	25	S. E.	18	51	Much floating ice in river
28	20	S. E.	34	S. E.	36	S. E.	30	39	Frost last night
29	29	S. E.	40	S. E.	40	S. E.	36	—	Floating ice increasing in river
30	30	Calm	55	Calm.	42	Calm	42	35	Floating ice increasing in river Fair

Remarkable Phenomena.—The atmosphere continued its smoky appearance until the 11th, appearing to be produced by southerly and south-easterly winds, and carried off by north and north-westerly ones.

BAROMETER.			MODIFICATIONS AND COURSES OF CLOUDS.					
			MORNING.		MID-DAY.		EVENING.	
Morning.	Noon.	Evening.	Clouds.	Courses.	Clouds.	Courses.	Clouds.	Courses.
28.70	28.63	28.73	Fair	—	Fair	—	Fair	—
28.75	28.45	28.50	C.	N. W.	C,	N. W.	C,	—
28.65	28.67	28.66	C,	N. W.	C,	N. W.	C,	N. W.
28.53	28.49	28.49	Cms,	N. W.	C,	—	C,	—
28.50	28.18	28.09	C,	W.	—	—	—	—
28.65	28.71	28.82	C,	—	C,	—	C,	—
28.95	28.64	28.48	Cs,	N. W.	—	—	—	—
28.35	28.22	28.30	—	—	—	—	—	—
28.68	28.60	28.60	—	—	—	—	Ns.	—
28.35	28.13	28.13	Ns.	—	Ns.	S. S. E.	Cml,	S. S. E.
28.53	28.53	28.47	Fair	—	Fair	—	Fair	—
28.59	28.80	28.80	Ns,	N. W.	Ns.	—	Ns.	—
28.89	28.70	28.56	Ns,	S. E.	Cs,	—	C,	—
28.41	28.33	28.35	C,	—	C,	N. W.	Cs,	—
28.10	27.90	28.10	Cs,	W. N. W.	C,	—	Cs,	W.
28.44	28.43	28.47	Fair	—	C,	N. W.	Cms,	—
28.60	28.46	28.51	C,	N. W.	Cs,	N. W.	Cs,	N. W.
28.90	28.70	28.56	Cs,	N. W.	Ns,	N. W.	Ns,	N. W.
28.30	28.21	28.31	Cs,	W.	Cs,	W.	C,	W. N. W.
28.75	28.76	28.80	Cs.	—	C,	W. N. W.	Cs,	—
28.94	28.83	28.76	Ns.	—	Ns.	—	Ns.	—
28.83	28.92	28.97	Ns,	N. W.	Ns,	N. W.	Ns.	N. W.
28.95	28.69	28.57	Ns.	S. E.	Ns.	—	Ns.	—
28.54	28.55	28.62	C,	S. W.	Fair	—	Fair	—
28.72	28.60	28.55	Ns.	S. W.	Ns.	—	Ns.	—
29.13	29.08	29.13	Cml,	N.W.	Cml,	N. W.	Cml,	N. W.
29.43	29.25	29.21	Fair	—	Fair	—	Fair	—
29.14	29.08	28.95	Fair	—	Fair	—	Fair	—
29.02	28.91	28.87	Fair	—	Cml,	N.W.	Cs,	—
28.85	28.77	28.77	Fair	—	C,	N. W.	C,	N. W.

November 10th, fall of rain ½ inch—23d, ¾ inch—24th, ½ inch.

Day of Month.	MORNING.		MID-DAY.		EVENING.		Mean. Temp.	Mean Temp. at Germantown.	AT ENGINEER CANTON-MENT.
	Temperature.	Wind.	Temperature.	Wind.	Temperature.	Wind.			REMARKS.
1	34	Calm	51	N. W.	46	N. W.	43	37	Thawing
2	32	S. E.	41	S. E.	43	S. E.	38	34	No floating ice in river
3	32	S. E.	53	S. E.	49	S. E.	44	30	Thawing
4	34	E.	39	E.	39	E.	37	39	Frost last night
5	33	S.	40	Calm	43	Calm	38	32	Rain at mid-day
6	42	S. E.	45	S.	42	S.	43	34	Drizzling, A. M.
7	36	S. E.	44	Calm	43	Calm	41	43	Frost last night
8	38	N. W.	42	N. W.	39	N. W.	39	45	Light winds
9	23	S. E.	32	S. E.	32	S. E.	29	42	Heavy frost last night
10	32	S. E.	34	S. E.	34	S. E.	33	—	Windy
11	31	S. E.	36	S. E.	34	S. E.	33	27	Windy
12	34	Calm	36	Calm	36	Calm	35	29	A little snow, hail, and rain last night. Float. ice this morn.
13	28	N. W.	32	N. W.	26	N. W.	28	30	Floating ice in river
14	20	N. W.	28	N. W.	24	N. W.	24	34	Floating ice in river
15	15	N. W.	20	N. W.	19	N. W.	18	33	Frost last night. Much floating ice this morning
16	14	S. E.	24	S. E.	21	S. E.	19	34	A little snow in flakes at noon.
17	21	S. W.	35	S. W.	37	S. W.	31	34	Frost last night
18	29	N. W.	28	N. W.	27	N. W.	28	33	Very windy
19	11	N. W.	38	N. W.	24	N. W.	24	45	Snow ¼ inch last night
20	17	S. E.	55	S. E.	42	S. E.	38	39	Thawing
21	35	S. E.	19	N. W.	17	N. W.	23	35	Very high wind ❀
22	1	N. W.	3	N. W.	1	N. W.	1	35	Ice made across river last night
23	—10	N. W.	3	N. W.	1	N. W.	-2	40	A little snow fell yesterday
24	— 8	S. W.	15	S. W.	19	S. W.	9	43	River entirely closed with ice
25	18	Calm						28	Stratus in horizon at midnight
26	20	N. W.	43	N. W.	35	N. W.	32	28	Frost last night
27	9	Calm						32	Frost last night
28	12	N. W.	21	N. W.	11	N. W.	14	25	Windy, slight snow. Icy particles in the air
29	4	S. E.	25	Calm	16	Calm	15	24	Frost last night
30	— 4	N. W.	2	N. W.	— 1	N. W.	-1	16	A little snow last night
31	— 4	S. E.	15	S. E.	19	N. W.	10	14	Snow ¼ inch to day

Remarkable Phenomena.—December 30th. This morning at sun-rise there appeared two images of the sun about 22° or 23° N. and S. of, and in a horizontal line with the sun; the whole sky being obscured by dense cloud: neither the images nor the sun appeared very distinct, but presented the appearance of luminous spots. The appearance continued until about 11 o'clock.—This evening at half past five o'clock, a similar phenomenon accom-

BAROMETER.			MODIFICATIONS AND COURSES OF CLOUDS.					
			MORNING.		MID-DAY.		EVENING.	
Morning.	Noon.	Evening.	Clouds.	Courses.	Clouds.	Courses.	Clouds.	Courses.
28.94	28.80	28.88	Cs,	N. W.	C,	—	Fair	—
28.90	28.85	28.72	Cs,	—	Cs,	—	Fair	—
28.56	28.55	28.63	Fair	—	Fair	—	Fair	—
28.88	28.78	28.80	C,	N. W.	C,	W.	Cs,	—
28.85	28.61	28.61	Ns,	S.	Ns.	—	Ns.	—
28.74	28.63	28.70	Ns.	—	Ns.	N. & S.	Ns,	—
28.87	28.73	28.74	C,	W. N. W.	Cs,	W. N. W.	Cs,	—
28.84	28.89	29.02	Ns.	W.	Ns.	—	Cml,	N. W.
29.28	29·00	28.97	C,	N. W.	C,	N.W.	C,	N. W.
28.77	28.60	28.58	Ns.	S. E.	Ns.	—	Ns,	—
28.75	28.70	28.70	Ns.	S. E.	Ns.	S. E.	Ns.	S. E.
28.57	28.44	28.44	Ns.	—	Ns.	—	Ns.	—
28.47	28.36	28.46	Cml.	W. N. W.	Ns.	N. W.	Ns.	N.W.
28.78	28.80	28.83	Ns.	N. W.	Ns.	N. W.	Ns.	N.W.
29.25	29.14	29.08	Fair	—	Cml,	N. N. W.	Ns.	—
29.09	29.04	28.91	Ns,	—	Ns.	—	Ns.	N.W.
28.72	28.62	28.50	Fair	—	C, Cml,	NW., SW.	C,	S. W.
28.49	28.54	28.50	Ns.	—	Ns.	—	Ns.	—
28.72	28.60	28.60	Fair	—	Fair	—	C,	—
28.56	28.50	28.40	C,	—	Cs,	W. N. W.	Ns,	—
28.14	28.30	28.49	Cml,	N. W.	Ns,	N. W.	Cs,	N. W.
29.00	28.73	28.83	Ns.	—	Ns.	—	Ns.	—
29.32	29.02	29.00	Cs,	S. W.	Cs,	S. W.	C,	S. W.
28.93	28.80	28.50	Fair	—	C,	—	Cs,	N. W.
28.64			C,	N. W.	C,	—	C,	—
28.58	28.31	28.51	Fair	—	Fair	—	Fair	—
28.68			C,	—	Cs.	—	Cs.	—
28.80	28.57	28.84	Ns.	—	Fair	—	Fair	—
28.84	28.80	28.66	Cs,	N. W.	C,	N.W.	Cs,	N.
28.98	28.95	28.95	Ns,	N.	Ns,	N.	—	—
28.83	28.50	28.54	Ns.	—	Ns.	—	Cml,	N. W.

panied the moon.—Around her there was a halo or luminous circle of about 45° in dia‑
meter. In the circumference of this circle, on each side the moon and in a horizontal line
with her, there appeared an image similar to those described of the sun, though not quite
so distinct. They did not continue long.

December 5th, fall of rain 1‑16th of an inch.

Day of Month.	MORNING.		MID-DAY.		EVENING.				AT ENGINEER CAN-TONMENT.
	Temperature.	Wind.	Temperature.	Wind.	Temperature.	Wind.	Mean Temp.	Mean Temp. at Germantown.	REMARKS.
1	16	N. W.	22	N W.	20	N. W.	19	12	A little snow fell to-day
2	13	N. W.	24	N. W.	18	N. W.	18	21	
3	4	S. E.	35	S. E.	28	N. W.	22	—	Mild and fair
4	13	N. E.	31	N. W.	21	N. W.	21	26	
5	0	S. E.	24	S. E.	19	S. E.	14	25	Fresh winds
6	20	S. E.	32	S. E.	28	S. E.	26	18	A little snow at evening
7	16	N. W.	40	Calm	35	N. W.	30	23	Thawing
8	24	N. W.	32	N. N. E.	27	N. W.	27	35	Snow in flakes at evening
9	7	N. N. W.	14	N. W.	14	N. W.	11	35	Windy. Snow ½ inch last night
10	— 8	N. W.	3	N. W.	— 3	N. W.	— 3	27	Windy. Slight snow last night
11	—16	N. W.	— 2	N. W.	— 3	N. W.	— 7	29	Moderate wind
12	7	S. E.	32	S. E.	36	N. W.	25	22	Strong wind, A. M. Little rain and snow, P. M.
13	10	N. W.	17	N. W.	13	N. W.	13	17	Snow, P. M.
14	2	N. W.	21	N. W.	— 1	N. W.	8	26	Fresh wd. Snow 6 inches last night
15	—14	N. W.	— 5	N.	— 5	N.	— 8	31	Fresh wind
16	— 9	N. W.	4	N. W.	1	N. W.	— 1	25	
17	— 9	S. E.	11	S. E.	11	Sy.	— 4	35	Snow ¼ inch at night.
18	—13	N. W.	9	N. W.	1	N. W.	— 1	25	Light wind
19	1	N. N. E.	9½	N. E.	2	N. W.	4	27	Snow 1 inch last night.
20	— 5	S. E.	9	S. E.	11	S. E.	— 5	22	Windy. Snow storm from 9 A. M.
21	10	N. W.	13	N. W.	1	N. W.	8	25	Snow till 3 P. M. Snow 5 inches on 19th & 20th
22	—15	N. W.	11	N. W.	— 8	N. W.	— 4	33	Light winds
23	— 9	S. E.	11	S. E.	12	S. E.	5	29	Windy. Thermom. at 17°, P. M.
24	19	N. W.	34	N. W.	19	N. W.	20	20	
25	— 5	S. E.	23	S. E.	23	S. E.	13	30	Windy
26	26	N. W.	33	N. W.	21	N. W.	26	23	Snow last night 4½ inches
27	19	N. W.	23	N. W.	4	N. W.	15	32	Light breezes. Snow
28	—15	S. E.	9	S. E.	5	S. E.	0	36	Windy
29	6	S E.	12	N. W.	— 3	N. W.	5	21	Windy. A lit. snow, A. M.
30	—26	S. E.	— 2	S. E.	0	N. W.	— 9	32	
31	— 2	N. W.	— 3	N. W.	—11	N. W.	— 5	30	Windy, A. M.

Remarkable Phenomena.—January 18th. This morning a parhelion appeared around the sun as he rose, consisting of a mock sun, or image of the sun on each side of him in a horizontal line. From the image northward of the sun there issued a cone of light, the vertex of which was directed from the sun. There was no halo, and the mock suns were not well defined by any outline, though the morning was fair, and the sun shone bright. At eight o'clock

BAROMETER			MODIFICATIONS AND COURSES OF CLOUDS.					
			MORNING.		MID-DAY.		EVENING.	
Morning.	Noon.	Evening.	Clouds.	Courses.	Clouds.	Courses.	Clouds.	Courses.
28.58	28.77	28.87	Ns.	—	Ns.	—	Cs.	—
29.00	28.91	29.00	Ns,	—	C,	N. W.	Cs,	—
28.98	28.76	28.87	C,	N. W.	C,	N. W.	Fair	—
29.04	28.97	29.03	Cs.	—	Cs.	—	C,	W.
29.19	29.02	29.04	C,	N. W.	Fair	—	Fair	—
28.88	28.74	28.66	Cs.	N.	Ns.	—	Ns.	—
28.60	28.44	28.57	Cs,	—	C,	—	Cs,	—
28.80	28.74	28.85	Cs.	—	Ns.	N. E.	Ns.	—
29.14	29.04	29.10	Ns.	—	Ns.	—	Ns.	—
29.15	29.12	29.21	Fair	—	Fair	—	Fair	—
29.48	29.27	29.21	Fair	—	Fair	—	Fair	—
28.63	28.58	28.62	Ns.	W. N. W.	Ns	—	Ns.	—
28.77	28.75	28.78	Ns	N. W.	Ns.	—	Ns.	—
28.97	28.97	29.13	Ns.	—	Ns.	—	C,	—
29.40	29.40	29.40	Ns.	—	Ns.	—	Ns.	—
29.22	28.98	28.96	Ns.	—	Cml.	—	—	—
28.82	28.76	28.86	Cs,	—	Ns.	—	Ns.	—
29.06	28.93	28.90	Fair	—	Fair	—	Hazy	—
28.83	28.83	28.86	Ns.	—	Ns.	—	Cs.	—
28.70	28.59	28.60	Ns.	—	Ns.	—	Ns.	—
28.85	28.99	29.15	Ns.	—	Ns.	—	Cml,	—
29.33	29.27	29.26	Fair	—	Fair	—	Fair	—
29.05	28.95	28.96	Cs,	W. N. W.	Cml,	—	Cs,	W. N. W.
29.19	29.15	29.19	Cs.	—	Cs.	—	Cs.	W.
29.08	28.95	28.84	Ns.	S. W.	Cml,	S. S. W.	Cml,	S. S. W.
28.42	28.42	28.61	Ns.	—	Cs.	—	Cs.	—
28.78	28.85	28.96	Ns.	—	Ns.	—	Cs,	—
28.90	28.77	28.80	C,	S. W.	C,	S. W.	Cs,	—
28.75	28.71	28.95	Cml,	S. E.	Cs,	N.	Cs,	—
29.07	28.95	28.93	C,	—	C,	—	Cs,	—
29.30	29.38	29.41	Cs,	W. N. W.	Cs.	—	Cs.	—

the distance of the mock suns from each other, measured by a sextant, was found to be 44° 40'. At half past eight they had assumed the appearance of extended planes perpendicular to the horizon, and about 5° or 6° in length; breadth a little more than sun's diameter; soon after which they disappeared. N. B. See *Remarkable Phenomena* continued, on page lxviii, at the conclusion of the *Meteorological Register.*

Day of Month.	MORNING.		MID-DAY.		EVENING.		Mean Temp.	Mean Temp. at Germantown.	AT ENGINEER CANTONMENT.
	Temperature.	Wind.	Temperature.	Wind.	Temperature.	Wind.			REMARKS.
1	—12	S. E.	— 3	S. E.	— 3	S. E.	— 6	8	A little snow, A. M. and windy
2	0	N. W.	7	N. W.	— 2	N. W.	2	21	Fresh winds.
3	— 5	S. E.	13	S. E.	20	S. E.	9	33	Windy
4	4	S. E.	30	S. E.	33	S. E.	22	28	Windy. Thermom. 34°, P. M. Snow melting
5	39	S. E.	45	S. E.	19	N. W.	34	24	Thawing at noon
6	7	S. E.	35	S. E.	29	S. E.	23	40	Fresh wind. Thawing
7	4	S. E.	33	S. E.	34	S. E.	23	32	Damp & foggy. Light wds.
8	21	N. W.	33	N. E.	31	N. W.	28	35	Damp and foggy. Icy particles falling all day
9	23	S. E.	41	S. E.	31	S. E.	31	31	Snow and ice melting
10	12	S. E.	31	S. E.	38	S. E.	27	22	Snow and ice melting
11	31	S. E.	44	W. N. W.	34	N. N. W.	36	31	Snow and ice melting
12	26	N. W.	35	S. E.	31	S. E.	30	33	A little rain and snow
13	33	S. E.	46	S. E.		S. E.		49	Rain and hail last night. Windy and warm to-day
14	34	N. W.	35	N. W.	37	N. W.	35	42	Violent wind all day with a little snow
15	33	S. E.	39	S. E.	44	S. E.	38	51	Snow chiefly melted. A little snow fell
16	32	N. W.	33	N. W.	29	N. W.	34	41	Violent wind last night & to-day, with some snow
17	20	N. W.	34	S. E.	31	S. E.	28	49	Moderate winds
18	27	S. E.	30	S. E.	30	S. E.	29	38	Windy
19	26	N. W.	23	N. W.	25	N. W.	24	29	Violent wind last night
20	20	N. W.	34	N. W.	30	N. W.	28	37	Moderate wind
21	33	S. E.	51	S. E.	47	S. E.	43	32	Thermometer at 55°. Ice rapidly dissolving
22	35	N. W.	45	S. E.	37	S. E.	39	39	Fresh brs. Ice melting
23	33	N. W.	47	N. W.	38	N. W.	39	44	Windy and squally. Geese flying northwardly
24	30	S. E.	54	S. E.	39	N. W.	41	53	Light breezes. Geese passing northwardly
25	33	N. W.	44	N. W.	35	N. W.	37	45	Light breezes. Ducks passing down river
26	25	N. W.	39	N. W.	35	N. W.	33	48	Snow last night 1-8th inch
27	21	N. W.	44	N. W.	40	N. W.	35	51	Frost last night
28	34	Calm	57	S. E.	49	W. N. W.	46	41	Frost last night
29	22	N. W.	60	S. E.	55	W. N. W.	45	32	Frost abundant. River begins to open

Remarkable Phenomena.—15th, Lightning in N. E. this evening between 7 and 8 o'clock—clear sky—fresh S. E. wind. During the violent wind to-day the rain guage was blown from its station and broken.

BAROMETER.			MODIFICATIONS AND COURSES OF CLOUDS.					
			MORNING.		MID-DAY.		EVENING.	
Morning.	Noon.	Evening.	Clouds.	Courses.	Clouds.	Courses.	Clouds.	Courses.
29.06	28.87	28.81	Ns.	—	Cs,	—	Cs.	—
28.80	28.77	28.88	Cs.	—	Cml,	—	Fair	--
28.85	28.69	28.67	C,	N. W.	Cs,	—	Cs,	—
28.84	28.65	28.60	C,	N. W.	C,	W. N. W.	C,	W. N. W.
28.32	28.22	28.72	Cs,	W.	Cs,	—	Cml,	—
29.00	28.87	28.78	Cs.	—	Cs.	—	Cml,	W. S. W.
28.95	28.76	28.83	C,	—	Fair	—	C,	—
28.75	28.60	28.69	Ns. S.	—	Ns.	—	Ns.	—
28.86	28.83	28.79	Ns.	—	Ns.	—	Ns.	--
28.84	28.58	28.66	C,	—	C,	N. W.	Fair	—
28.60	28.33	28.50	C,	—	C,	—	C,	—
28.80	28.50	28.60	Cs.	—	Fair	—	C,	—
28.33	28.16		Cs,	—	C,	—	C,	--
28.24	28.26	28.33	Cs,	—	Ns.	—	Ns.	—
28.24	28.00	27.80	Cs, Cml,	SSW,SSE	Ns.	S. S. E.	Cm,	—
27.96	28.21	28.43	Ns.	N. N. W.	Ns.	—	Cs,	—
28.76	28.55	28.66	Fair	—	C,	—	C,	—
28.86	28.73	28.55	Cs.	N. N. W.	Cs,	—	Cs.	—
28.44	28.69	28.89	Ns.	—	Cml,	N. N. W.	C,	—
28.96	28.86	28.87	Fair	—	Fair	—	Fair	—
28.74	28.50	28.42	Fair	—	Fair	—	Fair	--
28.53	28.47	28.49	C,	—	C,	N. W.	C,	N. W.
28.16	28.19	28.40	Cs,	—	Cms,	—	Fair	—
28.30	28.07	28.08	Cs.	W. N. W.	Cs.	W. N. W.	C, Cs,	—
28.11	27.96	28.05	Cs,	—	Cs, Cml,	S.W,N.W.	Ns,	—
28.21	28.25	28.38	Ns,	N. W.	Cs, Cml,	W.,NNW.	Cs,	--
28.67	28.58	28.63	C,	—	Cs,	—	C,	—
28.87	28.73	28.73	Fair	—	C,	—	Fair	--
28.90	28.65	28.57	Fair	—	Fair	—	Fair	—

22d.—Halo around the moon this evening at 40′ past 6—ascertained its diameter to be 45° 8′. Cirrus cloud all over the sky.

23d.—Halo around the moon this evening also.

Day of Month.	MORNING. Temperature.	Wind.	MID-DAY. Temperature.	Wind.	EVENING. Temperature.	Wind.	Mean Temp.	Mean Temp. at Germantown.	Rise or fall of Missouri r in the last 24 hours. Inc.	AT ENGINEER CANTONMENT. REMARKS.
1	20	N. W.	32	N. W.	21	N. W.	24	40	—12	Violent winds
2	16	N. W.	26	S. E.	26	Calm	22	24	+ 1	Frost last night. Icy particles falling in the morning
3	21	N. W.	28	N. W.	24	N. W.	24	24	+ 5½	Strong wind. A little snow
4	32	S. W.	50	S. E.	48	N. W.	43	31	+ 5	Frost last night. Fresh wind
5	30	N. W.	28	N. W.	25	N. W.	27	41	— 2	Very clear sky all day
6	5	N. W.	13	N. W.	9	N. W.	9	44	+ 2½	Snow ¾ inch last night
7	6	N. W.	15	N. W.	14	N. W.	11	26	+27½	Frost last night
8	15	N. W.	16	N. N. E.	12	N. W.	14	28	+20	Frost last night
9	24	N. W.	23	E. S. E.	24	S. E.	23	31	+ 4	Frost last night
10	20	Calm	35	S. E.	34	S. E.	29	33	— 5	Fresh wind. No geese, few ducks flying
11	28	S. E.	23	S. E.	25	S. E.	25	27	— 1½	Violent winds. Snow ¾ inch
12	31	S. E.	42	S. E.	37	S. E.	36	27	+ 7	Moderate winds
13	32	N. W.	46	N. W.	40	N. W.	39	34	+ ½	Rain last night
14	19	N. W.	33	N. W.	32	Calm	28	46	— 6	Frost last nt. Riv. break. up
15	22	N. W.	39	N. W.	34	N. W.	31	36	— 5	Frost last night
16	21	S. E.	51	N. W.	43	N. W.	38	40	— 3	Do. Moderate winds
17	24	N. W.	45	N. W.	36	Calm	35	43	— 3¼	Do. Light and var. winds
18	34	S. E.	61	S. E.	58	S. E.	51	40	—14¼	River open. Geese, swans, ducks, &c. flying up
19	39	N. W.	48	N. W.	41	N. W.	42	39	— 1½	A little rain, A. M.
20	25	Calm	48	N. W.	41	Calm	38	44	— 1½	A little rain, P. M.
21	25	Calm	58	N. W.	49	N. W.	44	42	+ 5	Frost. Geese, &c. flying Nly.
22	34	Calm	67	N. W.	58	N. W.	53	43	+10	Moderate wind
23	38	S. E.	65	S. E.	68	S. E.	57	48	+42	Violent wind all day
24	55	S. E.	65	S.	53	S.	57	54	+40	High wind, A. M. Showers P.M. Light. in N. E. even.
25	38	N. W.	51	N. W.	46	N. W.	45	56	+10	Drizzly, A. M.
26	38	N. W.	40	N. W.	42	N. W.	40	57	—12	Heavy rain till 7 A. M. Some rain and snow afterwards
27	29	Calm	56	S. E.	45	S. E.	43	57	+10	Frost last nt. A lit. rain P.M.
28	39	S. E.	45	E.	38	N. E.	40	50	— 4½	Rain occas. through the day
29	28	N. W.	34	N.	32	N. E.	31	51	— 6	Fresh winds
30	28	S. E.	56	S. E.	52	S.	45	34	— 2	Heavy frost last night
31	35	Calm	57	N. E.	40	N. E.	44	34	+ 6	Windy P. M. and all night

Remarkable Phenomena.—Halo around the moon on the evening of the 21st.—Continued several hours. Same on the evening of the 23d, from 7 till 11 o'clock.

The ice on the Missouri broke and commenced moving on the 29th February; but a few days after it blocked up and continued stationary until the 14th of the present month, when it began to move again; and on the 18th it was entirely open and clear of ice. In this register an extra column is added, containing the daily rise or fall of the river. The

BAROMETER.			MODIFICATIONS AND COURSES OF CLOUDS.					
			MORNING.		MID-DAY.		EVENING.	
Morning.	Noon.	Evening.	Clouds.	Courses.	Clouds.	Courses.	Clouds.	Courses.
29.27	29.27	29.50	Fair	—	Fair	—	Fair	—
29.42	29.10	29.00	C,	N. W.	Cs,	—	C,	—
28.90	28.90	28.94	Ns,	N. N. E.	Cml,	N. N. E.	Cml,	—
28.67	28.84	28.84	C,	—	C,	—	Cs,	—
28.88	28.75	28.86	Fair	—	C,	N. W.	Cs,	N.
29.14	29.04	29.12	Cs.	—	Cml,	N. E.	C,	—
29.16	29.10	29.16	Fair	—	Fair	—	Fair	—
29.32	29.18	29.20	Fair	—	Fair	—	Fair	—
29.14	28.96	28.98	Fair	—	Fair	—	Cs,	—
29.20	29.18	29.18	Cs,	S. E.	Ns.	—	Ns.	—
29.20	29.14	29.00	Ns.	—	Ns.	—	Ns.	—
28.95	28.80	28.74	Ns. S	—	Ns.	—	Ns.	—
28.74	28.62	28.55	Ns. S	—	Cs,	—	Ns,	—
28.76	28.67	28.67	Cml,	N. N. W.	Cml,	N. N. W.	Cml,	N. N. W.
28.89	28.81	28.84	Cs.	W. N. W.	Cs.	W. N. W.	Cs,	W. N. W.
28.94	28.72	28.77	Fair	—	Cml,	—	Cml,	—
29.05	28.90	28.90	Cs	N. N. W.	Cs,	N. N. W.	Cs,	—
28.82	28.60	28.50	Fair	—	C,	—	Cs,	—
28.75	28.75	28.88	Ns.	—	Ns.	—	Cml,	W.
29.10	28.90	28.83	Fair	—	Cml.	N.	Cml,	N.
28.88	28.74	28.48	Fair	—	C,	—	C,	—
28.38	28.25	28.49	C,	N. W.	C,	W.	Cml,	—
28.58	28.26	28.20	Cs.	—	Cs.	S. E.	Cs,	W.
28.30	28.30	28.40	Cs,	S. W.	Ns.	—	Cml,	—
28.62	28.52	28.50	Ns.	—	Ns.	—	Cs,	S.
28.31	28.37	28.60	Ns.	—	Ns.	—	Cml,	—
28.90	28.90	28.90	Cs,	—	Cs.	—	Cs.	—
28.87	28.91	29.02	Cml,	—	Ns,	E.	Cs.	—
29.27	29.30	29.28	Cml,	N. W.	Cml,	—	Cml,	—
29.03	28.89	28.72	C,	N. W.	Fair	—	Cml,	W.
28.53	28.60	28.34	Fair	—	C, Cs,	—	Cs.	—

sign — denotes the fall of the water during the last twenty-four hours, and the sign +
denotes its rise during the same length of time. When the register was commenced the
river was three feet above the low-water mark, or its lowest stage in the winter. Therefore on the 25th, when it was highest this month, it was thirteen feet five inches above its
lowest stage in the winter.

Day of Month.	MORNING.		MID-DAY.		EVENING.		Mean. Temp.	Mean Temp. at Germantown.	Rise or fall of Missouri ri in the last 24 hours. Inc.	AT ENGINEER CANTONMENT. REMARKS.
	Temperature.	Wind.	Temperature.	Wind.	Temperature.	Wind.				
1	29	N. N. E.	28	N. W.	20	N. W.	25	52	+ 5	A light snow fell to-day
2	15	N. N. E.	38	N. W.	27	N. W.	24	32	— 7	Geese, &c. flying S. to-day
3	14	Calm	41	S. E.	46	E.	33	—	— 3	Large frost last night
4	40	W. N. W.	64	N. W.	51	N. W.	51	—	+12	Strong wind
5	29	N. W.	59	N. W.	49	Calm	45	—	+22	Strong wind
6	41	S. E.	65	N. W.	55	N. W.	53	—	+ 5	Very windy. Large hail fell before sun-rise
7	41	N. W.	65	N. W.	52	N. W.	52	44	— 9	Windy. Light sprinkle of rain this afternoon
8	32	Calm	57	N. W.	47	N. W.	45	46	0	Strong wind
9	40	S. E.	76	S. E.	70	S. E.	62	47	0	Windy
10	50	S.	79	S.	69	N. W.	66	57	+28	Geese flying N. Strong wind
11	49	N. W.	69	N. W.	59	N. W.	59	—	+12	Strong wind
12	35	S. E.	65	S. E.	64	Calm	54	56	+14	Very strong wind
13	48	S. E.	80	S. E.	72	S. E.	66	52	—12	Lt. in N. and N. W. Windy
14	50	S. E.	68	S. E.	70	Calm	62	54	—16	Rain and thunder in aftern.
15	51	S. E.	71	S. E.	72	S. E.	64	55	— 7½	Fresh wind. Lightn. in N.W.
16	49	S. E.	62	S. E.	64	S. E.	58	49	— 4	Rainy
17	50	S. E.	66	S. E.	79	S. E.	65		— 4½	Lightning last night
18	53	S. E.	82	S. E.	82	S.	72		— 5½	Fresh wind
19	63	S.	79	S. E.					— 3	Strong wind
20	59	S.	65	S. E.	62	Calm	62		— 2½	Strong wind
21	54	S. E.	71	N. W.	74	N. W.	66		— 3	Fresh breeze
22	55	N. W.	76	S. E.	70	N. W.	67		— 3	Wind very strong at mid-day
23	58	S. E.	84	S. E.	83	S. E.	75		0	Strong wind
24	65	S. E.	79	S. E.	80	E. S. E.	74		— 2	Fresh wind. Violent rain and hail storm after sun-set, 1-3 inch rain in one hour
25	50	N. W.	52	N. W.	57	N. W.	53		— ½	Rain to-day
26	42	N. W.	63	N. W.	67	N. W.	57		— 3	Fresh breeze
27	49	N. W.	67	E. N. E.	69	E.	61		— 2½	
28	53	S. E.	59	S. E.	64	S. E.	58		— 1½	Fresh wind in morning
29	53	S. E.	65	E. S. E.	67	E. S. E.	61		— ½	
30	56	S. E.	68	E.	70	E. S. E.	64		— 8½	

Remarkable Phenomena.—20th, Halo and Corona around the moon.

In the hail storm of the 24th, hail stones fell of a very large size. One of the largest seen here was of the following dimensions, viz. length 2 inches, breadth 1½ inches, depth 1 1-8 inches.

BAROMETER.			MODIFICATIONS AND COURSES OF CLOUDS.					
			MORNING.		MID-DAY.		EVENING.	
Morning.	Noon.	Evening.	Clouds.	Courses.	Clouds.	Courses.	Clouds.	Courses.
29.00	29.03	29.10	Ns.	—	Ns.	—	Cs.	—
29.16	29.08	29.10	Fair	—	Cs.	—	Fair	—
29.08	28.90	28.70	Fair	—	Fair	—	Cs,	—
28.30	28.38	28.56	Cs,	—	Cml,	N. W.	Fair	—
28.56	28.70	28.80	Fair	—	Cml,	—	C,	N. W.
28.60	28.30	28.40	Cs.	—	Cs.	—	Cs.	—
28.45	28.56	28.73	Fair	—	Cm,	N. W.	Ns.	—
28.94	28.75	28.84	Fair	—	C,	—	Cs,	—
28.66	28.36	28.10	C,	—	Fair	—	Fair	—
28.00	27.44	27.50	C, Cm,	W. N. W.	C,	N. W.	Cml,	N. W.
28.32	28.32	28.39	C,	—	Cs,	—	Cs,	N. W.
28.48	27.94	28.35	Cml,	—	Cml,	S. W.	Cml,	S. W.
28.50	28.00	28.00	Cml,	N. W.	—	—	Cs, Cm,	S. W.
28.25	28.05	27.90	Ns,	S.	Ns.	—	Cs,	—
28.20	28.10	28.10	Cml,	S. W.	Cml,	—	Ns.	—
28.40	28.25	28.20	Ns.	N. E.	Ns.	N. E.	Cs.	—
28.23	28.05	27.96	Ns.	—	Ns.	—	Cml,	—
28.03	27.60	27.72	Fair	—	Fair	—	Cml,	S. W.
27.40	27.40		Cs.	—	Cs.	—	Cml,	—
28.30	28.30	28.33	Cs,	—	Cs,	—	Cs,	—
28.40	28.20	28.10	Fair	—	Cml,	—	Cs,	—
28.40	27.94	28.08	Fair	—	Cs,	—	Cs,	—
28.25	27.60	27.15	C,	—	—	—	Cml,	—
27.97	27.76	27.77	Cml, Cs,	—	Cs,	—	Cs.	—
28.54	28.60	28.50	Cs.	—	Cs,	—	C,	—
28.62	28.41	28.26	Fair	—	—	—	—	—
28.59	28.31	28.24	C,	—	—	—	—	—
28.68	28.50	28.52	Cs.	—	Fair	—	Fair	—
28.76	28.54	28.50	Cs.	—	Fair	—	Fair	—
28.89	28.65	28.53	Cml,	—	—	—	—	—

April 16th, Fall of rain 3-10 inch.

Day of Month.	MORNING.		MID-DAY.		EVENING.		Mean Temp.	Rise or fall of Missouri in the last 24 hours Inc.	AT ENGINEER CANTONMENT.
	Temperature.	Wind.	Temperature.	Wind.	Temperature.	Wind.			REMARKS.
1	57	N. W.	74	N. W.	71	N. W.	67	+ 1	10 P. M. few drops of rain
2	54	S. E.	76	S. E.	75	S. E.	68	0	
3	59	S. E.	71	S. E.	67	S. E.	65	— 2½	Fresh wind
4	64	S. E.	66	N. W.	61	N. W.	63	+ 4½	Violent storm last night with thunder and lightning
5	50	N. W.	69	N. W.	70	S. S. E.	64	0	
6	54	S. E.	68	S. E.	70	S. E.	64	+19	
7	40	N. W.	55	N. W.	51	N. W.	48	+26	Rain last night, with thunder and lightning. Strong wind
8	45	S. E.		S. E.	59	S. E.		— 6	
9	51	S. E.	77	N. W.	65	N. W.	64	— 9	
10	53	S. E.	59	N. W.	52	N. W.	54	+19	
11	46	N. W.	61	N. W.	63	Calm	56	+15	
12	56	N. W.	70	N. W.	64	N. W.	63	+ 8	
13	54	N. W.	67	N. W.	62	N. W.	61	— 5	
14	50	N. W.	69	N. W.	64	N. W.	61	— 5	
15	58	S. E.	67	S. E.	66	S. E.	63	— 7	
16	59	S. E.	65	S. E.	61	S. E.	61	— 7	Storm last night of wind, rain, and hail
17	61	S. E.	70	S. E.	68	S. E.	66	— 6	Rain last night, with much wind, thunder and lightning
18	59	S. E.	66	S. E.	66	S. E.	63	— 5	
19	56	S. E.	72	S. E.	68	S. E.	65	— 7	
20	54	S. E.	68	S. E.	69	S. E.	63	— 3	Rainy
21	56	S. E.	76	S. E.	71	S. E.	67	— 6	
22	60	S. E.	77	S. E.	75	S. E.	70	0	Light breezes
23	60	S. E.	83	S. E.	77	Calm	73	+ 5½	
24	67	S. E	69	S. E.		E.		+14	Rain with high wind this evening. Thunder and lightning
25	53	E.	67	N. E.	59	N. E.	59	— 6	
26	57	N. W.	68	N. W.	62	N. W.	62	—12	
27	50	N. W.	76	N. W.	72	N. W.	66	+ 1	
28	58	N. W.	79	N. W.	68	N. W.	68	+40	Light winds
29								+30	Light winds
30	59	S. E.	73	S. E.	71	S. E.	67	+15	Light winds
31	58	S. E.	66	S. E.	63	S. E.	62	—24	Light winds

May 4th, fall of rain, ½ inch—10th, 1 inch—20th, 1·8th inch—24th, ¾ inch.

BAROMETER.			MODIFICATIONS AND COURSES OF CLOUDS.					
			MORNING.		MID-DAY.		EVENING.	
Morning.	Noon.	Evening.	Clouds.	Courses.	Clouds.	Courses.	Clouds.	Courses.
28.80	28.46	28.44	Cs.	—	Cms. Cs.	—	Cs.	—
28.66	28.20	28.18	Cs.	—	Cm,	—	Cs,	—
28.41	28.07	28.07	Cs.	—	Cms.	—	Cs.	—
27.70	27.74	28.03	Ns.	—	Ns,	—	Ns.	—
28.03	28.38	28.33	Cs, C,	—	Cm.	—	Cs,	—
28.59	28.31	28.03	Cs.	—	Cs,	—	Cs,	—
28.23	28.29	28.81	Cm,	—	Cm,	—	Fair	—
28.72		28.53	Cs,	—	C,	W. N. W.	Cs,	—
28.60	28.08	28.37	Cs,	—	Cm,	—	Cml,	—
28.57	28.41	28.50	Ns.	—	Ns.	—	Ns.	—
28.63	28.40	28.40	Ns	—	Cml,	—	Cs,	N. W.
28.25	28.40	28.58	Cs,	N. W.	Cs,	N. W.	Cml,	N. W.
28.26	28.70	28.75	Fair	—	Fair	—	Fair	—
28.91	28.65	28.61	Fair	—	Fair	—	C,	N. W.
28.80	28.63	38.70	Cs.	—	Cml.	—	Cs,	N. W.
28.80	28.73	28.73	Ns,	S. E.	Ns.	S. E.	Ns.	E. S. E.
28.60	28.25	28.30	Ns.	—	Ns,	S. E.	Cml.	S. E.
28.37	28.30	28.24	Ns.	—	Cml.	S. E.	Cml.	S. E.
29.47	28.18	28.26	C,	—	Ns,	S. E.	C,	—
28.47	28.33	28.27	Ns.	S. E.	Ns.	—	Ns.	—
28.27	28.14	28.21	C,	—	C, Cm,	S.	C, Cm,	S'.
28.00	28.08	28.15	Fair	—	Cm,	S. W.	Cm,	—
28.22	27.70	27.82	Fair	—	Cm.	—	Cm, Cs,	—
28.02	28.07		C,	—	C. Cs.	—	Ns,	—
28.57	28.57	28.65	Ns.	—	Cml,	—	Cs,	—
28.55	28.68	28.60	Cs,	—	Cml,	N. W.	Fair	—
28.66	28.13	28.22	Fair	—	Cml,	N. W.	Cs, Cm,	—
28.48	28.00	28.29	Cml,	—	Cm.	N. W.	Cm,	—
			Fair	—	Cs.	—	Cm,	—
28.49	28.21	28.31	C,	—	Cms,	—	Cs.	—
28.76	28.47	28.66	C,	—	Cs.	—	Cs,	—

[*Remarkable Phenomena* continued from page lix.]

January 29th. Parhelion around the sun this afternoon, consisting of a halo circumscrib-ing the sun, in the circumference of which appeared the mock suns, and in a horizontal line with the sun. The diameter of the halo was observed to be 45° 20'. To the N. E. of the sun there also appeared a luminous arch inverted, or having its convex part towards the sun, and its extremities directed from it. It was about 60° of a circle of a smaller periphery than the halo, and well defined. The part nearest the sun was found to be 48° 17' distant from that luminary, so that it did not come in contact with the halo, but the points of their near-est approach were 25° 37' apart. The halo was indistinct, except in the vicinity of the mock suns, where it was well defined. Time of making observations half past three o'clock, P. M. Thermometer at the same time 5°, Barometer 28.88, atmosphere hazy, thin light clouds about sun, fresh N. W. wind.

This evening soon after the moon rose, there being a thick haze or mist in the atmosphere about her, there appeared two luminous cones of a reddish cast, whose bases coincided with the moon's disc; the one extending with its vertex above the moon directed towards the zenith, and the other with its vertex below her approaching the horizon. At six o'clock the paraselene appeared complete, consisting of the halo of the same diameter as that around the sun this afternoon, the mock moons or images, and the inverted arch to the S. W. of the moon, and of the same size and distance from the moon as that which appeared with the parhelion above mentioned. From each mock moon there projected a cone of light, whose vertices were directed from the moon. Soon after these appeared two more cones issuing from the moon, one on each side of her in a horizontal direction. The length of the one pro-jecting downwards was 8° 40'; that of the other three 2° 30', they being equal in length. Thermometer when the observations on the moon were made stood at 5°, Barometer 29.00, fresh N. W. breeze, atmosphere hazy, no clouds visible about moon.

January 31st. Parhelion around the sun this morning, consisting of the mock suns only, which appeared soon after sunrise, the distance between them measured 44° 30'

On the 12th the ice in the river was found to be 28 inches thick. Very little current where the measurement was made.

VOCABULARIES

OF

INDIAN LANGUAGES.

———◆———

FOR the accuracy of the words in the following Vocabularies we have to rely upon the knowledge of the Indians or interpreters from whom we received them, having carefully noted them down on the spot, as they appeared to be pronounced. I have much pleasure in acknowledging the ready and important aid which I received from Mr. John Dougherty, at present Deputy Indian Agent for the Missouri; indeed, the Omawhaw, Shoshone and Upsaroka vocabularies are chiefly set down agreeably to his pronunciation.

The philologist will observe, that in these vocabularies, the guttural sound is indicated by a †, a nasal sound by an *, and a ‡ accompanying the letter j, shows that the French sound of that letter must be given to it.

T. SAY.

VOCABULARY OF INDIAN LANGUAGES.

Fàte, fàr, fâll, fät ;—mè, mèt ;—pine, pìn ;—nò, mòve, nòr, nòt ;—tùbe, tùb, bùll ;—òll ;—pòùnd.

	Wäh-tòk-tá-tá, or Oto Language.	Kónzá Language.	O-máw-hâw Language.	Sioux, (Yancton band,) Lang.	Mìn-né-tä-ré, or Gros ventre Language.	Páw-né Language.	Chèl-á-kè, or Cherokee Language.
Head	nä-só	vé-ách-ré	pàh	pàh	än-too	päk-shù	ïs-kò
Hair	nä-tó	pä-heu	pä-hé	pä-hä	àr-rä	ò-shù	kä-tlùh
Face	ïn-jä		ïn-dä	é-tä	é-tä		ä-gä-tä-gä-nùh
Forehead	pä	päh	pä	é-tä-hò	é-ré	päk-shé-ré	ä-kä-tùh
Eye	ïsh-t äh	ïsh-täh	ïsh-täh	ïsh-täh	ïsh-täh	kè-ré-kò	còl-yén-sùh
Nose	pä-só	päh	(same as head)	pä-sò	ä-päh	tshù-shò	kád-lä-nùh
Ear	nän-tois	näh-täh	né-täh	nòng-kó-pä	lä-hòch-é	át-kä-rò	é-ä-nä-gä-lùh
Lip	é-hä	é-häh	é-hâh } same	é-hä			ä-hò-lé
Mouth	é	yéh or éh	é-hâh }	eé	é-éép-chäp-päh	tskä-ò	käy-én-äh
Chin	é-kò	égh	rä-bä-hé	é-kò		kä-kä	ky-tò-kä
Tooth	hé	héh	eé	hé	eé (teeth)	hä-rò	kä-nò-kùh
Tongue	rä-zä	yää-säh	they-sé or thä-sé	chä-dzhé	néigh-t jé	hä-tò	ä-hä-nò-lùh
Beard	é-hé	é-h-häh-hé	é-hé	pò-té-hé	ä-poò-té	rä-ròsh	kit-sänéor ä-gìt-ä-gä-nùh
Neck	tä-shä	täh-heu	pä-hé (same as hair)	tä-hò	ä-péh	tshù-shé-ré	
Skin	hò-hä	whùgh-hah	hä	hä	läugh-pä	skä-rét-kè	kán-ä-gùh
Arm	ä-grät-ché	äh	äh	ïs-tò	arròugh	pé-é-rù	kán-ò-gän
Hand	nä-wä	shä-géh	nòm-bä	nä-pä	shän-té	ïk-shé-ré	ò-woy-än-é
Fingers	no name for the fingers collectively.	shä-géh-häh	shä-gä	näp-chò-pä	shän-té-ïch-pò	hásh-pét	tä-kä-yä-sùt-én
Nail	shä-gä	shä-géh-hù-hah	shä-gä-hä	shä-kä	ïch-pò	hásh-pét	kä-sò-kùt-ùn

Leg hŏ	shä-gäh	näugh-pä-hĕ	hŏ	ĕh-tä-whĭr-tä	käsh-ŏ	kŭn-ŭns-kä-nŭh
Thigh rä-gä	shä-gäh-tŭn-gäh	‡jä-gŭh	chä-chä	ĕ-rĕ-kĕ	pĕ-kä-tä-kŏ	kä-gŭh-lung
Foot cĕ	sĕh	sĕ	cĕ-hä	ĭt-sĕ	äsh-ŏ	lä-sä-tä-nŭh
Toes no name for the toes collectively	sĕ-häh	sĕ-pä	cĕ-shäs-tä	ĭt-sĕ-shän-kĕ	äsh-ŏ-häsh-pĕt	tä-kä-nä-sŭt-ŭh
Copulation wä-tŏ		wät-chĕ	tow-ĕ-tŏng	ĕ-ĕ-pĕ	cär-ĕ-ŏ	ä-tŭh
Penis rä	shäng-a	‡jä	chä	ĕ-rĕ		ŏ-wĕ-däh
Vulva ŏ-yä		ĕ-‡jä	sŏ-sŏ	shĕr-räh	kĕ-shät-skĕ	kĕ-kŭh
Meat tä-tŏ-kä	tä-tŏ-kah	tä-nŏ-kä	tä-dŏ	cŭ-rŭc-tschĭt-tĕ	hä-tŏ	ŏ-nŏh-hwä
Blood wä-pä-gä	wäh-pĕ	wä-mĕ	oŭä	ĕh-rĕ	pĕt-sŏ	kŏ-lŭh
Heart nän-tchä	nä-chä	naun-dä	shän-tä	näh-täh	ärĕ-kŏ	hŭ-lŏn-ŭh
Bone wä-hŏ	wä-heu	*y-hĕ	hŏ, same as leg	ĕ-rouh		
Horn chä-hä	häh	hä	hĕh or hä	än-tjĕ		
Magician wäh-hŏ-bĕn-ne	nĕ-kŏs-shĭng-gŏh	nĕ-kä-shĭng-gŭh-hŏ-bä				
Chief wäng-ä-gĕ-hĕ		nĕ-kä-gä-hĕ				
Man wäh-shĕ-gä		nŏ	wĕ-chä-shä	mät-tzä	tsä-ĕ-ksh	ski-yŭh
Old man wä-shä-ĭn-gä	wä-kŏoh	ĭsh-ä-gä	wĕ-chäch-chäh	ĕ-tän-cä		
Soldier mŏĭ-ä-kĕ-tä		wä-nä-shä				
Woman näh-häk-kä		wä-ŏ	wĕ-äh	mĕ-yä	tsä-pät	kä-yŭh
Old woman nä-äk-shĭn-yä	shĕ-dŏ-shĭng-gŏh	wa-o-tjĭn-guh	wä-kŏnk-kä	gä-nŏ		
Boy chĭn-tŏ-ĭng-yä		nŏ-tjĭng-gä	hŏ-kĕ-shĕ-nä	shĭ-kän-tjä	pĕsh-kĕ	ät-sŏ-zŭh
Friend ĭn-tär-rŏ		cä-gä	wĕ-chĭn-chä-nŏ	mĕ-yä-kän-tja		
Girl chĕ-mĕ-ĭng-yä	shĕ-mĕ-shĭng-gŏh	mĕ-tjĭng-gä			tchŏ-rä-ksh	ä-gä-hĕw-tzŭh
Father än-tchä	ĕ-täh-chĕh	dä-dä or dä-dä-hä	ät-cŭ-cŭ	tän-tä	ä-tĕ-äsh	ä-tŏ-tŭh

VOCABULARY OF INDIAN LANGUAGES.

Fāte, fär, fȧll, făt;—mē, mĕt;—pïne, pĭn;—nō, mŏve, nŏr, nŏt;—tūbe, tŭb, bŭll;—ŏïl;—pŏŭnd.

	Wȧh-tŏk-tā-tā, or Oto Language.	Kónzá Language.	O-máw-háw Language.	Sioux, (Yancton band,) Lang.	Mĭn-ne-tȧ-rĕ, or Gros ventre Language.	Páw-nĕ Language.	Chêl-ȧ-kĕ, or Cherokee Language.
Mother	é-hóng, the mother	é-náh	é-hóng, the mother	hú-cō	é-kä	á-té-ráh	á-tsĭng
Son	é-ing-yá, the son	(See Boy)	é-ĭjing-gá, his son	ché-hét-cō	móŭ-rĭ-shá	pé-róŭ-tā-tā	á-quát-sé-át-sŭ-tsŭh
Daughter	é-óng-á, the daughter	(See Girl)	é-tjóng-gá, the daughter	wé-tách-nóng	má-cáth	tchŏ-rá-gé-lá-há	á-quát-sé-á-gá-hŏ-tsŭh
Pretty	ŏ-cóm-pé		ŏ-cóm-pé	ŏ-yŭk-cŏ-pé	é-tä-sŭk-ĕs	pé-róŭ	á-kȧh
Ugly	ŏ-cóm-pĭsh-cón-ná		ŏ-cóm-pé-á-íjá	ŏ-yŭk-shé-shá	é-tä-é-shé-ĕs		
Child	ché-chíng-á	shíng-góh-shíng-góh	shingá-shingá	ŏk-ché-chŏ-pá	mán-on-gáh, children	pé-róŭ	á-kȧh
Brother	é-ená, elder brother é-sóng-á, younger brother	wés-sŏn-gáh	wé-sŏn-gáh, younger brother ĭjé-ná-há, elder brother	hŏ.cówng-ĭjé-cŏ ché-á, my elder brother	bé-á-cáh, elder mát-tsŏ-gá, younger	é-rá-ré	á-ké-né-lé
Sister	é-tóng-á, younger sister é-ŏnuh, elder do	wét-tŏn-géh	tóing-gá	tŏw-ín-och-té	mát-tó-mé-yá elder, mát-ták-ké-é-né,younger	é-tá-thé	áng-gá-tŭh
God	wáh-cón-dáh—they call the thunder the same	wŏk-kón-dŏh	wáh-cón-dá	wá-cá-tŭn-cá, the Great Spirit	mán-hó-pá, Great Spirit	tlóŭ-wá-hót, Master of Life	ká-lŏng-lá-té-é-géth-té-rá, the Great Spirit above

Devil	wåh-cŏn-dåh-plsh-cŏ-na, bad god	wŏk-kŏn-dŏh-pĕ-shĕ, bad spirit	ĩsh-tĕn-ĕ-kĕ,bad spirit or witch	wå-cŏn-shĕ-chĕh, bad spirit	no corresponding word	tså-hĕ-ksh-kå-kŏ-hrå-wåh, bad spirit	skĕ-nŭh
Heaven	wåh-nŏh-å-tchĕ-nŭh, town of spirits	no corresponding word; wåh-nåhk-hĕ-ŏ-shŏngĕ-yåh-rĕ —road of the dead	wå-nŏch-å-tĕ, town of brave and generous spirits	wån-åch-å-tĕ-på house of spirits	å-påh-hĕ, good village	tskå-ŏ, same as mouth	kå-lång-å-tĕ
Hell	no name for this	no corresponding word in this language; o-shŏn-gĕh-pĕ-shĕ—bad road	wå-nŏch-å-tŏw-woin-på-tjĕ, town of poor or useless spirits	no word for this	no corresponding word	kå-kŏ-hrĕ-å-tŏ-rŏ, bad road	tsĕns-skĕ-nŭh
Heat	tåh-ån-åh	mŏs-chĕh	ŏn-å-brĕ	ŏh-dĕ-dĕ-tå	år-råse	tŏŭ-ĕts-tŏ	tĕlh-kåh
Cold	snĕ	snĕ-wåh-chĕh	snĕ	snĕ	cĕ-rĕ-å	tå-pĕch-ĕ	ŭh-lån-nŭh
Rain	nĕ-yŭ	nĕ-shĕ-hue-åh	nåun-shĕ	må-hå-tjou wåh	†thår-å måh-på	tåt-sŏ-rŏ	å-gå-skŭh
Snow	påh	påh-hue-åh	måh		mĕ-†roh-thĕ måh-pĕ-ich-tĕ-ĕt-snow large	tŏ-shå	ån-tsink
Ice	nŏ-thå	nåh-hĕh	nŏ-hå	chå-thåh	hår-å-å-pa rain together	lå-shĕ-tŏ	ŭn-å-stĕr-lång
Hail	på-sŏ		må-sĕ	wås-sŏ	må-pŭs-å-gŭs må-lå kĕr-åug-cŏ-tåh ŏh-påh		the same as ice
Summer	tŏ-kå		nŏ-gåh	min-tŏ-cå-tŏ		lĕ-åt	kŏ-kĕ
Winter	på-nĕ		måh-rå-dŏng	wåh-nĕ-åh-tŏ		pĭtsh-ĕ-kåt	kŏ-lŭh
Morning	hå-rŏ-tåch-tchĕ		cås-åht-tĕ	hĕ-hån-nå		kå-kå-rŭsh-kå	sŏ-nåh-lĕh
Evening	ĕh-tå-nå		påz-zå	ĕh-ti-å-tŏ		wå-tåtĕ-kåt-tåtĕ-kĕ-å	sŏn-ĕ-å-lĕh

VOCABULARY OF INDIAN LANGUAGES.

Fâte, fâr, fâll, fât ;—mê, mêt ;—pîne, pîn ;—nô, môve, nôr, nôt ;—tûbe, tûb, bûll ;—ôïl ;—pôünd.

	Wâh-tók-tä-tä, or Oto Language.	Kónzä Language.	O-mâw-hâw Language.	Sioux, (Yancton band,) Lang.	Min-nê-tä-rê, or Gros ventre Language.	Pâw-nê Language.	Chêl-â-kê, or Cherokee Language.
Day	hâng-wâ		ôm-bâh	âung-pâ	mâh-pâh, very like snow	shâk-â-rô-ê-shâ-rêt	é-kûm
Night	hâng-hâ		hôn-dâ	hâ-*hâ-pê	ôh-sê-tîs	é-râ-shû-â-tê	sôn-ô-yêh
Sun	pê		mê-nâ-câ-jä	ôuê	mâh-pê-mê-nê, sun of day	shâ-kô-rô	nâ-tôh
Moon	pê-tâng-wâ, sun that gives light		mê-ôm-bâh	hâ-yâ-tô-wê	ôh-se-â-mê-nê, sun of night	pâ	as sun, dist. by adding *night*
Star	pê-kâh-hâ		mê-câ-â	wêh-châh-pê	é-kâh	ô-pê-rêt	nôh-kôs-â
Earth	mâ-hâ		môn-ê-kä	mông-câ	â-mâh	ô-râ-rô	kâ-tûn
Water	nê		nê	mê-nê	mé-nê	kêt-sô	â-mâh, nearly the same as *salt*
Whiskey	pâ-jê-nê		pâ-gê-nê				
Medicine	mân-cóng		môc-công				
Mysterious medicine	wâh-hô-nê-tä		†thô-bâ				
Fire	pá-jä		pâ-dâ	pâ-tä	bê-râs	lâ-tê-tô	ât-sê-lûh
Wood	nâ		†jan	châ*	bê-râ	lâ-gish, forest	ât-âh
Tree	nâ-bô-shrâ-jä, standing wood		†her-â-bâ-mê	châ-ôn-gê-nâ, one wood alone	bê-râ-êch-tê-êt		hû-kûh
Bean	ô-nê		hîm-bâr-rîn-grâ â-bâ	wâht-pâ	â-pâ-bât-tô-sê	léts-kô-shû	
Leaf	nâh-wâ		wât-tân-zê				
Maize	wâ-tô-jä		wât-tâng				ü-gâh-lô-kûh
Pumpkin	wat-twôlng						

English						
Bark	ná-há	tjòh-nòh-hàh né-né	cháng-há chán-té	ês-sché ow-pá	lá-vét-tá-té	ù-thá-lù-kùh
Tobacco	rá-né					
Hazlenuts	quá-ìng-yá					
Hill	ò-há	*á-tjin-guh pá-há				
Valley	á-brás-ká	ò-tjé-nòsh-ká	thá-á-cá	ávo-cá-vé-cár-ish-tá	pá-hò-ké-vé-tò	òh-tát-lùh
River	nésh-nòug-á, running water né-wá-brù, water springing up	wá-tish-ká	sé-mòng-cá	á-mán-shé-é-pé, a bushy ravine án-gé	lá-kát-tòsh, a ravine kát-tòsh	ák-wŏ-né
Spring	shòng-á?	né-hùn-gá	wá-cò-pá	má-há	kéts-pá-lé,	á-mùk-á-nù-gò-gùh
Gelding		shòng-gá-sòn-gá-án-né	cák-cé-zá	it-ze-mát-shù-gá	á-rò-shá	
Horse	shòng-tò-ká?	shòn-gá-tùn-gá	shòn-kò-wá-cóng	án-tjù-cá-bá-tù bé-cá	á-shá-tsá-pát	tsá-wìl-é
Mare	shòng-mìng-yá	shòn-gá-min-gá	shòng-min-tò-cá shòng-wé-á-nòng	it-zé-bì-zù-gá-nòn-gá	á-shá-kish	
Colt	shòng-shìng-yá	shòn-tò-tjin-gùh	shòng-ché-chá-ná	mát-shù-gá		
Dog	shòng-ò-ká-né, unmeaning horse	shé-nò-tá	shon-ká	sá-tjá		ké-lèh
Wolf	shòng-tùng	shòng-tùn-gùh	shínk-tò-ká-chèh			
Fox	mês-rá-ká	má-nìk-ò-shier wàsh-ìng-guh	chá-tò-ká-ná	ìh-hòc-cá-tjé	lé-kòt-ské	sés-quàh
Bird	wá-ìng-yá	zé-zé-kàh	zé-cá-nò	sá-cán-gá		
Turkey	wá-ék-kùng-já	†hé-rá-skà				
War eagle	hé-rá	ŏm-pá-nù-gàh	héh-há-ká	má-ròn-gá-cá-ré-pé		
Buck elk				má-ròn-gá-bé-cá		
Doe		ŏm-pá-min-gàh	ŏ-pòng			

VOCABULARY OF INDIAN LANGUAGES.

Fáte, fär, fåll, fåt:—mé, mét;—pìne, pìn;—nó, móve, nór, nót;—tûbe, tûb, büll;—öll;—poûnd.

	Wáh-tók-tá-tá, or Oto Language.	Kónzá Language.	O-máw-háw Language.	Sioux, (Yancton band,) Lang.	Mín-né-tá-ré, or Gros ventre Language.	Páw-né Language.	Chél-á-ké, or Cherokee Language.
Egg	é-tchá	ét-táh	wá-tûh	weet-cá	sá-cán-gá-non-gá	le-kót-ské-pé-kó	ó-á-téh
Buck deer			tóch-tá-nû-gáh	tá-mìn-dó-cá	sé-é-ká-tûc-ké		
Doe			tóch-ta-min-gáh	tá-wé-á-nóng	sé-é-ká-tûc-ké-bé-cá		
Fawn			tóch-tá-tjìngûh-hin-gara-jjá	tá-ché-chá-ná	sé-é-ká-tûc-ké-nón-gá		
Fish	hó	hó	hó-hó	hó-hûng	bó-á	kát-tshé-ké	át-tsá-téh
Squirrel	áh-sìn-yá		sìn-gûh				
Prairie dog	mán-né-hó-já	vátz-áh	mán-né-thó-dá	wám-dósh-ká	má-bûc-shá	lót-pát-sét	é-náh-táh
Snake	wá-cóng		wáis-ûh				
Bison	chá		tá		ké-é-rá-pé		
Otter	tósh-nóng-yá		nósh-nóh	pét-tóng	mé-rá-pó-cá		
Black tailed deer	tá-sá-wá		tóch-tá-sin-já-sá-bá				
Bear	món-já	wás-sáh-bá	wás-sá-bá	wá-hûnk-cá-cé-chá	láh-pét-zé	kó-róksh	yóh-nûh
Raccoon	mé-ká		mé-cá	wé-chá	mé-rá-pá		
Beaver	rá-wáy		íjjá-bá	chá-pá	á-táp-péh		
Louse	há	háh	há	há-ûh			
Antelope	tá-tó		tá-tshû-gûh			péts	tá-nûh
Skunk	món-ká		món-gûh				

Flea	tá-grés-ká, deer that is going	no corresponding word	tát-á-gŭh, fool deer	há-nŭh	sá-cás-kè	té-rá-gŭh	tsŭ-kŭh
Muskrat	ŏ-tŏ-ák-ká		sìn-já-sná-já-wá-gé-rè				
Rabbit	mish-tsching-yá		más-tschìn-gá	másh-té-chá-nŏng	é-tá-kè		
Bow	mán-tŏ	sháh-mé-ja	mán-dá-sán-rá	é-tá-zé-páh	bé-ráh-háh	té-rá-gìsh	kĕlk-tsŭt-è
Arrow	má	máh	máh	wáng-hink-a-pá	é-táh	lèk-shŏ	kŭn-è
Knife	má-hé		né-né-báh	mé-ná	mát-zé		
Pipe	rá-nŏ-wá	pá-chéh		chán-dŏw-hŏ-pá	éh-ké-pé		
Canoe	pá-já		mon-dé-há-shin-gá	wá-táh	á-mán-tá	lák-ŏ-hŏ-rŏ	tsé-ŭ
House	ché	téh	té	té-pé	á-té, Ind. lodge	ák-ká-rŏ	kát-sŏ-dá
Copper	má-zá-zé	máhs-és-sé-hé	môn-zá-tjé-dá	mas-ah-shah, or red iron	ŏ-wás-sá-shé-rè	kŏts-tér-rá-há	tsál-yá-tál-ou-i-ká, red brass
Stone	éng-rŏ é-rŏ	éh	é-éh	é-yŏng	mé-é	ká-rét-kè	nì-yáh
Body	má-zá	máhs-sŭh	môn-zá	má-áh	ŏ-wás-sá	pá-bèt-dé-shŏ	ù-tál-li-gìs-kè
Iron	Hŏn-já	hŏo-éh	ŏh-hŏh*	háh or tóch	í, or ár-rŏch-ŏ-báh	ná-wá	ŏ-wáh
Yes	Hé-á-kŏ, by the men	hánk-kásh-éh		hé-yáh	ná-tjés	ká-ke	án-tlèh
No	Hé-á-ká, by the squaws		áuns-kásh-á				
None	nìng-yá		nìng-grá				
White	ská	skŏh	ská	scáh	hŏ-tèch-kè	lá-tá-ká	ŭ-ná-kŭh
Red	shŭ-já		tjé-dá	sháh	ìsh-shè		
Black	sá-wá	sáh-béh	sáh-bá	sá-páh	shŭ-pé-shá	ká-tèt	ŭn-nŭh-gá
Blue	tŏ		tŏ	tŏé	tá-hé		
Yellow	zé		zé	zé	shé-rè		

L

VOCABULARY OF INDIAN LANGUAGES.

Fàte, fàr, fàll, fàt;—mè, mèt;—pìne, pin;—nò, mòve, nòr, nòt;—tube, tùb, bùll;—òil;—pòůnd.

	Wàh-tòk-tä-tä, or Oto Language.	Kônzä Language.	O-màw-hàw Language.	Sioux, (Yancton band,) Lang.	Mîn-nè-tä-rè, or Gros ventre Language.	Pàw-nè Language.	Chêl-à-kè, or Cherokee Language.
Light	tä-kòng	hàum-pàh	ò-gò-òm-bä	òh-tjä-tjò	màh-pä-sůh-käs	shůk-shè-gät	è-gä-hèw
Darkness	ò-hän-zä	hàum-o-pàs-sè	ò-gä-hä-nò-pä-sä-wè	òh-yòk kä-pä-zä	òh-pa-tjè	same as night	ůl-sè-kůh
Me	mè-èh	bè-àh		mè-yä	mè-è		
I (ego)						tä	i-yèh
One	yòn-kä	mè-äkh-chè	mè-äch-chè	wän-chä	lè-mòis-sò	äs-kò	
Two	nò-wä	nòm-pàh	nòm-bä	nò-pä	nò-ò-päh	pèt-kò	
Three	tä-nè	yäh-bè-rè	rä-bè-nè	yä-mè-nè	nä-mè	tòů-wèt	
Four	tò-wä	tòh-pàh	tò-bä	tò-päh	tò-päh	shkè-tìksh	
Five	sä-tä	sàh-täh	sät-tä	zäp-tä	chè-thoh	shè-òksh	
Six	shä-qua	shàlp-pèh	shäp-pä	shäk-pä	à-cä-mä	shèk-shä-bïsh	
Seven	shäh-ä-muh	pä-òm-bàh	pä-nům-bä	shäk-ò-è	chäp-pò	pèt-ko-shek-sha-bish	
Eight	krä-rä-bä-nä	pä-yäh-bè-rè	pä-rä-bè-nè	shäk-ün-dò-hůh nůh-pèt-chè-wïng-kůh	nò-pặp-pè	tou-wet-sha-bish	
Nine	shän-kä	shänk-kůh	shòn-kä	wèk-chèm-in-ůh	nò-wäs-säp-pä	lòk-shè-rè-wä	
Ten	krä-bä-nůh	kerä-brah, or ker-à-bè-ràh	krä-bä-rä	à-kä-òng-tjïn	pè-rä-gäs	lòk-shè-rè	
Eleven	à-gèn-nè-yòn-kä	äh-rè-mè-äkh-chè	ä-gär-è-mè	à-kä-nò-pä	à-pè-lè-mois-sò	as-ko-lok-she-re	
Twelve	à-gèn-nè-nò-wä	äh-rè-nòm-päh	ä-gär-è-num-bä		à-pè-nò-ò-päh	pet-ko-shô-she-re	

Fåte, får, fåll, fåt;—mè, mèt;—pine, pin;—nò, mòve, når, nòt, &c.

Having but a small number of words of the two following Languages, it is thought proper to insert them separately from the above comparative tables, in order that the columns may not be too much extended.

Shòs-hò-nè Language.

Good, sånt	Antelope, wå-rè
Bad, kåtè-sånt	Elk, på-rè
Salmon, åu-gi	Awl, wè-ù
Come, kè-må	Beaver, hå-nîsh
Large, pè-ûp	Friend, hånts
Big river, påu-pe-up	Woman, wipè
To eat, bò-rè-cån	Water, på
White people, tåb-bå-bò—*people*	Horse, bùnk-ò
of the sun	No, kå-hè
Go, nù-mè-å-rò	Tåsh-è-på, pierced nose—*a nation*
To copulate, yò-cò	*of the Columbia*
To see, må-bò-nè	Påw-kees, black feet Indians
Did not see it, kå-ên-må-bò-nè	Pùn-åsh, root eaters—a band of
To love, kòm-mùh	Shoshones who call a horse tò-
A great many, shånt	îsh, and a squaw mò-cò-nè
Bison, kòt-zò	

Ùp-så-rò-kå, or Crow Language.

White people, måsh-tè-sè-rè—*yellow eyes.*	Knife, mît-sè
	What, så-på
Pawkees or Black-feet, è-chîp-è-tå	Near, åsh-kå
Poor, båts-îsh-cåt	Friend, shè-kå
Powerful or strong, båts-åtsh	To eat, bå-boush-mèk
Good, è-tschîck	Gunpowder, bè-rùps-spå
Bad, kåb-bèåk	Little, è-rò-kå-tå
Bison, bè-shå	Name which they give to the
Bison bull, chè-rå-på	Sioux nation, mår-ån-shò-bîsh-
Beaver, bè-råp-på	kò—*or the cut throats*
Tobacco, ò-på	Young woman, mè-kå-tå
Where, shò	Water, mè-nè
Far, håm-å-tå	Fire, bè-då
Mountain, åm-å-†hå-bå	Wood, mòn-å
Elk, è-chè-rè-cå-tè—*little horse*	River, ån-shå
Finished or completed, kår-å-kò-	Horse, è-chè-rå
tùk	No, bår-å-tå

Fåte, får, fåll, fåt;—mė, mėt;—pine, pin;—

The following promiscuous words are added for the further information of the philologist.

Wåh-tŏk-tå-tå, or Oto Language.

White people, måz-ŏnk-kå—*iron makers*

Americans, må-hė-hŭn-jėh—*big knife*

British, rå-går-råsh-ing, probably not an Oto word

Ioway nation, på-hŏ-jå—*gray snow*

Missouri nation, nė-ŏ-tå-tchå—*those who build a town at the mouth of a river*

Mississippi river, nė-ŏ-hŭn-jė—*the river that enlarges as it runs*, or nė-bėr-å-ṭjė, *water of knowledge*

Missouri river, nė-sŭ-jå—*smoky water*

Osage river, nė-skå—*white water*

Grand river, nėsh-nå-hŭn-jå—*big water*

Konzes river, tŏ-pė-ŏ-kå—*good potatoe river*

Nodowa river, nė-å-tŏn-wå—*jump over river*, or nė-wå-tŏn

Walk, må-nė

Distant, hår-rė

Deer, tåh-chė

Green, tŏh-tschė

Platte river, nė-brås-kå—or *flat water*

Little Platte river, nė-brėskå-ing-yå—*little flat water*

Tarkio river, tår-kė-ŭ

Nemehaw river, nė-mŏ-hå-hŭn-gė

Little Nemehaw river, nė-mŏ-hå-ing-yå

Nishnabatona river, nish-nå-bŏt-ŏnå—*canoe making river*

Weeping water river, nė-hå-gå—*weeping water*

Saline creek, nės-cŏ—*salt water*

Loup fork of the Platte river, Pawneeomawhaw-nė-ėtow-wå

Elkhorn creek, wå-tå-tŭng-yå

Konza river, Konza-nė-ėtow-wå—or *the river belonging to the Konzas*

Run, nŏng-å

Leap, tå-wå

Fight, å-kė-rå-gå

Eat, wå-rŏ-jå

Drink, råt-tŏng

Steal, mŏ-nŏ

Talk, ė-chå

Strength, brė-hrå

Weakness, wå-hå-hå

Poor, wå-wås-tŏng

Near, ås-kė

Different, ė-tån-tŏng

Good, pė-åy

Bad, pish-cŏ-nå

Mockeson, å-kŏ-jė

Gunpowder, åk-hŏ-jė

Ball, må-zå-mŭh

Looking-glass, må-zŏ-kå-tŏŭ-å

Long, thrå-jå

Short, sŭ-is-chå

Broad, år-rŭ-chå-hŭn-jå

Thick, shŏ-gå

Thin, brå-kå

Father, in-kŏ—used by a person when addressing his father. This word is said by Lewis and Clarke, p. 36, to mean *chief*, but this seems to be a mistake.

Twenty, krå-bå-nŭh-nŏ-wå

Twenty-one, krabanuhnowa-å-gėn-nė-yŏn-kå?

Thirty, krabanuh-tå-nė

One hundred, krabanuh-hŏ-yŏng

One hundred and one, krabanuh-hoyongagenneyonka

One thousand, krabanuhhoyong-hŏn-jå—or *big hundred*

—nò, mòve, nòr, nŏt ;—tŭbe, tŭb, bŭll ;—ŏĭl ;—pŏůnd.

O-måw-håw Language.

White people, wåh-hå—*makers*
Americans, måh-hė-tŭn-gůh—*big knife*
British, sůk-ån-åsh—not a proper Omawhaw word
Hat, wå-hå-på-gå-rŏng
Hatchet, måz-zå-på-‡jin-gå
Axe, måz-zå-på-tŭn-gůh
Prairie dog's burrow, mån-nė-†hŏ-då-tė
Grizzly bear, mŏn-tschů
White hare, mås-tschĭ-skå
Porcupine, på-hė
Bald eagle, hė-rå-på-sŏng
Grey eagle, hė-rå-grå-‡jė
Black bear, wå-så-bå
Dragon fly, tė-nė-nĭk-å
Sword, måh-hė-tŭn-gůh
Small knife, måh-hė-‡jin-gůh
Canoe, mŭn-då
Thunder, †gėr-rŏng
Breech-cloth, ‡jå-å-dė-går-rŏng
Niece, wė-tė-‡jėh by the men, wė-tŏ-‡jŏn-gå by the squaws
Brother-in-law, tå-*hŏng
Deer skin, tå-hå
Sweet maize, wåt-tån-zė-skė-rå
Common maize, wåt-tån-zė-sår-rå-gå
An ear of maize, wå-hå-bå
Abdomen, tå-zė
Paunch or stomach, nė-hå
Mammæ, mŏn-zå, same as *iron*
People, nė-kå-shĭng-gå, or nė-kůh-shĭng-gůh
Young warrior, wå-sė-sė-gå
Warm, måsh-tå
Nostrils, påh-shů-shå
Human skin, hė-hå
Deep blue, tŏh-chė
Dance, wåt-chė. Sometimes the word gå-hå, *to make*, is subjoined to this word in order to distinguish from their term for copulation
His child, ė-nė-sė

Me (I) make, på-†hå, very like the word for *hill*
My true child, wė-sė-‡jŭn-tschė-nů
It is said there is none, ning-gå-ům
Bad or ugly, på-‡jůh—a word used in anger, principally by the squaws
Poor as a turkey, wåh-på-nė-zė-zė-kå-å-gò
I am as poor as a turkey, å-måh-panezezekaago
You are as poor as a turkey, wår-ĭchpanezezekaago
It was red with blood, wå-mė-‡jė-då-kå
I will not go, å-brå-můj‡-‡jė
Come here, gė-gå-hå
Little Platte river, nė-bras-kå-‡jĭngůh—*Little flat water*
Konza river, Konza-nė-ėtå
Bowyer creek, nė-hå-ba—*shallow water*
Little Sioux creek, wå-tå
Run, tŏ-nå
Leap, wė-så
Fight, kė-kė-nå
Eat, wå-bråt-tå
Drink, bråt-tŏng
Steal, mŏ-nŏ
Talk, ė-å, very like *stone*
Strength, wåsh-cå-tŭn-gå
Weakness, wå-hå-hå
Poor, wåh-på-nė
Near, åsh-kå
Good, ŏ-dŏng
Bad, o-dong-buj‡-‡je, or ŏ-dån-‡jė, or pė-å-‡jå
Mockeson, *hån-på
Gunpowder, måh-†hŏ-då
Ball, måh-zå-můh
Lookingglass, nė-ŏ-kė-gårras-sė
Long, snå-då
Short, chå-shkåh
Broad, brås-kå
Thick, shŏ-gůh

Fåte, får, fåll, fåt;—mė, mêt;—pine, pĭn;—

Thin, brå-kå
Thirteen, å-går-ė-rå-bė-nė
Twenty, krå-bå-rå-nŏm-bå
Twenty-one, krabaranomba-kė-dė-mė-åch-chė
Thirty, krabara-bė-nė
Thirty-one, krabarabene-kė-dė-mė-åch-chė

One hundred, krabara-hė-mė
One hundred and one, krabarahe-me-kė-dė-mė-åch-chė
One thousand, krabaraheme-tŏn-gå
One thousand and one, krabarahe-metonga-kedemeachche
Nine thousand, krabarahemeton-ga-shŏn-kå

O-måw-håw Names of Persons.

MEN.

Yellow Belly, tå-zė-zė
Little God, wåh-cŏndå-ǂjĭn-gå
God, wåh-cŏndå
He that carries his feet, sė-gė-ė
He that has four feet, sė-tŏ-bå
Four hands, nŏm-bå-tŏ-bå
Two legs, ǂjå-gå-nŏm-bå
Four nails, shå-gå-tŏ-bå
Big hand, nŏmbå-tŭn-gå
Big eyes, îsh-tå-tŭn-gå
He who deliberates, wå-rů-gêr-rŏng
Buffaloe rib, tå-rė-tå
Buffaloe tail, tå-sĭn-då
Buffaloe head, tå-på
Buffaloe bull, tå-nů-gå
Buffaloe calf, tå-ǂjĭn-gå
Little white bear, mŭt-chů-ǂjĭngå
Black white bear, mŭt-chů-så-bå
Black bird, wå-ǂjinga-så-bå
He that walks on the edge, ŏ-hŏn-gå-mŏn-ė
He that makes signs as he walks, wå-bŏm-ėn-ė
He that walks behind, å-gå-hå-mŏ-nė
He that hunts as he walks, ŏ-nå-mŭn-nė
The walking cloud, måh-pė-mŭn-nė
The strong walker, wåsh-kå-mŭn-nė
He who walks when fruit is ripe, sė-då-mŭn-nė
He who cries as he walks, hå-gå-mŭn-nė

He who walks beyond others, kŏ-shė-hå-mŭn-nė
He who arrived in haste, wåsh-cŏn-hė
He who is not afraid of tracks, sė-grå-nå-på-bå
The white horse, shŏn-gå-skå
Seven, på-nŭm-bå
Ace of spades, ŏ-kå-dė-gå-rŏng
Little cook, ŏ-hŏn-ǂjin-gå
Head wind or North wind, kė-må-hå
Big skunk, mŏn-gå-tŭn-gå
Prairie wolf, mŏn-ė-kŭs-sė
Swan, mė-hŭs-cå-tŭn-gå
He who walks double, nŏm-bå-mŏn-nė
Black breast, mŏn-gå-såb-bå
No hand, nŏm-bå-ning-gå
Brave, wå-shů-shå
No knife, må-hė-nĭng-gå
Two tails, sĭn-då-nŭm-bå
The top of the tent-poles which are tied together, tė-shė-mŏ-hå
Big bullet, må-zė-måt-tŭngå
Medicine mouth, ė-wå-hŏ-bå
He who carries real medicines, måc-cå-n-ė
Wet mockeson, hŏm-på-nŏ-cå
Big leggings, ŏ-tånt-tŭn-gå
Smoke maker, shů-då-gŏch-hå
Two faces, in-då nŏm-bå
The twins, nŏm-bå-dånt
Yellow knife, må-hė-zė

SQUAWS' NAMES.

The first moon, mė-tå-ė
Nå-så-zå

—nò, môve, nòr, nòt ;—tùbe, tûb, bùll ;—òil ;—pòùnd.

Village, towoin
Mė-hủn-gủh
First thunder, ti-ėn-ė
Female sun, mė-tėh-hȧ
Female moon, mė-ủm-bủn-nė

Female axe, mȧs-ủp-pȧ-mė
Female deer that looks, wȧ-tủm-bȧn-nė
The first thunder that falls, tȧ-ing-gȧ-rȧ

O-mȧw-hȧw Interjections and Exclamations.

Zt!—This is used by the men when contemplating a fine trinket, looking-glass, &c.; they sometimes say zt-ȯ-dȧh!
Shėh-zt-zt-zt! or wah-zt-zt-zt! or ȯah-zt-zt-zt! is used by the men for driving dogs out of mischief.

²Ėh-zt-zt-zt-zt! by the women on the same occasion.

Hėh! an inspiration—used by the women when a sudden but trifling accident occurs—as it is also used by the white females.

Kė-ȧ!—the first syllable nasal— by the women for calling their dogs.

Wȯ-ȯh! by the men for calling their dogs or horses. It is a sound very similar to that used by the whites to halt horses.

Wȧh-mȧn-gȧr-ing-gȧ! Be off, or go away—spoken in anger—this would be the last word, an attack would succeed if disregarded.

¹Ȯ-hȯh! (drawn out very long) used to one who has been troubling them a long time—it would precede the preceding exclamation in the gradation of displeasure.

Gė-gȧ-hȧ! wȧh-gė-gȧ-rȧ! ȯ-hȯh-gė-gȧr-ȧ!—the successive expressions of impatience in calling a person to come.

Hi-ȯ! The answer of a squaw to one who calls.

Hȧ! The answer of a man to one who calls.

Dȧ-dȧnsh-tȧ-ȧ! An exclamation similar in signification to *O, alas, me!*

Fàte, fär, fàll, fàt ;—mè, mèt ;—pìne, pìn ;—

Sioux, (Yancton band,) Language.

American, mè-nà-hàs-hàh—*Long knife*
British, sà-kìn-dà-shà. This appears to be an adopted word.
Physician, wà-pè-à-wè-à-chà-shà
Village, ò-tòng-y-à
Eagle, hò-yàh
Green, tò-wè-tòy-yà, or " the blue to dye with"—they have no other word for this colour
Warm, màch-tà
Pawnees, pà-dàn-ò-tà
Sioux, dà-cò-tà
Run, è-òng-kà
Leap, è-èp-sè-shà
Fight, kè-chè-zà
Eat, wò-tàh
Drink, yà-tà-kòng
Talk, è-àh
Good, wàsh-tà
Gunpowder, chà-hùn-dà

Thirteen, à-kà-yà-mè-nè
Nineteen, à-kà-nùh-pèt-chè-wùng
Twenty, wek-chem-in-eh-nom-pah
Twenty-one, wekcheminehnom-pah-à-kà-òng-gè
Thirty, wekcheminuh-yà-mè-nè
Thirty-one, wekcheminuhyamene-a-ka-òng-ɫjìn
One hundred, ò-pàng-hà
One hundred and one, opangha-à-kà-òng-ɫjìn
One thousand, kòk-ò-tòng-ò-pàng-hà
One thousand and one, kokotong-opangha-à-kà-òng-ɫjìn
Ten thousand, kokotongopangha-wekcheminuh
The upper bands of the Sioux in their pronunciation substitute the letter *l* for the *d*.

Mìn-nè-tà-rè, or Gros ventre Language.

American, màn-cè-êch-tè-êt—*Big knife*
British, bò-shè-ìt-tò-†chrè-shù-pè-shà—*the men who bring black cloth*
French, bò-shè
Spaniard, wàs-shè-ò-màn-tì-quà
Crow Indians, pàr-is-cà-òh-pàn-gà —*the crow people*
Crow Indians, another band, êh-hà-tzà—*the people of leaves*
Snake Indians, mà-bùc-shò-ròch-pàn-gà
Flat-headed Indians, à-too-hà-pè
Pierced-nose Indians, à-pà-ò-pà
Black foot Indians, ìt-zè-sù-pè-shà
Gros ventre of the Fort prairie, a band of Black feet, à-rè-tèàr-ò-pàn-gà

Assinniboin Indians, è-tàns-kè-pà-sè-tà-quà
Shienne Indians, à-wàs-shè-tàn-quà, or ìt-ànsè-pò-ɫjè
Sauteur Indians, hà-hàt-tòng
Mandan Indians, à-ràch-bò-cù
Rickaree Indians, à-rìck-à-rà-ònè
Sioux Indians, ìt-àns-kè
Pawnee Loups Indians, sà-ɫjèr-ò-pàn-gà
Les Noire Indians, àt-tè-shù-pè-shà-lòh-pàn-gà
The Red Shield Chief, one of the principal chiefs, è-tàm-inà-gèh-iss-shà
The Borgne or One Eye, grand chief, a remarkable man, he was killed by the Red Shield, a few years since, kà-kò-à-kis

—nò, mòve, nòr, nòt ;—tùbe, tùb, bùll ;—òil ;—pòund.

Missouri river, å-månti-å-ꞩjè—*the river that carries canoes*
Little Missouri river, å-månti-cå-ꞩjå—*the river that carries little canoes*
Yellow Stone River, mît-zè-rè-å-ꞩjè—*the river of yellow rocks*
Physician, måt-zå-må-hò-på
Village, å-må-tèh
Prairie, å-mòn-sù-kèt
Eagle, ìch-prò-hîch
Arrow point, è-tåh-è
Tomahawk, wèèp-så-lån-gå
Green, ꜥthåu-tè-gè
Emasculation, ån-jù-cå-då-ꞩjus
Little wolf, bòt-sås
Blanket, wåsh-å-èchrè-ò-tùckè
Mountain, åvo-cå-vè
Kill, tå-hå
Die, tås
Scalp, å-råm-på-tsåk-kè

He or she, nè
Bison cow, mè-tè-yå
A thick forest of small trees, bè-rå-shè-è-pè
Run, tè-rè-å
Leap, tè-chrè
Fight, rè-kè
Eat, må-ròu-tå
Drink, bè-dè-hè
Steal, må-å-shån-rè
Talk, dè-då
Mockasin, ò-påh
Gunpowder, mèr-è-zè-bå
Nineteen, å-pè-nò-wås-såp-på
Twenty, nò-ò-påh-pè-rå-gås
Thirty, nå-mè-å-pè-rå-gås
Forty, tò-påh-å-pè-rå-gås
One hundred, pè-rå-gås-ìch-tè-êt
One thousand, pè-rè-gås-ìch-tè-êt-å-cåh-cò-rè

Påw-nè Language.

Grand Pawnees, tchå-wè
Loups or Pawneeomawhaws, skè-rè
Pawnee Republicans, zè-kå-kå or kèt-kå-kèsh
Tappage band, pè-tòù-wè-rå
Not, bùjꞩ-ꞩjè
Tool Robe, (the republican grand chief,) shå-rè-å-dèèksh-tåw-wè
Thirteen, tòù-wèt-lòk-shè-rè
Fourteen, låh-kò-kè-tå
Fifteen, shè-òksh-tå-rò-kè-tå
Sixteen, shròù-wè-ò
Seventeen, tòù-wèt-kå-kè, (twenty less three)
Eighteen, pèt-kò-kå-kè, (twenty less two)
Nineteen, ås-kò-kå-kè, (twenty less one)
Twenty, pè-tòù-ò
Twenty-one, petouo-ås-kò

Thirty, lùk-shè-rè-wè-tòù-ò
Thirty-one, luksherewetouo-asko
Forty, pèt-kò-shò-ò-rå-rò
Forty-one, petkoshooraro-as-ko
Fifty, petkoshoorarolokshere
Sixty, tòù-wèt-rå-rò
Seventy, touwetrarolokshere
Seventy-one, touwetrarolokshere askolokshere
Eighty, shke-tiksh-tå-rò
Eighty-one, shketikshtaroasko
Ninety, shketikshtarolokshere
Ninety-one, shketikshtaroaskolokshere
One hundred, shè-kòksh-tå-rò
One thousand, petkoshoorarolokshere-tså-è-ksh
The name of one individual of the Pawnee Loups is "The maker of God."

Fâte, fâr, fâll, fât ;—mê, mêt ;—pine, pin ;—

The two following Vocabularies were taken down by Major Long during his tour on the upper Mississippi in the year 1817.

	Winnebago, Puant, or Nippegon.	Naudowessies of Carver and Hennepin.
Arm	år-dåh	ish-tò
Axe	måhs	òntz-på
Arrow	måh	wåh-hèn-tè-på
American or Long knife	måh-èk-hå-tè	is-sòn-tåh-kåh
Brother	sùnk-hå-dèh	mè-sòn-kåh
Beads	wỳ-å-pér-ris-sipe	wè-ò-kè-å-tåh
Bread	wicè-kåp	åh-hò-è-å-pè
Beaver	nåh-å-påh	schåh-påh
Bear	òntsh	wåh-hånk-cè-chåh
Brass or copper	måhn-sè	måhnz-å-zè
Chief	òngk-pè	wich-åsh-tåh-yåh-tòp-pè— *good chief*
Canoe or boat	wåch	wåh-tå
Cards, playing	pèk	pèk
Child	nò-gò-nèk	òke-chè-ò-påh
Dead	åh-nò	kthåh
Deer	tchåh	tåh-kèn-shåh
Dog	shònk	shònk-åh
Elk		ò-pångh
Elbow	èyè-shòù-ùck	ish-påh
Eyes	shtås-sò	ish-tåh
Ears	nåhnt-shòù-åh	nòkh-rå
Feet	sè	sè-håh
Fingers	nå-åp	nò-på-tò-kå-håh
Fox	chå-òntz-sin-cèr-èt	shònk-grè-dåh
Fire	pychè	på-tåh
Father	chå-chè	åh-tå
Face		è-tå
Good	å-pè-nò	wåsh-tå
Garter	ò-å-kish-kè	wåsh-kin-chåh-hå
Gun	ish-òk	måhs-åk-khån
Ground	måk-kåh	måh-kòh-chå
Green	måh-nèch-ò	tåh-kò-tè
Grass	khåh-wèh	på-zhè
Hands	nåh-pùr	nò-på
Head	nåhs-sò	Fåk-è
Heart	nåch-kèh	chån-tå
House or lodge	tchè	tè-pè
Horse	shònk-håt-tå	shònk-å-wåk-kùngh
Island	wich	wè-tåh
Iron	måhs-ish-åh	måhnz-åh

—nȯ, mȯve, nȯr, nȯt ;—tůbe, tůb, bůll ;—ȯíl ;—pȯůnd.

	Winnebago, Puant, or Nippegon.	Naudowessies of Carver and Hennepin.
Indian	wȧnk-shȋch	ȋk-ė-chȧ-wȋch-ȧsh-tȧ
Knife	mȧh-hė	ės-sȧnh
Lead	ȋsh-ȯ-cȯ-mȧh	mȧhnz-ȧs-sȯ
Legs	ȯ-rȧh	hȯ
Louse	hȧ-dȧh	hȧh-yůr
Maize	wȧ-chȯ-ȧs	wȧh-mė-nȧh-zȧh
Man	wȧnk-shė-grȧh	wȋch-ȧsh-tȧh
Mother	nȧh-nė	ė-nȧh
Musket	shȯů-ůck	sȋn-tė-pȧh
Meat	tchȧck	tůn-dȯ
Meal	wȯȋs-tȯp	ȧh-hȯ-ė-ȧp-pė
Mockasin	wȧ-cȯ-chėh	hȧm-pȧh
Moon	hȧh-hėh-wė	wė ?
Mouth	ė	ė ?
Mosquetto	nȧh-wȯnk	chȧh-pȯn-gȧh
No, or nothing	chȯnch-quė-nė-nȯ	hė-yȧh
Nose	pȧh	pȧgh-rȧ
Oar, or paddle	nȧsh-ůck	wȧ-mė-nȧh-hė-chȧh
Old	ȧh-chȋn-shůn	wȋch-ȧ-hȋn-chȧh, *old man*
Otter	tȯ-shėn-ůk	ptůngh
Owl	wȧhk-chėh-hė	ė-ȧngh-kȧh-hȧh
Powder	ȯk-hůn-nė	chȧh-hůn-dė
Pond or lake	tȧh-hȧt-tȧ	mȋn-dȧ, or tȯng-gȧh
Porcupine	wȧh-hȧne	
Pipe	tȧh-nė-hȯ	chȧn-dȯ-ȯ-pȧh
Road	nȧh-kȯh	chȧng-kȯ
River	nė-shȧn-nůk	wȧh-tė-pȧh
Red	wȧs-sėh	shȧh
Sister	nȯk-ȧch-ȧp-pė-tȧh	tůnk-shė
Silver	shȯ-dė-ȧh	mȧnz-ȧs-kȧh
Squaw	hė-nȯ-kȯ-tȧh	wȋn-ȯ-khė-jȧh
Sun	wė-dȧh	wė ?
Star	kȧh-dȧch-ȯ	wȋch-ȧnck-pė
Thunder	wȧh-kȯn-jȧh	wȧk-kė-ȧh
Tree	nȧh-nȧh	chȧh
Town or village	mȧh-kėt-tė-chė-nůk	ȧh-tȯng-wȧ
Tobacco	tȧh-nė-nȧh	chȧn-dė
Teeth	hė	ė ?
Universe	hȧn-nȧjh-pė	ȧh-wȧs-sė
Wax	i-sȋc-wė-kė-nė-chȧh	tȯk-mȧh-hȧh-sės-sėn-dė
White	skȧh	skȧh
Water	nė-nȧh, or nėh	mėn-nėh
You	nė-ėh	nė-yȧ

Fàte, fàr, fàll, fàt ;—mè, mêt ;—pìne, pìn ;—nò, mòve, &c.

	Winnebago, Puant, or Nippegon.	Naudowessies of Carver and Hennepin.
Yes	òn-chàh	hàh
One	jhìng-kè-dè	wàn-chàh
Two	nòpè	nòm-pàh
Three	tàh-nè	yàh-mèn-nè
Four	chòpè	tòh-ò-pàh
Five	sàch	sàh-pè-tàh
Six	kùh-wè	shàhk-pè
Seven	shà-kò	shàhk-ò-wìn
Eight	nò-wùnk	shàh-hùn-dà-hàh
Nine	jhìnk-ìch-òs-cò-nè	nòp-chèh-wùnk-kàh
Ten	khèr-à-pùn	wè-kè-chà-mè-nàh
Eleven	jhìnk-hè-rà-shò-nè	àk-kà-wùn-ghè
Twelve	nòpe-ash-ò-nè	ak-kà-nùmè

GENERAL INDEX.

A

Agama collaris, ii, - - 252
Agriculture of the Pawnees, i, - 447
Alleghany mountains, i, - 4 & 6
Alleghany mountains, some of their
rivers considered, i, - - 9, 10
Alleghany ridge, i, - - - 11
Ameiva tesselata described, ii, - 50
America, town of, i, - - - 36
American bottom, i, - - 49
American character, estimation of by
the Omawhaws, i, - - 323
Ancient works, i, - - - 13, 23
Animals, catalogue of, i, - - 369
noticed, i, - - 474
Antelopes, i, - - - 348, 485
Ant hills, i, - - - 346, 493
Apple creek, ii, - - - 285
Apus obtusus described, i, - - 461
Aquilegia cœrulea described, ii, - 15
Aralia spinosa, ii, - - - 294
Argemone alba, described, i, - 461
Argillite of the Washita, ii, - 288
Arkansa, arrival at one of its tributaries, ii, - - - 15
arrival and encampment at,
ii, - - - - 39
remarks on its valley near
the mountains, ii, - - 44
the party commence their descent of, ii, - - - 50
remarks on its scenery, ii, 51
of its character, ii, - 66
great bend of, ii, - 206
below the great bend, ii, - 258
country on, below Belle
point, ii, - - 264 et seq.
little, ii, - - - 214
Arrapahoes, ii, - - - 176
war party of, ii, - - 192
their attempt to take one of
our horses, ii, - - 193
medicine bag, ii, - - 194
Arrow rock, i, - - - 100
ASTRONOMICAL RECORDS, Appendix
ix et seq.
Atmospheric phenomenon, i, - 490
Attack by the Indians on a block
house, i, - - - - 80

B

Badger, ii, - - - - 93
Baldwin Dr., his duties, assigned, i, 2
his sickness, i, - 21
his death and character,
i, - - - 93
Bald-pated prairie, i, - - 142
Bartonia nuda and ornata, i, - 497
Battery rock, i, - - - 42
Bats, ii, - - - - 65
Batsoah creek, i, - - - 485
Bayou Cura, ii, - - - 280
Bear, grizzly, ii, - - - 35
described, ii, - 52
black, ii, - - - - 136
ferocity of when wounded,
ii, - - - 146
Beaver, i, - - - - 464
Bees, i, - - - - 141
a swarm taken, ii, - - 151
Bell, captain joins the exp., i, - 404
his duties, i, - - 423
detached with a party to
ascend the Arkansa, ii, 42
his springs, ii, - 43
his detachment to de-
scend the Arkansa, ii, 173
account of their move-
ments, ii, - 172 et seq.
Belle Fontaine, arrival at, &c., i, - 67
Belle Point, description of, &c., ii, 260
arrival at, ii, - 172
Capt. Bell's party arrive
at, ii, - - 258
product, diseases, &c. ii, 262
departure from, ii, 264
Big Black river, ii, - - - 383
Big horn, ii, - - - 13
Bijeau, his account of the Rocky
Mountains, ii, - - 63
Bijeau and Ledoux, join the expedition, i, - 450
their character,
usefulness, and
separation from
the exp., ii, - 202
Birds, i, - - - 32, 49
ii, 35, 80, 97, 115, 137, 142, 159

Biscuit, or bread, allowance of to the individuals of the party, ii,   49
Bison, description of, i,   -   470 et seq.
    account of, i,   -   -   480
    crossing the Platte, i, -   481
    more afraid of whites than of the Indians, i,   -   -   482
    some account of, ii,   78, 125, 135, 204, 207
Bistineau lake, ii,   -   -   308
Black hills, i,   -   -   -   471
Blowing flies, i,   -   116
    ii,   -   -   135
Blue earth river, i,   -   -   134
Blue water river, ii,   -   -   316
Body of a white officer interred by the Indians, i,   -   -   91
Boggy river, ii,   -   -   316
Boiling spring creek, ii,   -   35
Bones of a serpent found in an Indian grave, i,   -   -   64
Bon Homme creek and village, i,   408
Boon, Daniel, anecdote of, i, -   105
Boonville and lick, i,   -   -   89
Botanical notes, i,   -   -   18, 54
    by Dr. Baldwin, i,   44
Boy, Pawnee, attending horses, i,   349
Boyer river examined by the party, i, 344
Bradbury, John, Botanist, i,   -   58
Bread exhausted, i,   -   487
Breccia, ii,   -   -   -   25
Briar creek, or Skin Bayou, ii,   257
Bridges, probability of their construction, across the Ohio and Mississippi, i,   -   47
Buck eye, or horse chesnut, i,   -   22
Bufo cognatus described, ii, -   190
Bull pen, source of north fork of the Platte, i,   -   -   464

C.

Cacti noticed, ii,   -   -   19
Cado chief, his interview with Freeman's party, ii,   -   311
Calloway capt., his skirmish with the Indians and death, i,   76
Camancias, remains of their encampment, and a recent grave, ii,   -   116
Camp Missouri, sickness of the troops at, i,   -   195
Canadian river, north fork of, ii,   81
    its valley bounded by high precipices, ii,   82
    its mouth, ii,   -   161
    arrival at its source, ii, 84
    its bluffs, ii,   -   87
    its water, ii,   -   96
    its tributaries, ii,   -   99

Canadian river, width of its bed, ii,   120
    opinions concerning its source, ii,   -   316
    supposed Rio Rajo of Humboldt, ii,   317
    remarks on the country, ii, 132, 143, 148, 152
    little north fork of, ii,   162
    arrival at its confluence with the Arkansa, ii,   -   167
Cane brake, i,   -   -   -   41
    difficulty in passing through, ii,   -   168
Canis nubilis described, i,   -   169
Cannon ball creek, i,   -   500
Canoe, skin, mode of constructing, i, 429
Cape Girardeau, arrival at, i,   -   45
    reassembling of the party at, ii,   -   321
    account of, ii,   -   323
    departure from, ii,   324
Cash river, its mouth a harbour for boats, i,   -   -   38
Cassis cornutus found in an Indian mound, i,   -   -   64
Castle rock and creek, ii,   -   16, 52
Catalpa tree, i,   -   -   35
Catfish, i,   -   -   -   142
Cavaniol mountain, ii,   -   -   169
Cave Inn rock described, i, -   32, 41
Cervus macrotis described, ii,   -   88
    major, ii,   -   -   89
    verginianus, manner of decoying, i,   -   -   103
Chains or rocky bars in the Ohio, i,   37
    in the Mississippi, i,   -   45, 47
Chalk banks, i,   -   -   38
Charaton village and river, i,   97
Charbonire, i,   -   -   70
Charcoal included in the argillaceous sandstone, ii,   -   80
Chattahooche mountain, ii,   -   274
Chenal au Barre, i,   -   -   102
Cherokee Indians, ii,   -   262
    remarks concerning, ii,   -   268
    origin of their quarrel with the Osages, ii, -   269
    their improvements, ii,   -   271
    some account of their government, ii,   -   272
Chesnut ridge, i,   -   -   12
Chirotes lumbricoides, i,   -   488
Cincinnatti, i,   -   -   21, 23
Climate, remarks on, i,   476, 393
    ii.   115, 124, 317

Climate, general remarks concerning, ii, - 320 et seq.
Coal, localities of, i, - 12, 29, 40
Coashatay village, ii, - 308
Coluber obsoletus described, i, - 140
testaceus described, ii, - 48
Conglomerates in the Ozark mountains, ii, - 70, 299
Cornfield, Indian, ii, - - 220
Cornice rock, i, - - 47, 50
Corn island, i, - - 28
Corn mills, i, - - - 75
Cote Sans Dessein, i, - - 80
Council Bluff, scenery, &c., i, - 152
Country north of the Missouri, journey through, i, - 406 to 423
at the base of the Rocky Mountains, ii, - 71
between the Cherokees and Little Red river, ii, - 273
Cove of Washita, ii, - 298
Cow island, arrival at, i, - 110
Crotalus tergeminus described, i, 499
confluentus described, ii, 48, 199
Cucumis perennis described, ii, 20
Cumberland river, i, - - 35
Cupressus disticha, ii, - 217
of remarkable size, ii, 318

D.

Dance, calumet, i, - - 332
of discovery, i, - 334
bear, i, - - 335
beggar, i, - - id.
bison, corn, i, - - 336
of the Minnetarees, i, 337
Dangers and difficulties suggested by the Indians and others, i, 426
by the Pawnees, i, - 477, 442
Dardenai, ii, - - 288
Datche bayou, ii, - - 307
Davidsonville, ii, - - 281
Deer, black-tailed, ii, - - 75
described, ii, 88
Deer, Virginian, their combats, ii, 300
Defile creek, ii, - - 11
Delaware Indians, ii, - - 285
Delineation, Indian, ii, - 265
Demun's creek, ii, - - 203
Deserters, Nowland, Myers, and Bernard; their theft, and the privations to which Captain Bell's party were subjected thereby, ii, 234
Devil's oven, i, - - 47
Diamond island, i, - - 110
Division of the Exp. party, ii, 63
Dogs, sufferings and death, ii, 213, 221

Dougherty, John, and others, overtake the steam boat at Wolf river, i, 115
remarkable instance of his knowledge of the country, i, 127
his adventures with grizzly bears, ii, - 56
Dry fork of the Canadian, ii, - 116

E.

Earthquakes felt at Cape Girardeau, ii, - 325
anecdote of, &c., ii, - 326
Eleven point river, ii, - 281
Elk noticed, ii, - - 89
instance of its behaviour when wounded, ii, - 166
Elk Horn river, passage of, in a skin canoe, i, - - 428
Emberiza amoena described, ii, 47
pecora, ii, - 199
Encampment, mode of, i, - 430
Engineer Cantonment, site of, i, 146
records made there, i, 146, 403
outfit and departure of the exp. from, i, 425
Esox osseus?, ii, - - 154
Excursion from Point Pleasant, on the Arkansa, to the Hot Springs of the Washita, ii, - 287 et seq.
Exhalations, luminous, account of, i, 412

F.

Fairy hills of the Minnetarees, i, 274
Falco lineatus, i, - - 33
mississippiensis, ii, - 121
Falls of the Ohio, i, - - 26
passage of, i, - 30
of the Canadian, ii, - 160
False Washita, ii, - - 316
Fields, Lieutenant, with fifteen men joins the Expedition, i, - 113
Flint island, i, - - 30
Floerkea proserpinacoides, i, - 413
Fluat of lime, i, - - 42
Forks of the Platte, arrival at, i, 463
passage of, i, 466
Formica, a species of, used as food by the Indians, i, - 214
Fort Chartres, i, - - 50
Osage, arrival at, i, - 99
account of, i, - 104
remarks on the inhabitants, i, - 105

Fort Lisa, arrival at, i,   -   145
    Smith, arrival at, ii,   -   172
        described, ii,   260 et seq.
Fortification, Indian, ii,   -   478
Fossils, extraneous, i,   -   33, 42
Fox, small species of, i,   -   486
Franklin, arrival at, i,   -   88
Freeman, account of his expedition
    up Red river, ii, 306 et seq.
    met by the Spaniards, ii,   313
    resolution of his sentinels, ii, 314
    compelled to return, ii,   314
Frenchman, singular hardihood of
    one wounded, i,   -   428
Fringilla grammacea described, i,   139
    psaltria and frontalis de-
    scribed, ii, -   -   40
Fuel, bison dung used as, i,   -   467
            ii,   -   68
Fulgur perversus found in an Indian
    mound, i,   -   -   64

G.

Galeodes pallipes et subulata, ii,   3
Games of hazard, i,   -   -   444
Gaura linifolia described, ii,   100
    mollis described, ii,   -   77
Gasconade river, i,   -   -   79
Geographical land-marks, want of, ii, 128
Geological boundary, i,   -   146
GEOLOGY, see tab. con. vol. ii. ch. XIX.
Gerbillus like canadensis, ii,   -   17
Girl, Ietan presents a horse to Major
    O'Fallon, i,   -   -   360
Glen, Mr., his trading house on the
    Verdigris, ii,   -   -   251
Glycirrhiza lepidota, i,   -   460
Granite crumbled, ii,   -   -   25
    of the Ozark mountains, ii,   298
Grand tower, i,   -   -   45
    anecdote of, i,   -   46
    prairie, i,   -   -   76
    river, i,   -   -   98
        remarks on the country
        of, i,   -   -   416
        island in the Platte, i,   4.3
        forest of the Platte, i,   495
        camp creek, grand encamp-
        ment, i,   -   -   502
Grapes, abundant and delicious, na-
    ture indicates the proper
    mode of culture, ii,   -   126
Grasshoppers, great flights of, ii,   31
Graves of the reputed Lilliputians, i,
            60 et seq.
Great swamp noticed, ii,   -   284
Greenstone, amygdaloidal and por-
    phyritic, ii, -   -   81
Grizzly bear, account of, ii,   -   52

Grouse, apparently a new species de-
    scribed, ii,   -   -   14

H.

Hailstorm, i,   -   -   409
    ii,   -   -   -   124
Herculaneum, arrival at, i,   -   52
Heuchera americana, i,   -   409
Hieracium runcinatum described, i. 453
Hirundo lunifrons described, ii.   -   47
Hop, common, on the Rocky Moun-
    tains, ii.   -   -   8
Hornblend in connection with the
    granite of the Rocky Moun-
    tains, ii.   -   -   5
Horses, and mules belonging to the
    expedition, i.   -   -   425
    of the Pawnees, i.   -   445
    whole number belonging to
    the expedition stated, i.   450
    frightened by bisons, i. 479, 484
    wild, noticed, i.   -   485
    remarks concerning, ii. 95,
            97, 123, 137
    a large gang of, ii.   -   140
    one shot, ii.   -   95
Hospitality, Indian, i   -   - 321
    of Mr. Billingsly, ii,   265
Hot Springs of the Washita noticed,
    and remarks on the cir-
    cumjacent country, ii.   288
            et seq.
    visited by various per-
    sons, ii.   -   -   290
    their individual temper-
    ature, locality, and com-
    parative discharge, ii.   291
Human feet, impressions in lime-
    stone, i.   -   -   57

I.

Ietan war party, ii. -   -   208
    their attempt to rob, ii.   211
Ilex opaca and I. cassine, ii.   -   294
Illinois river of Arkansa, arrival at, ii. 254
    creek or bayou, ii.   -   271
Indians, detailed account of, i. 167 to 403
    wandering, trade with the
    Shiennes, i.   -   -   502
    met by Captain Bell's detach-
    ment, ii.   -   -   174
Indian villages, ruins of, i.   -   145
    speeches, i.   -   -   395
    peculiar odour, i.   -   482
    estimation of inferior ani-
    mals, i.   -   -   320
    interpreters and guides, diffi-
    culty in obtaining, i.   -   443

Iron, banks on the Mississippi, i. 38
   ores of, i. - - - 42
Isle Au Vache, see Cow Island.

J.

Jackson, arrival at, ii. - 284
James, Dr. E., joins the Expedition, i. - - 404
   his duties, i. - 424
   his excursion from the camp
   on the Platte to the Rocky
   Mountains, ii. - 4 et seq.
James's Peak, distant view of, ii. - 22
   explored, ii. - 23
   described, ii. - 25, 32
   view from its summit, ii. 30
   accident of the party, ii. 32
Journey from St. Louis to Engineer
   Cantonment—account of the
   soil, products, &c., ii. 404 to 423

K.

Kakoakis, a Minnetaree chief, rav-
   ishes and kills a squaw, i. 309
Kaskaia Indian, and his squaw, ii. 60
   his account of a bat-
   tle, ii. - 66
   their true charac-
   ter, ii. - 175
Kaskaias, party of met by Major
   Long, ii. - - 102
   their want of hospitality, ii. 106
   their disposition to pilfer, ii. 109
   remarks concerning, ii. 110
   the country they frequent, ii. 112
   their diseases, habits, and deportment, ii. - 113
   another party met, ii. - 176
Kaskaskias river, a town at its
   mouth, i. - 48
Kenhawa river, i. - - 19
Kiamesha river, ii. - - 315
Kiawa Indians, ii. - - 174
   council, their fond-
   ness for tobacco, ii. 176
   their horsemanship,
   vermin, ii. - 178
   appearance, dress,
   &c., ii. - 180
   visit to their lodg-
   es, ii. - 182
   their grand chief
   Beartooth, ii. - 184
   subordinate chief of,
   ii. - 185
   their language, ii. 186
Kinnecanick, or mixed tobacco, i. 331
Kite, Mississippi, i. - - 101

Knife chief, interview with, i. - 441
Konzas river, arrival at, &c., i. - 109
   remarks on the country
   of, i. - - 137
Konza Indians, council of, i. - 111
   reception of the party, i. 118
   deputation proceeds to Isle au
   Vache, i. - - 119
   description of the village, dwellings, and furniture, i. - 120
   food, mode of cooking, and culinary apparatus, i. - 122
   government, marriage ceremony, i. - - - 123
   mourning for the dead, polygamy, ties of relationship and
   friendship, and denominations
   of consanguinity, i. - 124
   diseases, origin, superstitions, i. 125
   physical description, clothing,
   ornaments, i - - 126
   occupations of the women, ablu-
   tions, chastity, courtezans, i. 128
   sodomy, mode of plucking out
   their hair, i. - - 129
   matricide, i. - - 130
   Pawnee prisoner, i. - 131
   the party exchange a horse with
   an Indian, i. - - 131
   dog dance, i. - - 135

L.

Lake Erie tortoise, i. - - 32
Lampyris, different modes of corrus-
   cating, i. - - 78
Lands, public, provision for schools,
   &c., i. - - - 52
Land-title, anecdote of, i. - 51
Language, i. - - - 342
   Indian, of signs, i. 378
Lathyrus polymorphus, i. - 433
Laurel ridge, i. - - 12
Lead mine district, ii. - - 286
   ores of, i. - - 42
Legends, fabulous, i. - - 323
Le Mine river, discovery of the body
   of an officer buried near,
   i. - - - 91
   extensive diggings near
   it, i. - - 100
Lepidium virginicum, i. - 488
Lilliputians, i. - - - 275
Limestone, metalliferous, i. - 13
   compact, i. 21, 34, 40, 42, 47
   ii. - - 324
   sparry, ii. - - 323
Limosa scolopacea described, i. 170
Little Red river, ii. - 273
Little rock, or Arkopolis, ii. - 300

Little rock, notice of, ii. - 312
    missionaries at, ii. - 319
Lodge, earthern, described, i. 436
    skin, of the Kaskaias, ii. - 105
Long, Maj., his detachment com-
    mence their march towards
    Red river, ii. - 67
    their privations, ii. 33, 93, 101
Long Hair, remarkable instance of
    his magnanimity, i. - 161
    his austerity and reserve, i. 350
    interview with, i. - 437
Loss of one of the party, ii. - 149
Loup fork of the Platte, i. - 432
    passage of, i. 448
Louisville, arrival at, i. - 26
Loutre island, i. - - 73
    prairie, i. - - 76
Loutre, an Indian, his death, i. 159
Loutre lick, &c., i. - - 411

M.

Maclura aurantiaca, ii. - - 158
Magnanimity, instance of, i. - 319
Magpies, i. - - - 489
Malva coccinnea, i. - - 53
Manito rocks, i. - - 87
Marmot, ii. - - - 28
Martynia proposcidea found, na-
    tive, ii. - - 51
Maysville, religious meeting near, i. 20
Meal, parched maize, allowance
    of, i. - 487
    exhausted, ii. 140
Medicine stone of the Mandans, i. 276
Menard creek, or bayou, ii. - 253
Merameg river, visited, i. - 54
METEOROLOGICAL REGISTER, ap-
    pendix XLIII.
Miegia macrosperma, ii. - 252
Migration of birds, i. - - 197
Milk sickness, i. - - 82
Miller, Mr. Joseph, noticed, i. 465
Mimicry, i. - - - 324
Minute Tern, i. - - 32
Minnetarees, belief in the resurrec-
    tion of the bison, i. - 278
    tradition of their origin, i. 279
    their idea of heaven, i. 280
Mirage, or optical illusion, i. - 419
    with inverted images, i. 490
Mississippi, river, arrival at, i. - 43
    scenery, i. - 45, 50
Missouri, arrival at, and its charac-
    ter, i. - - - 66
    scenery, i. - 70, 79, 87
    width and depth of its val-
    ley, i. - - 113
    upper and lower, i. - 459
    hibernial, state of, i. - 196

Missouri Indians, i. - - 340
    destroy a party
    of Spaniards, i. 340
    dispersed by the
    Sauks and Foxes, i. 341
Monongahela river, printed Alle-
    ghany, i. - 13
Mont Cerne, ii. - - 264
Mounds, natural, ii. - 59
Muriate of Soda, i. - - 34
Mus floridanus described, - 54
Mygale avicularia, ii. 157, 254, 259

N.

Navigation of the Alleghany and
    Ohio, i. - 16
    boats suited to, i. 37
    of the Missouri obstructed
    by rafts, i. - 86
Negracka, or red fork, ii. - 217
Negroes, their funeral ceremonies, ii. 328
Nemawhaw river, grand, i. - 141
    little, i. - 142
Neosho, little, ii - - 220
Neosho, or Grand river, ii. - 253
Neshetongo river, ii. - 224
New Bourbon, i. - - 48
Nishnebottona, river and grand
    pass, i. - 142
Nitrate of lime, i. - - 34
    potash, i. - - 35
Nodowa river, i. - - 114

O.

O'Fallon, Indian agent joins the ex-
    pedition, i. - 70
    his speech to the Sauks, i. 222
    other speeches, i. - 395
Ohio river, remarks on the scenery
    of its upper portion, i. 19
    below, Cincinnatti, i. - 23
    near its mouth, i. - 36
    mouth of, its importance in
    geography, i. - 39
    general marks concerning, i. 39
    remarks on the scenery
    near its mouth, i. - 42
Oil, bituminous, i. - - 15
    stone quarry of Washita, ii. - 293
Olean village, i. - - 16
Omawhaw Indians, council with
    the, i. - 174
    chiefs visit us, i. - 193
    surprise at the properties
    of quicksilver, i. - 194
    predestination, i. - 194
    war party, i. - - 197
    account of the Omawhaws, 200
    their village and hut, i. 200

Omawhaw, occupations, preparations
    for national hunt, i.   201
    departure on a hunting ex-
    cursion, i.   -   -   205
    ceremony on discovering a
    herd of bisons, i. -   206
    surrounding a herd of bi-
    sons, i.   -   -   208
    dissection and preparation
    of the meat, i.   -   210
    return to the village, i. -   212
    employments, i.   -   212
    different preparations of
    maize, i.   -   -   213
    pumpkins, i.   -   213
    canibalism, i.   -   -   214
    lice eaten by the Indians, i.   215
    amusements of the men, i.   215
    winter hunt, i.   -   217
    employment of the squaws,   218
    trade, i.   -   -   218
    return by the village and
    proceed on to hunt the
    bisons, i.   -   -   220
    manner of preparing the
    hides, i.   -   -   221
    government. i.   -   222
    the grand chief *Blackbird*, i. 223
    matrimony and the marri-
    ed state, i.   -   230
    jealousy, i.   -   -   233
    punishment of adultery, i.   233
    catamenia, i.   -   -   235
    parturition, i.   -   236
    diseases, i.   -   -   237
    monsters, abortion, infant
    children, i.   -   -   238
    girls, their chastity, &c. i.   239
    boys, their propitiation of
    the Wahconda—disobe-
    dience, i.   -   -   240
    an 'dote of a father, i.   241
    young man, his home till
    married, i.   -   242
    his house and furniture, i.   243
    mourning for the dead, i.   243
    love—maternal love, anec-
    dote, i.   -   -   244
    quarrels and duels, i.   249
    titles of consanguinity, i.   251
    anecdote of a father-in-
    law, i.   -   -   253
    fraternal love, i.   -   254
    old age, i.   -   255
    diseases, i.   -   -   258
    medical and surgical know-
    ledge, i. -   -   262
    burial, i.   -   -   281
    lamentation for the dead, i.   282
    physical description, i.   283

Omawhaw, senses, i.   -   -   286
    mechanics and fine arts, i.   287
    astronomical and geogra-
    phical knowledge, i.   -   288
    culinary, horticultural and
    martial instruments, i.   290
    domestic animals, i.   -   291
    war parties and war, i.   292
    battle with the Pawnee
    Loups, i. -   -   -   300
    battle with the Pawnee re-
    publicans, i. -   -   300
    with the Puncaws, i.   301
    with the Otoes, i.   -   301
    with the Padoucas, i.   302
    with the Konzas, i.   -   302
    manner of intrenching, i.   304
    fidelity of Wacora, i.   -   307
    migration, i.   -   338
    drunkenness, i. -   -   264
    sodomy, i. -   -   266
    ideas of futurity, i.   -   267
    of God, i. -   -   268
    magicians, i. -   -   268
    superstitions, i.   -   272
    peculiar odour, i.   -   482
Orbicular lizard, i.   -   138
            ii.   -   -   35, 89
Orchidae, i.   .   -   44
Orders, Major Long's, detailing the
    duties of the individuals of
    the party at the commence-
    ment of the expedition, i.   1
    relative to the duties of the
    party during the winter can-
    tonment, i.   -   165
    issued at the departure of
    the expedition from Engi-
    neer Cantonment, i.   425
Ore of iron, haematitic, ii.   -   292
Organic reliquiæ described, i.   22, 38
            84, 90, 106, 147
            ii.   49, 219
Orthocera, i.   .   -   22
Osage river and town, i. -   -   85
    Indians, ii.   -   -   237
    their mode of hunting horses ii. 243
    some account of, ii.   -   244
    number of children of a
    chief, ii.   -   -   251
Oto Indians, dance of, i. -   -   154
    council with, i.   -   158
    attack the Konza village, i.   305
    party of, attacked by the
    Konzas, i.   -   -   305
    their nation, village, and
    name, i.   -   -   338
    their migration, i. -   -   339
    bravery, i.   -   .   341
    hunting grounds, i.   -   342

Oto Indians, ceremony of marking a
   squaw, ii. - -   189
   their knowledge of insects, ii. 189
   intoxicating bean used by, ii. 194
Out-fit and departure from Pittsburgh, i. - -   4
Out-lying hills, ii. - -   11
Owl, Coquimbo described, ii. 36, 37, 200
Ozark mountains, remarks concerning, ii. - -   276
   rivers of, ii. - -   281
   account of soil, minerals,
   &c. ii. - -   287

P.

Padouca Indians, ii. -   65
Papillon creek, i. - -   427
Pawnee Indians, their attack on Mr.
   Say's detachment, i. -   133
   deputation of, i. -   159
   visit to their camp, i. -   160
   attack the Konza village, i. 303
   village destroyed by Wa-
   sacaruja, i. - -   306
   their council, i. 353, 366
   presents made them, i. 353, 361
   dance, i. -   354, 361
   mode of receiving distinguished strangers, i. 355, 365
   Petaleesharoo, i. -   356
   human sacrifices, i. -   357
   battle with the mountain
   Indians, i. -   362
   civil dissension, i. -   365
   shield, i. - -   367
Pawnee villages, arrival at, i. 435 et seq.
   population, i. - -   445
   situation and surrounding
   country, i. -   446
Peak, James's, ii. -   28
   a distinguished land mark, ii. 78
   Spanish, ii. - -   58, 77
Peale, Mr. his duties, i. -   2
   his sickness, ii. -   87
   accidental separation from the
   party, ii. - -   118
Pear, prickly, ii. - -   19
Pelecanus carbo, i. - -   4
Pelidna pectoralis, described, i. 171
   cinclus, var. described, i. 172
Petrosilex of the Washita, ii. 288
Phenomenon, atmospheric, ii. 490
Phryganea, i. - -   32
Pigeon, apparently new, described, ii. 10
Pike's blockhouse, ii. -   40
Pilots, at the falls of Ohio, i. 26
Pine, Weymouth, i. - -   12
   species of, on the Rocky Moun-
   tains, ii. - -   34

Pinus flexilis, ii. - -   27
   described, ii. - -   34
   fruit eaten, ii. - -   35
   resinosa, ii. - -   288
Pipe stone, Indian, i. - -   31
Pittsburgh, departure from, i. 4
   noticed, i. - -   14
Plantago attenuata, i. -   445
   lagopus, i. - -   433
Plants of the Rocky Mountains
   above perpetual frost, ii. 27
   colour of their flowers, ii. 28
Platte river, its mouth, i. -   143
   its valley, i. - -   429
   arrival at, i. -   450
   scenery of, i. - 454, 468,
                483, 488
   remarks concerning, i. 459
   temperature of, i. 489
Point Pleasant, i. - -   19
   a Cherokee village on the Ar-
   kansa, i. - -   268
Poison Spring, near the Hot Springs
   of Washita, ii. -   292
   anecdote of, ii. - -   293
Pond Fort, i. - -   408
Populus Angustifolia, i. -   497
   Angulata, ii. - -   164
Portland, i. - - -   48
Portulacca pilosa, ii. -   68
Potamogeton natans, i. -   455
Poteau river, ii. - -   260
Prairie fly, i. - - -   75
   wolves, their sagacity, &c. i. 168
Prairies, their origin and character, i. 404
Prairie dog described, i. -   451
   their villages, i. -   498
Precautions used by the party, ii. 35
Precious metals, fabulous accounts
   of, ii. - -   277
Prickly pear, (cactus ferox and
   mammillaris) i. -   452
Provisions, seasonable supply of, i. 462
   scarcity of, ii. 38, 49, 83, 93, 101
   particularly plenty, ii. 127
   Capt Bell's party in great
   want of, ii. -   227
   supplied by Lieut. Swift, ii. 228
Psoralea esculenta, i. - -   448
Purgatory creek, ii. -   69
   difficulty in ascending its
   bluffs, ii. - -   76

R.

Raft, Great, of Red river, ii. -   307
Ranunculus amphibius, i. -   498
Rat, Florida, i. - -   54
Rattlesnakes, i. - -   116, 499
Red Mouse, a Kaskaia chief, ii. 106

Red River of Louisiana, account of,
    from Freeman's MS. jour-
    nal, ii.   - 302 et seq.
    forests of, ii.   -   303
    settlement of, ii.   -   304
    colour of its water, ii.   305
    difficulty in ascending, ii.   307
    remarks on the tributaries
        and country of, ii.   -   314
    sources unknown, ii.   -   316
Revenge, with anecdotes, i.   -   317
Ribes Aureum, i   -   -   501
Rigolet de Bon Dieu, ii.   -   304
Rivers of the Ozark mountains, specu-
    lation concerning, ii.   281, 294
Road, national, i.   -   -   17
    or trace from Charaton to
        Council Bluff, i.   -   415
    to Columbia river, ii.   34
    Spanish, ii.   -   -   69
    to Santa Fe, ii.   -   94
Robins, i.   -   -   -   502
Rock, remarkable, in Canadian ri-
    ver, ii.   -   -   162
Rocky Mountains descried, i.   -   489
    arrival at, i.   -   503
    remarks concerning, ii.   -   1
    scenery of, ii.   -   9
    examined, ii.   -   -   14
    penetrated by the party, ii.   18
    view of, from the summit of
        James's Peak, ii.   -   30
    scenery in their vicinity, ii.   77,
                                        79, 82
Rosa mutabilis, i.   -   -   69
Rudbeckia tagetes described, ii.   68

S.

Sabbath observed by the party as a
    day of rest, i.   -   457
Sacrifice to the Great Star, i.   -   357
Saddle, Indian, speedy construction
    of, by a Squaw, ii.   -   62
Saline springs, i.   -   15, 16, 33, 48
Saline, U. S. near Shawneetown, i.   33
    on a branch of Le Mine ri-
        ver, i.   -   -   100
    on Neosho, or Grand river, ii.   251
    on Illinois river of Arkansa, ii.   254
    river of Washita, ii.   -   300
Salt, native, procured by an Arika-
    ra, i.   -   -   449
    unsuccessful search for, ii.   80
    obtained from the Kaskai-
        as, ii.   -   -   115
Sandhill crane, i.   -   344
        ii.   -   -   328
Sandhills, or drifts, ii.   -   147
Sand rat, or goffer. desc. i.   406

Sandstone, crystalline, i.   -   417
    argillaceous, i.   27, 34, 40, 47
    at the base of the Rocky
        Mountains, ii.   1, 5, 11, 13
    slaty, ii.   -   -   39
    organic remains in, ii.   -   48
    inclined, of the Arkansa, ii.   44
    formation, extent of, ii.   76
    on Red River, ii.   -   304
    of the Ozark Mountains, ii.   288
Santa Fe, road to, ii.   -   -   94
Say, Mr., detached with a party at
    St. Charles, i.   -   71
    adventures of his detach-
        ment, i.   -   -   75
    detached with a party from
        Franklin, to fort Osage, i.   95
    detached with a party to ex-
        plore the country between
        fort Osage and the Pawnee
        villages, i.   -   108
    account of his journey to the
        Konzas, i.   -   -   116
    his party plundered by a Paw-
        nee war party, i.   -   132
Sciurus lateralis, ii.   -   324
    macrurus, i.   -   -   115
    quadrivittatus, desc. ii.   45
    lateralis, desc. ii.   -   46
    grammurus, desc. ii.   72
Scolopendra, ii.   -   -   98
Selenite, ii.   -   -   98
Settlers, first, their character, ii.   279
Shawneetown, arrival at, i.   -   31
Shawnee Indian's head elevated on
    a pole, ii.   -   -   285
Shell of the Omawhaws, object of
    superstition, i.   -   325
Shienne chief, ii.   -   -   177
    war party, ii.   -   195
Shippingsport, i.   -   -   27
Short Mountain creek and settle-
    ment, ii.   -   -   266
Sickness of the exploring party, and
    its cause, ii   -   -   10
    at Cape Girardeau, ii.   321
Sienite of the Rocky Mountains, ii.   5
Signals, Indian, ii.   -   -   140
Silver creek, i.   -   -   28
    hills noticed, i.   -   29
Sink holes, i.   -   -   58
Smithland, i.   -   -   35
Solanum triflorum and heteran-
    drum, i.   -   -   453
    tuberosum, i.   -   -   94
Spaniards, their measures to inter-
    cept Freeman's party, ii.   312
Spider, bird-catching, ii.   -   157
Springs, boiling, ii.   -   21, 23, 32
    mineral, ii.   -   -   43

Springs in the red and gray sand
    stones, ii. - - 71
Spring river. ii. - - 281
Squirrel, striped and spotted, ii. 174
Stanleya integrifolia, desc. ii. 17
Stewart, Mr. Robert, noticed, i. 465
Stipa, hygrometric, i. - - 500
Stinking fork, ii. - - 218
Strawberry river, ii. - - 281
St. Louis, arrival at, i. - 55
    notice of, i. - - 56
St. Charles, arrival at, i. - 70
St. Charles' river, ii. - 58
St. Francis' river, ii. - - 283
Swallow, cliff described, ii. - 47
Sycamore, i. - - - 23
Symphoria glomerata, i. - 449
Sylvia celata described, i. - 169
    bifasciata described, i. 170

T.

Tabanus, or prairie fly, i. - 75
    ii. - 198
Table lands. ii. - - 12
Tarkio river, i. - - - 141
Tarrarecawaho, his speech to his
    warriors, i. - 352
Tell-tale sandpiper, i. - 4
Tennessee river. i. - - 35
Tern, black-headed, i. - 67
Testudo, geographica, its oviposi-
    tion, i. - - 32
Tetrao obscurus, described, ii. - 14
Ticks, seed, the party annoyed
    by, ii. - - 144, 256
    described, ii. - 256
Tikatok, his village, ii. - 272
    character, ii. - 273
Toad, a new species described, ii. 190
Tobacco fumes highly relished by
    the Indians, ii. 176
TOPOGRAPHY, see table of contents,
    vol. ii. ch. 18,
Tortures, expiatory, of the Minneta-
    rees, i. - - 276
Trap formation, its scenery, ii. 79, 82
Travelling, order of observed by the
    party, i. - - 421
Treaty of peace, ceremonies of, i. 310
Trees imbedded in the banks of the
    Missouri, i. - - 68
Tribes and bands of the Omaw-
    haws, i. - - 325
Triton lateralis described, i. - 5
Tumuli, or Indian mounds, i. - 59
    in Illinois, on the American
    bottom, i. - - 66
Turkey buzzard, i. - - 4
Tyrannus verticalis described, ii. 60
    forficatus, ii. - - 224

Tyawapeti bottom, i. - 44

U.

Ulmus alata, ii. - - 204
Ursus horribilis described, ii. - 52

V.

Vaccine virus, accident to, i. - 434
    unsuccessfully applied, i. 439
Valour, i. - - - 309
Venus, planet, seen at mid-day, i. 488
Verdigris river, little, ii. - 220
    arrival at, ii. - 250
Vermillion creek, i. - - 502
Vespertilio novaboracensis et subula-
    tus described, ii. 65
VOCABULARIES OF INDIAN LANGUAGES
    appendix LXIX et seq.
Volcanic rocks, ii. - - 86, 88
    remarkable ridges of, ii. 91
    appearances, ii. 327
Volcano pseudo, subterranean explo-
    sion, i. - - 196

W.

Wabash river, i. - - 81
Warreruza creek, i. - - 116
Washita river, its source, &c. ii. 294
    its tributaries, ii. 301
Waters, their colour considered, i. - 10
Water, want of, the occasion of un-
    avoidable filthiness, ii. 141
Water of the red sandstone forma-
    tion, ii. - - 96
Wealth, superior, indicated by the
    number of corn cribs, i. 77
Wharf creek, ii. - - 59
Wheeling, arrival at, i. - 17
Whipporwill, i. - - 4
White river, ii. - - 273
    remarks concerning, ii. 274
    cut off, ii. - 275
    country of, ii. - 276
    its bed and valley, ii. 278
    natural growth and pro-
    ducts, ii. - 279
Witticisms, i. - . - 309, 330
Wolf river, i. - - 114, 115
Wolves, their ferocity, ii. - 78, 82
Wolf, black, i. - - 102
    ii. - - 157
Wood, scarcity of, ii. - - 69
Wormwood, species of, ii. - 475
Wren, new, described, ii. - 4

Y.

Yankee, to whom applied, i. - 2
Yucca angustifolia, i. - - 46

R. Seymour del.

Pub. by H. Colnry & Alea 1827

H. Bay dr.

Drawn by T.R. Peale.

Engraved by Young & Walker.

MOVEABLE SKIN LODGES of the KASKAIAS.

F. Kearney sculp.?

A. Lawson Del.

Pub.d by H.C. Carey & I.Lea, 1822.

J.G. Fields Sc.

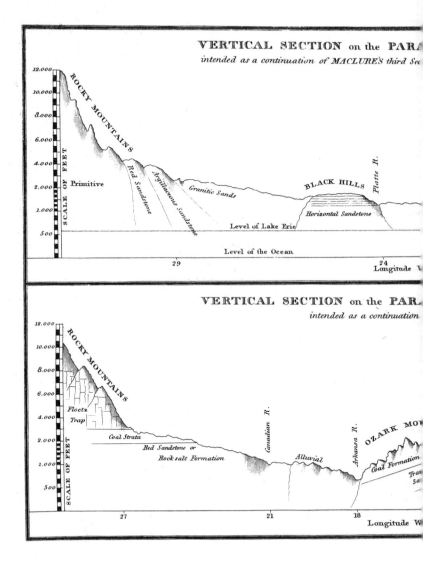

VERTICAL SECTION on the PARA

intended as a continuation of MACLURE'S third Sec

ROCKY MOUNTAINS

SCALE OF FEET

12.000
10.000
8.000
6.000
4.000
2.000
1.000
500

Primitive

Red Sandstone

Argillaceous Sandstone

Granitic Sands

BLACK HILLS

Platte R.

Horizontal Sandstone

Level of Lake Erie

Level of the Ocean

29

24
Longitude

VERTICAL SECTION on the PAR

intended as a continuation

ROCKY MOUNTAINS

SCALE OF FEET

12.000
10.000
8.000
6.000
4.000
2.000
1.000
500

Floetz
Trap

Coal Strata

Red Sandstone or
Rock salt Formation

Canadian R.

Alluvial

Arkansa R.

OZARK MO

Coal Formation

Tra
Sa

27

21

18

Longitude W

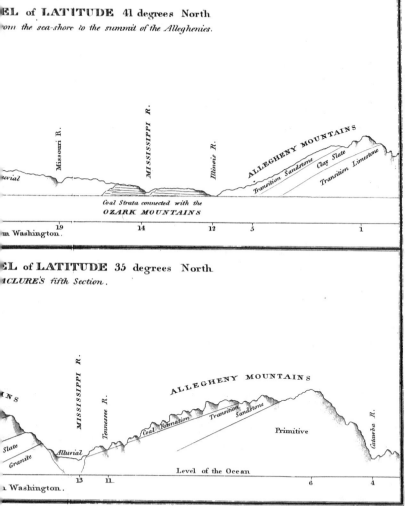

EL of **LATITUDE** 41 degrees North
rom the sea-shore to the summit of the Alleghenies.

Missouri R.

MISSISSIPPI R.

Illinois R.

ALLEGHENY MOUNTAINS

Transition Sandstone *Clay Slate*

Transition Limestone

uvial

Coal Strata connected with the
OZARK MOUNTAINS

m Washington.   19   14   12   5   1

EL of **LATITUDE** 35 degrees North.
ACLURE'S fifth Section.

MISSISSIPPI R.

Tennessee R.

ALLEGHENY MOUNTAINS

Coal Formation *Transition Sandstone*

Primitive

Catawba R.

Slate

Granite   *Alluvial*

Level of the Ocean

a Washington.   13   11   6   4

Engrav'd by Young & Delleker